THE FOREMAN ON THE ASSEMBLY LINE

THE FOREMAN on the ASSEMBLY LINE

Charles R. Walker
Robert H. Guest
Arthur N. Turner

INSTITUTE OF HUMAN RELATIONS
YALE UNIVERSITY

Published by HARVARD UNIVERSITY PRESS
CAMBRIDGE · MASSACHUSETTS · 1956

Distributed in Great Britain by
GEOFFREY CUMBERLEGE · Oxford University Press
London

Library of Congress Catalog Card Number 56–6525
Printed in the United States of America

ACKNOWLEDGMENTS

This study was made possible through the generous cooperation of many persons: officers of the XY Corporation, the plant manager, the personnel manager, and all members of the plant staff.

Thanks are due to Warren G. Bennis of the Massachusetts Institute of Technology, and to Donald S. Pitkin of Boston University, who conducted many of the interviews. Our associate, Frank J. Jasinski, contributed many helpful criticisms based upon his separate study of foremen in another plant. Valuable suggestions were made by Chris Argyris, George P. Murdock, and E. Wight Bakke of the faculty of Yale University; Mrs. Donald B. Rock prepared the diagram at the end of the book.

Finally we are grateful to the fifty-five production foremen at Plant X without whose enthusiastic cooperation the project would never have succeeded.

CONTENTS

1 INTRODUCTION

The foreman, the forgotten man of a few years ago, has become almost the most talked about in the industrial world. Any employer who does not declare that his foreman is a member of "management's team," and that he occupies a peculiar place of honor as management's "front-line" representative, is behind the times. Enormous amounts of energy and dollars have been invested in "educating" the foreman in everything from basic economics to psychology. But despite this interest and effort resulting in a growing literature of and for the "supervisor," few studies have attempted to relate the foreman and his problems to his own industry, and to particular work environments which it is his duty to master and supervise. And fewer words still have been written about the foreman as seen by himself.[1] One purpose of this book is to help supply these deficiencies for what is believed to be a strategic section of the American economy — the automobile assembly line.

In 1950 the Institute of Human Relations at Yale initiated a series of studies dealing with various phases of the impact of mass production on human behavior. Two studies of the worker on the assembly line have been made, others will follow.[2] It is clear that the "technological environment" influences the life of the average worker in many important ways. The effects are as great or nearly so in determining the kind of working life experienced by the supervisor.

[1] Some notable exceptions are mentioned in the Selected Bibliography.

[2] Publications based upon this research are included in the Bibliography on pp. 183–188.

Our approach has been similar to that of an earlier study, *The Man on the Assembly Line*: observation and interviews. In that inquiry we looked at the technological environment and at the foreman and management generally, from the standpoint of the worker. He was our bench mark, our vantage point of vision. Here, the foreman assumes that role.

All the production foremen in the plant chosen for study, fifty-five, were interviewed. The approach of the interviewer was semi-directive. Every aspect of the foreman's situation was covered as far as practicable, with emphasis given to actual duties and what he thought of them, and to his relationships with other people and with his environment. The plant chosen for study, which we have called Plant X, was the same selected in 1950 for our survey of hourly wage earners. The parent company of which it is a part has been called "The XY Company."

Throughout the chapters, liberal quotations are included from what the fifty-five foremen actually said to the interviewers. This has been done in the interest of accuracy, and also in the hope that some of the dynamic atmosphere of the plant might find its way onto the printed page.

Although most of the material as given is descriptive and qualitative, it points the way, we believe, toward generalizations susceptible of quantitative study and experimentation. In "A Foreman's Day," and in the material from which it is drawn, a beginning has been made toward a quantitative analysis of the foreman's job in time and space. For a detailed description of the method and the categories used, the reader is referred to pages 152–159 of the Supplement.

Categorization of topics in nearly every chapter has followed closely the raw data as they came from the interviewers. The book presents case-history material, but behind this presentation and controlling it are certain broad concepts, of which one of the most important is that of a "technological work environment." This is a way of conceiving any factory through an emphasis on the close tie between process and social and psychological phenomena. A

German scholar calls it a "socio-geographic" approach; a French scholar, a "psycho-technical" one. And an Englishman, using the same frame of reference, speaks of studies of "socio-technical production systems."

Finally, we have made an effort to relate our study of a "segment of a segment" in American industry to the broader problems of man's relations to work in the modern world, and have suggested generalizations appropriate for future experiment and research.

Throughout our study we found much to admire, some things to criticize. As in previous studies in the XY Company, what impressed us most was the willingness both at Plant and Company levels to acknowledge the existence of problems and to make every effort toward their solution.

In a sense the *foreman* is one species in a very large genus of human beings. The genus may be said to include all who directly supervise men and women, such as the lower ranks of officers and non-commissioned officers in the armed services, head nurses in hospitals, senior clerks in banks and law offices, and many others. It is hoped that some light may be thrown on this important role played by so many individuals in so many regions of society. But it is a conviction of the authors that the fruits of research, whether theoretical or practical, will be richer if there is a concentration not only on "species," but also on "sub-species." The species in this case is the foreman in any industry; the sub-species is the foreman on an automobile assembly line. We believe that not only is his job a particularly difficult and dynamic one in the modern world, but that some of the social and behavioral problems related to his function are critical for a civilization based on men and machines. The achievements of modern technology are a mounting tribute to man's imagination, industry and courage. But technological advance, like every other kind, means not only progress, but problems. Mankind is still trying to adjust to an unfinished technological revolution which began a hundred and fifty years ago, and whose end certainly is not yet in sight. The man and the supervisor on the assembly line as participants must adjust and readjust day by day and year by year to that continuing revolution.

In the chapters which follow we will look first at the environment itself within which factory society is built, and where both worker and supervisor spend their working lives. It is a very remarkable one and has often and justly been celebrated for its almost miraculous ingenuity. We will then let the foreman speak for himself.

2 THE FOREMAN AND THE PRINCIPLES OF MASS PRODUCTION

This is a study of foremen in a particular work environment. Before we can usefully explore what being a foreman means to the individual, it is important to look at the physical geography of the plant and the engineering rationale of work organization.

Plant X is known as a final assembly plant. It is the last step in a series of manufacturing and fabricating operations prior to distribution of the product to the dealer. At a prescribed moment in time and space, thousands of parts and partially assembled units arrive at the plant and are fed into a maze of conveyors and machinery, emerging as completed automobiles at a rate of over 350 each eight-hour day.

The plant itself covers twenty-three acres of floor space. The dominant feature to the observer, as well as to the foreman and hourly wage earner, is the great conveyor which winds through the plant for a total length of over two and a half miles. Feeding into the main line are two miles of overhead and auxiliary lines carrying small parts, materials, and unit assemblies to appropriate stations along the line. Off the main line at many points are sub-assembly operations, some on conveyors, some on stationary "bucks" or benches.

The plant is divided into two main areas, each fed by a rail spur. In one area, metal sections, fabricated in the "home" fabricating plants, are taken from railroad cars and distributed to the metal department. Here, the raw parts, underbody, cowls, quarter panels, doors, etc., are welded together to form the metal body of the car. Transferred to another section of the conveyor (the paint department), the body undergoes a series of paint operations: a rustproof covering is fused to the metal, primary coats of paint are sprayed on the body, and then the final coat is applied. (Later, and in another separate area, the body undergoes polishing operations.) Next the body is "dressed up," in the trim department. Fittings are installed, glass is inserted, and mouldings, chrome trim, cloth linings, instrument panels are put in place. Here, too, after arriving from a separate series of conveyor operations, the seats and seat backs are made up and installed.

After the body is polished and "fitted up," it moves to the second major plant area known as the chassis department. While the car body has been going through the operations just described, the car chassis has started on its way. Frames, arriving by rail, have moved along a spring-and-axle assembly line. Engines, sent from an engine plant several hundred miles distant, were attached to the built-up frame and wheels put on. After many other operations, the chassis arrives at the final line where the body is lowered at "body drop" and fastened to the chassis. Among the several operations which follow are attachment of hoods, grilles and front fenders, bumpers, lights, and many more units. The completed automobile is then tested, adjusted, and given final conditioning in the last department, car conditioning.

All of the above operations in the assembly of a car are divided among five areas or departments, known as metal, paint, trim, chassis, and car conditioning. Each of these departments is headed by a superintendent who reports to the general superintendent of the plant. The latter in turn reports to the plant production manager. Under each superintendent are two to three general foremen; under each general foreman, two or more production foremen. The production foremen are the subject of this study.

Each production foreman is in charge of a section of the operations described above. In the metal department, for example, a foreman has a group of soldering operations located on the main conveyor. The preceding section welds the metal seams of the car body and the succeeding section files the seams which are covered in the soldering operation. Some sections are entirely sub-assembly and off the main line. Other sections combine both sub-assembly and main-line operations.

The work performed on the different sections of the line makes use of a variety of hand power tools — welding guns, paint spray guns, air-driven wrenches. Simple hand tools such as files and hammers are also used in certain sections. With a few exceptions, the number of operators per foreman ranges from twenty-five to thirty-five men.

Each operator has a few prescribed tasks to perform as the product is delivered by the conveyor into and away from his work station. The average time cycle for each operator's job is about one and one-half minutes. By having their work fractionalized in this way, most operators, even in a section performing similar work (spot welding, paint spraying, etc.), have a minimum of contact with others because there is no *functional* reason for them to work interdependently with one another. As a result the foreman in many respects deals with an aggregate of men performing work *independently* of one another, rather than with an integrated team, working together and assisting one another.

A remarkable feature about operations, and of considerable importance to front-line supervision, is that many different types of cars are assembled. There are three distinct "makes" of automobiles, each with many models and styles. Each body is painted with one of forty-five distinct colors and these colors can be applied in more than two hundred two-tone combinations. There are over one hundred twenty-five separate accessory specifications. In addition the various models have different color combinations for instrument panels and upholsteries. Because of the three different makes of cars, and the variety of color and accessory specifications, the possible combinations are, as one member of management put it, "astronomical." Theoretically, the line could run for more than a year at a maximum rate and the plant would not produce two identical automobiles.

There is, of course, much standardization of parts, which makes it possible to draw from stock any part with a given specification and put it on any model with similar specifications. But a unique feature of the operations is that the schedules are so contrived as to permit each car in sequence to be preceded or followed by a car of completely different type, instead of a "run" of similar models. The system has many advantages for distribution to dealers and also for balancing the work load, but as we shall see, at times it adds to the many practical problems of the individual foreman.

Operations as complex as those in automobile assembly require an enormous amount of planning and coordination by specialized technical service groups. In fact, for every two and one-half persons in the direct production departments, there is one in a staff or service position. It is well known that in all industry the ratio of technical to production groups has been increasing. This is eminently true of automobile assembly operations, and as will be seen, is of critical importance in understanding the foreman's functional role in any assembly plant.

In this brief tour of the plant we have taken a quick look at an extremely complex technical and human organization. And yet the whole labyrinth of men and machines is organized in accordance with the relatively simple principles of mass production, or more accurately, the principles of progressive assembly. These principles involve the basic concepts of standardization, interchangeability, precision, synchronization, and continuity. For assembly-line operations, they may be described as follows:

1. Orderly progression of the product through the shop in a series of planned operations so that the right part arrives in the right place at the right time.

2. Mechanical delivery to and from the operators of these parts and of the product as it is assembled.

3. A breakdown of operations into their simple constituent components.[1]

Everyone familiar with an automobile assembly line recognizes that the work performed by hourly wage production workers, materials handlers, schedule men, and standards personnel is directly related to these principles of progressive assembly.

But what about the production foreman? What is the underlying engineering rationale of *his* job? Do these same principles apply? In a strict and technical sense, no. If the engineering of the tools and the product were perfect, if processes were flawless, if every operation were perfectly executed by all of the operators, materials handlers, etc., if schedules were balanced and kept stable – then it could be argued that the foreman was superfluous and performed no essential role within the scope of these engineering principles of progressive assembly.[2]

There were a few intervals during the course of the present study when operations in a given foreman's section were running close to this ideal and, indeed, during such times it appeared as if the foreman could be dispensed with. Such occasions, however, were rare, and it was apparent that most of the time the foreman's day was taken up with hundreds of tasks essential to the continued operation of the line. Nevertheless, it will perhaps enlighten the reader to understand that the foreman's role is not formally defined by the principles of engineering design. At point after point, machines or technical experts have absorbed many of the duties normally associated with front-line supervision.

To illustrate, compare the assembly foreman's technical role

[1] See C. R. Walker and R. H. Guest, *The Man on the Assembly Line* (Cambridge: Harvard University Press, 1952), p. 10.

[2] It should be added that in practice he is not wholly relieved of purely technical responsibility, such as minor repairs and adjustments.

with that of the foreman in an industry not so highly rationalized, or with the foreman in an earlier period of technological development. On the assembly line, the movement, the amount, and the placement of stock (parts to be assembled) are determined for the foreman by materials-handling experts. The product is moved into, through, and out of his section on a moving conveyor. The foreman does not control its rate of movement, except in an emergency; i.e., when he stops the movement completely. He does not determine the number of units which are to be produced in a given period of time. Schedules are predetermined elsewhere by technically trained experts. The sequence of styles, colors, etc., or in other words the distribution of models, is not planned by the foreman. He can, to be sure, redistribute the elements of each individual operator, but he cannot change the time established for each of the elements of a job. These times have all been carefully established by technically qualified specialists in the standards department. Also, only very minor changes in processes, tools, and fixtures may be made by the foreman.

Look now at other types of industry. In less highly rationalized operations a foreman is often directly responsible for initiating the process, moving materials, scheduling, setting up jobs, and performing many duties which in a mass-production plant are carried out by the technical experts. Does it follow then that the elaborate plan of operations described above has been worked out to such a degree of technical refinement that the foreman has no real responsibility? The answer, strongly negative, will be found in the later chapters. This remarkably well-conceived system of production, in the last analysis and in spite of considerable mechanization, is operated by people and as such is subject to human error. And it is the foreman, located at the critical point in operations, who must deal directly with the one set of imperfect tools which have not been "engineered out." These tools, of course, arc his men. The quality of the relationship between a foreman and his group of operators in large measure determines the success or failure of the whole process of production.

SUMMARY

The final assembly of an automobile is performed at Plant X. It is here that parts and materials flowing in from many fabricating plants are assembled into a completed product ready for distribution to the dealer and the customer. The complex organization of men and materials is predicated on certain basic engineering principles which involve the orderly progression of the product through the shop in a series of planned operations, the mechanical delivery of materials, and a breakdown of work into simple constituent motions. Human effort at the level of production workers, materials handlers, schedulers, and many others is organized primarily around these engineering principles.

The foreman's role is more difficult to define. His job is not determined by any principles of engineering design, but his function remains of critical importance, and in part because no designer can be expected to account for all the many variables of human behavior.

3 THE FOREMAN AND THE WORKER

Each foreman at Plant X appeared not only willing but eager to talk about every aspect of his foremanship. But no one part of it was discussed more readily or more fully than relations with his own men. Nearly every foreman stated unequivocally that this was the most important part of his job – several newly-promoted foremen said it was the hardest part – and all thought it the key to their success or failure as supervisors:

People — that's your big problem right there. You have to get the men to see things your way. If you can do that, everything is smoother. If you can't get the men to go along with you, you have trouble and you never will get the job done properly.

The man on the line makes your job. If he wants to work for you and is doing a good job, then things are easier. If he doesn't want to work for you, then it's just too bad.

Ninety per cent of my job is knowing how to break in and handle the men. . . . It's very easy for the men to rebel, and then things go to hell before you know it, and the foreman is left holding the bag.

And here is a comment that gives a little insight into the doubts and difficulties of the *new* foreman:

Well, there are a lot of different problems; most of mine are with the men. Trying to create an impression and how to handle them. Things that seem big to them are little to you. If they have problems, you have to help them . . . It was tough for me. I never had supervised before. The hard thing is to figure out the way to explain what to do. There's so much to learn and to get everyone to do everything right. It's kinda tough, because a while before,

I was a partner with the workers on the line, and they still expect you to be.

Why were relations with men so important? Did not the moving line determine how men should work and keep them at it? Some foremen said it did, and that this mechanical compulsion made less human supervision necessary. For example:

The line does a lot of your work for you. The men have to keep up with it. If I stand down at the end of my section, I can see if anything has been done wrong by one of my men, and I can find out why.

I like the moving line because you know where your people are. The first thing I do when I come into a department is to try to do away with sub-assembly operations. I don't like them at all. The line here, the moving line, controls the man, and his speed. Then no matter how slow a man is, he has to keep moving. We're all human, we like to go as slow as we can unless we are pushed, and this line controls him perfectly.

But even these foremen made it clear that the moving line did not solve their two biggest problems: absenteeism and quality. Because of the need of keeping the line continuously manned, absenteeism presented unusual difficulties to an assembly-line foreman, as we shall see later. As to quality, in order to maintain standards it was necessary for the foreman to keep his eye continually on tools, materials, and men. To be sure, the conveyor moved the car past the man, but it was the man's hand that picked up the parts and fitted them together. Foremen who said the conveyor helped were saying it helped the quantity, not the quality, side of their foremanship.

Moreover, a majority of the foremen were acutely aware of morale and personal adjustment problems directly related to the pacing of the line, and to the repetitiveness of most jobs:

As the men develop speed, they can get to where they can sit down for a minute and take a rest. Not every man can. Some men fight the job all day long. A man has to learn not to fight the job.

Many foremen told us that their biggest job was breaking in new men. Excessive fatigue from unused muscles, nervous tension, and fear of "going into the hole" (failure to complete an assigned sequence of operations in the time allowed) were some of the difficulties of the new assembly worker which it was the supervisor's job to mitigate or dissolve. And too often, the foremen would complain there was not enough time to break in a man and teach him not to fight his job.

In several ways the technological elements of the work mentioned above, together with some of its psychological effects, were related to the matter of discipline. Checking up on a man to see that he did not "go in the hole" too often, and that he did an acceptable job were a foreman's preoccupations all day long. But what did he do if men did fall down on the job? What sort of discipline did he impose? That question was very much on the foreman's mind.

As in plants of any kind there were various formal penalties that could be imposed: verbal warnings, written reprimands, suspensions, discharge. But besides such punishments, there were ways in which a foreman could, and sometimes did, "make it tough for a man." However, the evidence from observation and intensive interviews with both men and foremen showed that such measures were only called into play with certain individuals and as a last resort. Most foremen had discovered that simply relying upon negative disciplinary measures as a normal way of operating did not pay off. Furthermore, there was widespread recognition that driving the men only reinforced existing pressures and tensions and hence lowered morale. And with the men against him, a foreman's job became intolerable for the average supervisor. Finally, there had been a marked change in management philosophy over the years, according to foremen. They frequently referred to the company's positive emphasis on human relations:

I've noticed a big change since I came into the outfit. Before, in the old days, I had never heard of human relations. Now, the job is really more enjoyable. The men are treated as human beings. . . . You used to drive them to work, now you talk them to work. . . . It started in 1939 that they began to treat people like human beings. That's a bad way to put it, but anyway it is much pleasanter to do the job now than it used to be. . . . If you meet the fellows in the street or in a gin mill, they greet you, while in the old days they would have crossed the street to avoid seing you. They hold no malice like before.

Sometimes foremen connected this general change directly with their own experience:

I've changed myself a lot, the way I handle people. I used to be rough on this job, plenty rough. Now, I explain things to the boys. I tell them what they're doing wrong, what they should do, and I don't bawl them out the way I used to. I don't rant and roar any more. See how it goes now. I could just stand here all day at this desk and the job would get done, but I used to run up and down the line and get into a sweat, blowing my stack all the time.

My men are a good bunch. About one out of every four foremen interviewed emphasized that his own men were a "good bunch" or a "good crew," or gave special emphasis to the good relations which he said existed between the men and himself. Foremen were not asked specifically what they thought of their men; consequently, it was striking that many of them went out of their way to praise the workers for whom they were responsible. In almost every case these favorable attitudes towards the men seemed genuine and strongly felt. They also seemed to indicate that these foremen thought of their men and themselves as members, more or less, of the same *group*, striving together to accomplish certain common goals:

Several of these men are green. The oldtimers help in training them and getting them used to the job. Fortunately, they are all good boys. If I couldn't run this line, it would not be their fault, it would be mine. That's what I told the plant production manager one time, because these men are good fellows.

This is a good crew, and I know that I would get 100 per cent co-

operation from them if anything happened, and they know that I would do all I could to help.

I never had a better crew anywhere . . . I can't ever remember any grievance here which had to do with the way I handle the men. I'm very satisfied with these guys.

I have had every line in this department but one, but this is the best one I have had yet. This is a very good crew. They always help you. They never let you down.

I've got a good crew here. They all know they have a job to do, and furthermore, they are all friends of mine. I used to work with them.

These foremen clearly believed in the capacity and willingness of their men to do a good job, and accordingly acted toward them with this basic assumption in mind. The men, therefore, tended to react in ways which justified the expectations held of them.[1]

Out of the interviews there emerged a kind of norm for the behavior of a good assembly-line foreman toward his men. Those foremen accounted by both their superiors and subordinates as "good" approached, without ever wholly reaching, this norm. There are certain ways of behaving which characterize good foremen anywhere: in a toy factory, a textile mill, or a shipyard, for example. Nearly everyone agrees — and Plant X was no exception — that a foreman should be fair, be friendly, treat his men as individuals, and so forth. But what was arresting, as well as especially appropriate for this inquiry, was the particular form and stress which such generalizations assumed when applied to the foreman on an assembly line. Besides a special emphasis given to well-worn items in the norm, there emerged a few novel qualifications. The most important of these was the ability to act as a

[1] For an "analytical scheme" which emphasizes the way in which a pattern of human relationships is determined and reinforced by the dominant assumptions of the individuals involved, see H. O. Ronken and P. R. Lawrence, *Administering Changes: A Case Study of Human Relations in a Factory* (Boston: Division of Research, Harvard Business School, 1952), especially pp. 166–170.

shock absorber, or as the average foreman put it, the "ability to take pressure from above, but not pass it on."

The items most often mentioned by the foremen (though the weight attributed to the item varied with the respondent) of how a good foreman behaves toward his men were these:

Treat your men as individuals on the job, since each one is different.

Establish a personal relationship with your men, apart from the job relationship.

Teach and promote your own men as far as possible.

Be a shock absorber. ("Absorb pressure and don't pass it on.")

Stand up for your men and interpret their needs and wishes to upper management.

Consult your workers and delegate responsibility to them.

It is obvious that these items do not include all the duties or obligations of a foreman. They say nothing about the many precepts that every well-trained foreman has by heart – and no alert management allows him to forget – such as: watch out for costs in both manpower and materials; be a good housekeeper; etc. They concern solely his relations with his men, and they are strictly what the foreman said or implied about how a foreman on an assembly line *should* behave. One more point before we look at them more closely. In a few cases, the foreman in talking with our interviewers was clearly voicing what he thought upper management – or the interviewer – would like to have him say. The majority, however, gave every evidence of talking out of their own experience and believing what they said.

TREAT YOUR MEN AS INDIVIDUALS

This precept was mentioned more often and perhaps more fully elaborated in our interviews than any other. Why? There is internal evidence in the language used that one reason for the many mentions was the stress this point had been given in training sessions. But there is also plenty of evidence that foremen had really thought hard about this particular point and were doing something about it in their daily work.

A simple and thoroughly practical application of the principle of treating men as individuals was given by one foreman, when he pointed to a worker whose job kept him isolated and at some physical distance from the rest of the section. "Most men couldn't stand that job, but this man likes to work by himself so I put him there." Another foreman showed his awareness of personal differences by remarking: "That man down there is slow as molasses, but he's a good worker. If I should try to needle him, he'd go even slower."

A third: "That guy over there has an unusual, highly skilled job. You can't tell him anything, he feels so important. He *is* good, too, but he's hard to handle, and I'm one of the few foremen who really understands him."

All this appears as wholesome human relations. When the foremen, however, turned from such simple examples to the ever-present problem of how to be "*fair* to *different* men doing the *same* thing," a significant dilemma arose. The dilemma is found, of course, to some degree in any modern factory, but on an assembly line it becomes acute.

All jobs on the line are standardized — that is, one is as much like the next as it is humanly possible for engineering to make them. Furthermore, they are designed, according to the thinking of management engineers, so that an average, normal, worker may perform any of them at the rate the conveyor moves. The question that thrusts itself forward, however, is this: are the operators who perform similar operations themselves similar? How many under foreman X are average; how many are above or below average? To be specific, here are two men on the "jungle line" with the same job, which is to weld small metal sub-assemblies on to the body shell. The time cycle, one and one-half minutes, the number of operations, and the speed of the conveyor are all the same for both men. But operator A is several years older than operator B. Operator B has high manual dexterity; operator A has low. Furthermore, on this particular day operator A is suffering from anxiety over the illness of his child.

The net result is that operator A frequently "goes into the hole"; i.e., is unable to complete his required operations before the conveyor moves on. Operator B works so fast that he is continually piling up for himself what the standards department calls "idle time." What should the foreman do, take work away from operator A and give it to operator B? And if he did so, would that be "fair"?

As noted above, this dilemma, though in a less extreme form, is found in most modern factories, and indeed outside them as well. But with manufacturing processes which are less standardized, individual human differences can more often be matched with operational differences. Here the infinite variations of the human physique and personality are thrown into sharp contrast with the rigorous sameness of assembly-line jobs.

So far as the foreman on the line goes, he describes the dilemma in very simple terms:

Some men take as long as two weeks to break in on this kind of job. But that new kid got to do it well in an hour. He is way above the average. That man next to him is below the average. [The interviewer then asked the obvious question: "Tell me, were both men given the same amount of work to do?"] Yes, because I try not to take advantage of a man who is a good worker.

To make this explicit: the foreman who is taking this approach to the dilemma is arguing that the fair thing is to allow the unusually able worker to earn a spell or "breather" by his unusually fast and skillful work. It is unfair to penalize him, so to speak, by making him work harder than the next man "just because he's good."

But the foreman quoted above added that this approach was not always possible. The exigencies of the line and pressure from above; i.e., from the general foreman or the superintendent, often made it necessary "to pile the work on."

As one foreman put it:

Here's a man who's fast, but you have to watch out, because he'll get his job done ahead and then stand around, which will look bad to the general foreman.

A broad conclusion would appear to be that the tremendous standardization of operations made it very difficult and at times impossible to do more than pay lip-service to the precept that every man is different and should be treated differently. Nonetheless, a majority of foremen were doing their best to adhere to the principle. A specific finding was that in the matter of work loads, as in so many other decisions, foremen were baffled as to what really was fair.

ESTABLISH A PERSONAL RELATIONSHIP WITH YOUR MEN, APART FROM THE JOB RELATIONSHIP

This meant any one of a dozen things, ranging from "Hi" and a grin to actual counselling about personal problems in or out of the plant. Some talked about "listening to what he has to say," understanding a man's feelings, talking about his sports, knowing his family troubles. There was, as might be expected, a touch of the stereotype in some of the foremen's discussions of these points. Nevertheless, it was clear that the average foreman felt that he must establish some sort of personal relationship with his own men if he was going to be successful. Here are typical comments:

We go to foreman school once a week where we learn that every man is an individual. So you have to talk to your men, find out what they do outside, how many children they have, how a man's wife is feeling, and everything.

It seems pretty clear that the foreman who recited the above sentiments very much hoped that his teacher would give him an "A+" in human relations.

On the other hand take this frank comment by a practical therapist:

If I see one of my men is steamed up over something, I just take him off the line, take him around the corner, and say to him: "Now let it blow off, boy, go to it!" And he'll tell me everything on his mind.

Or this foreman who feels himself entangled with the personal lives of his operators whether he wants to be or not:

A lot of the men bring me their problems, personal problems which I really don't have any reason or right to hear. And these sorts of problems affect their work a hell of a lot. Take a man with a sick child — he goes around all day as if he were in a daze. It helps a lot just to let a man speak and say what's on his mind.

Here is another foreman who is taking a psychosomatic approach:

If a feller comes up to me and tells me he has a stomach-ache, well he may or may not have a stomach-ache, but I try to find out what is bothering him because something must be to have him say that.

A few foremen went so far as to maintain social contacts with their men outside the plant. Talking about an outing he was planning with his men, one foreman said:

It's got to be an annual affair now. I started it a couple of years back. . . . We have a lot of fun. It's something the fellows talk about before it happens, and something to remember and talk about for months afterwards.

As we have emphasized before, the social atmosphere of an automobile assembly line is a peculiarly impersonal one. In the above comments it is obvious that a counter force is at work. We know that the foremen who made these remarks were in effect counteracting the monotony, the mechanization, and the impersonality of the conveyor and of the standardized task. As our minute-by-minute observations showed, the imperatives of production, especially for the less experienced foremen, rigorously limited the amount of time and also the amount of energy available for "personal relationships." To this point, which is a vital one, we shall return for further discussion in later chapters.

We have already remarked that some of the foremen who discussed personal relationships with the men they supervised appeared to be echoing a company policy which had been made explicit in a supervisory training course in human relations. This suggests the obvious danger of an artificially stimulated sociability. Not all men want to be sociable with the boss. Others are reluctant to discuss their private lives, problems, or even hobbies with their supervisors. It is important for a foreman, or any other counsellor, to know when to be friendly and when not to be. Not every good foreman, nor every good worker is outgoing and sociable. Some of the best foreman-worker relationships depend more on unspoken feelings of mutual respect than upon picnics or clinical conversations.

With the above reservations and recommendations, it may nevertheless be concluded that an informal personal relationship between supervisors and workers is important, and especially so on the assembly line.

One foreman discussing his men said:

I often try to put things in a joking way. If you tear into a man, it injures his pride. Of course, I lose my temper sometimes, but before 12 o'clock I see him again.

While another foreman was working on the line to meet an emergency condition, one of his workers said to the interviewer:

He's a good guy. He doesn't push you too hard. He was one of us, you know. I don't hold it against him that he's got to be a foreman. If he could make the grade, more power to him. If we get into a hole, he always helps us out.

TEACH AND PROMOTE

It is characteristic of the mass-production method that it tends to minimize differences in skills between jobs and hence reduce opportunities for promotion.[2] But nowhere is this more obvious than in the case of the automobile assembly line. The pay differential between the lowest paid, least skilled jobs and the highest or most skilled (with the exception of a few specialists' jobs) is around twenty cents.[3] Nonetheless, there were minor gradations of skill and desirability among jobs, and the good foreman was alert to these differences and did his best to make assignments whenever possible in accordance with some scheme of advancement. In addition it was recognized as desirable shop practice, though not always observed, to allow a good man to transfer out of one section into another, if by so doing he could better himself. Finally, there was one highly important stepping-stone open to hourly wage earners under every foreman, the job of utility man.[4] The alert foreman was always trying to develop one or two of his senior men, for their own good as well as in the interest of production, to become utility men. It was recognized by everybody in the shop that a utility man's job was a kind of school for promotion to the ranks of supervision. These sentiments were expressed particularly by the older foremen:

Over there . . . that man I am trying to develop . . . I had a talk with him yesterday. I asked him if there was anything the

[2] See R. H. Guest, "Work Careers and Aspirations of Automobile Workers," *American Sociological Review,* vol. 19, no. 2 (April 1954), pp. 155–163.

[3] This may be compared with a typical fabricating plant in the metal industry in which a range of from 50 to 75 cents is often found.

[4] Utility man is a special job classification, to which management assigns qualified workers who are capable of stepping into any of the jobs within a given section and, without instruction or guidance, performing them immediately in good and workable manner. Utility men are used to relieve operators for personal or emergency reasons or for repair work. Sometimes they fill in when workers are late or absent.

matter. He said: "Yes, I'm not getting anywhere. I hear where you're going to make another utility man. What are my chances for it?" I told him: "It's up to you. I will put you on pickup work so you can start to learn every operation, and then after a while I will make you a repair man, so you can learn all the jobs." He is happy as hell about it now. . . . A man likes to get ahead. . . . Basically, my job is to get quantity and quality and to develop the men as much as possible.

My men have an incentive to learn because they know that I will promote them when they know the more skilled jobs. . . . Most of the men on those jobs throughout the plant started out under me and learned their jobs here.

Not long ago I saw an opening for a man to a better job. He didn't want it because he wanted to stick with me. I convinced him to go and now he can't thank me enough. The average man, if given a chance, wants to better himself.

They had a man in the next section who wasn't working out. So I took this man over and gave them one of my good men, and I want to see if I can turn a good man out from this rather poor man.

These foremen clearly imply that it is possible on the assembly line to have a system of job progression, to teach men how to perform jobs calling for increasingly more skill, and to help them get promoted when they qualify. This is possible, but it is not easy. Foremen are usually too preoccupied with immediate matters of production. Also, in making promotions seniority has to be considered. Even so, greater emphasis by management on promotion and job progression seemed indicated.

BE A SHOCK ABSORBER

Most foremen and many general foremen and superintendents agreed that an essential supervisory skill on an assembly line is the ability to absorb pressure – either coming from management or implicit in the process – and not transmit it in the same way to subordinates. Some foremen made this point explicit:

I used to get excited on the job and run around all the time. But not now. I have learned how to take it easy. It's easier for me that way, and the men respect you for it too, if you don't get too excited.

A man has to learn not to fight the job. . . . At first when I was made foreman, I got all flustered. I got all nerved up on the job which just makes it worse for you. I take it calm now. That man over there said to me once: "How the hell can I get you flustered? I've tried everything!" You see, I never holler at a man. When I feel like hollering, I just walk away.

The significance of these comments lies in their assumption of a very great temptation to "holler," and of a climate of tension which requires, therefore, a determined effort of will to remain unflustered. In talking about absorbing pressure and not passing it on, however, foremen did not mean compromising their disciplinary powers by letting men disobey direct orders or violate rules.

Explicit recognition of the importance of this shock-absorbing ability was given by the more perceptive members of middle management. Here is a general foreman's comment on the point:

. . . Some people, let's say in higher management, have got to recognize the fact that by putting too much pressure on the foreman, you are only going to drive him to do things that lead to friction on the job. . . . As for myself, I have a thick skin, and I absorb a lot of that pressure and only pass on what I think should be passed on. The foreman has the toughest job in the whole plant — he catches hell from both sides. He gets it from me and from my boss, and he gets it from the hourly men.

All workers naturally like a boss who is on their side when a tough situation comes up and who is willing to "stick his own neck out" in order to give his men the help and protection they need. For the man on the assembly line, this kind of protection is far more important than in most other working environments. Most workers feel that the moving line is compelling them to perform, over and over again, operations which of themselves have little intrinsic interest. For many of them, management may be looked upon as another source of unwelcome pressure. Some foremen, therefore, realized that the only way they could establish a mutually satisfying and constructive relationship was by consciously acting as a buffer or shield to protect their men from such pressures, and also by going out of their way to help a man out of a tight spot whenever the occasion arose.

While helping out on a repair job, one foreman said:

I always get in there to help them out when something goes wrong. If a man knows that you're for him instead of against him, you gain his confidence. He knows that you are ready to help him. And by gaining his confidence that way, everything goes smoother.

The foreman who discussed pressure and the importance of absorbing it attributed its origin either to the work itself as paced by the conveyor or to management, to his own boss, or to some known or unknown persons above him.

Here, for example, is a foreman who is quite explicit about where the pressure comes from, and even more so, about his duty not to pass it on:

The general foreman is always trying to put the pressure on me to get more work out of the men. He sees a man idle, so without waiting to find out why, he tells me to find some work for him to do.

Note how two sources of pressure in this case are actually interdependent. The general foreman is pressuring the foreman to put an idle man to work. But the reason he appears to be idle is because of the general foreman's assumption that a conveyor-paced shop should keep every man busy every minute. The foreman sharply disagrees with this assumption:

If I treat a man right and he figures a way of doing a job which gives him a little rest, then so much the better for him. My boss doesn't understand that, so you might say I'm the concrete wall between the general foreman and the men. I have to take it one way, but not give it out the same way. I suppose the general foreman gets it from his boss, and his boss gets it from his boss.

As might be expected, there were differences in both practice and philosophy in this matter of transmission of pressure above the foreman's rank. A little later we shall look at the relation of those echelons to the foreman. So far as the foremen themselves went, a majority believed that a good foreman on an assembly line must train himself to be a human shock absorber. Otherwise, "it's just too bad" both for the men under him and for his own constitution.

STICK UP FOR YOUR MEN

Related to absorbing pressure and not passing it on was the idea that a good foreman stands up for his men. Few foremen made this point explicitly, perhaps feeling that it would be inappropriate to their role as members of management. Nevertheless, we found that a majority recognized in practice, if not in theory, that a good foreman is *not only a* representative of management; he is also the leader of his group of workers and in this role will fail unless he is seen by his men as one who stands up for and interprets their interests and needs to upper management.

Workers, when interviewed, made the same point. As one of them put it:

> My present foreman is the nicest guy I ever worked for. The other foremen respect him also. I saw him stick his neck out with the general foreman over work loads. You won't find a lot of other foremen doing that. He'll argue a point with the general foreman if he thinks he's right.

Both supervision and workers gave many examples of foremen who stood up for the rights or interests of the hourly wage earner. As a rule they concerned cases where the foreman was an advocate for his own men in the face of what appeared to him as arbitrary, hasty, or misinformed action by a general foreman or a superintendent. The questions at issue might concern work load assignments, alleged negligence in a matter of quality, alleged unauthorized absence, failure to learn a new job quickly enough to satisfy a superior, and a hundred other matters minor in themselves, but by no means trivial or minor to the parties at interest. There are differences that stem from a leader's temperament, or from management's policy, as to how much trouble and how many risks he will take for his own group. And there is, of course, always a danger that he will neglect his duties as management's front-line representative in doing "favors" for his men. But in Plant X there appeared to be a norm of behavior on this point, which was well recognized by both management and the hourly wage earner.

CONSULT YOUR WORKERS AND DELEGATE RESPONSIBILITY TO THEM

This was emphasized particularly by the more experienced foremen. In fact there might almost be said to be a range of policy and practice in this matter, from the foreman, for example, who ran his section — or tried to — as a one-man show to the foreman who had trained his men as a team to be able to solve nearly all day-to-day problems without his help. Foremen with a "do-everything-myself" philosophy naturally said nothing about delegating responsibility, but the foremen who believed in and practiced the principle were articulate and often emphatic on the point.

To give some examples, here is a foreman who, although he did not emphasize the general principle nor mention the word responsibility, believed strongly that his men should be *consulted* when changes were made, so that they themselves could make suggestions:

> In this automobile game, change is the standard thing. . . . Most people don't like to be told that they are going to be changed and to take it or leave it. They like to know about it ahead of time, and they like to feel they've had a part in it.

Another foreman said that he gave each of his men as much

responsibility as possible. For example, he pointed to two men working off the line, and he said that they were allowed to decide for themselves when they had made enough sub-assemblies for one line of cars, and when it was time to shift to another series:

One man can't possibly run everything in a department. The foreman can't do everything, but he has to rely on his men. And his men appreciate it when he gives them responsibility.

Here is another who named specific duties that had been delegated:

There is so much on the assembly line that even a utility man can't do everything. Now what I have trained my utility men to do is to get the men themselves to take a lot of responsibility themselves. If they see that they are running short of parts, why it is the usual practice for the utility man to check with the stock man. But in my section the men themselves know enough to take care of it.

The above are examples of the delegation of responsibility which are elementary and limited compared with what is possible in a less mechanized work environment. They are nonetheless important to the workers and supervisors involved. In fact by their apparent triviality, they dramatize the degree to which many jobs on an assembly line have been denuded of the duties commonly associated with many other kinds of work.

We now come to a more complicated example:

I have often put it up to a group of men as to how they are going to break their work down. You take the seven men on that sub-assembly job over there. I got them together and said: "Now you boys know more about the job than I do. Do you want to break it down in any way you think best?" I went on to explain to them that I wanted it broken down so that any of the men could do any of the different jobs. . . . Now there are some people who wouldn't go for that. . . . [But] if he [the foreman] can put some trust in his men, they'll break it down fair enough.

It is worth looking closely at this example. This foreman, like many others, retained full responsibility for the quality of the work, yet by giving the men a say in the breaking down and assignment of duties in a sub-section, he had enlarged the interest of the men in their own jobs. Also, their role was changed, if only slightly, from that of operator to that of participant—from persons who had always been told, they became persons who were now in some degree being consulted, about their work.

But besides thus assisting the foreman in the breakdown of the jobs, each man could learn the other men's jobs in the sub-section; as a result men could be rotated between jobs and so the element of *variety* was added to otherwise monotonous tasks. Such shared knowledge of all the jobs brought, in addition, a special advantage to the foreman and to the group. If any man was absent, any other man out of the sub-section could take over his job. All of this added up to a sense of membership in a bona fide work team. Finally, in the foreman's opinion, the quality of the product had been substantially improved through this arrangement.

Since assembly work has been designed to minimize the responsibilities of individuals and to exist without reference to team-work, it is striking that a sense of individual responsibility, an appreciation of variety, and a sense of team membership have all reasserted themselves.

Every foreman's most experienced workers, to whom he could and did delegate special responsibilities, were his utility men. But here again, as in the case of his other workers, the amount of responsibility delegated varied widely. Such foremen as we have just been quoting, who recognized that they could not successfully do everything alone, had come to rely heavily on their utility men, not only in emergencies, but also in the day-to-day administration of their sections. Here are discussions of the point by two old timers recognized by plant management as thoroughly experienced and highly successful foremen:

Once a foreman starts to poke into everything, he is lost. The utility man loses self-confidence and doesn't feel that he can make a move for fear that the foreman will step in and say something else. I can see that in certain kinds of industries under very stable conditions perhaps it is best to have the foreman keep his fingers on everything. But on an assembly line you must design your whole personnel setup for emergency conditions, because everything is in a constant state of emergency. As I like to tell my friends, an assembly line is just one damn emergency after another.

I have four utility men, and they relieve and also do repair work. There is one of them over there. Watch him work. I have the men trained to go to him on most mechanical problems, unless the problems are very serious, when they come to me. That gives me time to look after the schedules, to constantly check on my quality and other things. I think that foremen around here do not delegate responsibility enough.

There are workers, on assembly lines as elsewhere, who do not want responsibility delegated to them, even such responsibilities as we have just been discussing. But from our own investigation of assembly lines, such workers appear to be in a minority. As noted earlier the foremen at Plant X differed both in policy and practice in this matter. It is worth restating, however, that the more experienced and more successful supervisor (in plant management's opinion) advocated and practiced a maximum delegation of responsibility to his operators.

SUMMARY AND CONCLUSION

We began this chapter by looking at the direct effect of the moving line on the foreman's job. Did the conveyor make that job harder or easier? A discussion of this question by the foremen themselves was related to the problem of discipline, of keeping the men at their jobs, of checking up on them, and so forth. And on this question a minority took the position that the moving line made the job easier by substituting, so to speak, mechanical compulsion for human supervision. The majority disagreed. These were the reasons: first of all, the conveyor obviously did not solve a foreman's major problems, maintaining quality and keeping the line manned; second, the moving line, coupled with the repetitive character of most jobs, created problems of adjustment and morale. Then too, most foremen felt that to get production by getting tough too often merely reinforced the disagreeable aspects of the job, and so lowered morale. In emergencies and in special cases, driving was necessary, but it was generally considered an outmoded supervisory technique. Many foremen volunteered to the interviewers that a good crew did not need to be pushed.

Attitudes and opinions about the effects of the technical process upon human motivation were reinforced when the characteristics of good foremanship were discussed. A good foreman on an assembly line, according to foremen in Plant X, should treat his men as individuals on the job; establish a personal relationship with his men apart from the job relationship; teach and promote his men as far as possible; be a shock absorber; stand up for his men; and consult his men and delegate responsibility to them. Each of these points tended to counteract some of the pressures or tensions inherent in the technological environment, and to substitute an individual approach for an anonymous and impersonal one.

Ever since the early work of Elton Mayo, and especially since the publication of *Management and the Worker* by Roethlisberger and Dickson, there has been much emphasis on the importance of sound relations at work, especially where the job itself lacks intrinsic interest. In this matter supervision is always an important factor in *any* factory society. But on the assembly line the first line supervisor is a particularly important factor in good human relations. He is strategic in the swift adjustment of the novice to the unique experience of a mobile work environment, to the solution of day-to-day personal problems as they arise on the job, to promotion, to a sense of individual worth and an acceptance of responsibility, to "protection" from hostile forces whether personal or impersonal. In order to assure maximum effort among his subordinates, a good assembly line foreman must be able to absorb enormous pressures from many sources and still not become a symbol of pressure to his men.

We will now look at the foreman's own supervisors. What are an assembly-line foreman's relations to management: to his own boss in particular (the general foreman) and also to the other ranks of management above him?

4 THE FOREMAN AND MANAGEMENT

Throughout their discussion of management groups, foremen emphasized one criterion of value above all others. This was *helpfulness.* Foremen had a difficult job to do, were subject to many and conflicting pressures. Therefore, when talking about their own boss or other members of management, they almost invariably reported whether these persons helped or hindered them in coping with the problems of the job.

RELATIONS WITH STAFF AND SERVICE DEPARTMENTS

In Plant X a majority of foremen said that the staff and service personnel were helpful to them. For instance, in discussing Labor Relations, the typical comment was, "When anything comes up they will help you out":

The staff people give me all the help I've ever wanted. I haven't had too much contact with them, but Labor Relations has always given me all I wanted.

If there is anything I need help on, all I have to do is call on the telephone and they will help me out.

Service groups were generally recognized by foremen as having specialized skill and experience in a particular area. As might be expected, when a foreman thought this way about a staff function, he found it easier to accept advice which might contradict his own judgment. In short, staff personnel were commonly conceived as a source of help rather than unwelcome interference:

If we need some help on works standards or something, we go to the phone and they get someone down here right away to help us out.

We work here and we know the operations, but perhaps we can't see all the problems. Someone else can come around sometimes and see some things we couldn't see ourselves.

We have unlimited resources to draw on. There are men who specialize in process engineering, methods engineering, and so on. Maybe they couldn't take a foreman's job because they are not as close to the job as we are, but they see things that we don't.

Even when complaints were made, foremen generally recognized that the purpose of the service department was to assist them. The complaints, therefore, were likely to be either that the particular department was not as helpful as the foreman had a right to expect, or that the reasons for certain policies should have been more fully explained.[1]

The importance of this good relationship between line and service departments can hardly be exaggerated. As technological processes have grown more elaborate, especially over the past twenty years, the number and importance of staff departments have enormously increased. The result is that the foreman, instead of being "king of his own castle" and competent to decide most technical or administrative questions himself, depends increasingly on experts. The experts or advisers to front-line supervision are numerous and of critical importance in most modern manufacturing plants. Any misunderstandings or jealousies, due, for example, to power grabbing, among them, may wreck the efficiency of the whole arrangement.[2]

[1] Two or three foremen made a point of mentioning the helpfulness of the plant doctor. He was someone, they said, you could really talk to about your worries. Although this example of helpfulness to foremen is different in nature from the others given, we believe that it is important. Many foremen clearly benefited from an opportunity to talk freely about things that were troubling them.

[2] At the time this study was nearing completion, the authors began investigation of another manufacturing plant where misunderstandings among inspection, engineering, and the line seriously reduced output of the com-

The need for a large number of specialists in maintenance, engineering, inspection, and other staff and service departments is one major result of a mass production technology. In Plant X at least, a minimum of human relations problems appeared to be connected with this development.

RELATIONS WITH OTHER FOREMEN

Again, the general theme of comments made by foremen about their fellow foremen was helpfulness; indeed, "We help each other out" was most often heard. For example:

We have very good cooperation between foremen here. Like if I get into some trouble, why the next foreman will come down and help me out, and I will do the same for him. That is a very important thing, too, and it means a lot to the men to see that the foremen are not on each other's necks all the time.

The foremen here help each other out. It has to be that way. . . . Like if one foreman's man hasn't done something right, the other will come over and say, "Can you get that bolt back further for me?" and so you say, "Sure, I'll see what I can do." Ninety-nine per cent of the foremen are good Joes. If they can, they'll straighten it out.

Other ways in which one foreman could help another included taking over the other's section when he went to a training session, getting a new worker a job in another area where he would be better suited to the work, lending another foreman a man to replace an absentee, and redistributing operations more equitably between two adjacent sections. All such forms of mutual assistance showed that many foremen thought in terms which were broader than the short-run advantage to their own particular sections:

---

pany's major products. Staff departments, as in this instance, frequently infringe on the legitimate functions of the line. For a provocative discussion of this problem and of the frustrations of foremen in such a situation, see F. J. Roethlisberger, "The Foreman: Master and Victim of Double Talk," *Harvard Business Review*, vol. 23, no. 3 (Spring 1945), pp. 283–298.

The other night I wanted to borrow a man from Art (another foreman) and I went over, saw him about it. Art said, "What in the hell are you trying to pull on me now?"; but we talked about it and made the switch. He gained nothing, but I did. The next time he'll gain something. . . The other day one of my boys got out of position on the line, he got behind. Bob came along and threw one of his utility men on. I didn't ask him to do it, but he fixed it up on his own.

Well, as for the foremen, there is no problem. Everyone helps each other out. Like Charlie now. He's over there watching my line while I'm talking to you, and this morning he gave me a man because I need a man pretty badly. Sometimes I take over for him. He really has helped me out quite a bit.

There were five other types of statements made about relations with other foremen:

Other foremen are not helpful.

Other foremen interfere too much.

My own section comes first.

Foremen do not get together enough.

There is too much competition among foremen.

Other foremen are not helpful. There were a few foremen who did not find their relationship with other foremen helpful, and did not expect it to be. Occasionally, a foreman complained about what he called "cliques" among other members of supervision:

I don't hobnob very much with the other foremen. I know that lots of the people in supervision have their cliques, and that they go around together, but I don't do that.

A few other foremen, who prided themselves on their independence, made complaints about the other foremen, such as: "The trouble is too many of these bosses forget they were once on the line themselves." And foremen in car conditioning, during periods of unusually high and sustained overtime, sometimes talked with bitterness tinged with envy over the shorter and more regular hours of other foremen.

Other foremen interfere too much. Much of the interaction that took place between foremen was concerned with mistakes made by workers in the assembly process. For instance, suppose Foreman B's operations are being disrupted on account of bad work by one of the men under Foreman A, who precedes him on the line. In order to clear the situation up, Foreman B has to go to Foreman A and show him what is wrong. This type of contact occurred constantly, and not only between adjacent foremen. Often a bad weld or paint job or some other operation would cause trouble not for the next foreman in line, but for a foreman several sections down, or even in another department. Thus, foremen were frequently, in effect, finding fault with each other. That is why they found it so difficult and yet so important to get along well with each other.

A new foreman remarked:

> Then there are problems with the other foremen, too. I mean like being called back on complaints; and then when you go around to them with complaints, they say they don't have time to listen to 'em. But we get along pretty well.

This same foreman complained that other foremen came around, interfered with his men, and gave him unwelcome advice. As a new foreman, his contacts with other foremen had been a source of friction, not of help, to him. This could have been either his fault or theirs; probably, it was a little of both. In any case, the few foremen who talked in this way implied they would rather see less of other foremen, not more. As one of them said: "Around here, no news is good news, but it shouldn't be that way."

My own section comes first. It was natural for a foreman to be primarily concerned with his own operations; he was supposed to be. However, when carried too far, this attitude was more conducive to friction than to helpfulness. A strong statement of this kind was sometimes coupled with equal emphasis on the importance of good relations with other foremen. "My job is in this one section. I don't give a damn about other places. My job is here." Yet a few minutes later the speaker remarked:

Another thing that is important is for the foremen to get along well with each other. It don't pay for foremen to clash. The way it is here, there is enough petty quarrelling without the foremen fighting each other. So we cooperate pretty good. If two foremen get to arguing, the men get a big kick out of watching them, and you lose their respect.

Foremen do not get together enough. Several foremen, recognizing that smooth relationships with each other were necessary if they were to get their work done well and at the same time keep the respect of the men, said that more interaction and cooperation between foremen should be permitted and encouraged. To these men, contacts with other foremen were highly desirable; the trouble was that they did not occur frequently enough:

There's no time during the day to talk with the other foremen. I wish there was.

You see two foremen a lot; you see the foreman in front of you and the one in back of you practically all day long. Now, one of the troubles around here is that the foremen are so busy, they don't contact you unless it's a point where the line is going to break down. . . . For example, if the foreman before me has a man doing something wrong, all I can do is to finally have the line stopped and then go down and speak to the foreman about it. Now, if I were free at all times and that other fellow were free at all times, this line stopping just wouldn't happen. They ought to make a rule that foremen should meet and talk these things over at least twice a day.

There is too much competition among foremen. As a method of controlling costs, management computed an "efficiency score" for each foreman. Most of those interviewed felt this practice led to unnecessary friction, and that in evaluating a foreman's performance management should pay more attention to the essential interdependence of all supervision along the line. This feeling was all the stronger since many foremen had little understanding of how the "efficiency report" was calculated or used.

Here is how one foreman made the point:

I have seen in the last ten years that there has been an increase in the competition between one foreman and another. I don't know if this is a good practice. They are carrying it too far. Of course, you have to realize that everything is competitive, but there is too much between individual foremen. Competition between plants, sure, that's all right. But you see, each foreman is rated for efficiency, and this tends to make for too much individualism and not enough emphasis on working together. The ratings are posted in the superintendent's office.

It can be seen from the preceding discussion that, despite the necessity for foremen to point out errors or omissions in each other's work, and despite competition, spontaneous or stimulated, among them, most foremen had successfully resisted impulses towards conflict or friction. Because the sections under different foremen were so *closely related to each other by the moving line*, and because of the recurrence of sudden emergencies which were not allowed for by the technical organization of the work, cooperation between foremen is perhaps more important than in other types of plants. Foremen, as they were being interviewed, talked about the importance of helping each other out, not simply as a way of helping themselves, but because they knew intimately the interdependence of the various sections and because helping the other fellow seemed to them the natural thing to do in these circumstances:

I get along good with the other foremen. In this business you've **got** to. That's the only way to work. If I went over and told the other foreman I need some help or to correct a certain part, he'll go out of his way to help, which means a lot.

I think the closer we foremen work together, the better it is; and I always feel that the sooner a foreman ahead of me tells me what's wrong, the better it is, too.

THE FOREMAN'S OWN BOSS

It is a familiar principle of organizational procedure that a superior should not "jump levels" in dealing with a subordinate; that is, orders and communications, either up or down, should follow lines of organization. The authors have interviewed supervisors in many industries, but never has this principle been so firmly or so frequently stressed as by foremen on automobile assembly lines. Why? The character of the interviews, together with what we know of the general climate of relations on the "line," suggests two reasons for the foreman's emphasis. First, that the principle was all too frequently broken, and second, that it was broken chiefly because of very great pressure on department superintendents to keep the line moving. When a superintendent or general foreman sensed trouble, his instinct, unless he had a strong organizational conscience, was to rush straight to the sore spot and cure it himself. And in so doing he was often tempted to reprimand workers in front of their own foremen:

In some places the superintendent thinks nothing of going down to the line and bawling a man out or bawling a foreman out right in front of his men. You don't see that in this department. This superintendent is very strong on following strictly the line of organization. He always deals with the general foreman, and the general foreman talks to the foreman. If something comes up that applies to all the foremen, why then we have a department meeting and the general foreman speaks his piece to us all, and after that the superintendent might add a word, but the general foreman talks first. They are very good that way here on going strictly by a line organization.

Besides all the reasons given by this foreman for wanting a strict observance of the principle, foremen on assembly lines, like foremen everywhere, wanted as much autonomy as they could get, and "jumping levels'" was viewed as an assault on home rule:

When it comes to running my particular section, I don't think the superintendent should enter the picture. As a matter of fact, I see very little of him. The general foreman is the only one I come into contact with, which is right. He is the one who is closest to us.

Or take this comment on the same point from another foreman:

If something goes wrong on the line, it is the foreman's job to take care of it. Because in his own section, he knows all the angles of any particular situation.

Thus, foremen valued highly the principle of "going by the line of organization." It was difficult, however, always to adhere to the principle under existing pressures. Foremen would forgive lapses if the boss tried and intended to follow it.[3]

It was striking that nearly all the points which emerged when foremen discussed how they ought to behave toward their men appeared in one way or another when they discussed how their own bosses — general foremen or superintendents — ought to behave toward them. That was particularly true of these two items of foreman behavior: be a good shock absorber; and consult your workers and delegate responsibility to them.

Consider the first of these. The reader will remember that foremen recognized that the ability to receive pressure but not to transmit it — or at least not all of it — to their workers was a vital supervisory skill on an automobile assembly line. Similarly, foremen praised general foremen and superintendents when they

[3] There was some disagreement on the applicability of the principle to a situation when Foreman B wanted to correct faulty work done under Foreman A who was in another department. Should B go over and talk to A directly, or should the contact go up and down through the two sets of general foremen and superintendents involved? Some said they preferred to deal directly with the foreman responsible. A few on the receiving end of the contact preferred to be notified by their own boss, not by another foreman. Presumably the suitability of either route in practice would depend on (1) the urgency and seriousness of the particular instance, and (2) on the kind of personal relationship existing between the two foremen in question.

exhibited a similar ability and criticized them when they did not. Here is an example of the kind of behavior by a superior that a foreman resented:

We have a certain item come up, like the other day, and my boss comes around and wants to correct it right then. He doesn't want to waste any time. Well, the other day I had two men out—emergency situation. I was all tied up, and the committeeman was screaming to me about something. My boss kept coming around and coming around, hounding me. He knew I was busy, but he kept hitting me on this one item. And because he's on your tail you do a half-ass job.

The interviewer asked what the general foreman should have done, and the foreman answered promptly:

Well, he **could** come up and ask you a question instead of telling you what you are supposed to do. You could have him watch the line while you go up and repair the thing, for instance.

The foreman volunteered this explanation for the general foreman's behavior:

Well, they are not on the line; they don't realize our problems. But I guess we all need patience. He's being pushed, too, of course, but then that's the test of the man.

The conclusion was widely expressed that pressure from superiors, after a certain point, creates needless friction and defeats its own purpose. Or, as some put it, the pressure designed to increase efficiency operates in reverse. It is also of interest that several foremen, though critical, boasted of their ability "to take it."

An old-timer, talking about how his bosses kept "hollering" at him, said:

I don't like to mention any names, but some of the foremen have not been able to take it. They have had to just give up and go home. It **can** be pretty rough, but I figure that I have learned how to take it without letting it get me down.

Another foreman, when asked what was the outstanding characteristic of his job, said, "Pressure." But he added he had learned to act so that it didn't bother him:

When they pull that pressure stuff on me I tell them to leave me alone or else I walk away from them.

There was interesting evidence that what was important in influencing the way a foreman felt about his boss was not solely what the boss *did* in a particular situation, but also the way the foreman interpreted underlying *attitudes* behind the boss's action. Sometimes foremen would describe, for example, things they thoroughly disliked which their boss did, but said they still respected him because basically he wanted to do right by them. They added that he often did things because he could not help himself. Foremen knew how tempted the general foreman or superintendent must constantly be to relieve some of his own tension by taking it out on the foreman:

I have a very good boss. Nothing ever excites him. He's honest and fair. His boss will crack down on him, but he won't on us. Too often around here, if one man jumps . . . the other does too. The mood of the foreman reflects the mood of his boss.

The truth of the last statement — the mood of the foreman reflects the mood of the boss — was recognized by several of the department heads and general foremen with whom we talked. For this reason, the best of them tried hard to keep calm. And some succeeded:

Right now I have never worked for more cool-minded people. They seem to stay collected at all times, and that is a very important thing. . . . Yes, I am working for a boss who expects you to keep your head at all times. His boss is the same way, and so is his boss's boss. . . . I am willing to say that you will find that relations with the foremen are pretty fair in this department. And when you have that kind of relations, it's got to come from up above. It's the people on top that make the difference.

Or, as others put it, when your superior acts calmly and approaches your problem without excessive tension or excitement, he is more likely to "help you out, not just condemn you, when something goes wrong." These words obviously correspond to the qualifications of a good foreman, as seen by his workers: "He is ready to help when you're in trouble" (see p. 26). The foreman's boss appears at his side most frequently when there is trouble in his section. When things are running smoothly, the department superintendents and the general foremen are generally out of sight. This situation was no cause for resentment to the average foreman; he did not expect to see his boss except in time of trouble. What mattered very much, however, was the boss's temper and attitude during these emergencies.

Did the foreman's boss use an emergency as another occasion to tell the foreman he was in trouble (which he already knew) and to imply that he was incompetent (which he resented)? Or did the general foreman or department superintendent use the opportunity to *help* the foreman solve the difficulty and to *teach* him how to deal with similar situations in the future?

My boss thinks that whenever anything goes wrong it's always the foreman's fault. . . . He never says what he can do to help you, but he always picks your job apart. He tries hard, but he's too ready to condemn rather than help.

My boss is the best man I have ever worked for. He finds out what's troubling you before he tells you what to do, and he'll ask why. . . . Other supervisors come down here and start yelling at you before they find out what's wrong. But not him.

When I have to make a tough decision, my boss will help me out. He is a wonderful man, never raises his voice, gets more from the men than anyone I know. And if he sees something wrong, he'll make a **suggestion!**

Consider now what we put down as the final item of good foremanship: consult your workers, and delegate responsibility to them. Foremen felt that they should observe this principle in dealing with their workers and just as strongly that their own bosses should observe the same principle in dealing with them, but that too often they did not:

This place is penny-wise and pound-foolish. Instead of arguing against the judgment of the foreman at every turn, it would be a lot healthier if our bosses did this: Let the foreman stick his neck out, and then really put it up to him if he's wrong. If they'd do this, it would show where the best foremen are.

Here is another foreman who took a more extreme position:

It seems to me that if I can't be trusted to judge how many men I need, I shouldn't be a foreman. . . . We just get treated as if we can't be trusted. . . . They call us members of management, but they don't treat us like we were. I'm not one of those fellows that has a strong drive to go places. . . . but I do have a strong drive to do a good job, and be trusted to do it.

There were two specific areas wherein this foreman felt he should be given responsibility and be trusted. The first was in staffing his section, as indicated above; the other was in the amount of discretion allowed to procure necessary materials and supplies within the limits of his established budget:

If a foreman gets out of hand and makes outlandish demands for materials, why, of course, management should step in. But otherwise, the general foreman and his boss should leave it up to the foreman to say when he needs materials and how much.

If some foremen were critical of their bosses' behavior in matters of authority, a majority were not:

They're pretty nice fellows. . . . They never come around unless we really have trouble, and they never stand over you like they do in some departments. They're reasonable, show you consideration and you can get help from them. Like, take this morning with the trouble we had. My general foreman and my superintendent didn't bawl hell out of me. They got together and made a decision, which we all understood.

To summarize, let one of the bosses the foremen have been talking about speak for himself. Foremen under him, while they referred to incidents where he had become excited or blamed them without reason, also forgave these lapses because they recognized that his basic attitude was one of helpfulness:

If the foreman is in some trouble, it doesn't do any good to tell him that he is in trouble — he already knows it. But the thing to do is to see how we can help him. Sometimes I know I do say to a foreman, "You solve it. I don't care what the difficulty is." But when I do that, I think it has a bad effect. I try not to push the foremen. I try to be as much help as I can. . . . Dealing with a foreman is just like dealing with anyone else. You have a group of different personalities, and you have got to understand the point of view of each one of them.

THE FOREMAN AND UPPER PLANT MANAGEMENT

When foremen talked about members of management above the level of superintendent, their comments were almost always favorable. For instance, one foreman gave this explanation for good cooperation between departments in the plant:

One reason is the Plant Manager. He has a knack of having people work together. And the Production Manager has a lot to do with it, too. . . .

Most foremen agreed, although several pointed out that the plant and production managers were seldom seen on the floor:

The Manager should try to get to the man on the firing line more. I know he's busy, but he's not **that** busy.

Our observation of Plant X foremen showed few direct contacts between foremen and upper plant management. In part this was because of the strong emphasis throughout management on the importance of following the line of organization. Foremen did not want or expect upper plant management to deal with them directly on important production matters. What several of them did want was more frequent, *informal* contact with these superiors.

Some foremen felt that more frequent plant-wide meetings would help establish closer relations with management. Occasionally a foreman complained in a half-humorous fashion that plant meetings were only held when things were going badly.

Another reason for wanting more frequent management meetings was to help foremen learn more about practices and policies which affected them. Throughout our interviews there were scattered complaints against certain corporation or plant policies. One example was the policy concerning discounts on the company's products; another concerned the requirement that foremen report to work on days when there was no production. In almost every case complaints were not so much about the policy itself as about the lack of adequate explanation of that policy to the foremen:

I might feel differently about it if I knew the reason why. We're supposed to have the answers, and if someone has them before you, that's no good. . . . It makes you feel as if you weren't in management's confidence.

In the authors' experience, front-line supervisors in most organizations feel inadequately informed about current developments and the reasons for policies that affect them. As a matter of fact, complaints of this nature were less frequent in Plant X than is usually the case.

In spite of those comments which criticized the lack of closer personal ties with local management, most foremen had a favorable attitude toward the production and plant managers. Especially important here, as in other relationships, was the feeling that these managers acted as "shock absorbers," and refrained from passing down unnecessary pressures. In describing human relations within the plant, many foremen agreed with the supervisor already quoted who said, "It's the people on top that make the difference."

Foremen felt that they belonged to the management of Plant X, but they did not have the same sense of belonging to the corporation as a whole. Nor did they think that corporation management above the local plant level really understood what it was like to be a foreman. A synthesis of foremen's attitudes on this subject may be stated as follows:

We are often told that top management thinks of us as the most important member of management. But those on top sometimes make decisions without first-hand knowledge of what happens here on the firing line. Too often, top management, in deciding how to get us to do the best possible job, shows little understanding of the foreman's point of view.

We are told to make decisions affecting our subordinates only after we understand their point of view and the problems they face. This pays off in quality and efficiency. Local management, by and large, follows the same principle, but we don't see it applied higher up. If those on top understood our problems better, we think we could help make this an even better organization than it is.

To a degree, this feeling of distance between foremen and top management is inevitable in any large organization. Yet much can be done to increase the front-line supervisor's sense of identification with the company as a whole and with the objectives of top management. Foremen in any industry are not only interested in being *told* that they are members of the management team. They want to be *treated* as members of management, which means being consulted on decisions that affect them. At the same time they want those on top to realize that the effective foreman is necessarily the leader, and in a very real sense a member, of his own immediate group of workers. The foreman's position is difficult; it helps him when his superiors recognize his difficulties, and understand his point of view.

SUMMARY AND CONCLUSIONS

1. The main criterion by which foremen evaluated other members of management was "helpfulness." Foremen identified themselves to a considerable extent with management's objec-

tives. But the circumstances of a foreman's job were difficult. They wanted and expected help in accomplishing these objectives — help from each other, from staff people, and from their superiors.

2. A majority of foremen said that they *were* being helped on the job by other members of management. Foremen who did not agree made the following points:

a. The staff departments probably mean to be helpful, but they do not adequately explain the reasons for some of the things they do.

b. Other foremen would be helpful if there were more opportunities to get together, and less emphasis on competition between foremen.

c. General foremen and department superintendents sometimes seem more ready to condemn than to help when something comes up. Of course, they are under pressure too, and the most important factor is whether or not they show a basic *intention* to be helpful.

d. Some foremen felt the need for closer personal contact with plant management, and for more adequate explanation of plant and company policies.

To some extent, different foremen perceived the same behavior by the same individual differently. Some foremen felt too pressed for time, or were too worried about immediate problems, to be able to see that other people were *trying* to be helpful to them.

3. Foremen generally agreed on what specific actions and attitudes by another member of management made a particular relationship helpful:

a. Staff departments were helpful when they addressed themselves to the foreman's problems *as he saw them*, when they gave advice and listened, and when they carefully explained the reasons for policies and actions which affected him.

b. Other foremen were helpful when they were willing to inconvenience themselves and even to subtract from the short-run efficiency of their own section in order to help a neighboring foreman when he needed it. Also when a foreman came over and pointed out some bad work in another foreman's section, the contact could be seen as helpful to both, provided a good informal relationship between them had already been developed.

c. The foreman's boss was helpful when he avoided merely condemning a foreman if something went wrong, when he followed the line of organization in transmitting orders or criticism, and when he was willing to protect a foreman from pressure, trust a foreman, listen to him, take his advice on problems, delegate authority to him, and back him up.

d. Management was helpful when it kept foremen informed concerning problems and policies, when there was as much informal contact and friendliness as possible within the organization, and when those on top, including corporation officials, showed a basic appreciation of the foreman's position and point of view.

5 THE FOREMAN AND PRODUCTION

In an automobile assembly plant, the moving line controls production. In a certain sense it guarantees that a given quantity of the product be manufactured in a given increment of time. If the conveyor is "set" for forty-four cars an hour, eleven cars will be produced every fifteen minutes. This statement, of course, is not strictly accurate. Cars will be produced as scheduled only if certain *other* conditions are fulfilled. And of these other conditions, perhaps the most important are:

1. That the line be kept continuously moving during the increment of time.
2. That each station on the line be adequately supplied with parts and materials.
3. That tools and equipment be in good working order.
4. That all the stations along the line be manned by operators who, in the time allowed, perform their jobs as planned.

Of these four conditions, the first three are not the *direct* responsibility of the assembly-line foreman. For instance, if the line breaks down, it is up to the foreman immediately to notify his superiors and the maintenance department of the trouble. But repairing the breakdown, and keeping the line in good working order, are the direct responsibility, not of the production foreman, but of the maintenance department itself. In the same way, if parts run short or equipment stops working properly, the foreman usually must take immediate action, but it is essentially the responsibility of the appropriate service departments to come to the foreman's rescue and to prevent such occurrences as much as possible. On the other hand, keeping each station of the line manned with operators who perform their assigned jobs in the time allowed *is* more nearly the foreman's responsibility.

This is why turnover and absenteeism created special difficulties for Plant X foremen. Absenteeism in particular was often discussed as the production foreman's most pressing and difficult problem. Unlike the situation in other industries, production could not be temporarily slowed down when a man quit or was absent, and made up later. On the assembly line, each work station on the line had to be manned continuously. Unless a qualified replacement was immediately available, there was often a danger that a whole section of the line would have to be shut down entirely, with serious results for planned production throughout the plant. Compared with other industrial plants, absenteeism at Plant X was not high. Yet, because of the nature of assembly operations, *any* absenteeism was bound to create serious difficulties.

In this chapter, we will describe the regular procedure for covering absentees, the difficulties as described in the foreman's own words, the remedies suggested by foremen for improving the present system, and their suggestions for eliminating some of the causes of absenteeism.

The first and immediate need for the foreman is getting someone to man the operation when the regular incumbent is absent. The replacement might be someone normally engaged in off-line bank-building operations. It might be another line operator. It might be someone "borrowed" from another foreman, or it might be the utility man. And in instances where absenteeism is excessive, it might be the foreman who in an emergency replaces the absentee himself. But whoever happens to be the replacement, operations are apt to be, as one foreman put it, "thrown out of gear." Drawing from other hourly operators often means a reshuffling of several men in the unit. Frequently it means putting a man on the job who is unfamiliar with it. If the foreman steps into the emergency, his other supervisory duties are suspended.

One of the practices for "covering" an absentee is to assign a utility man to a vacant operation. Each foreman is provided with one or more utility men who are capable of performing all the jobs in a section. Some utility men spend most of their time on repair work; some are used to provide personal relief during the day for operators working on the line. This latter function is made difficult when the utility man is covering the job of an absentee. Under these circumstances the system of relief may be upset. Failure to provide normal relief was found to be one of the critical factors in workers' dissatisfaction with their jobs, and foremen become very much disturbed when faced with the question of relief as affected by absenteeism.

Another kind of problem relating to utility men was revealed in this study. It was discovered that most utility men were actually performing a great many more functions than simply that of substitute operator, relief man, or repair man. Many foremen, particularly those with considerable supervisory experience, had developed their utility men to the point where they were capable of assuming some responsibility in such matters as training new operators, checking materials and tools, watching quality problems, and performing other trouble-shooting functions. When a foreman was "hit" by absenteeism, he lost not only the experience of the absent operator, but also the informal but important aid of his utility man.

Under such conditions, with the problem coming up frequently throughout the plant, foremen had less time to give instructions to their men, to observe quality performance, and to deal with personal problems. Bogged down in immediate emergencies, the foreman had too little time to prepare for and to avoid future emergencies. He could not pay adequate attention to new trainees. He could not keep his superior informed of potential trouble and he neglected the important coordinating relationship between himself and the foremen in preceding and succeeding sections.

The seriousness of the absenteeism problem from the foreman's point of view is revealed in the comments below:

The toughest job you can get is being a foreman. You need iron nerves all the time and the biggest strain is absenteeism. You get an excessive amount of absentees that just can't be covered, then you have a mess, with your utility man, with other men, and particularly in time of relief. When there is absenteeism, there's a never-ending pressure on the foreman. Absenteeism has been terrible during the last three months.

One of the troubles around here is that foremen get so busy because of absenteeism that they have to work on the line themselves. When this happens, the other foremen know it, and they don't contact you on important problems, unless it reaches a point where the whole line is going to break down. If you stand at the end of the line and watch the cars as they go into car conditioning [the final repair section] you can tell which departments are having absentees.

The two biggest problems we have here are absenteeism and relief. For example, we have a certain amount of work, and to do it we get a certain amount of manpower. Now, if I have two or more men out, that takes up my utility men, and then I have trouble getting relief for the men. This results in quality trouble.

One of the problems which creates grievances is absenteeism. Say I have three utility men and three absentees. Who'll cover the men for relief? If the three utility men cover the absentees, there just aren't enough men to handle the relief of all my men. That's what causes grievances. A foreman's job all depends on absenteeism. Once that happens it really hurts a foreman. You're licked.

If some men are out, I can cover operations, but I can't relieve the men. I have to work on the line myself sometimes. The more time that a foreman is forced to work on the line, the less time he has to look for trouble.

When you have one man out and only one utility man as I have, then things really get tough. As it is now, even when you have a full crew there is enough for a foreman to do by way of improvement quality-wise, safety-wise, and product-wise. This past week has been very bad. Just take right now — the regular operator has to be relieved and so I have to perform the job myself.

These are but a few of the many comments by foremen which reflect the strength of feeling they have toward the problem of absenteeism. Some foremen are less disturbed than others, and differences between departments were also noted. But it was rare to find that absenteeism was no problem whatsoever to a foreman.

As indicated earlier the most disturbing over-all effect of absenteeism is that it upsets the relationship between the foreman and his men. Workers wanted variety, but they resisted being shifted arbitrarily between jobs and being forced to run their operations in make-shift fashion. Every foreman was fully aware of the fact that such conditions engendered a certain amount of hostility between his men and himself. He recognized the simple but frustrating cycle of events when men stayed out: the time when his men needed him the most — when there were absentees — was also the time when he and his utility man were least able to help them.

With a few exceptions most foremen agreed that no wholly satisfactory solution has been developed by management to remedy the day-to-day effects of absenteeism. They also generally agreed that the simple organizational device of using utility men to substitute for absentees is not the full answer to the problem. Special attempts at a solution have been made in the past, but none appear to have been adequate.

Many suggestions were offered as possible solutions. Some represented an extension of practices now used by certain foremen. Other suggestions involved a marked change in the present system. In all of the comments, there is a strong emphasis on the need for flexibility. Certain foremen were able to achieve some flexibility by teaching some of the operators several jobs:

One way I try to handle absenteeism is to break in as many men as I can so that they can do several jobs within a job classification. I have several old-timers lined up so that they can take over any place. When I have a man absent, I get a substitute from the general foreman and I put the substitute on the easier job and move the rest up into different jobs.

Another suggestion emphasized the use of replacements drawn from off-line operations. In several sections it was noted that certain operators, working at off-line jobs, were able to build up "banks" or surpluses. Foremen found it sometimes possible to pull a man off temporarily and put him on the line to substitute for an absentee. Here are a few typical comments from foremen with such off-line operators:

I have an advantage in my section because one section of my operations is off the line. The men there can make up quite a lot of stock ahead of time. If I am short of men on the regular line I can pull as many men off as I need and it won't affect my off-line operations. . . This gives me a great deal of flexibility. I make a point of teaching the men different line jobs. The men like it, because when I ask them to fill in they are not afraid. So I have a cushion for the shock of absenteeism and it helps a lot.

A key to my flexibility in case of absenteeism is that I have these off-line operations you see here. It's a great help. The boys who are on these off-line operations are capable of going onto pretty much any other job, so I frequently pull them off. There is a mutual understanding that this is the thing to do. Most of the time I'm the one who moves the men around, but there is a certain amount of voluntary movement. I encourage this sort of thing. Now there is a large number of men capable of moving in wherever I need them.

One of the foremen had purposely moved some of his operations off the line with the specific idea of minimizing the effects of absenteeism on the line. As he put it:

Let me show you how I have pulled a lot of operations off the line. Over here I have worked it so that a man can make up these mouldings and get a large stock of them built up quite far ahead of time. Then, if I have an absentee on the line, I can throw this man onto the line. I've done this throughout my group, and it allows me to ride a long time. This kind of thing could be done much more in this Department than it is. Some foremen have the theory that you must try and put every operation on the line. The secret is to train men to do a lot of different jobs. Some men like to do different jobs, and others don't. You have to play that one by ear.

Another comment related to flexibility points out the importance of helping out other foremen when there is absenteeism. One foreman said:

My operations are right next to the other department. The time sometimes comes when the foreman over there needs a man. I have a few men who have done that kind of work, even though their regular job is completely different. I think the men like it because it gives them broader experience.

One attack on absenteeism that was suggested concerned creating some form of labor pool from which men might be drawn temporarily to replace absentees:

It would help the foremen out if they had some kind of employee pool. If they had ten men, say, in the paint department to do the jobs, sort of like utility men, then when a foreman had a man out, he could draw on one of those to fit in. If a foreman had some men out, then the men in the pool could be drawn on and take the load off the foreman. I was a foreman in an aircraft plant during the war, and they had a pool. It worked out very well.

Down at T——— they always had a pool of men. The men in the pool when they weren't working on the line were doing odd jobs that needed to be done some time. We didn't have any absentee problem at all. The men in the pool had been there for years and knew the jobs. They don't have this kind of system here. They say it costs too much money. But you take last Monday when I had four men out. I got by okay, but I sent jobs down the line that weren't right. Later on they had to be repaired, and that cost much more money than the cost of a pool. They have it figured out that there are enough men to take care of the average amount of absenteeism, but actually in an emergency you can't find these men.

A foreman with an unusually high efficiency rating made the following observation about a pool of men:

They have tried many kinds of pools in this and other plants to take care of absenteeism but they failed for two reasons. First, they were not administered right. Superintendents and general foremen did not see to it each day that the men in the pool were utilized most efficiently by the foremen. And second, whenever management put on a drive to cut down on labor costs, they always knocked off the pool first. This is wrong because they were just looking at the immediate labor costs. They are not looking at the long-range savings in repair and car conditioning costs.

Here is what I would like to see tried out. Give a general foreman three or four men, depending on the size of his sections. These men should be the best all round operators drawn from the different sections. They would be utility men. Assign them around the department wherever there are more absentees than the regular utility men can cover. When they are not being used as substitutes there are any number of duties they could perform. They could move in and help train new operators. They could suggest more efficient ways of doing different operations. They could be used as substitute foremen during vacation time, or when a foreman was out sick or when a foreman was out of the section for other reasons. We could watch them to see which ones were permanent foreman material. They could be used, when they were not substituting for absentees, to follow through on some particular quality problem which is giving the foreman a lot of trouble. I don't mean they would take over any regular foreman responsibilities. But there are times when a foreman is trying to check up on a lot of things at once, and he needs someone to get some information from car conditioning or from some other department where there is quality trouble with the work done in our section.

This idea won't work unless the general foreman keeps it under control. I'd like to see the thing tried in one or two areas where the general foremen were top-notch. If there was some way for management to measure the long-range savings against the direct labor costs of such a pool, I'm convinced they would save a hell of a lot of money.

The idea of a labor pool, suggested by Plant X foremen, is not a new one, either in the XY company or in the industry. On the surface it appears to be an obvious and simple solution for assuring a full complement of manpower for the line at all times.

Actually the idea is difficult to put into practice. First, there are the immediate costs to consider. When absenteeism is low on any given day, the wages of the extra men serve to boost labor costs. Also, operating a pool system has many administrative difficulties. Unless closely controlled, there is the natural tendency for foremen and others in supervision to ask for more than their share of reserves to make sure that all emergencies in their section will be met. And, unless those operators in the pool are shifted out of a section as soon as a foreman has his full complement, the extra men may become more or less permanently absorbed in the regular production force. Labor-relations difficulties may also arise because the men in the pool in time come to learn several jobs and then claim that, being all-round operators, they should get utility-man wages.

These are but a few of the difficulties posed by the pooling suggestion. Actually, a form of pooling was installed shortly after this study was made. The general superintendent reported that despite difficulties of administration the plan had a markedly favorable effect on quality performance and that in time it would reduce repair costs in the car conditioning department.

So much for the effects of absenteeism on assembly operations and for suggested solutions. Foremen also discussed the reasons for absenteeism and ways of reducing the absentee rate itself.

As in any industrial plant many absences are caused by sickness and accidents sustained on the outside. Such absences are difficult for management to control. Plant X maintains an elaborate health program. Also, personnel are constantly being reminded of the importance of safety and of avoiding accidents. In our study of foremen, we were struck by the recurring theme of "safety first." Almost no criticism was heard of either the hospital facilities or the safety program.

But sickness and accidents do not always explain why many workers often stay away from work. There are probably some who stay away without a valid excuse. The better foremen were quick to track down chronic offenders and to take disciplinary action against them. Failure to do so, they recognized, was demoralizing to the conscientious workers. Our studies of foremen and hourly workers suggest that in addition to absenteeism resulting from causes either patently justified (sickness, etc.) or completely unjustified, there were still other causes which were somehow related to the tensions and pressures of assembly operations themselves. In the study of hourly workers at Plant X, it was found that workers on more highly repetitive and conveyor-paced jobs tended to be absent more frequently than workers whose jobs had more variety or were less rigidly paced.[1]

Some foremen seemed to recognize that absenteeism among operators was tied in with this constant pressure of the line. They reasoned that every once in a while a man would have to "let off steam," and one way of doing it was to stay home. During long periods of sustained overtime in certain sections, the pressure of production was particularly acute; under such circumstances management devised methods of systematically allowing the men to go home at the regular time once or twice a week.

Too much overtime was frequently mentioned as a cause of above-average absenteeism. "It's been rough lately," remarked one foreman in car conditioning. "We have been working long hours. The men get tired and run down and just don't turn up the next day." A costly walkout in another final assembly plant was caused, in the opinion of a majority of supervision, by too much sustained overtime. Foremen recognize and accept the fact that some overtime has to be expected during the period of changes in models, but a morale problem is to be expected if at the same time production schedules are increased.

Foremen believed that the most important factor in good operations was the maintenance of congenial relationships between themselves and their men, and that to sustain this kind of relationship during periods of high production with excessive overtime a certain amount of tolerance was required in the matter of absenteeism.

[1] *The Man on the Assembly Line,* pp. 117–120.

In the opinion of some foremen, this sense of tolerance is not always shared by higher supervision, as the following comment illustrates:

On absenteeism, the bosses discourage it, but I do let the men off for pretty much any kind of a reason when they tell me in advance. That fellow right over there went to Vermont last Friday because he wanted to spend Easter weekend with his family up there. Now, he helped me out on some off-line jobs ahead of time, and when he came back on Monday he worked like the dickens. The boss didn't know about it, and in fact if they knew that I let a man off for any other reason than an emergency they would be sore about it. You take that other man over there, he got feeling sick yesterday and I sent him to the doctor, but he wouldn't go home because I was in a jam on his stuff, so he worked the rest of the day.

Some foremen brought out the fact that workers themselves, especially the older ones, informally discourage their fellow workers from arbitrarily staying away from work. As one said:

Some of the men put pressure on other men not to stay out. You take in my particular section, it just so happens that to do the work requires the men to work as partners. They get to pace one another and if one of them is absent then a new man comes in and it breaks up the rhythm. If a man abuses absenteeism, his buddy puts pressure on him.

Most operations on the assembly line do not lend themselves to team or partnership relationships. But in spite of this fact, the more experienced foremen were able to instill group loyalty and foster group morale in their sections. They testified that this generated a force which kept down absenteeism.

SUMMARY

Since the foreman has no control over the speed of the conveyor, his direct responsibility for production is to see that the line is adequately manned. For this reason absenteeism, even when the over-all rate is not high, creates serious problems for the assembly line foremen. In a fabricating plant it is not necessary, as on an assembly line, that every work station be manned on pain of causing all operations to shut down.

The various steps that foremen took in trying to solve the absenteeism problem were all efforts at introducing flexibility into assembly-line operations. Teaching men to do more than one job, using replacements from off-line operations, "borrowing" a man from another foreman — in these and other ways foremen tried to gain flexibility for temporary manpower shortages in spite of the rigid manpower requirements of the assembly line. In the same way a manpower pool, most frequently suggested by foremen for dealing with the absenteeism problem, would, if successfully administered, provide the needed flexibility.

Some foremen believed that in addition to the usual causes of absenteeism, many men stayed out because of production pressures at work, especially during periods of sustained overtime. In counteracting such pressures they felt they were helping to reduce absenteeism. Experienced foremen successfully counteracted absenteeism by developing a team relationship among their men. Unfortunately, all too frequently more than one operator failed to report to work.

6 THE FOREMAN AND QUALITY

In the previous chapter it was stated that "the moving line controls production" if certain other conditions are fulfilled. A major condition was that "all the stations along the line be manned by operators who, in the time allowed, perform their jobs as planned." Manning the line from the foreman's point of view was principally a problem of absenteeism. The emphasis in the present chapter is on *performing the job*, which shows itself primarily as a problem of quality.

Quality has many different connotations in industry, depending upon the nature of the skills required to produce an acceptable product. In XY corporation's foundries, where motor blocks are cast, the skills derive from the art and science of metallurgy. In plants making high-precision instruments, quality rests on the delicate skills and long experience of the instrument maker.

On an automobile assembly line quality requires something different. Work is relatively simple and repetitive, requiring more knack than judgment. Nonetheless, a certain amount of surface mental attention and skill in using the human element of hand and eye are required. Quality still depends in the last analysis on the individual worker: the way he performs his operation, simple as the elements may be, and the attitude he has about the work.

Certainly the most striking general conclusion that emerged was the decisive importance of interpersonal relationships, particularly those of worker and foreman, in determining individual job performance and maintaining the worker's interest in quality.

All production foremen at Plant X were encouraged to talk

about both general and specific problems related to quality. Their comments revolved around the two aspects of quality – the human and the technical. More often than not the two aspects were in the foreman's opinion closely interrelated.

When foremen talked about the technical problems, they were speaking of:

1. The condition of tools and materials.
2. The supply of materials and parts to the unit.
3. The interdependence of operations from one unit to the next along the moving conveyor.
4. The fluctuation of line speeds and its effects.
5. The "balance" of work between each of the operators at the various stations along the line.

When foremen talked about the human problems in quality, they were speaking of:

1. How they acted toward others and how others acted toward them in solving the above technical problems.
2. The attitudes of workers toward quality and how attitudes were influenced.

Foremen often discussed the condition of tools and materials and its effect on quality. They spoke about the merits of various hand tools – the welding guns, grinding wheels, spray guns, files, polishers, air-driven screwdrivers, and the hundreds of other tools used by operators. Most foremen recognized the great improvements which had been made in tools and materials over the years. Nevertheless, a number of foremen were convinced that the practical operating experience of foremen was not yet fully tapped. The company to some extent sought the advice of front-line supervisors as to the merits of various tools. Yet foremen believed that their practical experience could be utilized much more than it was when engineering changes were being considered. One member of upper supervision put it this way:

I simply cannot understand why the corporation, when "they" design the product, make engineering changes, or set up their tooling – why they can't pull some grass-roots foremen right out

of the shops and ask them what they think of the changes. I know they tell us that they have practical people working with the engineers, but the ones I've had direct contact with are not practical. They were not people who came up from the ranks and they are not people who are on top of the situation day by day. Only a foreman is in this positon. We've got some who could save many thousands of dollars in quality and production improvements.

This kind of comment and the sort of remarks heard so often from the foremen are interesting in light of suggestions made by hourly workers in previous studies. Many workers were critical of management's failure to seek their advice about tools and equipment, and to a lesser extent about engineering changes. We were in no position to evaluate their complaints from a technical point of view, but their opinions appeared to reflect a wide-spread sentiment. There was little evidence to indicate that the suggestion system alone was the answer.

The condition of materials as they arrived in the plant for assembly was a subject of comment by foremen and to many this subject had a direct bearing on quality. One foreman said, for example:

If we didn't have so much mutilation in materials shipped to us, we would not have to have so many finishers on the line to get the stuff up to quality standards. Mutilation goes in cycles. I don't know why, but perhaps it is the way the railroads bump the freight cars around. They bump 'em a little and it causes a ding [dent] which we have to take out.

Another technical area related to quality concerned the flow and supply of materials and parts within the plant. Any shortage of materials or parts, whether such a shortage lasted for several days or for only a few minutes, upset operations, created a certain amount of human irritation, and indirectly affected quality. It was observed that the greatest number of complaints about handling of materials came from foremen in those sections where there appeared to be the greatest amount of personal antagonism between foremen and the stock men (the latter were not under the jurisdiction of production foremen). A few experienced foremen described the importance of developing good relations with the stock men. Our observations on the line showed clearly that the stock men who did a good job at anticipating needs for parts and materials were those who took the greatest personal interest in the success of the foremen whose unit they serviced. Similarly, foremen who had the least difficulty with the condition of their tools were usually foremen who had established a friendly personal relationship with maintenance personnel.

The functional interdependence of one unit of the line with the next was another technological factor which had a direct bearing on quality. Any error in performance not spotted in one unit often created a more serious problem later in succeeding operations. Defective finishing of the raw surface of the body metal, for example, could and often did cause trouble in the paint operations further down the line. Poor alignment of a door, if not promptly remedied, could show up with serious consequences later on. A characteristic of such errors was that the longer they were left uncorrected, the more difficult and time-consuming their correction became as the product neared final completion.

Such conditions, technical in one sense, place extraordinary emphasis on the need for close coordination between the foremen themselves. Where quality complaints about "the other foreman's section" were the fewest, we observed that:

1. A foreman in succeeding operations showed a sympathetic interest in the difficulties of the preceding foreman.

2. The foreman in preceding operations spent considerable time in the succeeding foreman's area and spoke freely and frequently with the foreman *and his men.* A comment often heard in this connection was, "How's my stuff coming through to you guys?"

Another technical problem of quality, obviously connected with human relations, concerned changes in the speed of the line. This study happened to have been made toward the end of a period in which production increased approximately sixty percent in a period of three months. Although a rise as sharp as this was somewhat unusual for this particular plant, a certain amount of fluctuation month by month is characteristic of all automobile operations. It is interesting to observe how the increased schedule affected the problem of maintaining quality standards. A first and obvious effect of an increase in the production schedule was that new men had to be hired and trained for the jobs. Quality at a particular part of the line naturally suffered because of the lack of experience of trainees. Of course, mistakes were ultimately corrected in car conditioning before the product went to the dealer. But because foremen were forced to spend so much time with new operators, they were unable to spend as much time checking on the condition of the product both in their own area and in areas contingent to their own section. And it was precisely during this period that quality suffered for other reasons, including the following:

1. The change in speed meant a rearrangement of each operator's work elements, some of which were unfamiliar to the man.

2. With increases in the line speed, it became necessary to add new foremen in certain sections.

Some foremen, especially those with long experience, were able to meet the quality problems of changes in line speeds with a minimum of difficulty. They had had practical experience at breaking in new men and at rearranging jobs so as to keep quality errors at a minimum. Old-timers, it was also observed, had some advantage over newer foremen because, being more experienced, they were able to demand and to procure new personnel when they needed it. As one of them put it:

> If I honestly feel I need more men, I go in and tell the general foreman. I always have an explanation for it and the general foreman will listen and let me have them.

Efforts are made at the local plant management level to anticipate personnel needs in the light of advance schedules from the central office, and it is recognized that men must be hired *before* a given production increase in order to allow for some break-in time. Unfortunately, it is not always possible to hire the right kind of operator for the job for which he is best suited. Nor is it always possible to bring in men far enough in advance to be properly trained. Even so, many foremen felt that production was unreasonably stepped up before the foreman had the opportunity to break in new men. One foreman, considered by management to be one of the best in the entire plant, said:

> With the present increase in line speed the company is losing quality. All this overtime you hear about is defective workmanship. They come around and tell me my jobs aren't done right. Hell, nobody has to tell me that, when I don't have enough men to keep up at thirty-eight cars an hour. . . . I know he can't do it right. So then the shortcomings must be picked up in car conditioning before the car goes out to the dealer.

This same foreman went on to acknowledge that many forèmen failed to utilize their manpower properly and had only themselves to blame for poor quality.

Closely allied to the problem of quality and changes in line speed was that of "balancing" the line. In its simplest terms, balancing means the equitable distribution of operations among the workers.

Many foremen described concretely how the problem of balancing was related to quality performance. Take, for example, a typical situation on the main line. The line is operating at the rate of say forty cars per hour. A group of twenty men under a given foreman have a total of twenty operations to perform. Each operation for each man is made up of "elements" or motions connected with the assembly of various parts on the car. Some men may have only five elements, some fifteen depending upon the length of time it takes to go through the motions for each element. At a production rate of forty cars per hour the operation (or sum of elements) of each man takes approximately one and a half minutes.

The foreman distributes the elements in such a way as to make certain that each man has time enough to do his work properly; i.e., to meet quality standards. Then a change in the schedule is made, and the line speed is increased by one, then two, or three cars per hour. The foreman must then rebalance the line. That is, he takes some of the elements away from one or more men and gives them to a new man who has been hired or transferred into the section. Being new, the man is bound to make mistakes. Or, in the course of rebalancing, some of the other men may have job elements changed. They, too, may make errors until they become thoroughly familiar with the job.

Under certain conditions it may not be possible to add a new man for such a small increase. The twenty men may then have to absorb the increase, and this in turn will call for redistributing some elements. Here is where skill and experience on the part of the foreman is crucial. If the men perform their operations at a faster rate, then the foreman must make sure that the men are not working at a rate faster than that called for in the time standards. If they are, he is open to a grievance and he is also subjecting himself to quality difficulties. Usually, the increase results in a new work pace and a redistribution of elements to be completely equitable according to the time standards set for the job. But as many foremen pointed out, in actual practice a change in pace, even if only a slight one, often results temporarily in faulty performance on the part of some of the operators. As one foreman put it:

> My biggest problem is balancing operations. I will get operations all set up for thirty-seven cars an hour, and get all the setups laid out and the men distributed in a certain way. The next thing I know the schedule is changed. I am quite sensitive to change. After a lot of experience you learn to figure out when a man might be overloaded if the speed goes any higher and when you're going to have to rearrange operations. You gotta watch for the point where it looks as if a man might start to put out poor quality. It is at this point that action has to be taken.

This foreman then went on to describe how he placed a new man on the job and how he balanced out the elements among the other operators.

The "zone of difficulty" brought about by changes in line speeds is an extremely complex matter calling for considerable judgment and experience. The foreman must know how far he can go before his operators reach the limit of the time standards. He must know precisely where and when action should be taken so as to avoid any threat to quality performance. Having secured additional personnel, he must know how to break the men in and how to rebalance elements in the jobs of other men. Newer foremen expressed much concern about their ability to balance operations and maintain quality at the same time.

An older foreman made the following typical comment:

When you have been around as long as I have, you learn that one of the most important things is to equalize work. I've seen many a foreman having one man doing three quarters of the work he could do and another man doing one and a half times more than he is supposed to do. That is heading for trouble all way around. It hurts quality because the man with too much will shyster [take short cuts] on the job.

In the course of our discussions with foremen, the suggestion was made that a conscious effort should be made by management to use experienced foremen for training newer foremen how to balance operations most efficiently.

There is still another problem related to balance and quality. It is recalled that Plant X makes not one but three different automobiles, each with different style, paint, trim, and accessory combinations. Certain operations on one car may be more complicated than on others. In the initial scheduling of cars at the start of the line, every effort is made to maintain a balanced distribution of cars and to avoid running a continuous sequence of the more complicated or difficult models. This is done for a very important reason. If an operator at any given station on the line were to have four or five "tough jobs" come down the line, one after the other, he would soon find himself getting behind in his work and unable to keep up with the line. The operator might be forced to do his work too hastily or he might have to skip a job which is then either pulled off the line into the foreman's repair section or sent on to the car conditioning department for final repair. In either instance proper quality performance is jeopardized as the result of this "bunching up" of the more difficult models.

In spite of the efforts of the scheduling department to maintain an equitable distribution of models, it frequently happens that somewhere along the line this distribution or schedule balance is upset. Two, three, and sometimes more, difficult jobs may hit a foreman's section of the line. This is not usually due to poor initial scheduling. It is more often the result of shortages in materials or of defective jobs that have been removed from the conveyor and replaced with other cars previously removed and repaired. The replacement in any given instance might be another difficult job, and it might by chance follow or precede other jobs requiring more time to assemble.

In any given day the difficult and the less difficult jobs usually balance out one another. But for certain periods of five or ten minutes during the work day, it was frequently noted that an operator at a given station was hard pressed to keep up with his work because of the bunching up of complicated jobs. Everyone agreed that it was during such periods that quality performance was most likely to suffer. This was particularly true when foremen had new men to break in or when absenteeism forced them to put others on who were less familiar with the operation.

The following comment regarding this condition accurately reflects an opinion shared by all production foremen at Plant X:

> One of the most important things is the schedule. It messes me up pretty bad at times. The schedule may start out all right, but somewhere my line gets messed up so that I get several of the same models in a row at once. When you get this kind of jam-up, it makes it tough on quality. If we could ever get the right kind of balance, we could save a barrel of money.

This foreman was not saying that the product as it went to the dealer was not up to quality standards. He was saying, as others did, that not having the work performed right at the proper time was costly, because it meant high repair costs later on.

We turn now to the influence on quality of workers' attitudes as reflected through the foremen at Plant X. Foremen often emphasized the importance of differences in the way men performed their tasks. "Some men you can leave alone for days and not worry about quality. Others, you have to keep after several times during a day." Most foremen believed that the average worker basically *wanted* to do a good job. This belief was supported very fully by an earlier study of hourly workers, which showed that over ninety percent of the men *wanted* to do a quality job. We observed that those foremen who had the greatest difficulties with quality were often those who blamed the condition on the men "because most of them just don't give a damn." In other words, if a foreman did not believe that his men had the desire to do a good quality job, then his attitude was quickly sensed by his men, with the result that they actually *did not do* a good job. And this continued behavior of the men only tended to reinforce the foreman's conviction about his operators' attitudes and abilities. One of the foremen (respected by both management and by the union) said:

> I just wanted you to watch that man for a while. What do you think of him? Pretty hot operator, right? Well, when I first was made foreman I was warned by the general foreman to watch the quality of that man's work, because the foreman before me (who was relieved) had kept harping about the bad work the man turned out. And his work **was** bad — the inspector knew it and so did I because I was utility man before they made me a foreman. It looked to me, though, like the guy was being picked on all the time by the foreman — you know, giving him the needle. When I became foreman I let the guy alone, except to tell him that if he needed any help to let me know. He's the best man I've got now.

In each of the fifty-five interviews with foremen, some mention was made of the crucial importance of "breaking in" new men to become "quality-conscious." Here is a typical comment by one of the foremen:

> It's got to be done slowly. It has been very tough [to do this] when we stepped up production. What you have to do with a new man is to give him just a small portion of a job and have him so he does it right. Don't push him too much into a number of different things. If he knows all the jobs but doesn't know them too good, then he will learn early in his life here to shyster [short-cut] the jobs. Once he gets in the habit he'll shyster forever.

Others stressed the importance of encouraging workers to speak up voluntarily about an error without waiting for it to be caught later by the foreman or by the inspector. "I know what's going wrong," said one of the foremen. "I know from the operators. They tip me off." An interview with another foreman reads:

> Interviewer noticed that men would signal to the foreman just to indicate to him that there was some bad work coming to him from previous operations. The foreman explained that the men did not have to wait for an inspector to tell them that they could take it upon themselves to signal him.

Experienced foremen stressed the importance of delegating as much responsibility for quality as possible to their utility men and to the men themselves:

> A foreman cannot possibly keep up on all the quality trouble spots, especially when there is a model change or when we have a lot of new operators. A good foreman knows how to use his utility men and his experienced operators.

SUMMARY

The application of mass-production methods to the assembly of an automobile does not automatically assure perfect quality. The human factor is still primary. The essence of a foreman's job is to promote "quality-mindedness" and to minimize human error wherever possible. The quality of his relationship to other people in large measure determines the quality of the product itself. In this chapter we have tried to show how many of the foreman's so-called technical problems of quality are tied up with the human relationships involved. The kind of personal relationship a foreman has with maintenance and with materials personnel is crucial to good quality no matter how well the technical services of these departments are organized. Balancing work loads requires technical ability, but more important is the foreman's skill in shifting men around and in revising elements of individual jobs.

Foremen recognized that in the last analysis quality performance is a matter of attitudes, of both the individual worker and the group as a whole. Foremen who were prone to consider a lack of interest in quality as some innate attribute of workers were also likely to be the ones who tried to dictate a "you-do-it-this-way-or-else" policy. Those foremen who assumed that the average man wanted to do a good job, who gave careful training to the new operator, and who helped out all of their operators when they needed it were more likely to be rewarded with good quality work.

The present study lends support to the administrative principle of delegating responsibility to hourly wage earners and especially to utility men. Those foremen most highly thought of by management were those who freely admitted that they could not possibly check on all the quality problems throughout the working day. It was their conviction that a foreman must depend upon his whole team – his utility man and his other operators – to speak up on quality problems and so prevent bad work from going through to the inspector. Quality consciousness, it may be inferred, is not something developed *solely* between a foreman and the individual worker. The men must take on a self-disciplinary *group* responsibility for doing a good job and doing it for a foreman who is their leader in fact as well as in title.

7 THE FOREMAN MEETS EMERGENCIES

Anyone acquainted with industrial operations knows that much of any foreman's time is taken up in resolving unexpected difficulties, major or minor in character. This is certainly the conclusion the authors have reached from a variety of studies involving hundreds of foremen in many industries. Supervision on the assembly line is no exception. We often heard the foremen at Plant X remark, "Emergencies are normal." This remark is more than a paradoxical wisecrack. It reflects a condition basic to the foreman's role in all assembly operations.

Changes of all kinds are characteristic of assembly plants, due to fluctuations in demand, model changes, manpower shortages, mechanical failures, materials shortages, and many other causes internal and external. An earlier chapter emphasized the complexity of operations and the fact that *men*, not automatic machines, do the actual work on the product. In that kind of a work environment it is not hard to understand why any kind of change is likely to create difficulties. And to the foreman these difficulties sometimes translate themselves into "emergencies."

It would be impossible fully to discuss here all the types of emergencies with which foremen had to deal. But most of them had their origin in changes and fluctuations in production schedules, and such change and fluctuation were caused primarily by the following factors:

1. The industry is highly competitive, and the volume of cars produced is related directly to the company's month-to-month competitive position. An increase or a decrease in demand has an

immediate effect on production, including the actual speed of the line in the final assembly plant.

2. The industry is somewhat seasonal in character. Not only does the volume of production change with the seasons, but the proportion of various body types also fluctuates over the course of a year.

3. Model changes take place once a year. Some, involving trim and accessories, are minor in character. Others involve completely new body designs. Materials, equipment, and processes change, and thereby require rearrangement of operations, new systems of parts distribution, different production schedules, new analyses of jobs, changes in skills required, and new applications of work standards. It usually takes two months before operations settle down to "normal" following a model change.

Other factors must also be considered which tend to accentuate the effects of fluctuation and change. We shall mention five:

1. Of consumer products, the modern automobile is one of the most complex. And in the case of the type of final assembly plant here studied, not one but *three* makes of cars are assembled. Such a multiplicity of parts for the different makes and models places an unusually difficult burden on management to see to it that the right part arrives at the right place on the line at the right time.

2. The schedule is further complicated by the fact that every part is shipped in from an outside source – some from plants of the corporation, some from outside suppliers. A production change in the final assembly plant naturally requires a change in the shipping schedules on the part of suppliers. Good communications and perfect coordination are essential. A breakdown for whatever cause in the shipment of parts to the final assembly plant can have an immediate and disastrous effect on production. Because of this sensitive schedule balance, it is not unusual for a supplier to ship by air essential small parts or accessories.

3. The nature of assembly-line technology is such as to make it more sensitive to labor turnover and to absenteeism than indus-

trial operations which are not dominated by a central conveyor system.

4. The substantial size and bulk of the product plus the fact that each car is built on a specific order from a dealer forces a quick disposal of inventory. An automobile, unlike many small consumer goods such as soap, pharmaceuticals, non-perishable goods, small appliances, etc., must be assembled and distributed to dealers with a minimum of time lag. It is physically impossible and too costly to build up a large inventory to be kept in stock at the plant. The product has to move in direct response to customer demand. Other consumer-goods industries can often set a steady production schedule throughout the year in such a way as to meet projected seasonal rises and dips in sales by drawing on inventory. The same leveling process is not possible in the final assembly plant.

5. The final assembly line with all its mechanization is still essentially a "hand-operated" business. The product at every stage of assembly is worked on with tools that are directly manipulated by human hands. Any substantial change in schedule, by way of increased or decreased production (or simply by a change in product mix), appreciably changes the amount and distribution of elements in the operator's immediate job. If the rise in schedule is great enough to require the hiring of new operators, the entire job of a given operator may be completely changed. A reduction in force can have the same effect. As we have already noticed, even a small change in the schedule can have important repercussions on quality performance and on the morale of the immediate work group under the foreman.

Certain broad effects of fluctuations in production were recorded statistically as a series of graphs maintained in the central offices of the company. Thus, monthly rises and dips in schedules were recorded for each of the company's assembly plants, including the one described in this study. Also, labor grievances were plotted chronologically under the production record. Sharp rises and dips in production schedules often correlated with variations in the other items plotted on the graph: for example, with a corresponding rise in turnover, labor costs, absenteeism, and grievances.

As might be expected, few foremen described the problem of schedule changes in terms of the broad facts underlying the industry itself. But they were keenly aware of what fluctuations in schedules and other changes meant to them in their day-to-day experience on the line as we have seen.

A foreman considered himself the one who "kept the show going" by facing up to the emergencies which arose in day-to-day operations. Some – though not all – of these emergencies were accepted as a normal part of automobile manufacture. For example:

In this automobile game, change is the standard thing.

Every day is an emergency here.

As I like to tell my friends, an assembly line is just one damn emergency after another.

Every foreman had a comment to make about how a major increase in the production schedule affected him. Here are two typical remarks:

This is something that makes a job rough. You break your neck to get the schedule up to so many cars an hour. . . . You go up and you move all your older seniority workers up as the new men come in; then when the schedule goes down you move everyone back down, making sure that seniority is properly handled. I've seen this happen so many times that in one way it doesn't bother me any more, but it's not a healthy situation.

The up-and-down schedules are very bad. You move up to a certain schedule, train the new men to working at the right work load, have the line all balanced out, and . . . just at that time there is a change, and it throws you all off again.

Quite apart from major fluctuations were those occurring from hour to hour during the day. Taken individually they would not be considered as serious emergencies, but in the aggregate and from the foreman's point of view they were perhaps more frustrating than the big changes. (See Chapter 5, "The Foreman and Production.")

One foreman described the effects of a small change as follows:

> It is quite easy to say that next month so many cars are to be produced. You can break this down by the number of days and the number of hours, and from that you set a standard of performance of a man which on paper looks very good. But you just don't balance it out in practice as easy as all that, because within any given hour a man gets a run of difficult jobs which makes it tough to keep up with, and that's not saying anything about what happens when a condition like this is aggravated by turnover, absentees, and training new workers.

Assembly-line foremen accept and expect the fact of change — up to a certain point. They fully recognize that customer requirements change and that schedules must change to meet them. They are conditioned to yearly model changes and realize that their job and the continued success of the product they make depends upon their success in bringing the line up to maximum speed and maintaining quality performance. As one supervisor put it, "Change is our bread and butter." They know that materials shortages are often caused by difficulties with suppliers that are beyond anyone's control. They are quite aware that despite mechanization the final assembly of an automobile is essentially a hand operation and subject to human error. Mistakes cause delays and minor but important shifts in the schedule. All these are accepted as "part of the game."

However, almost without exception, foremen said that fluctuations and changes, *whatever their cause,* were the source of their greatest frustration on the job, and that this was also true for their men. Almost every problem they discussed, whether it concerned quality, production, or relations with men or management appeared related to fluctuations.

Foremen were convinced more could be done to reduce fluctuations and hence reduce the amount of time they had to spend "putting out fires." As they saw it, fluctuations could be attributed to one of three levels – to the industry, to the corporation, or to the local plant. Not much was said about any industry-wide solution. Something further might be done at the plant level, although there was little criticism of local plant management for the way it ran the operations. As to the corporation level, foremen recognized that they as foremen were not in possession of all the facts. They were unanimous, however, in believing that more could be done at higher levels to eliminate sharp rises and dips in the schedule. They believed it would be desirable if persons charged with the planning understood better the human and financial costs of fluctuations at the doing level.

SUMMARY

As stressed in an earlier chapter on the principles of progressive manufacture, a foreman's primary role on the assembly line is to take care of minute-to-minute problems which arise and which are the result of the failure of a highly rationalized work process to operate perfectly. There the principal factors which produce emergencies for the foremen have been discussed. Underlying most of them are fluctuations in schedules, and accentuating all of them are the complexities of the products and the technical imperatives of the assembly line. Foremen at Plant X were conditioned to accept change, but they made no effort to conceal the frustrations it created for themselves and their operators. In their judgment some of the extremes in schedule, if given adequate study, could be modified. And finally, they were convinced that the human and financial costs of change were greater than top management realized.

8 A FOREMAN'S DAY

The previous chapters have presented a general picture of how the foreman views his job. In this chapter and the next, the several dimensions of the foreman's job are brought together in time and space and focussed on two specific foremen. First, we shall examine what a particular foreman actually did in the course of a day at work.

Pat is our foreman. He works in the Metal Department, called the Body Shop, of Plant X, where pre-formed sheet metal is delivered to the department, undergoes a series of welding operations, and ends up as a car body ready to be painted, trimmed, upholstered, and dropped onto the chassis in later operations.

Pat's own section, an area 100 feet by 135 feet, is the "jungle," appropriately named because of the hundreds of wires, lines, and hoses hanging down from overhead trolleys and pulleys. Attached to each set of lines are electric spot-welding guns of various sizes and shapes. Car bodies move through the work stations in this section along the continuous conveyor. On the side are several stationary benches, where small parts are welded together and placed in stock adjacent to the line according to schedule, then welded to the body shell. The parts themselves comprise stamped and welded metal reinforcements and moldings, most of which are not seen in the finished automobile. The parts are set in place with jigs and fixtures which serve as supports and are spot-welded to the body by the operator. As parts of the jungle's equipment are Pat's stand-up desk, an electrician's bench, several stock bins, and many racks to hold the fixtures when not being used. Twenty operators work for the foreman. He also has three service-department workers assigned to his area, an electrician, a jig and fixture man, and a materials handler.

Let us now consider and analyse how Pat spends an eight-hour day in this crowded, complex "jungle" area. We have based our analysis on a minute-by-minute observation made of Pat's working day, a complete record of which will be found on pages 159 to 181 of the Supplement.[1] We will then give some general comments by the observer in summary form. These observations are intended to illuminate the significance of the study of this foreman's day, and to relate it to the material in other chapters based upon the interview study.

In the course of the eight hours (excluding the lunch period), foreman Pat walked more than twenty-one thousand feet or over four miles. He took part in 387 separate observable incidents, each lasting from a fraction of a minute to several minutes. Each incident was analyzed according to six "dimensions," namely, what it concerned, whom he had contact with, how it was done, where it took place, what the nature of the personal interaction between the foreman and someone else was, and finally, how long it took. To illustrate, at 3:16 p.m. the following incident took place:

Repair man calls Pat over to his station and points out that a part is not coming through properly welded in place. Pat and repair man discuss it and Pat tells the repair man that the trouble is coming from an operation in the preceding department. Pat leaves and quickly goes to the preceding section.

What did the incident concern? It concerned a problem of quality. With whom did he have contact? It involved the foreman and his repair man. How was it done? It was an activity of talking, as contrasted to one involving reading, writing, or manipulating. Where did it take place? It was at a work station right

[1] A later observation study was made for fifty-six production foremen. More than 32,000 incidents of behavior were recorded, categorized, and analyzed by the methods described in this chapter. A report on findings is now in process.

on the production line. What was the nature of the personal interaction? It was one in which an operator initiated a contact with the foreman, followed by a reply or reciprocal discussion. How long did the incident last? It took approximately three-quarters of a minute. A new incident began when the foreman left to check on the operation in a preceding section of the line. The 387 incidents for the entire day were summarized according to each of these six dimensions: topic, contact, activity, place, interaction, and time.[2]

WHAT DID THE INCIDENTS CONCERN? (TOPIC)

The table below breaks down this foreman's behavior into seventeen "topic" categories, and shows the total number of minutes spent on each topic and the per cent of total time.

Topic	Total minutes spent	Per cent of total time
Foreman's performance of an operation	94	19.5
Quality	88	18.2
Personnel administration (assignment, procurement, etc.)	79	16.5
Materials	66	13.8
Equipment, tools, jigs, and fixtures	47	9.8
Work progress	34	7.0
Employee job performance	24	4.9
Personal relations with other non-job related topics	20	4.1
Production schedule	2	.4
Safety	1	.2
Housekeeping	1	.2
Work standards	0	0
Grievances	0	0
Injury or illness	0	0
Meeting	0	0
Miscellaneous	2	.3
Topic unknown	25	5.1
TOTAL	485[3]	100.0

[2] Complete definitions of behavior categories falling under each of the six dimensions of an incident are given on pages 154–159 of the Supplement.

[3] There are 480 minutes in an eight-hour day. The extra five minutes in the table is because some incidents lasted only a few seconds but were coded at the minimum code allowance of fifteen seconds.

As might be expected, this foreman's work was concentrated on production matters. Quality and the progress of work consumed one quarter of his day. Another quarter concerned materials, tools, and equipment. Almost twenty per cent of his day was spent by Pat performing an operation himself in order to help out his operators. This percentage is considerably higher than average,[4] but it illustrates an important point which is brought out in other chapters: namely, that even minor changes in schedules substantially affect the foreman's job. On the particular day observed, a change occurred in the distribution of models running through the line. No change in the speed of the conveyor took place, but there were greater numbers of one model requiring more than average work at one of the sub-assembly stations. The operator got behind in his work and could not keep up. An emergency condition was created. The foreman, while waiting for additional temporary help, took care of the emergency by performing work himself periodically. During such periods he was unable to perform other supervisory duties. The identical condition would probably not repeat itself the next day and thus not warrant a permanent increase in manpower. But other conditions of an emergency character could and frequently did come up with all foremen. Since the line had to be kept moving, most foremen filled in the breach by performing operations themselves in such emergencies. These emergency conditions, whether due to absenteeism, mechanical breakdowns, schedule increases, or as in this case, a change in model distribution, created some of the most important problems which a foreman had to face. (This and other observations of foremen at work clearly illustrate how an excessive amount of time spent on any one phase of the job substantially reduces the amount of time available for other phases. The foreman who was forced to spend time working on the line himself or who had to chase around after materials had less time available for more important supervisory functions.)

[4] The average for all production foremen was 8.1 percent of the time, or 39 minutes per day, for performing a manual operation.

As to the other topics in the above table covering foreman Pat's day, notice that 16.5 percent of his time was devoted to personnel administration. Most of these incidents involved his seeking additional help to cover the emergency condition described above.

Little time was recorded for non-production activities such as safety, housekeeping, grievances, or other items.

WITH WHOM DID HE HAVE CONTACT? (CONTACT)

Nearly half of the foreman's time was spent in direct contact with other people. This involved verbal and non-verbal interaction (hand signals, nods, performing work together) with someone else. These interactions are summarized in the table.

Contact	Number of incidents	Total minutes spent	Percent of total time	Average time per incident (mins.)
Own Men:				
Regular operators	87	67	13.8	¾
Utility man	14	10	2.1	¾
Repair man	13	12	2.4	¾
Peers:				
Other foremen	23	33	6.9	1½
Superiors:				
General foreman	7	28	5.8	4
Department Supt.	3	15	3.0	5
General Supt. or higher	0	0	0	0
Service Personnel:				
Maintenance	20	24	4.8	1¼
Materials Handling	5	5	1.1	1
Inspection	8	10	2.1	1¼
Works Standards	1	1	.2	1
Others:				
Other hourly	6	4	.8	¾
Observer	30	20	4.2	¾
All others	11	10	2.1	1
No contact	176	244	50.7	1½
TOTAL	404 [5]	483	100.0	

[5] This figure is higher than the recorded 387 incidents because some contacts involved more than one other person.

During the eight hours, foreman Pat interacted 227 times with 47 different individuals. These contacts consumed just under 50 percent of his time.[6] Pat interacted most often with his own men — 114 times in all — or for 18 percent of the time during the work day. The breakdown shows that 27 of these interactions took place with only two of his men. The two were his utility man and his repair man, both of whom had a strong functional importance to the foreman. The repair man was responsible for catching all errors made in "jungle" operations, and the utility man was responsible for giving other operators relief spells and for helping the foreman with minor administrative details. Pat averaged just over five contacts with each of his 18 regular operators during the work day.

In addition to his own men, there were three other hourly-rated workers in Pat's section. These were the stock man, the electrician, and the jig and fixture man. These men did not report to him in the line of organization, but they were assigned to service his unit. Twenty-five contacts were made with these workers: five with the stock man and twenty with the two maintenance men.

Notice that the contacts with everyone were brief in duration. The average incident involving interaction with Pat's own utility man, repair man, and operators lasted less than a minute. Interaction time involving other foremen, inspection, materials handling, and maintenance personnel was slightly over one minute on the average. Contacts with his immediate superior averaged four minutes and with his superintendent, less than five minutes. Rarely during the day did the foreman spend more than ten minutes at a time with anyone, including his own operators. Observations of other foremen substantiate the fact that the foreman's job on the assembly line allows little opportunity for any long, sustained interaction. More often than not a conversation between the foreman and someone else was cut short because the

[6] Other foremen spent somewhat more time in contact with others. In one case, for example, as much as 80 percent of a foreman's total day was spent in face-to-face contact with others.

foreman had to attend to some other immediate emergency. Discontinuity and interruption, these characteristics of the foreman's contacts with others, may be traced to the compelling demand to keep the line moving and to take immediate care of any source of difficulty which might cause a stoppage.

HOW WAS IT DONE? (ACTIVITY)

Each incident was recorded in terms of the physical activity involved, such as talking, reading, standing, manipulating, walking, etc. If the foreman watched a particular operation while walking, it was considered primarily as looking rather than walking. If he stood by his desk explaining something to an operator, the activity was recorded as talking rather than standing. If he picked up a piece of material and gave it to someone, it was recorded as "hands, touches, or carries." The total of the day's physical activity is summarized in the accompanying table.

Activity	Total minutes spent	Percent of total time
Talks	183	37.8
Looks	108	22.5
Manipulates	98	20.3
Hands, Touches, Carries	34	7.0
Walks [7]	32	6.6
Signals	7	1.5
Listens (without talking)	6	1.2
Shows	6	1.2
Stands	5	1.0
Reads	4	.9
Writes	¼	0
Sits	0	0
TOTAL	483	100.0

Notice that the foreman devoted the largest segment of his working day to some kind of verbal activity. This fact appears to

[7] Walking was listed as an incident only when the foreman was going from one place to another without being engaged primarily in observing something, talking with someone, or carrying an object. His actual total time walking, including all incidents when doing something else while talking, was one hour and twenty minutes.

be true in varying degrees for all of the assembly-line foremen. The finding underscores a fact we have emphasized in other sections; namely, that even in a highly rationalized operation like an assembly line, verbal interaction of foremen with others is still an important element in the total work picture.

As noted earlier, primarily because of an imbalance in model distribution, the foreman spent more than the usual amount of time performing work himself (manipulates). He also had to carry tools and material from one place to another, and these two activities together accounted for the next largest segment of the foreman's day. It should be pointed out that such work was done only in response to an immediate emergency and was not a regular part of his job.

Third in order of time were those activities in which the foreman observed his over-all operations or in which he was inspecting materials, parts, tools, or the actual work of the operators (looks).

An important observation to make is that the foreman – and this was true of most foremen in this plant – had very little paper work, either writing or reading. The company had long recognized the importance of relieving foremen of every possible clerical duty and giving him as much time as possible to run operations and to handle personal contacts on the job.

Finally, notice that the foreman did not sit down once during working hours.

WHERE DID THE INCIDENTS TAKE PLACE? (PLACE)

We were interested to know where the foreman spent most of his time. Seven categories were established: specific work stations (i.e., right next to a specific operation), general work area of the foreman's section (not immediately adjacent to a work station), his desk, a preceding section of the department, a succeeding section, the departmental office, and some other department. The results are given in the table.

Place	Total minutes spent	Percent of total time
Specific work stations	196	40.5
General work area	159	32.8
Succeeding section	57	11.8
Department office	25	5.2
Other department	20	4.2
Desk	18	3.8
Preceding section	8	1.7
TOTAL	483	100.0

Notice that over 40 percent of the foreman's time was spent right beside the line (or sub-assembly operation) at work stations. Another 32.8 percent was spent in general work area or section. This foreman spent very little time at his desk—just under 4 percent, and only 5 percent in the departmental office. The remaining time was spent in preceding (1.7 percent), or in succeeding (11.8 percent), sections, or in other departments (4.2 percent).

WHAT WAS THE NATURE OF THE PERSONAL INTERACTION BETWEEN THE FOREMAN AND SOMEONE ELSE? (INTERACTION)

We have already determined (a) how much time this foreman was in personal contact with other people (approximately 50 percent), (b) with whom he was in contact, and (c) the average duration of the interactions. It was considered important also to find out how often the foreman initiated a contact with, or was first contacted by, someone else.

Excluding those incidents in which the foreman was in the presence of someone but not speaking, we observed that of the 179 contacts with forty-seven other persons, 104 were incidents in which he first contacted someone else and seventy-five were when someone came to him. When these figures were further broken down, a considerable difference was noted in initiations of contacts between the foreman and his own men as contrasted with those between the foremen and all others (superiors, other foremen, and service personnel).

When the foreman initiated contact with persons outside of his own immediate work group, he did it twice as often (69 times) as they did with him (33 times). On the other hand, his own operators contacted him somewhat more often (42 times) than he initiated contact with them (35 times).[8]

COMMENTS BY THE OBSERVER

Our foreman, while relatively new to the job (less than a year), was rated distinctly above average by management. He was highly regarded by his fellow foremen. What generalized statements can be made which support or deny what has been said before about "what makes a good foreman?" Here are some which the observer himself considered worth noting about the personal characteristics of this foreman.

Relations with his men. The observer's general impression about Pat was that he was both highly respected and warmly liked by his men. The number of contacts he had with his men did not seem too important. Some men he talked with several times, others only once or twice, if at all. What *was* important in his relationship to them was the quality of the interactions which did take place.

Certain clues as to the quality of his relationship to subordinates may be given as follows:

He issued direct unilateral orders to his men only nine times during the day.

When he wanted an operator to do something, his order was never in a "do-it-or-else" manner. He invariably paused, giving time for acknowledgment, a response, or a counter suggestion.

[8] The reader is reminded that this interaction pattern is not necessarily typical for all foremen. Further analysis to date reveals considerable variance in interaction patterns from one foreman to the next. The significance of these differences will be explored in a later report.

If an operator was having no trouble with the job, the foreman did not stand over him and watch.

Whenever requests for information, supplies, material, or help on the job was made, he almost always followed through at once. In the few cases where that was impossible, he explained why.

At one point, Pat was advised by a member of a staff department that someone from the central office of the company was present, inquiring about a certain operation. Unlike other supervisors whom we have observed under similar conditions, he did not at once tell his workers that "Detroit was complaining." Rather, he pointed out to the man responsible that "*We* have to watch the operation carefully"; furthermore, he explained what an error was doing to the finished product. He used instruction rather than reprimand as his method of correcting errors, whenever that was possible.

When an operator forewarned the foreman that some difficulty with tools or materials was to be expected, he acknowledged the message with a wave or a nod.

There was some friendly joking between the foreman and the men during the day, but such incidents lasted only a few seconds.

He checked to see that the men were being given their regular relief period in the morning and afternoon.

He sought advice from his own operators, his repair man, or the jig and fixture man on three or four problems for which he himself did not have an answer.

He showed considerable anxiety over the fact that one of his men, due to emergency conditions, had more than his normal share of work to perform.

He kept this man posted on the progress or lack of progress he was having in getting help, but he avoided placing personal blame on any other foreman or on his superior.

Although on the move and under constant pressure to keep up with the line because a change in the model distribution had caused a temporary manpower shortage, he did not translate this pressure to the men by "flying off the handle" or by showing personal irritation.

He was available to his men most of the time and notified his utility man the few times he was not.

His men knew that he was able to perform every job in the section by himself.

Relations with superiors. Pat showed no reluctance to speak up to his general foreman and vigorously make a plea for an extra temporary operator.

He appealed to the superintendent for an extra operator, doing so in the presence of his general foreman.

He acknowledged to the general foreman of another department that an error was his own personal fault – that he had done it while operating the equipment himself. He later acknowledged to his own repair man that he, the foreman, had "pulled a boner."

Relations with other foremen. He kept his fellow foremen in previous operations posted on the quality of their work, although in some instances his own section was in no way affected by some of the previous operations.

A few times during the day he noticed workers from another section doing some of their work in his section, thus crowding his own men. He did not speak to them directly but dealt with the matter through their own foreman. At other times, he spoke directly with operators in other sections to ask them about the work being done in his own section.

The emergency condition. In a real sense this foreman's day was dominated by the single problem of a temporary shortage of one man for only two hours. Over one-third of his time was taken up with this situation in one way or another. He performed work, carried materials, helped to break in a temporary man, and spent a large segment of his time trying to get assistance from his fellow foreman and superiors (almost twenty-eight minutes with the general foreman alone).

While it was clear to the observer that the immediate condition was caused by factors beyond the control of the foreman and his immediate superiors, it was equally clear that longer-range planning up and down the line and a more systematic method for allocating manpower would have measurably reduced the chances of such an emergency condition arising.

Although the emergency condition cut deeply into the foreman's time, he was still able to maintain a healthy relationship with his subordinates. Interestingly enough this foreman did not act as if he had consciously thought out any principles of human behavior, nor behave as if someone had instructed him in the do's and don'ts of foremanship. From his observed behavior and from his remarks, his philosophy might be summarized in this simple way:

A foreman has to see to it that each job is done right, that the men keep up with the line speed, and keep up with as few kick-backs as possible from the inspector, my boss, his boss, Detroit, the dealer, and the customer. The job can be done right only if the men **want** to do it right. As a foreman it's my job to make it so the men **want** to do the job right. You don't push them. You help them. Then they help you. You keep their tools in top shape, make sure they have stock on hand, be right on the spot when they are in trouble, explain why a thing has to be done, listen to them, stand up for them if they are right, leave them alone unless they want you.

9 PROFILE OF A FOREMAN

Here an attempt will be made to get into one foreman's shoes, so to speak, and to understand his role as he sees it.

We will call our foreman Frank Vitelli. Frank is not a "typical" Plant X foreman. No one is. But his history, his past and present activities and attitudes do represent some important general themes which have run through the interviews of all foremen. He has been chosen mainly because there are available complete interviews [1] with him over a period of time and because his story is an interesting one.

The first interview with Vitelli was in September, 1950, when he was a worker on the line. He was seen again in March, 1953, on his first day as a foreman, and again in May, 1953, after he had been a foreman for six weeks. Finally in June, 1954, he was observed for a full day, during which we recorded everything possible that he said and did as a foreman on the job. These interviews and observations are the basis of this chapter.

Most of Vitelli's six years at Plant X, both as worker and as foreman, have been spent in the "wet sanding" section in the Paint Department. After bodies are given their "prime and glaze" coat they go to wet sanding. Here they are sanded to a very smooth finish prior to receiving the next coat of paint in a subsequent section. Wet sanding is a very important operation; much of the success of the final paint job depends upon it. As Frank himself put it, "This job can make or break a paint job.

[1] Some of Vitelli's statements quoted in this chapter have been used to illustrate points in preceding chapters as well.

It is the key job right here." At the same time wet sanding appears to an outsider to be almost a primitive operation, in marked contrast to the advanced technological environment of the plant as a whole. It is an excellent example of the importance of the human element on the assembly line.

Frank himself, as a worker, described his job accurately and simply: "We prepare bodies for painting. We use sandpaper and water and sand down prime and glaze coats." Here is a more detailed description of the job, given by another wet sander:

I pick up a piece of sandpaper, hold the water hose in my other hand. I wet down the upper quarter, where the body slopes down, and the quarter panel. With both hands I use an up and down movement, about ten strokes the whole length of the "breakdown." I finish with eight more strokes around the drip rail and then using my left hand go over it — up and down six times. Then six strokes on the left corner panel — two or three strokes around the detail. Then using my right hand I rub the bottom edge seven or eight strokes. Under the quarter panel — using my left hand — I give it about two strokes. Then I move to the upper quarter — using both hands — and rub six strokes on the "breakdown" and finish with eight strokes along the weld and the same on the trunk to the bottom. At the bottom there's another weld and I give it six strokes with each hand. Then after I do two jobs I throw the paper away and wait for the next car.

Another wet sander said of his job:

All I use is a piece of sandpaper and a hose. They call it unskilled labor, but I disagree with that. It's a rubbing job. If you press too hard, you kill yourself and you still won't get it off. Then the paint varies and you have to go the way that goes. If you start fighting it, boom! You're dead at the end of the day.

Superficially this would seem to be a highly unpleasant and monotonous job.[2] Actually in Plant X and in other assembly plants it was found that wet sanders often felt a sense of cohesion

[2] Since our first study, many of the wet sanding operations are now performed with rotary disc sanders requiring less muscular effort than when the sanding was done entirely by hand.

as a group and pride in doing a good job together which compensated to a degree for the unpleasant nature of the actual work itself.[3] Indispensable, however, to group cohesion and pride is a good relationship between management and worker. The foreman is crucial.

VITELLI AS A WORKER

As in the case of most Plant X workers, the nature of Vitelli's job on the line was in marked contrast to his previous work. Since boyhood he had worked at many different laboring jobs, but none of them had been in a mass-production plant. He had been, for example, both a laborer and a group leader in a construction company. The company was small and his chances for advancement were good. He liked construction work, not only because of good pay and good bosses, but because he was interested in the job itself. He liked the variety of the work, having a say in how to do it, being able to set his own pace, and to move around on the job. As he said:

> The good thing about it was you did lots of different things. . . . I could use my judgment on the job.

In spite of unsteady work and rather poor working hours, he would have liked to stay in construction work.

But the construction company left town and Frank came to Plant X as "the only available job I could get around here." When he came, he was twenty-six years old. After three years at Plant X, his attitude towards his job as wet sander on the line is indicated by the following comments.

He explained why he only talked with one other worker:

> It's very noisy. You have to holler to talk to the guy across the line from you and it gets tiring. . . . I'd like to be able to talk more.

[3] Wet sanders were also paid five or ten cents more an hour than the average worker on the line.

He mentioned that he performed only one operation all the time and found the job "not at all interesting":

My job is very monotonous. . . . You learn the job in two days and then there is nothing more to learn.

He discussed the difficulty of doing good quality work on the job:

The line is too fast. I'd like to get satisfaction. All the guys would. I get satisfaction when I really do the job right. But I don't usually have time to get it right.

He described his wife's reaction to his job at Plant X:

She thinks I've gotten grouchy since I started working there because I'm so tired. But she likes the pay.

Concerning his overall attitude towards the company's treatment of the men, Frank said:

You're a number, but that's the only way I suppose it has to be in a big company. Still, they should give more warning before working overtime, and those things.

When asked whether given the chance he would take another job, or stay at Plant X, Frank answered:

If I could get almost the same pay and the security, I'd take another job. I'd take any outdoor job with these conditions. Ideally I'd like to be a construction foreman.

And summing up his attitude as a worker at the end of the interview, Frank remarked:

I like the job because it gives me better living conditions. That's the main thing when you've got a family. And I like the medical service. But the monotony of the job and the speed are very bad. . . . It's a tough place to work.

Frank's reactions as a worker to his job at Plant X were typical of most workers interviewed in our first study.[4] He disliked being

[4] *The Man on the Assembly Line.*

paced by the moving line and working indoors. He found the work uninteresting, monotonous, and physically tiring. He also objected to being unable to talk to other workers or to move around on the job. On the other hand, these negative features of the work were compensated for primarily by good pay and steady work, and also by good working hours, nearness to his home, having good bosses, the company's benefit programs, and having a union which, to him, was necessary in such a plant. In other words, he liked his former job on the construction gang because of the actual nature of the work, but disliked it because it did not provide economic security; in contrast, he disliked the pacing and repetitiveness of his Plant X job, but liked the pay and security. On both jobs he felt he had good bosses.

As a worker Frank wanted to get ahead but was discouraged about his chances for advancement. The next job in his department which he wanted was "oil sanding" off the line, because "you set your own pace," but he thought there was a poor chance of getting it.

Or I'd like to be foreman, where I'd get good pay and feel like I'm accomplishing things myself. I don't like to be absorbed by the machinery.

To Vitelli, becoming a foreman seemed a way to free himself from the technology of the moving line. But when asked what he thought his chances were of becoming a foreman, he said:

They're poor. I don't want to stay at Plant X. I want to leave.

Frank was ambitious, as he still is. In his earlier work he had always progressed rapidly to a position of leadership. He was a man who wanted to accomplish things for himself. His chance for advancement did come, quicker than he thought it would. If it had not, it is a fair assumption that he would no longer be at Plant X.

The comments given so far show the importance of the nature of the immediate job, in determining a worker's attitude. The mechanical pacing of the work, confinement to one station on the line, and a job which required little skill or imagination were the main reasons Frank Vitelli gave for his feeling that as a worker he was not accomplishing things. In a sense he appeared to be looking for an escape. He wanted to become a foreman, for example, because "I don't like to be absorbed by the machinery." When he did become a foreman, as we shall see, the technology of the moving line was still the most important single influence upon the nature of his job. What had been a burden, however, now became a challenge. As a foreman Frank felt less restricted and that he *was* accomplishing things.

Significantly, his ability to handle the new job depended a good deal on the experience he had gained on the old one, and especially on his first-hand understanding of the human implications of assembly-line technology.

On his first day as a foreman, for example, Frank pointed out that the tough thing about wet sanding on the main line was the constant pacing of the work. "You can't let the line beat you." New men, he said, often found the work too hard; they had to use muscles they had never used before. But if they got through the first two weeks, they got used to it; and the job came to appear preferable to some of the other jobs on the line, primarily because it was cleaner and less complicated; that is to say, the work was "right there in front of your eyes." There was also some satisfaction in that good judgment was required to do the job right. Eighteen months later Frank was still just as concerned with the relation between his men and the actual work they had to do. Explaining the importance of the first crucial weeks of adjustment to this type of job, he said:

They seem to get a lot of troubles when they first come to the wet deck. They get nosebleeds and all kinds of things wrong with them. I think it is because when you get into an industry like this, at first you find that the job takes more out of you than you have to give. Later you get used to it. That's why I watch them very, very closely when they are new.

From his own experience as a worker on the line, Frank knew the importance of a foreman who understood the reactions of his men to their jobs, who was able to manage his section with sympathy and fairness, and who promoted a human situation which compensated for the disliked characteristics of the work itself.

As a worker, Frank thoroughly appreciated the importance of the foreman-worker relationship. He had a good foreman, and to him this was a very important factor in determining his total attitude about working at Plant X. As he said, having a good foreman was "the only reason a lot of the guys stay." As a foreman, he continued to believe that the human relationship which a foreman could establish with his men was probably the most important part of his job.

VITELLI AS UTILITY MAN

The most important experiences which prepared Frank to become a foreman occurred during his two and a half years as a utility man in the wet sanding section, during which time increasing responsibility was delegated to him by the boss. As a utility man he became thoroughly familiar with all the jobs in the section and with the many problems of production, quality, materials, etc., that arose from day to day. More than this, he became familiar with other sections in the plant, the work of which affected or was affected by wet sanding.

In many respects Frank was an unusual utility man. In fact, through listening to the other men and representing their point of view to the foreman, he came to assume to a degree the role of informal leader of the wet sanding group some time before his own promotion to foreman.

In his second interview as a foreman, when he was asked about relations with the union, Frank said:

I haven't had any trouble in the four and a half years I've been here. I explain to all the men that if they have any grievances and if they insist on seeing their committeeman, I'll get him right away, right off the bat. I've had a lot of experience on this, because before I was foreman — when I was utility man — the guys would come around to me on these questions and ask my advice. . . . I explained their rights, their privileges, what they could do, what they couldn't do.

Later Frank gave a still more unusual example of his informal status as utility man. He said that often he used to go into other sections of the plant to find out about items which were causing trouble in wet sanding. Sometimes he would talk to the foreman and operators involved. He admitted that "some of them resented it," but on the whole, he thought, it "worked out pretty well."

As already suggested, the extent of Frank's responsibilities as utility man was not typical. However, it had had at least one very important advantage, as far as Frank himself was concerned. It helped him become a better foreman than he could have been without this experience. The eight hours' observation of Frank as a foreman amply confirmed this statement. In particular he showed an unusually accurate knowledge of where in other departments various operations affecting his line were performed. He told the observer that his experience as utility man had been very valuable in teaching him where to go to track down particular items which were causing his men trouble. He had learned to make contacts with foremen and operators in other sections in such a way as not to cause resentment. When he was promoted, he had already handled many of the problems involved in relationships between himself and men in his own and other sections. Most important, he had learned to understand himself in such a role and thus to prepare himself to cope with administrative responsibilities.

Discussing why he thought he had been made a foreman, Frank recognized that the ability to get along with the men, which he had demonstrated as utility man, was the most important reason:

I knew that if I kept at it long enough, something would break. I get along with the fellas, too. I listen to their problems, ones they have about the job and private ones, too. I tell them what I think they should do in their case. If a fella comes up to me and tells me that he has a stomach-ache, well he may or may not have a stomach-ache, but I try to find out what **is** bothering him, because something must be to have him say that. I have seen hundreds of fellas come in here and they are all different.

Frank as a utility man had learned to listen to the men, not only to what they said, but also to what they meant. This is one of any successful foreman's most important skills.

As a foreman Vitelli had the same point of view towards his utility man that his former foreman had had towards him:

I want my utility man to do all the necessary things without having to be told. If he sees something wrong, if he sees a man doing something not right, he should correct that guy. . . . Also, it makes a smart utility man if he knows what's going on in other departments.

During the day when he was observed, Frank demonstrated in his behavior towards his utility men a high regard for their ability to make decisions and to take minor administrative action when he was away from his section. In one incident, for instance, the senior utility man in effect directed some of the men in "housekeeping" part of the area after the foreman had mentioned in passing that this needed to be done. There were several other incidents in which Frank's utility men exercised considerable initiative. Frank himself spent over thirty percent of the total day outside his immediate section, looking into matters in other sections and departments, or making brief visits to the department office. He knew that his men would continue to turn out good work while he was away. This was in large measure due to the confidence he placed in the three utility men and in the inspector in his section. At the same time, before leaving, he usually told at least his senior utility man where he was going in case an emergency requiring his presence should arise. On his desk, for his utility men's use, he had a list of important telephone numbers, such as the maintenance and jig and fixture offices, the tool room, etc., to be called in case of emergency.

During his lunch period Frank discussed at length with the observer the importance of delegating responsibility, especially to the utility men. He described the subsequent value to him of the extra duties he had been given as a utility man, and he emphasized that now he wanted his utility men to take on increasing responsibilities so that they too could better prepare themselves for promotion:

I believe that by enlarging the job of the people under you, that is the best thing you can do to get ahead yourself. Certainly I want to be sure that whoever takes over my job, if I should be moved, knows the section thoroughly, and also knows about the other things, and has a good knowledge of the whole job. By letting the utility man run the line when I am away, by having him take care of many of the details, filling out the forms and so on, and by letting him go into other sections to check on quality the way I do, I am making it that much easier for myself to move ahead to a better job.

In short, Frank recognized that the more he could help his key subordinate to qualify for promotion, the more likely he was to qualify for promotion himself.

VITELLI AS FOREMAN

We have seen that as utility man Frank came to feel himself in some respects the informal leader of the other men. As a foreman he continued to exercise much the same kind of informal leadership, combined, of course, with considerably more formal authority. The attitudes of his men continued to be of first importance to him. In talking about them, he often referred to the importance of having a group which worked well together. While he recognized that each man was different and that they could not all be handled the same way, he thought of his men primarily as a *group*, and one of his important functions was to promote harmony within it. In the following comment he discusses two specific instances in which he, as foreman, had taken action to correct something his men were doing. One was an individual problem, and was corrected by discussion with the individual worker. In the other instance, Frank saw the problem and solved it in terms of the group. Running through his account is the conviction that a foreman has a dual function: (1) to correct promptly *individual* deviations from the proper way of doing things (e.g., individual action to improve quality by correcting mistakes in the work); and (2) to foster the development of a group under his leadership with common objectives (e.g., action to increase cohesion and morale of the group which in turn improves the performance):

In here the men used to bark sometimes back and forth at each other. They don't do that any more now. And what's more they're even working harder. (Function 2) If a man does something wrong, I don't bawl him out. I point out to him the mistake he's making. I had a man here who when he was sandpapering made the lines kinda curve, gave a little back flip at the end of each movement. It didn't look right. . . So I point out to him what he's doing wrong. (Function 1) . . . And some of these guys, when they get through with their sandpaper they try to flip it over into the can. Well, out of ten tries perhaps they get one in okay, and the rest of it falls on the floor. And so I tell him "Look, it's better not to do that, because one of you guys has got to sweep it up." I try to show them that they're all working together here, and they gotta have respect for each other. (Function 2) Any time I see a fella doing something wrong, I go right over to him and tell him about it. I don't waste any time. I don't let it go by. (Function 1)

Like most successful foremen, Frank thinks highly of his men. Because of his confidence in them, he acts in ways that encourage them to deserve the good opinion which he has of them in the first place. (See Chapter V, "The Foreman and Production.") After he had been a foreman for six weeks, he described his men this way:

I have a range here from twenty years of age to forty-one years, and both the man who is twenty and the one who is forty-one are damn good workers. Usually the married men stick it out the longest. They have more responsibility, having a wife and kids and so forth. But the younger men are good workers, too. Most are easy-going fellows. They are not, well, what should I say, exuberant. . . . Right now I haven't got a wise guy in the bunch. I figure that anything I can do for the man, I give it to him. It pays off in the end. . .

On the day when Frank was observed, soon after the line started, he systematically toured the section on what he called his "howdy rounds," greeting and exchanging a few words with nearly every man about his work or about some outside interest. In response his men brought up problems which were causing them trouble and Frank made notes of all important items. Out of all the problems he took the three most troublesome, traced the trouble down to its source, and saw to it that the condition was corrected. One involved faulty material; two, incorrect work in a preceding section. In short, he assumed that his men knew what they were talking about and he made it his job to correct the conditions about which they complained. Finally, he told them what he had done and checked later to see if the condition had been improved. This same cycle – receiving information from his men, acting on it, and telling them about the action taken – was repeated many times during the day.

After the first hour and twenty minutes, Frank said to the observer, "We have checked the three major complaints. Now we can pay more attention to the fellas and see how they are coming along." Obviously, one of the most satisfying parts of his foreman's job was going to the men, kidding with them briefly, and finding out if there was anything he could do which would be helpful to them. Much of his time he spent this way. He also spent time outside his section, tracking down quality problems which his men had told him about or which he had discovered himself in watching the work.

It is impossible to describe briefly all of Frank's activities as a foreman on the day he was observed, but in order to give characteristic examples of his attitude towards his job, here are four series of incidents from the minute-by-minute record of his eight hours on the job. (Typically these series were intermittent in nature. They constantly interrupted each other. One of the most important abilities which Frank and other assembly-line foremen demonstrated was to tolerate frequent interruptions without being distracted from accomplishing what needed to be done.)

One succession of incidents occurred sporadically from 8:51 in the morning to 2:35 in the afternoon. At 8:51 Frank's senior utility man gave him a suggestion for making a certain job easier to perform and more efficient. To implement the suggestion required a series of actions and interactions by the foreman and by others, including procurement of certain tools with which to work upon a piece of equipment, enlisting the services of a maintenance man (who was busy until 11:21), and consultation with the several workers who would be affected by the change. The latter were enthusiastic when they heard about it. By around 2:30 the change had been fully incorporated into everybody's routine and the episode closed.

Another series of incidents involved considerable work by the foreman in order to make some of the wet sanding operations easier to perform. These specific operations were performed with a rotary disc instead of by hand. Frank had decided the job would work better if the abrasive discs were placed on circular sheets of corrugated rubber instead of canvas. Because he was very anxious to see how well this idea would work out, he spent over half an hour in the storeroom area cutting rubber discs and showing one of his utility men how to cut them. When he returned to his section, he showed them to the workers involved, asking one of his men, "Do you think that will do it, Eddie?" Intermittently throughout the rest of the day he checked back with his men to see how the new method was working.

Another, more complicated series of incidents occurred during the afternoon and illustrated Frank's interest in his men both as individuals and as members of a group. It involved cooperation with other members of management, particularly with Ray, the foreman of an adjacent section, with whom Frank worked closely throughout the day. The general foreman, Frank's immediate superior, was spending most of the day supervising some important repair work in the car conditioning department. At 12:42 he called Frank and Ray together and explained to them that he needed another experienced operator from one of their two sections to do some repair work in car conditioning. He would be required for the rest of the day. Frank explained that it would be difficult for him to spare a man, because one of his repair men who had the experience necessary for the work in car conditioning had left on an excused absence for the afternoon.

After considerable discussion the three supervisors agreed on the following solution to the problem. Frank would lend the general foreman one of his experienced operators who was qualified to do the work in car conditioning. To replace this man on Frank's line, Ray would lend him Smitty, a less experienced operator whom Ray could spare by making certain other arrangements within his own section. (To the observer Frank remarked: "That's the good thing about my general foreman. Notice the way he listened to what I had to say and thought about it carefully before making up his mind.")

Frank explained the reassignment to his own experienced operator, who left with the general foreman for car conditioning. Frank also had to explain the situation to his utility men since the relief schedule would be affected. (One of them would have to help Ray out later on.) Then Frank led Smitty to the job he was to fill in on for the rest of the afternoon. Smitty had not worked in this section before, so Frank showed Smitty the job, and got the utility man's help in making sure that Smitty understood it. He kidded Smitty in passing several times after he had started in on the job, but never stood over him.

After Smitty had been working in Frank's section for half an hour, he had trouble with his job and broke a tool. At the time Frank was at his desk, going over data with a man from the Work Standards department. One of Frank's regular operators, Jack, who worked next to the operation to which Smitty was assigned, came up and told Frank that Smitty had broken a tool. Jack also suggested that he and Smitty should change jobs, since his own regular job would be easier for Smitty to perform. Frank nodded and continued conferring with the Work Standards man for another five minutes. (The Work Standards man had been at Frank's desk for ten minutes, but their conference had been repeatedly interrupted.) Then after the Work Standards man left, Frank went to Smitty and asked him if he would like to switch jobs with Jack. Smitty said, "Why, because I broke the tool?" Frank said, "No, but Jack's job is easier, and he has had experience on the one you're doing." Smitty agreed to make the switch, and Frank briefly showed him how to do the simpler job. As he did so, Frank nodded to Jack to indicate that his suggestion for the switch was a good idea. To the observer, Frank said, "On something like this, I wait for them to make the suggestion themselves. That's how to get them thinking for themselves."

This series of incidents is typical of the chain reaction of events which often follow when the reassignment of a single worker is required. To solve the various problems which came up as a result of the need for another man in car conditioning required certain administrative skill and tact. Note the foreman's appreciation for the position of Smitty as a newcomer in an unfamiliar section where he did not know the work. Forty minutes after the original reassignment Smitty had settled down to Jack's regular job, which he could do without difficulty. On several occasions during the rest of the afternoon Frank found a chance to joke with Smitty briefly. For instance, at 2:13, while away from his own area, Frank passed Smitty going on relief. Frank asked him lightly how the job was going. Smitty said, "Okay." To the observer it appeared that Smitty had been somewhat apprehensive at first at being assigned to a strange section, but that during the afternoon he came to feel that he was a real member, if only temporarily, of Vitelli's group.

The final incident we want to describe briefly here occurred during the last hour of the day. Outwardly trivial, it is worth recording for three reasons: (1) it was in fact by no means trivial to at least one of the people involved; (2) it is typical of the many incidents, each unimportant by itself, which over a period of time have a cumulative effect on foreman-worker relations; (3) it illustrates Frank's concern for his men not only as individuals but as members of a group. This incident involved some horseplay between the wet sanders which had to be stopped because it got out of hand. Occasionally, the wet sanders aimed their hoses and squirted water at each other playfully. Officially this was an infraction of the rules, but a certain amount of it may well have had a good effect upon the operators' attitude towards their jobs. As Frank explained to the observer:

> I realize that they squirt water, but I don't make too much of an issue out of it unless it gets out of hand. Of course, you have to watch it and not let it go too far.

At 3:21 the squirting did go too far, and the subsequent action taken by the foreman indicated his concern not only for company regulations but also for his men as a group who had to work constructively together. Frank saw one of the wet sanders, whom he called "the rebel," angrily squirting another operator. Frank spoke to the rebel, who loudly complained, "They started it, and if they squirt me again, I expect you to stop them." The rebel appeared to be furious, and several operators laughed at the fuss he was making. Frank went over to see who had squirted the rebel, and found out it was Tony, one of his more experienced men, who had left for relief. Ignoring the other men who were kidding him, Frank returned to his desk. When Tony returned from relief, Frank talked with him quietly at his desk for several minutes. He then talked with Tony's partner, who had also been involved. He told them both that the only way he could stop the rebel from causing trouble was to crack down on squirting generally and he expected them to cut it out. Frank said, "I know the rebel does more squirting than anyone else, and then whenever he is squirted he makes a big stink about it. Wherever we put that guy, we have trouble. Now, I don't want you to get involved with him. You just stay clear of him." To the observer Frank explained, "I don't want to get Tony into trouble. He's a good man, but if I'm going to stop this, I've got to treat everyone the same."

On a subsequent day Frank told the observer that since that time he had had no trouble with squirting. He said that the men realized that it had gone too far and had corrected the situation themselves. He also reported that the rebel on two or three occasions thereafter had come up to him and apologized for the trouble he had caused.

To the observer there were several interesting aspects to this little affair. In a potentially difficult situation the foreman had kept his head. Furthermore, he had interpreted the incident as a group problem and had acted accordingly. It was obvious that the wet sanders as a group were not on the rebel's side. By making the squirting a serious issue to the foreman and by losing his temper, he had violated the group's ideas of appropriate behavior. In their eyes he had made himself ridiculous. The foreman, therefore, could not openly take the rebel's side without himself violating the group's code. Neither could he ignore the fact that the rebel had been squirted. By remaining calm, by waiting for Tony to come back from relief, by refusing to get into an argument with the rebel, by talking firmly with the men who had done the squirting and yet in a way that showed understanding of their point of view – in these and other ways, the foreman appeared to help his men solve a group problem in a constructive way. For the rest of the day Frank and the rebel did not speak to each other. At the end of the day, standing by the line near the rebel's work station, Frank got into a friendly conversation with another worker there about a famous incident in the past when horseplay had caused a serious accident. Apparently the way Frank handled the situation eventually persuaded the rebel that he himself had been in the wrong, and he apologized to his foreman for causing the trouble.

In the comments which Frank made about his men and in his actions in relation to them which we observed, notice that he displayed three important attitudes or practices. (1) He was conscious of the men as individuals and paid attention to their individual attitudes and needs. (2) He was conscious of the men as a group and acted as the leader of the group responsible for strengthening their group bonds and encouraging their group objectives. (3) In what he said and in how he acted he showed a basic respect for his men as well as faith in their willingness and ability to do a good job.

VITELLI AND QUALITY

As mentioned earlier, Frank said that he and the other wet sanders would like to get satisfaction from their jobs. When wet sanding is done well the job feels right, and to most workers there is a real satisfaction in doing good work. But when "the line is too fast" and you "don't have time to do it right," the job becomes irritating. As a foreman Frank still remembered this important relationship between job satisfaction and quality. He believed that his men wanted to do a good job, and he did what he could to help them.

Of course, Frank also had to check up on his men and correct them when they made mistakes. But he did not attempt to check their work in great detail. If he had, he would have had time for little else. In fact for long periods Frank left his section entirely, yet the work continued to be done well. Most of the incidents directly concerning quality occurred towards the beginning of the day. As Frank explained, both he and the general foreman had been away from the section, working in car conditioning, for the last several days. Consequently, in the morning he found several things being done wrong which he had to correct. As he pointed out to the observer in the afternoon, when talking about how smoothly the section was running:

It's a big difference now from this morning. Of course, they knew I was away and the general foreman was away, so they were not on their toes as much as they are now. It's natural. It's only human for that to make a difference. Once they see that you are checking on a couple of guys, then the others all tighten up, too.

Frank's method of "checking on a couple of guys" was interesting. It seemed almost casual. He would be walking past a worker and notice a job not being done quite right. He would call the operator's attention to it by a gesture or a word; the worker would nod in acknowledgment, and Frank would proceed on his way. Once on noticing a bad wet sanding job he showed it to the operator and said, "That will never go," then immediately left to do something else.

Over eighteen percent of Vitelli's total day was made up of incidents directly concerned with quality. Let us illustrate by noting the following incidents, all of which occurred between 10:59 and 11:04:

1. Frank looks into several trunks and talks to a worker about an item in the trunks needing attention.

2. Asks utility man how the work is coming and tells him, "If you get a chance, see what you can do about those tabs [some faulty work from a previous section which had to be corrected]." Utility man says, "I got them already." Frank replies, "That's using your head, boy."

3. Feels a tail pan to see how the putty is coming through [a job performed in a previous section about which Frank had talked with the operator involved].

4. Walks up the line looking at several bodies which had been wet sanded, occasionally feeling one of them.

5. Yells across to a wet sander, "Try to give me a little more down there," showing him the place. Worker nods. Frank examines the next body at the same place and yells back to the

same wet sander, "That's good on that one. Let's have more like that." Worker nods.

6. Asks another wet sander how the jobs are coming. Worker says he needs more emery paper to do the job right. Foreman leaves to get him some.

Here were six separate incidents concerning quality which took place in five minutes. There were at least ninety-three similar incidents during the day. Many of them were initiated not by Frank himself, but by his men telling *him* about items that needed to be corrected.

For the first hour and a half and on numerous other occasions during the day, Frank spent his time tracking down various troubles which his men told him about. Often he went into other sections to investigate things being done wrong there which were causing his men trouble. Sometimes he talked with the foreman about them; other times he went directly to the operator involved and explained to him how he should change the way he was doing his job. The observer never noticed that this activity on Frank's part caused any resentment in the other sections. Especially did the two foremen immediately preceding and following Frank's section feel free to go into one another's section in order to track down trouble and correct it at its source. To them this was helpful; it did not seem like interference or criticism. Because of the mutual understanding between the three foremen, Frank said, they each felt free to talk directly with workers in another section in order to get something cleared up.

Once when Frank was in the preceding section on the line, an operator there came up to him and told him about something wrong. Frank followed the man into the spray booth to investigate. When he came out, Frank said to this operator, "Thanks, Al, for showing me." This attitude of helpfulness between foreman and worker, even in another section than the foreman's regular one, seemed to be characteristic of Frank's relationships.

VITELLI'S IDENTIFICATION WITH HIS JOB

According to Frank himself he always had a drive to get on top. In his comments on his earlier life some of the reasons why he became a foreman can be seen:

I've had a crazy kind of life. When I was fourteen I started in working. Then I went into a road gang. In four days I was made a gang leader. Then I went on to another job, and I was made leader there, too. I used to think sometimes I was going out of my mind. I've always worked in tough places. I used to box for a while. . . . I had a rough time in the Navy. . . . Then I decided I really better settle down. . . . So I came over here. They didn't want to take me at first — they said I was too small. But I told the boss, I guess I can take it. That didn't go over too good, but I stuck with it.

Frank has settled down. His experience at Plant X has taught him how to control and channel his energy, but the basic ambition and drive remains. He would probably say that whereas before he was primarily a "driver," now he has developed into a "leader." Just before the comment given above, in his second interview as a foreman, Frank said:

I'm still new here, of course, and I've got a lot to learn yet. . . . I can get real mad. Before, I used to back some of these guys up against the wall and there'd be a fight; but a couple of years ago I decided I'd have to change. Now, when I get mad I take a walk. I stay away about five or ten minutes and try and cool down. I haven't flared up yet for two years.[5] I just don't like to take orders.

Towards the end of this interview Frank indicated what was possibly a very important source of help to him in adjusting to Plant X:

Another good man to know is the [plant] doctor. I go over to talk with him. I've gotten to know him pretty well. I discuss cases

[5] During his eight hours' observation as a foreman, in spite of several provocations, Frank was never seen to lose his temper, to raise his voice, or to show any obvious outward signs of inner tension.

with him. My own, too. He's a good man. I thought he was kind of queer at first, but I think he's probably got about the hardest job here in the plant. Most of the foremen think the Doc leans too far on the side of labor. I don't think so. I think he's fair.

When interviewed as a worker, Frank showed no great interest in his work. But by the time he became foreman he thought of himself as an integral part of Plant X and he was thoroughly absorbed in his work and in the importance of succeeding at it. He frankly enjoyed being a foreman, and at the same time he felt compelled by an inner drive constantly to improve his performance, as the following excerpts from the interview, held six weeks after he became a foreman, make clear:

I like being a foreman. There are ups and downs, and you have to make a lot of decisions, so there's some pressure. But about these decisions, I've figured out it's better to make them right away. If you don't, then things pile up and it becomes hard to make decisions.

The interviewer then asked what Frank meant by "pressure":

It is a matter of quality, for one thing. Then you have to keep cost at a minimum. And then there's the whole business of labor relations. You get the most work you can out of the men. Then there's the problem of working with new men.

The interviewer asked if Frank felt there was any pressure on him from his superiors:

I don't feel any pressure from above. I just feel the **pressure inside myself.** I feel I should be doing a better job, and a better job should be done, but they haven't started to get tough about it yet. The simple fact is that they're getting some paint jobs over on the final line that we could give them some help on over here. [Emphasis added.]

An example of his interest in his job came up later in the interview when he was discussing his belief that many grievances could be eliminated, especially those having to do with distribution of overtime work:

I feel that a foreman should teach all his men all the jobs that require overtime. Then there needn't be too much of a gap between a high man and a low man. If you get so you have one man that's good on a job that gets a lot of overtime, then he's the fella that gets all the overtime. That's no good. I've spent a lot of extra time working extra hours overtime without pay myself in order to break guys in right, so they could do all the jobs.

The pressures of a foreman's job on an assembly line did not bother Frank excessively; he was used to them and accepted them as an inevitable part of the framework within which he tried to do as good a job as possible. Because he trusted his men, he was no longer tied to the section. Without constantly worrying that something terrible would happen, he felt free to go to other areas in his search for ways to make his men's jobs easier and more productive. Towards the end of the day Frank suddenly remarked to the observer, "I love this work. When I have my day off, I'm all keyed up. I seem to be waiting for something to happen. You get so used to it. . . ." It seemed clear that being a foreman on the assembly line had become *natural* to Frank. On the job he felt at home.

At the same time he did not have a static point of view towards his role. He liked the responsibility of the foreman's job and wanted more of it:

I like to get away from having just one kind of job under me. I used to have just the wet deck; then I got those other operations. Now, I would like still more. It gives you more responsibility and it makes the foreman's job more interesting.

In preferring to have more rather than fewer men under him, Frank was not typical of Plant X foremen. However, the few others who mentioned the same preference were those who, like Vitelli, followed the practice of delegating an unusual amount of responsibility to their utility men and in general based their behavior on the assumption that by and large their men could and wanted to do a good job without constant, close supervision by the foreman of each operation.

CONCLUSIONS

The following inferences might well be drawn from the information about Frank Vitelli which we have presented:

1. As a worker he found his job tiring, monotonous, unsatisfying; he stayed on it mainly because the pay was good and the work steady.

2. Ambitious all his life, Frank, the worker, wanted to become a foreman. However, he thought his chances were so poor that he might as well leave.

3. Two important and related reasons for wanting to become a foreman were: (a) to escape from the physical and psychological confinements imposed by assembly line technology ("I don't like to be absorbed by the machinery"), and (b) to realize his full capacity for increased responsibility (to "feel like I'm accomplishing things myself").

4. Frank's experience on the line was invaluable to him. As a foreman he demonstrated an awareness of the importance of the worker's relations to his immediate job, especially in the case of new men.

5. The informal patterns of relationships in the wet sanding section were not disrupted when Frank became the foreman. As utility man he was already in an *accepted* position of informal leadership. This made his new position easier for him and easier for his men to adjust to. As utility man he had learned many of the technical and the human problems of administering the section. Most important, he had learned a lot about himself.

6. His activities and attitudes as a foreman are best illustrated by examining some of the series of incidents which occurred during an eight-hour day. The fundamental characteristic of these series of incidents was that they were *intermittent*. They overlapped each other and were constantly interrupted by other incidents that arose to demand his attention.

7. As a foreman Frank was constantly dealing with problems involving quality. (No other *single* topic involved as much of his

time.) In his contacts with his own men, with other men, and with other supervisors concerning quality problems, no feeling of resentment or atmosphere of fault-finding prevailed. Considering the pressures under which these interactions took place (imposed in this case by the moving line and by Frank's own drive to excel at his job), this is remarkable, but to the observer it appeared that both Frank *and* those he dealt with had learned to live with pressure and to insulate their relationships against its potentially disrupting effects.

8. As a foreman Frank had adjusted to his job, but he did not stand still, either literally or figuratively. He retained a strong drive to succeed and to earn positions of increasing responsibility. He was thoroughly wrapped up in his job as a foreman, and as part of the social and technological environment of Plant X. In this larger sense he was still "absorbed by the machinery," but this was an absorption he accepted and enjoyed.

9. As a foreman Frank believed in delegating responsibility to his men, especially to his utility men. He trusted them to be conscientious and to do a good job, and he tried to teach them through experience to do better.

10. Frank believed "that by enlarging the job of the people under you, that is the best thing you can do in order to get ahead yourself." In delegating added responsibilities to his utility men, he was frankly acting in his own best interest.

Finally, we repeat three generalizations which characterized Frank's behavior and attitude as a foreman.

1. He was conscious of his men as *individuals* and paid attention to their individual attitudes and needs.

2. He was conscious of his men as a *group* and acted as the leader of the group, responsible for strengthening their group bonds and encouraging their group objectives.

3. In what he said and how he acted he showed a *basic respect* for his men as well as a *positive assumption* that they were willing and able to do a good job.

Of course, Frank Vitelli did not always follow these generalizations, but these were the things he intended to do. And these intentions, we suggest, are essential ingredients of any successful leadership of people engaged in productive work. Furthermore, while it is easy to express such intentions verbally, actually demonstrating them in specific instances on the job is a difficult and absorbing task.

A final point on these three generalizations has to do with their relative importance. Often management appears to give more emphasis to the first, paying attention to *individual* needs, than to the other two. Yet according to our observation each of the three is equally important; any one of them operates successfully only when combined with the other two. For example, attention to the individual, apart from his position as a member of his group and from the group relations involved, ignores many of the most important factors which should be considered in any administrative problem. And even outwardly "correct" action directed towards either the individual or the group, which is not based on fundamentally constructive assumptions about other people's intentions and capacities, runs the danger of becoming barren and insincere. Workers when discussing their superiors agreed that how your boss felt about your ability to do a good job had a great deal to do with how good a job you did.

10 MASS PRODUCTION AND THE INDIVIDUAL

In this chapter and the ones following, we shall no longer report, but make an effort to integrate the material from the other chapters around two major themes — the individual and the human group. The problem of the individual who loses his identity in the mass is a typical problem of the modern world. There is much talk of our huge overgrown institutions, of governments that are bureaucratic because they are too big, of corporations that are impersonal because their operations are so large. Historians and editorial writers indeed have long been busy recording and deprecating the submergence of the individual in the mass. David Riesman's vivid phrase, "The lonely crowd," perhaps sums up the phenomenon and the reaction to it which most of us acknowledge. But on the assembly line this problem has a special character and origin. It is rooted not so much in the circumstance of large-scale operations as in the formal logic of job design, and job design as related to a moving conveyor. As we have already seen, as far as engineering ingenuity can devise, individual skill, judgment, and initiative have been subtracted from jobs at the production level. This we have illustrated by many examples. Consider only five which particularly emphasize the effect on the individual, and with which the reader of this book is already familiar:

1. The number of units of work performed in any given moment of time is determined by the speed of the conveyor. Accordingly, in doing his job the individual must subordinate his own natural rhythm to the unvarying rhythm of the machine.

2. For the application of human ingenuity or of personal choice in doing his job, or of experience and judgment, a series of simplified motions are substituted and repeated throughout the working day.

3. The exigencies of the moving line compel the strict regulation of relief. In attending to bodily and other personal needs, the worker must conform to a schedule, and be dependent on a system of organized relief. Rigid conformity to this relief system serves continually to remind the worker of the primacy of the mechanical.

4. There are fewer opportunities for interpersonal relationships than in less rationalized factories. As a result many workers feel a frustating sense of anonymity.

5. Since there is comparatively little difference in skill between one job and the next, the difference in pay and prestige is small. As a result the average worker feels his chances of promotion are slim, unless he ceases to be a production worker altogether, and becomes a foreman.

To meet all of these and other elements in the work environment that tend to reinforce a sense of the impersonal, and that seem, according to some workers, to swallow up the individual in the mass, the good foreman provides as many counterweights as he can.

In any organization the function of the front-line leader is to mediate between the rigidities and impersonalities of command and the infinite variety of human nature. In assembly lines, the advanced sectors of a rationalized and standardized economy, technology affects the individual as an added force, and a very impressive one, on the side of the impersonal, of the *de*-individualized, of the *non*-human. Those who experience compulsions which are non-human or mechanical are apt to accuse the agents of these compulsions of themselves being inhuman. Hence, the obsessive hostility sometimes exhibited by assembly workers toward corporation managements.[1]

[1] See *The Man on the Assembly Line*, pp. 137–140.

Thus the greater part of the foreman's activity in relation to his men, as recorded in this book, may be looked upon as a spontaneous effort to supply the component indispensable for a successful organization – dignity of the individual.

In the light of this record of the foreman's own efforts to solve the problem, what can the upper ranks of management, including top corporation management, do to assist him? Our answers would be:

1. Give priority in choosing foremen to those who have the skills which enable them to counterbalance anonymity with a personal relationship, to absorb excessive pressures, and to exhibit the other characteristics of successful foremen we have recorded.

2. See that the foreman, apart from his technical duties, has the *time* to establish such personal relationships, either by giving him less to do, or by teaching him to organize his time more effectively, or both.

3. See that there is sufficient continuity of employment of the work force so that more sustained and satisfactory relationships between men and supervision can develop.

4. See that all above the rank of foremen act toward them as the best foremen act toward their men, and especially see to it that the pressure from above is never so great as to transform the foreman from a leader into a driver.

We have considered the impact of assembly-line technology on the individual worker. What about its impact on the foreman as an individual? In certain ways this effect appears as the reverse of that on the worker. At the root of the worker's objection to assembly-line technology are the pacing and repetitiveness inherent in his job.[2] It is necessary for the foreman too, in his own way, to "keep up with the line," but far from "doing the same thing over and over," the essence of the foreman's job is doing something *different* every minute. In fact the typical foreman engaged in some four to six hundred *separate* episodes in the course of his

[2] *The Man on the Assembly Line,* pp. 51–56.

working day. If the conveyor kept the average worker at or near one work station doing the same thing, it kept the foreman, on the other hand, moving rapidly from place to place and doing many different things.

This contrast deserves emphasis because it illustrates how any one characteristic of a job, if pushed to an extreme, is repugnant to the normal personality and causes excessive fatigue. Extreme routine on a job is unpleasant and unduly fatiguing to most, if not to all, persons.[3] Excessive discontinuity, an interruption every minute of the day, for example, also is unpleasant and very fatiguing to most people. And in this case both extremes stem directly from the technology of the same work environment.

It is obvious that nearly all supervisory and executive jobs are characterized to some degree by discontinuity and by the pressure of unwanted interruptions. But as in other instances, the technology of the assembly line appears to produce a far more extreme manifestation of a familiar phenomenon. For this reason, just as tests have been suggested to measure workers' limits of tolerance to *routine*, so it would be advisable also to test limits of tolerance to *discontinuity* in the working day.

The foreman, like any good executive, needs the ability to hold simultaneously in his mind details of many incompleted actions, so that later, at the appropriate moment, he may close the episode. He needs the ability to tolerate arbitrary interruptions without forgetting about what he was doing at the moment and without losing his sense of proportion. This suggests a solution on two fronts: (1) careful selection and promotion based on a candidate's ability to withstand interruptions with a minimum of frustration; and (2) alteration wherever possible of conditions which produce excessive interruptions. The foremen at Plant X clearly believed there were too many arbitrary interruptions, and among them they counted those that stemmed from excessive fluctuation in schedule.

[3] *The Man on the Assembly Line,* p. 53.

Tolerance of routine or of overspecialization, tolerance of discontinuity, of arbitrary interruptions, are phrases which obviously have connotations for our time far beyond that of assembly lines, or even of modern industry as a whole. We will return to them for a final comment in the last section of this book.

11 MASS PRODUCTION AND THE GROUP

We saw in the last chapter that the assembly-line foreman plays an important role in modifying the impact of mass-production technology upon the individual. But we have also discovered that some of the foremen at Plant X talked about the men they supervised as a group or team, and very consciously thought of themselves as that group's leader. Furthermore, they made reference from time to time to concrete results of group or team spirit in improving quality or in solving such problems as absenteeism and turnover.

In this chapter, then, we shall examine the foreman's role in relation to work groups, and in particular seek answers to these five questions:

1. What is the nature and importance of groups on the assembly line?
2. What factors tend to weaken these groups?
3. What are the characteristics of strong groups?
4. What is the nature of the foreman's dual role, (a) as a leader (and member) of his group of men; and (b) as a member of management?
5. What conditions and circumstances encourage productive group strength?

Before we answer the first question, we should go back one step. What *is* a group, a human group? A definition on which nearly everyone who has studied the subject agrees is that personal contact or interaction between its members is basic. In other words, without some pattern of interaction, you may have a crowd or an aggregate of individuals, but not a group. Interaction, however, is not simply talking. It includes signals, gestures, facial expressions, and any other form of face-to-face communication. For example, an interaction can occur simply through one person handing another person a tool, or a piece of metal, and this is often the way interactions do occur in factory work groups. George Homans begins his book, *The Human Group*, with this definition: "We mean by a group a number of persons who communicate with one another often over a span of time, and who are few enough so that each person is able to communicate with all the others, not at second hand, through other people, but face to face. Sociologists call this a primary group."[1]

NATURE AND IMPORTANCE OF GROUPS ON THE ASSEMBLY LINE

Enough has been said about the technology of the assembly-line environment to suggest that the workers under any given foreman are not the same as the close-knit groups or crews and teams common to many industries, where all members have separate but strictly interdependent functions, and tend to think of themselves as a "baseball nine" or a "football eleven." But on the assembly line, men do work that is rarely related, team-wise or in a strict functional sense, to what other members of the group do.

[1] G. C. Homans, *The Human Group* (New York: Harcourt, Brace and Company, 1950), p. 1. For a fuller definition of a group in terms of the interactions of its members see especially *ibid.*, pp. 82–86. "If we say that individuals A, B, C, D, E . . . form a group, this will mean that at least the following circumstances hold. Within a given period of time, A interacts more often with B, C, D, E . . . than he does with M, N, L, O, P . . . whom we chose to consider outsiders or members of other groups. B also interacts more often with A, C, D, E . . . than he does with outsiders, and so on for the other members of the group. It is possible just by counting interactions to map out a group quantitatively distinct from others." (p. 84) Note also Homans' warning: "One point does need to be made clear. Saying that a group is defined by interaction is not the same thing as saying that interaction is the whole of group life." (p. 86)

For this reason in our early study of assembly lines, our first impression was that technology had eliminated the work group altogether, leaving merely a tenuous relationship between individuals and the foremen.

But this is not true, whatever the logic of engineering. Every segment of the line under a foreman is an actual or potential work group or team. Sometimes the men under a given foreman qualify as a primary group and sometimes do not. Sometimes they "communicate with one another often over a span of time" because of a certain type of foreman's leadership or other circumstances, and at other times they do not. There are "few enough" for all to communicate face to face, but, as we shall notice, technological and other factors sometimes make interaction difficult or impossible.

Social scientists in discussing groups use the term cohesiveness, rather than strength. This, as commonly understood, means a measure of the durability of the group. One brief definition of cohesiveness is "the resultant of all the forces acting on all the members to remain in the group."[2] We are interested in the durability and the cohesiveness of a group as so defined; but more precisely we are interested in the resultant power of its members to think and act as a single unit and to fulfill their common objectives by so doing.

Before examining why groups vary in cohesiveness, we need to state two assumptions which should be kept in mind throughout this discussion:

The first, which is perhaps implicit in Homans' definition of a group, is that there tends to be a positive correlation between the amount of interaction among members and the cohesiveness or strength of the group. In other words, the more frequently people

[2] Dorwin Cartwright and Alvin Zander (editors), *Group Dynamics Research and Theory* (Evanston, Illinois and White Plains, New York: Row, Peterson and Co., 1953), p. 78. Cartwright and Zander summarize a number of studies concerned with the concept of cohesiveness, pp. 73–91. See also S. E. Seashore: *Group Cohesiveness in the Industrial Work Group*. Ann Arbor: Survey Research Center, University of Michigan, 1954.

in a group talk with one another — or otherwise interact — the stronger the group.[3]

A second assumption is that a strong and cohesive group with the foreman as its leading member is desirable. Personal satisfactions of its members are increased. Frictions are reduced. A sense of purpose develops which can lead to improved efficiency and quality. These assumptions can be justified, we believe, not only by our own observations and research at Plant X and elsewhere, but also by reference to the large volume of recent social-science research into the nature and functions of groups in industry and elsewhere. For example, recent field studies of work groups in different industries by the University of Michigan[4] indicate the probability that "pride or involvement in the work group and productivity are interacting variables, and that an increase in either one tends to bring about an increase in the other."[5] Furthermore, "the relationships in the primary group are also important among the determinants of morale, especially satisfaction with the job and with the large organization. Workers in the tractor company [one of the companies studied] who reported that they really felt a part of their work group . . . tended to be high in satisfaction with job and company."[6] A number of recent similar

[3] There are obvious exceptions to this statement and yet it remains a useful generalization. One exception is this: if the members markedly disagree on the group's goals, increasing interaction may increase their disagreement and so reduce the group's cohesiveness. For a discussion of this and related points, see W. F. Whyte, "Leadership and Group Participation," (Ithaca, New York; New York State School of Industrial and Labor Relations, Bulletin 24, May, 1953) especially pp. 28–30. See Homans, *The Human Group*, pp. 110–117, 243, 444. See also the "Note" by Paula and Robert Brown, and Homans' reply, in *American Sociological Review*, vol. 20, no. 1 (February, 1955), pp. 83–86.

[4] For a summary of some of the major studies by the Survey Research Center at the University of Michigan, see R. L. Kahn and Daniel Katz, "Leadership Practices in Relation to Productivity and Morale," in Cartwright and Zander, *Group Dynamics*, pp. 612–628.

[5] Cartwright and Zander, *Group Dynamics*, p. 624.

[6] Cartwright and Zander, *Group Dynamics*, p. 625. See also Katz and Kahn: "Some Recent Findings in Human Relations Research in Industry," in G. E. Swanson, T. M. Newcomb, E. L. Hartley, and others (editors), *Readings in Social Psychology* (New York: Henry Holt and Co., revised edition,

studies confirm the earlier ones of Elton Mayo and others on frequent positive correlations of group cohesiveness with productivity, as well as with job satisfaction.[7]

One fundamental reason that a feeling of belonging to a cohesive group of men at work increases the average worker's satisfaction with his job and with the company may well be that without a group to identify with, there is in most large organizations a feeling of anonymity which most people dislike. Certainly this has been true for the automobile assembly workers interviewed in our studies. In both plants surveyed, considerable bitterness was expressed against what appeared to them as "impersonal treatment" by the company. A surprising number of workers felt that "the company isn't interested in people," or "you're just a number as far as they're concerned."[8] This feeling of anonymity, caused at least in part by the relatively impersonal nature of the work itself on most assembly-line jobs, can create or accentuate problems of morale, absenteeism, turnover, and quality.

Our evidence is that the successful foreman at Plant X intuitively recognized the importance for the average worker of belonging to a group, and purposely related himself not only to each individual but to his group of men as a whole. This constituted another method, and an important one, by which the foreman counteracted the pressure and impersonality of the work environment.

We are now ready to look at the factors which weaken, and those which strengthen, work groups on the assembly line.

1952), pp. 650–655; and F. C. Mann and J. K. Dent, "The Supervisor: Member of Two Organizational Families," *Harvard Business Review*, vol. 32, no. 6 (Nov.–Dec. 1954), pp. 103–112. Also see Seashore: *Group Cohesiveness in the Industrial Work Group*.

[7] See especially Elton Mayo and G. F. F. Lombard, *Teamwork and Labor Turnover in Southern California* (Boston: Harvard Business School, Division of Research, Business Research Studies, no. 32, 1944). See also our Selected Bibliography for other studies of work groups.

[8] See *The Man on the Assembly Line*, pp. 135–140. These attitudes were still more strongly expressed by the longer-service men in the second assembly plant studied.

FACTORS THAT TEND TO WEAKEN GROUPS

These factors are important because it is only by counteracting them that a foreman derives the advantages of a cohesive work team, and significantly, nearly all of them appear as barriers to interaction between men on the assembly line.

The first and most obvious barrier is noise. In many of the sections along the line, *verbal* interaction, at least, is difficult or impossible. (The section called "the jungle," described in the chapter on "A Foreman's Day," is a good example.) Even where noise does not inhibit interaction, the average worker has to pay close attention to the line, which is always moving in front of him, if he isn't to "go into the hole." He can seldom or never stop even for a moment to chat with his neighbor. And unlike some assembly jobs in other industries, the work on an automobile assembly line often requires a degree of "surface mental attention"[9] which makes it difficult or impossible to work and talk at the same time, except for the occasional exchange of a few words – for example, when there is a gap in the line. Also, except when he takes personal relief, the average worker must remain at his station throughout the work day, which sharply limits the number of men with whom interaction is possible.

A more important and basic limiting factor is one we have already mentioned. The process, the technical nature of the work of an assembly line neither suggests nor compels interaction. Interaction connected with the work, such as interchange of tools, signals, reciprocal or team activity, is not usually necessary. In other words, there are fewer absolute *functional* requirements for interaction between men in an assembly plant than in many other industries.

Group cohesiveness is also limited by the fact, characteristic as far as we know only of assembly lines, that every group under a foreman is, so to speak, blurred at both ends so far as interaction goes. To illustrate: imagine a moving line, let us say, a hundred

[9] See *The Man on the Assembly Line,* pp. 12–13.

and fifty feet long with three groups of workers each occupying fifty feet of the line. The men are on each side of the line, and let us say each group of twenty men has ten on one side and ten on the other. The actual interaction of the workers with each other can be diagrammed and this we did in our earlier study of hourly wage earners at Plant X.[10] Without reproducing those diagrams, it is nevertheless easy to show something of the character of intra-group interaction. Because of the noise and close attention to work, interactions can only occur with men who are near each other. If five workers are A, B, C, D, and E, C, for example, can only interact, unless he shouts, with B and D, or with those opposite to him on the line. Thus, an individual worker is likely to interact, in the course of a day or a month, with only a fraction of his own work group, and then only briefly and infrequently. And the workers at either end of the section interact as frequently, because of proximity, with members of the next group as they do with their own. Because of this interaction pattern, the boundaries between groups are blurred, and all the individuals in the group with which a worker tends to interact do not necessarily come under the same foreman.

Not only is the cohesiveness of the men in a foreman's section limited by this overlapping at the edges; equally important are changes in the composition of work groups caused by fluctuations in production, turnover, and absenteeism. Even when interaction among members of a potential group is frequent, it takes time for cohesiveness to develop. Whenever schedules fluctuate sharply up or down, the composition and size of the groups change, and often individual members report to different foremen. In the same way turnover and absenteeism disrupt the composition of a group, and make it more difficult for foremen to develop that feeling of belonging and loyalty which comes from stability of membership. Several foremen, it will be recalled, stated that developing among their men a feeling of loyalty and team spirit was an effective way to combat absenteeism. Yet if absenteeism increased, cohesiveness

[10] *The Man on the Assembly Line*, pp. 74–75.

decreased, and with less cohesiveness, absenteeism tended to increase still further. Some foremen were able to transform this potentially vicious or negative circle into a positive circle. In such sections, when absenteeism or turnover decreased, the group's cohesiveness was strengthened, and the stronger it got, the fewer men were absent from work.

CHARACTERISTICS OF STRONG GROUPS

In spite of these inhibiting factors, some foremen *were* able to build with and between their men a strong sense of belonging to a group. Under the foreman's leadership, members of that group helped each other out in performing what they thought were their common objectives in getting the work done. How was this possible? How did these foremen manage to overcome the various handicaps to group formation discussed above? Let us look first at the particular pattern of interaction which was observed between the foreman and his men, and then at what the foreman conceived his role to be.

This study did not include a quantitative study of workers' interaction patterns, but our interviews and observations lead to certain conclusions concerning the nature of interaction between the more successful foremen and their men that are conducive to quantitative testing. The evidence suggests that in those sections in which the foremen had been able to develop a sense of group or team spirit:

1. Interactions were more frequently reciprocal than unilateral between foreman and workers;
2. Key operators served as channels of communications;
3. Interactions between operators were functional or problem-solving. Some self-determination and informal job rotation was practiced.

When there were more reciprocal than unilateral interactions between the foreman and his men, that meant as a rule that when the foreman talked with a worker he was asking a question and listening to a response, rather than merely making a demand or transmitting an order. It was natural for such a foreman to delegate a certain amount of informal responsibility to his utility men or other key operators, so that there was more frequent interaction between the foreman and these operators than between the foreman and his other men.[11] Thus, the group structure in such instances did not simply comprise two levels of communication, the level of the formal leader (the foreman), and the level of all his subordinates. There was in addition a third, informal level, consisting of one or more utility or other key men.

A foreman who believed that his section operated more effectively when greater responsibility was distributed to his key operators practiced the same philosophy when he also allowed and encouraged his regular operators to take some of the responsibility for ensuring that good work was done in the section. Thus this meant that there was more interaction between operators concerning the work than in other sections. Without waiting for the foreman or inspectors to point out trouble, the operators themselves kept each other posted about actual or potential trouble encountered in the section, and, furthermore, advised one another as to steps which should be taken to correct the difficulty.

This kind of interaction among the men also reflected a certain amount of group self-determination allowed by some of the foremen. Though they maintained full responsibility for the end results, some foremen allowed the operators to determine how the work load was to be distributed among the group. At times the group, with the foreman's guidance, established informal systems of job rotation, and so, over a period of time, the average man in the group came to interact with most, if not all, of the members of the section. He was not tied to one location or limited in his interactions to those immediately adjacent to his work station.

[11] See for instance chapter 8, "A Foreman's Day." Foreman Pat interacted 227 times with 47 individuals. Eighty-seven of these interactions were with his 18 regular operators, and 27 interactions were with his two utility men. And see also chapter 9, "Profile of a Foreman."

Our previous studies indicated that informal job rotation among hourly workers increased their satisfaction.[12]

THE FOREMAN'S DUAL ROLE

It is obvious that the more successful foremen, in whose sections these patterns of interaction were observed, had particular ways of perceiving their role. Most important were their willingness and ability to think of themselves as the leaders (and therefore members) of a group of men, and to delegate to them a greater amount of initiative and responsibility than was strictly called for in the formal organizational structure. In some ways these foremen violated management's expressed beliefs as to the foreman's role. But these were the foremen regarded by upper management as the most successful. Their beliefs about the foreman's job and his relations with his men have been given in our chapter, "The Foreman and the Worker," especially in the quotations on pages 27 to 31. A description of how one of these foremen acted and thought is given in "Profile of a Foreman," in which an attempt was made to illustrate concretely how a successful foreman not only pays attention to his relations with his men *as individuals*, but also *as a group*, with a certain group attitude and structure. It is natural for him to take this group attitude and structure into account, because he thinks of himself as also a member of the group.

Not only is such a foreman sensitive to the group as well as to the individual needs of his men, but he bases his approach to them upon the assumption that they are willing and able, individually and as a group, to help each other and himself out by doing the work well. Perhaps the most important characteristic of a good foreman, especially in helping him to strengthen group cohesiveness and loyalty among his men, is this readiness to think well of his men, to make a partial identification with the men's feelings and viewpoints – an identification not as a rule shared by upper

[12] See *The Man on the Assembly Line*, pp. 148–151.

management. This was especially true of one of the points made most strongly by some foremen; namely, a good foreman should "stick up for his men." The foreman who was more willing to "stick his neck out" in the interest of his own group of workers found it easier to build with and among his men a feeling of cohesiveness and loyalty. This contributed to his winning recognition for good performance from management. In the case of such a foreman, as we pointed out earlier, "there is, of course, always a danger that he will neglect his duties as management's 'front-line' representative in doing 'favors' for his men. But in Plant X, there appeared a norm of behavior on this point. . ." This "norm" was accepted, informally, by workers, supervision, and upper management alike.

But a question now comes to mind. If a foreman thinks and acts not only as the leader but also as a member of his group of workers, how is it possible for him at the same time to be a member of management? Can a foreman belong to a group of workers and to the group called management at the same time? The answer, of course, is that it is not only possible but *inevitable* that a foreman perform this dual role, nor is it abnormal or undesirable. As has often been pointed out, it is the essence of the foreman's job to be "the man in the middle."[13] Indeed this may be the successful foreman's basic function: to act as the intermediary between the purposes of management and the attitudes and activities of his men. As a member of management, as management's "front-line representative," he interprets company policy to his men, maintains

[13] See, for example: B. B. Gardner and W. F. Whyte, "The Man in the Middle: Position and Problems of the Foreman," *Applied Anthropology* (*Human Organization*), vol. 4, no. 2 (Spring 1945), pp. 1–28; F. C. Mann and J. K. Dent, "The Supervisor: Member of Two Organizational Families," *Harvard Business Review*, vol. 32, no. 6 (November–December 1954), pp. 103–112; F. J. Roethlisberger, "The Foreman: Master and Victim of Double Talk," *Harvard Business Review*, vol. 23, no. 3 (Spring 1945), pp. 283–298; D. F. Wray, "Marginal Men of Industry, the Foremen," *American Journal of Sociology*, vol. 54, no. 4 (January 1949), pp. 298–301; and D. N. Ulrich, D. R. Booz, and P. R. Lawrence, *Management Behavior and Foreman Attitude: A Case Study* (Boston: Division of Research, Harvard Business School, 1950), especially pp. 29–46.

discipline, transmits orders, hires (or participates in hiring), discharges (or participates in discharging) the work force. But at the same time, the successful foreman also transmits the needs, complaints, and attitudes of his men to management and defends and interprets the workers' viewpoint. On occasion he goes further and stands protectively with the workers against what appear to him as arbitrary or inequitable actions by management. In this role, he is not only an overseer of work, but for the occasion, the leader and representative of his men.

The danger is that a foreman will fail to appreciate the duality of his role, that he will lean too far in one direction or the other. At times it requires a careful sense of proportion to avoid this temptation. In studying other plants and industries the authors have observed that the foreman's role ranges between extreme management-mindedness on the one hand, to extreme identification with workers' interests on the other.

An example of strong orientation toward management occurred in another automobile plant. During a period of crisis top management felt impelled to place unusual burdens and exert abnormal pressure on all ranks of plant management. As a result most foremen felt they were forced to act always as pushers or transmitters of orders with no hint of sympathy, understanding, or interpretation of the attitudes of their men. Workers and foremen distrusted each other, and openly demonstrated this distrust. As a result, workers were mere time servers, strongly interested in putting their bosses in the wrong. For their part, supervisors rarely defended a worker but instead took occasion to discipline and often humiliate their men in the presence of fellow workers. Instead of being liked and respected, many foremen became feared and hated. Foremen felt much the same way about their superiors as their men felt about them. The final result was a strike in which management in a week lost all the production gains it had painfully amassed through months of pressure. Subsequently, management made some important changes, both in personnel and, more important, in underlying philosophy, and the situation greatly improved. This was an example, obviously, where the necessity for foremen to think and act as belonging to their own group of men had been neglected, and management (as well as foremen themselves and their men) suffered the consequences.

An instance of the other extreme occurred in a steel fabricating plant. Certain foremen had become so closely identified with the workers' and the union's interests that they had virtually abdicated as supervisors. Repeatedly, in matters of discipline, work load, and work assignment, they followed uncritically the men's wishes. Here again both sides suffered. Management lost control of production, and the men also found, as the plant's competitive position declined, that their future became steadily less secure. In addition the union, having involved itself in all kinds of decisions normally reserved to management, became vulnerable to the charge by its members that it was trying to *be* management. When the situation was fully recognized, both union and management representatives took steps to restore a sounder balance of rights and prerogatives for both sides.

The lesson for management to learn from such examples is that both extremes of supervisory behavior are equally undesirable. What causes these extremes? Our answer is that as a rule and over a period of time the nature of the foreman's role in any plant is determined more than anything else by the principles and practices of top management. And perhaps the most important and practical thing which management can do is to understand and accept the necessity for a successful foreman to fulfill the dual role that we have been discussing:

> If . . . management fails to recognize this duality and attempts to enlist a supervisor's undivided loyalty, he may lose his ability to act as a representative of his employees and eventually his effectiveness in helping management gain its objectives.[14]

Nothing helps a foreman more than to know that his superiors,

[14] Mann and Dent, "The Supervisor: Member of Two Organizational Families," p. 112.

while eager to have him a member of management's team, are still not afraid to have him belong, as leader in fact as well as in name, to his own group of men.

SUMMARY AND CONCLUSION

This chapter started with a discussion of certain terms: "group," "interaction," and "cohesiveness." Next, certain basic assumptions were given which, we believe, were justified by evidence from our own research and from other studies. We assumed that at least a *potential* work group existed under every foreman, that a strong group helped production and personal satisfaction, and that strength or cohesiveness increased with interaction between group members.

We named several factors which weaken cohesiveness and noted the fact that the assembly process itself does not call for functional work teams or crews. Because of the geographical distribution of men along the line, each group under a foreman is blurred at the edges, which gives it a limited and overlapping interaction pattern. Finally, because of fluctuations in schedules, the membership of any section under a foreman is subject to frequent and sudden change, which hinders the development of a strong group.

In spite of these handicaps, some foremen successfully built strong work groups or teams. The interaction patterns of their groups showed more reciprocal and fewer unilateral interactions between them and their men, more frequent interaction between foreman and utility men, and a greater amount of functional interaction between operators.

The more successful foremen tend to think and act towards their men as a group, to think well of their men's capacities, and to stick up for them. In these ways the foreman becomes an informal member and representative of his group of workers as well as their formal "leader."

It is inevitable, we emphasized, that a successful foreman belong to his group of workers as well as to management. And it strengthens his hand when his superiors understand the necessity for this dual role. Given such understanding by management, the foreman is able to avoid extremes in his relations with his men.

The final question which grows out of this discussion is: what conditions encourage group strength and cohesiveness? We suggest at least five:

1. When management encourages the foreman to think of his men as a group or team with himself as their leader;

2. When foremen are selected who have the ability not only to perform their jobs technically, or to establish individual relationships with each man in each group, but to identify themselves with the group they lead;

3. When production schedules are stable, permitting group relationships to develop more readily. Fluctuations in group membership interrupt the growth of cohesiveness, increase the costs of absenteeism and turnover, and make it more difficult for foremen to build productive relations with their men;

4. When foremen hold periodic meetings with their men. Such meetings, either weekly or once a month, tend to develop effective group relations, and are becoming increasingly prevalent in American industry. Their special importance on the assembly line is accentuated by the limits to interaction imposed by technology. The foreman who regularly meets with his men increases quality-consciousness, gains valuable production suggestions, and increases group morale.[15]

5. A more fundamental requirement for realizing the potential benefits of greater group cohesiveness would be a basic re-design of assembly jobs themselves with a view toward satisfying and tapping more fully the plant's human resources. When engineers take fully into account individual and group dynamics in the de-

[15] In an assembly plant, obviously such meetings cannot be held when the line is moving. It is necessary rather to stop production temporarily or to hold the meetings after regular hours, paying foremen and workers for the small amount of overtime involved.

sign of jobs and processes, more enthusiasm and initiative will be released at work than is possible within the present limits of mass-production technology. This point requires and will receive a separate volume for its development. Some hint of its scope and importance is indicated in our next and final chapter.

12 THE PROBLEM IN PERSPECTIVE

In the Introduction to this study it was stated that workers and supervisors were participants in an unfinished technological revolution which began one hundred and fifty years ago. One of the human problems of this continuing revolution is essentially that of adjusting human behavior to the technical demands of work itself.

It is important not to read into the quoted comments of foremen at Plant X a criticism of the assembly process as such, or as an engineering device. All the supervisors, as far as we could judge, accepted the advantages in economy and speed of manufacture, of the principles of progressive assembly, and took their work environment for granted. However, they had their own ideas as to how they and their men should adapt to conditions as they found them. These ideas we have reported in this book.

The long, frank discussions by fifty-five foremen of the character of their jobs and of those under them and above them, showed that several concepts, widely held by the public and even by some members of management, about the effects on human behavior of the assembly process were mistaken. It also underscored certain unsolved problems in the important area of a social and psychological adjustment between men and machines.

To illustrate: it is believed by many outside of industry that the assembly line has not only denuded the jobs of any skill but taken from the worker any desire for assuming responsibility. It is true that most jobs require little skill. However, the most successful foremen — both in management's view and in the opinion of the hourly wage earners — were those who delegated responsibility as widely as possible.

The belief is widespread with the general public and in some management circles that an assembly-line foreman is and must be merely a pusher or driver of his men. But the evidence from our study of Plant X points to a different conclusion. The foremen at Plant X who supplemented the compulsions of the moving line with external pressure (nagging, demanding, threatening) were the least successful. Foremen who made the most of positive internal motivations, who established with their men a relationship of reciprocal responsibility and respect were the most successful in maintaining production, quality, and morale. Such a reciprocal relationship is difficult but possible in this work environment under normal conditions of relatively stable employment, *and when encouraged by upper management.*

When we look at the relations of the foreman not only to his own workers, but to others, the influence and importance of technology is clear. As the number of mass-production operators in our economy has increased, so has the number of service and maintenance personnel. The latter, besides the executive, supervisory, and clerical force, included substantial crews of electricians, mechanics, jig and fixture men, materials handlers, and others whose job was to keep all the machines along the route of the conveyor and the conveyor itself moving and in good repair.

With these service men, the foreman was in frequent and friendly contact. However, their number and strategic importance points up the difference between the foreman's job today and yesterday. Before the advent of the conveyor, before the extreme mechanization of the modern factory, the foreman was of course his own mechanic and electrician. He also set up his tools and laid out his work. Others now do these things for him. This technological revolution introduces two new problems in human relations, and in the case of Plant X both appear to have been recognized by management. The first is the maintenance of good relations between service and line. In some modern plants, the foreman feels that staff specialists have been robbing him of his prerogatives. So jealousies over pay or function frequently intervene to damage efficiency. Since frictions in this area were rare in Plant X, the problem did not detain us long in this study. The second problem can be accented by a question. Since the foreman's job, once rich in many technical skills and duties, has been stripped of most of them, what is left? On what today rests his status and authority? In Plant X at least his authority rested largely on personal leadership and the exercise of supervisory skills within a frequently frustrating but always dynamic work situation. Top management of Corporation XY appears to have consciously and deliberately followed the logic of technology by putting all specialized services into other people's hands, but at the same time it attempted to build the foreman's role by giving him as much authority in personal relationships as possible within the limits of the labor agreement. This included letting him have the last word in hiring his own personnel, in training, and in administering discipline. As we have seen, however, many foremen in Plant X did not feel that the company had gone far enough in giving them management responsibilities or recognition. They felt they should share more than they did in management decisions on new tools and processes, and insisted they should *always* be told the reason behind any policy change which it was their duty to carry out. These criticisms and requests are common ones among foremen in modern industry. In some ways perhaps it may be more difficult to satisfy them on assembly lines, because so many decisions and directives "flow from blueprints," as one man put it, and so many decisions must be made by technical experts. But by the same token, we believe, it is the more important that they be satisfied; that the foreman's point of view be considered and that he be made a participant in as many management decisions as possible.

In attempting to put the foreman's role at Plant X into perspective, it is important to say that on the whole and in spite of "rough times," difficulties, and frustrations, the foremen at Plant X *liked their jobs.* A majority were glad they were foremen, and glad they were foremen in the XY corporation. They liked their economic rewards. The corporation policy of paying salaries at least twenty-five percent higher than those of the men they supervised reinforced the foremen's status as members of management and was an important factor in their over-all job satisfaction. On the job they liked dealing with people and meeting the challenge of a dynamic work environment. This positive side in our appraisal of the influence of technology should not be lost sight of, nor the fact that many of the "likes" were due to enlightened management policies.

Nevertheless, real dissatisfaction existed and real problems stemmed from the technical environment for the foremen themselves, for upper management, and for the hourly wage earner. We have accordingly concerned ourselves more with areas where human problems or conflicts existed than with those areas where foresight and good-will had already reduced such difficulties to slight importance.

In the course of this study, fifty-five foremen discussed nearly every aspect of their foremanship that they could think of — or that we could. What light, if any, does this testimony throw on the *general* problem of mass production and human nature?

"Industrialization has introduced a new division into society," wrote Alexander Lindsay, the British philosopher, "the division between those who manage and take responsibility, and those who are managed and have responsibility taken from them. This is a division," he adds, "more important than the division between rich and poor." This comment touches upon one of the basic human problems which the foremen at Plant X were trying to solve. They were attempting, through personal contacts, through emphasis on individual differences, and through delegation of responsibility, to heal the division between those who were managed — both by their superiors and by machines — and management. But Lindsay was, of course, not talking about any particular plant or specific industry, but a social condition common to

Western civilization. Broadly speaking, certain features, like the "division" he mentions, are characteristic of most of society in the modern world. As to the extreme specialization or simplification of jobs on assembly lines, what is unique or extraordinary in that for modern man? Is not *overspecialization* simply a problem of modern times, the problem, for example, of science today, or scholarship, or government, or education? Even in technology, which is the parent of specialized knowledge, the deans of our engineering schools warn against the narrowing of curricula and seek breadth and a more rounded "training for life." In a similar fashion the concept and the problem of "discontinuity" are surely not confined to foremen on assembly lines or to sectors of industry that rigorously practice the principles of mass production. The daily life of most of us who live at or near the centers of Western civilization is apt to be discontinuous. Interruptions, pressure, discontinuity, and finally frustration are words applicable to the work and sometimes to the leisure of millions more than the employees in mass-production factories.

We make this point of broad association for two reasons. The first is to emphasize that that segment of American industry upon which we have focussed in this book should not be singled out as alone posing or alone responsible for these problems and dilemmas. Fundamentally, they are the problems of all of us living in a Western industrial culture and in the present century.

The other reason is to re-emphasize why we chose this particular sector in which to explore these problems, and why we are glad we did. We chose it because often in science, and particularly perhaps in the biological and social sciences, it is possible to learn more surely and sharply about a phenomenon of nature or society if it can be examined in an advanced and fully developed stage or sector.

We are glad to report that our first studies of this advanced sector are in a measure encouraging. First of all, because so many persons in positions of leadership and responsibility not only have recognized the problems posed as important — both for industry and for society – but have welcomed analysis and with an open mind are seeking solutions. In examining in detail this environment, first in our earlier studies from the point of view of the hourly wage earner, and now from the point of view of plant management and especially of front-line supervision, nothing was so striking as the *usefulness of normal human characteristics.* Although the logic of technology was to dispense with individual skill, initiative, and group loyalties, all of these human phenomena have nevertheless emerged. It is only through such individual and group qualities that the specialized technology can be made to function effectively.

For some years the authors have referred to their work at Yale as a study of "differing technological environments." Other scientists use other terms. Recently A. T. M. Wilson of the Tavistock Institute in England referred to similar work as "comparative and experimental studies of socio-technical production systems." He added, "Perhaps the most striking fact about the work is its independent appearance in various countries and centres; and from this, the emergence of similar trends with largely comparable findings."[1]

A particularly interesting example of work in this field is taking place at the University of California. There, research is under way which includes both engineers and representatives of the social sciences devoted to the discovery of basic criteria for designing and redesigning jobs. The criteria when reported upon will have taken account not only of what students of materials and machines have discovered about job design but what sociologists, psychologists, and others have found.[2]

Through such efforts it may be possible not only to introduce

[1] A. T. M. Wilson, "Some Contrasting Socio-Technical Production Systems in Industry." A paper given in a symposium on "Social and Technological Organization in Industrial Production Systems" at the 14th International Congress of Psychology, Montreal, June, 1954. An abstract of this symposium has been published in *Acta Psychologica*, vol. 2, no. 1 (1955), pp. 170–175.

[2] The project, which is entitled "Job Design," is directed by Louis E. Davis of the Department of Engineering and Ralph R. Carter, Department of Psychology, University of California, Berkeley.

more widely such measures of balance and counterweight, as we have been suggesting, but perhaps to take a deeper look at certain traditional factors in the design of both jobs and factories. Some of what might be called the socio-technical variables in work situations of which our knowledge, both practical and theoretical, is still scanty are elements, time cycles, group size, etc., and their most productive combination.

A study of recent technological trends will show that there are two directions in which factory work environments are moving. The first is toward greater emphasis on mechanization and automation; in other words, toward giving machines more and more to do. The second is toward employing more fully and intelligently the human being, who in the final analysis builds and controls the machines.

The emphasis of this book, and of others in this series, is upon behavior and attitude as affected by machines. The underlying assumption — or prejudice, if the reader wishes — is that the fuller development of the character and personalities of men and women while at work, whether men or management, is called for and is *possible without forfeiting the advances and advantages of modern technology.*

In the broadest sense this inquiry and the others in the present Yale series have been concerned with *work* and with man's relation and attitude toward it in the modern world. For a good many years industrialists and social scientists have been tackling the problems of introducing machines, and more recently mass-production methods, into the pre-industrial or "backward" areas of the world. But only recently have the problems of adjustment to a modern work environment in all its dimensions been recognized as also important for advanced countries.

The successful operation of a machine economy rests upon certain attitudes toward work, on acceptance of certain responsibilities, and on acceptance of particular ways of behaving and feeling. This point was made recently with great clarity and eloquence by the chairman of the Industrial Section of the British

Psychological Society. In urging a deeper study of work in the modern world he said:

> We have insufficiently realized the unusualness, and perhaps the precariousness, of the kind of attitudes to work upon which our civilization rests. . . . Work . . . as a mastery of technique, as control, attention, and service is the lynch-pin of modern society. And work in this sense depends . . . on the attitudes of those who perform it. Attitude to work then, is fundamental to the very continuance, still more to the progress of society.[3]

[3] L. S. Hearnshaw, "Attitudes to Work" (Chairman's address to the Industrial Section of the British Psychological Society, London, January 14, 1954), *Occupational Psychology*, vol. 28, no. 3 (July 1954), p. 138.

SUPPLEMENT

DETAILED OBSERVATION OF A FOREMAN'S DAY

The quantitative analysis of a foreman's activity, in the chapter, "A Foreman's Day," was based upon a detailed, minute-by-minute report of what one foreman did at Plant X for an eight-hour period. The record of this observation is presented here, together with a fuller explanation of behavior items used in the tables in the earlier chapter. This observation is one among fifty-six similar observations for all production foremen at Plant X. A complete analysis and a report of the results are now being prepared.

PURPOSE OF THE OBSERVATION

The underlying purpose was to find out more precisely what foremen actually do on the job. In spite of everything which has been written about "the foreman" in American industry, there is little empirical data showing what he does under actual shop conditions. It was believed that observing incidents of behavior over a time continuum would be of practical as well as theoretical value. Such information reveals a variety of behavior patterns which in turn may be used to answer the following kinds of questions:

1. Are there significant differences in behavior patterns between the more successful and the less successful supervisor?

2. Management has certain preconceptions about a foreman's essential duties and about how his time should be spent. How do these judgments agree with or differ from the actual behavior of the more successful foremen (success measured by objective standards of efficiency and quality)?

3. What are the technical or organizational problems beyond the foreman's control which interfere with his other essential supervisory functions?

4. What is there about the interaction pattern (frequency, duration, and origin of contacts) which throws additional light on the qualities of leadership?

METHOD OF OBSERVATION

Prior to the observation of each foreman on the job, the observer spent approximately three hours in his immediate work section, charting the work stations and the work flow; learning the names of parts, tools, and equipment; identifying key people in the work group; and establishing rapport with the foreman. (Almost all of the foremen had been interviewed previously and were well acquainted with the Yale group.)

Next morning, the observer started at the beginning of the work day to record in turn each incident in which the foreman *did* something. We noted the time that each incident began and ended, what the incident concerned, what the foreman did, with whom he did it, where the incident occurred and the direction and nature of the interaction. To do so, the observer stayed with the foreman at all times, enlisting, whenever necessary, his aid in completing gaps in the report (as in the content and contact of telephone calls and momentary conversations).

As soon as possible, usually the following day, the observer dictated the report. It was then transcribed and the section diagram mimeographed. At this point, the observation was returned to the foreman for corrections of nomenclature, omissions, and any other errors. These were subsequently discussed with the foreman and incorporated into the file copy. (The observations were shown to no one without the foreman's permission.) The thirty-two thousand incidents for the fifty-six foremen were then analyzed, coded, and tabulated.

DEFINITIONS OF INCIDENTS

An incident refers to behavior with a certain integrity of its own, and which may be classified under six major dimensions: What the incident concerned (topic), with whom it was done (contact), how it was done (activity), where it was done (place), what the nature of the interaction was (interaction), and how long it took (time).[1]

By analyzing all incidents in this manner, it becomes possible to summarize the gross distribution of the number of incidents and the time spent on various aspects of the job. It is also possible upon further analysis to answer questions like these:

How often did the foreman's own operators speak to him about quality?

How much time did the foreman spend in the succeeding section speaking to the foreman in that section about a quality matter?

How much time did the foreman spend actually carrying stock and materials himself?

Mathematically, over 206,000 combinations are possible. For practical purposes approximately three hundred will be used.

The definitions of incidents used in the coding system are listed below[2]:

[1] See "A Foreman's Day," pp. 84 to 91.

[2] The basic system of classifying incidents and many of the definitions are drawn from the Army Report No. 946, "Activities and Behaviors of Production Supervisors," Personnel Research Section, PR&P Branch, The Adjutant General's Office, Department of the Army, Washington, D. C., 1952. The principal difference between the two studies is that the Army study recorded only the number of incidents and not the time elapsed for each incident.

CODE *TOPIC*

0. *Topic Unknown:* Content or purpose of phone call, action, or interaction not known to observer.

1. *Foreman Performance of an Operation:* The performance by the foreman of elements or operations customarily assigned to operators. Does not include investigation of reported or observed malfunctioning of equipment (2) nor the demonstration of equipment operation to an employee as in training (8).

2. *Equipment, Tools, Jigs, and Fixtures:* Includes investigation of observed or malfunctioning of equipment; all replacements, repairs, or adjustments; and preparation of equipment for a changeover.

3. *Materials:* The quantity, quality, and movement of any stock used in assembly, as well as desk and production supplies. Does not include procurement and replacement of tools, jigs, and fixtures (2). Apparel necessary to job.

4. *Quality:* Any activity relating to the quality of the product whether it be about work done in previous sections while the work is being done in the foreman's section or reports from other sections about the work of the foreman's section after it has left that section. Includes the foreman's examination of a specific product. Does not include his observation of work progress generally (5) nor his speaking to an operator about his method of performing his operations (8).

5. *Work Progress Status:* The activities of his section or of a group generally. Does not include: examination of a specific product for quality (4) nor the direct observation of the work performance of an individual operator (8). May include how many jobs completed.

6. *Production Schedule:* Problems, decisions or action to implement the production schedule: short-term immediate production planning; improvisation of substitute activity when some unexpected turn of events disrupts the intended schedule or sequence of jobs.

7. *Work (Time) Standards:* The setting, explanation, or modifications of time standards; standards for rate of output by employees. Pace of line.

8. *Employee Job Performance:* The performance of element-opera-

tions by employees. Includes: demonstrating specific operations to employees; the manner in which an employee is doing or has done his job (employee-centered rather than product or equipment-centered, although it may necessarily have implications for product, quality, or production method); informal reprimands (verbal) or formal (written) reprimands, and suspensions for employee's unsatisfactory job performance.

9. *Personnel Administration:* Any activity relating to employees apart from specific job performance (8). Includes: assigning employees to specific jobs either at the outset of the shift or during the shift; overtime, layoff, bumping, transfer to another section or department, irregular work hours, vacations, time for special functions or events; records of work assignment, attendance, exit passes, merit rating; the need for additional personnel or a surplus of employees; search or inquiry concerning the whereabouts of an employee; and the distribution of pay checks, explanation or computation of pay, pay at irregular times or special or overtime pay.

10. *Grievances:* Employee-originated complaints concerning working conditions, compensation, remuneration, etc. May or may not involve formal union-management relationship or infraction of union contract.

11. *Injury or Illness:* Injury is usually job-connected, the result of some accident bringing bodily harm to an employee. However, it may concern an injury incurred outside the plant. The topic usually includes consideration of visits to the plant infirmary. Illness usually refers to illness current at the plant, but may include the cause for some past absence. Action usually involves some form of first aid, or the transfer of the individual to the plant dispensary for medical attention.

12. *Safety:* Aspects of safety hazards and safety practices, usually, but not necessarily, referring to unsafe conditions or practices.

13. *Housekeeping:* Neatness of a department, cleanliness, proper as opposed to scattered storage of stock or equipment, use and location of trash cans and cigarette-butt dispensers.

14. *Meeting:* Instances where a foreman receives notices about, plans to attend, or attends, a meeting or conference of an official, formal nature. It may be with peers, staff men, or superiors.

15. *Personal Relations or Non-Job Related:* Discussions of personal matters with employees, foremen, or others. Non-job related ac-

tivity of foreman such as taking personal relief, having a mid-morning snack, taking a drink of water, etc.

16. *Miscellaneous:* Activities of foreman not classifiable in any other topic.

CONTACT

0. *No One:* Where the activity of the foreman does not involve any other individual, such as desk work, operation of a machine when there is no demonstration, instruction, or assistance to a subordinate involved, and scheduled or unscheduled rest period taken by himself.
1. *General Foreman:* The foreman's direct superior.
2. *Department Superintendent:* The head of the foreman's department.
3. *General Superintendent, Production Manager, Plant Manager.*
4. *Other Foremen:* Another line foreman in another section of the department or in another line department.
5. *Other Production Supervision:* General foreman and department superintendents of production groups, other than the foreman's.
6. *Inspection:* Any individual (inspector, inspection foreman, or others) assigned to the inspection department.
7. *Material Handling:* Any individual (materials handler, materials supervision) assigned to the material controls department.
8. *Maintenance:* Including janitorial staff (but not the foreman's sweeper) electrical, jig and fixture, millwright, plumbers of the maintenance department.
9. *Department Clerk:* Clerk in the foreman's departmental office.
10. *Work Standards:* Any individual (work standards or supervisor) assigned to the work standards department.
11. *Repair Man:* Individual in the foreman's section whose responsibilities are defined as "repair."
12. *Utility Man:* Individual in the foreman's section whose responsibilities are to substitute for absentees and for employees otherwise not at their work stations.
13. *Own Operator:* Operators (including sweeper) in the foreman's section both on line and sub-assembly stations but not including repair and utility men.

14. *Union Representatives:* Individuals who are at the moment acting as union representatives.
15. *Other Hourly Production Workers:* Hourly line operators of other sections including repair men, utility operators, line and sub-assembly operators.
16. *Observer.*
17. *All Others:* Includes individuals not enumerated above such as engineers, employment director, personnel manager, training director, accounting or other non-line department employees. Also persons whose identity is not known to the observer.

ACTIVITY

0. *Listens:* Principally passive listening to the comments of another individual. This would not include a discussion or conversation in which the foreman participates with comments of his own, even though he is alternatively listening to the comments of others. Such activity would fall in code 8. This may also include listening to a machine operation, to a public-address system signal, or the like.
1. *Looks:* Visual observation other than reading. May include a visual survey of the department, looking at machine operation, product, stock, activities of others, or incidental visual observations. Does not necessarily include the particular connotation of "looks for" or searches, unless the principal aspect of such searching is visual.
2. *Manipulates:* Does manual labor, works with his hands; handles some object, stock material, or the like; operates a machine; helps another person, as in moving stock from one position to another, or in adjusting a machine.
3. *Hands, Touches, Carries:* Examines an item tactually; hands, carries, or takes an object such as a piece of stock, product, or paper, to or from another person; re-positions, picks up, or lifts an object.
4. *Reads:* The particular visual activity indicated by the word; not to be included in code 1 above. May include scanning, perusing, poring over, or studying written, printed, or typed material.
5. *Shows:* Exhibits or demonstrates an item, plan, schedule, condition, or method to another individual.
6. *Sits:* Not involved in another principal activity, such as discussion, reading, listening, etc. Usually indicates a period of inactivity,

either a rest period or time when there is no demand on the foreman's attention, and he is waiting, making himself available for questions or problems from subordinates or others.

7. *Stands:* Instances where standing is the principal activity. Not to include the many occasions when the foreman is at the same time involved in some other principal activity, such as talking, manipulating, showing, listening, or looking. It usually implies that he is taking a rest period or simply remaining in his area of supervision available for questions or problems.
8. *Talks:* Includes discussion with any other individual, or a monologue; i.e., both "talking with," and "talking to"; this code is used alone when part of the activity may be standing or sitting, listening, or showing, and when the discussion or instruction given orally is the principal activity.
9. *Walks:* Indicates the foreman's movement from one place to another, or trips to other departments. This code is used only when the walking is the principal activity, and is omitted when it is incidental to looking, manipulating, or talking.
10. *Writes:* Making out any sort of forms or paper work; notes for his own use, memoranda for peers, subordinates, or superiors; personnel passes, time schedules, check lists, drafting, and inscribing on charts or graphs.
11. *Signals or Gestures:* Any signal or gesture, such as a wave or a nod, which does not involve verbal activity.
12. *Telephones:* Uses a telephone whether to receive an incoming call or to make a call. Includes attempts to make a call which are not completed.

PLACE

0. *Specific Work Station:* Any work station, production machine, fixed apparatus, or equipment bench. May also include incidents not at a specific work station but within arm's length from the line.
1. *General Work Area:* Area of supervision outside of an enclosed office and away from desk on floor. Around machines, conveyors, or the like, but not at a specific work station. This is limited to the area of responsibility of the foreman in question, and does not include the entire production area of the plant.
2. *Desk:* Where the foreman has a desk or deskstand in the work area, not separated or closed off from the work area by a partition.

3. *Preceding Section* in department.
4. *Succeeding Section* in department.
5. *Other Department,* whether preceding or succeeding.
6. *Department Office.*

INTERACTION

0. *No Interaction:* No observable interaction with anyone.
1. The *foreman contacts* someone else who makes *no observable* verbal or non-verbal *reply.*
2. The *foreman contacts* someone else who makes a verbal or non-verbal *reply.*
3. *Someone else contacts* the foreman who makes *no* verbal or non-verbal *reply.*
4. *Someone else contacts* the foreman who makes a verbal or non-verbal *reply.*
5. *Initiation indeterminate.*
6. *In the presence* of someone else with no observable interaction directly between them (interaction taking place through some third person or object).

Following is the eight-hour observation of Foreman Pat, beginning at 2:15 p.m. on one day, ending at 4:12; then starting at 7:30 a.m. the next day and continuing to 2:15 p.m. that afternoon. A layout diagram, found at the back of the book and to be folded out for ready reference, indicates by number the particular work station on the main line. The letters A through G are sub-assembly stations.

OBSERVATIONS OF FOREMAN PAT — JUNGLE LINE

(*For a general description of operations, see p. 82, "A Foreman's Day."*)

2:15 p.m. Pat checks with scheduler S. Looks at hourly report of number of cars coming through body shop.

2:16 p.m. Walks over to R (repair man) on pickup line and checks to see if earlier repair trouble was corrected.

2:17 p.m. Calls over inspection foreman to show him a hole missing in a piece. Inspection foreman acknowledges will notify the trim department.

2:19 p.m. Pat tells repair man to locate the hole by eye until it comes through all right. Pat has a drink of water.

2:20 p.m. Pat walks over to station 5 and asks his utility man how many men he still has to relieve. (In the morning and in the afternoon, the utility man relieves each of the fourteen men for a period of 8 to 10 minutes.)
Pat moves along the line – stations 5, 6, 7 – checking visually on the quality of work.

2:21 p.m. Checks a loose nut on a fixture at station 7. Speaks with operator.

2:22 p.m. Man at station 3 calls for materials. Pat tells man at subassembly bench E to make up more material.

2:23 p.m. Walks over to MH (stock man). Tells stock man the line is getting low on hinges. They discuss the number short and agree there is enough for tomorrow.

2:25 p.m. Walks from MH to station 1 and makes visual check on the car body to check on the hole discussed earlier at the pickup line.

2:26 p.m. Pat sees foreman from preceding section and tells him about the missing hole. A hand signal from welder at W.

2:27 p.m. Walks over to W. Asks how jobs from jungle line are coming along. Walks from W over to station 2. "I often go back to my operators and tell them how things are coming along." Goes over to R and discusses problem.

2:29 p.m. Goes to bench, opens desk, and gets out pair of safety glasses.

2:30 p.m. Goes from bench over to station 3 and back to bench. Blows whistle for electrician. Walks to electrician's bench (EB). Pat instructs electrician to fix gun with a leak.

2:31 p.m. Pat takes out a cigarette. Goes from EB to station 8. Checks on back light fixture. Operator nods and continues to spot weld.

2:32 p.m. Pat stands watching gun in operation. Discusses it further with the man. Works on the gun and rearranges some of the tubes. "I gotta fix those tubes so that the fumes blow away from the operator."

2:34 p.m. Moves from station 8 to EB to get friction tape.

2:35 p.m. Starts to return. Hailed by inspection foreman at station 7. Discusses problem with inspection foreman and trainee.

2:36 p.m. Moves from station 14 to station 6. Checks with utility man on how many men have been relieved. Walks from station 5 to D. "I like to build up my sub-assembly so that I can fill 'em in on absentees. Today, things are going good and I don't have any absentees."

2:40 p.m. Moves over to station 8 and points out hole in the metal to superintendent. Goes back around the body of the car and points out another imperfection in the rear.

2:42 p.m. Picks up ding hammer and works on quarter panel of body at station 4. "That thing is caused by something going wrong down at the gate line."

2:43 p.m. Over to station 5 and checks on another hole. "With a thing like that coming through, I have to check every half hour." Walks from station 6 up to station 10. Inspection foreman says a few words to Pat.

2:45 p.m. Pat returns to station 4, jumps into car, and helps man work on rear window fixture. Inspection foreman comes over, together with jig and fixture man. Pat discusses problem with them.

2:46 p.m. Pat jokes with the operator at station 10, leaves the car, and goes to gate line to talk further with jig and fixture man.

2:48 p.m. Returns to station 3 and watches for more trouble with Bailey Molding.

2:49 p.m. Pat jumps into the rear of the car. Works a minute, leaves.

2:50 p.m. Discusses the same problem with the operator. Walks back to station 2. Pat observes, "I don't know what is causing it, whether it is the fixture itself, or the man that isn't doing it right, or that something is happening in the gate line, or maybe it's in the previous fabrication of the metal." Pat moves over into the next car.

2:52 p.m. Pat and jig and fixture man have a discussion. Pat points out the trouble to the jig and fixture man, who nods, and indicates that he knows what it is.

2:53 p.m. Pat asks operator for a small fixture. Operator at 3 puts it on the car, and Pat stands back and watches him, then moves over and discusses another fixture with the jig and fixture man.

2:55 p.m. Pat moves over to E and talks with the operator on how much stock there is available. Operator indicates it is getting low, and Pat acknowledges.

2:56 p.m. Called by man at station 3. Pat walks over. On the way he says, "One thing I have the men doing, which helps a lot. They always call for me and don't wait for me to have to find out the trouble myself. You take that man on subassembly. He is one of the best, and he knows I'm trying to do what I can for him. When it comes right down to it, it's all how you treat your men. The men can make or break a foreman; and if they want to break a foreman there's not much a foreman can do about it. These fellows here all knew that I worked on the line and that I know the job."

2:58 p.m. Pat takes a drink opposite station 9. Then checks his watch to see whether his utility man will be able to relieve all of the men.

2:59 p.m. Pat goes over to station W and checks a red inspection tag; then looks at several surfaces of the body.

3:00 p.m. Pat speaks with the foreman of this section and then moves down the W line to inspect a number of cars.

3:01 p.m. One of the men on the line asks if the jobs look O.K. Pat says they do.

3:02 p.m. Walks back to his own section along the line at stations 17 and 16. At H he checks with the supply of material on the racks. Observes that a small, stamped metal piece is coming in bent. Pat tries to straighten some of them out at the bench himself. "Gee, these are coming through bad. I guess I'll have to check into it."

3:04 p.m. He continues to work at the bench himself at H to fix up the pieces.

3:05 p.m. Continues the same thing. "I do not have to do much complaining about this condition, because these are the last ones we have to run through, since we are running into the new model. The new cars do not have them."

3:06 p.m. Pat discontinues checking metal parts and observes men at stations 13 and 14.

3:08 p.m. Pat moves back to the W station, lights a cigarette, and looks at a couple of the jobs.

3:09 p.m. Pat moves over to station F where he is called by a bench man and shown a bad piece. "Send it over to salvage. Don't scrap it." Pat explains, "It's always an easy thing to send these things to scrap, but I know them good enough so that we can salvage them and save the company money."

3:10 p.m. Makes a circle all around the A, B, C, G area, in the stock area. Goes over to a bench where the stock man keeps his list of jobs coming through. Pat comments to stock man, "We are going to be running out of these things and won't need them later on, so try not to get overstocked." Stock man nods.

3:13 p.m. Moves over to station E and checks one of the bench jobs.

3:14 p.m. While standing there, observes, "Things are going good now. There's no whistle. As long as I don't hear the whistle, I know things are fine." Utility man goes by and nods, indicating that he is on schedule for the relief of the men. Pat smiles and says, "Good."

3:15 p.m. Pat observes aloud, "Utility man looks as if he has plenty of time now to relieve the men. Sometimes the relief man has to relieve for more than the regular relief period, like if a man has to go to the hospital for a while. When this happens, and I'm getting close on my relief time, then I call in a sub-assembly man. That's one of the big advantages of having a sub-assembly area. It gives you a chance to move the men around and keep up on the job." Several agitated whistles. Call for the foreman. Pat looks through the jungle and sees his repair man R on the gas weld line signalling to him. Moves over quickly.

3:16 p.m. Repair man calls Pat over to his station and points out that a part is not coming through properly welded in place. Pat and repair man discuss it and Pat tells him that the trouble is coming from an operation in the preceding department. Pat leaves and quickly goes to the preceding section.

3:17 p.m. Reaches the foreman at the gate line and indicates to him the kind of trouble they are having.

3:18 p.m. The two foremen discuss the trouble. Pat observes, "There's a loose clamp on the fixture which is causing all of this trouble."

3:19 p.m. Pat stands and watches the foreman as the foreman talks to the man about one of the gate clamps which is obviously not tight enough.

3:21 p.m. Pat starts from the gate line and walks slowly back to W line (pickup). Tells repair man that they found the trouble, and the repair man smiles and goes on working.

3:23 p.m. Pat moves over to his bench and meets the specifications man and they discuss a visit by an official from the central office. "The specs man is around reminding me to make everything perfect since the man from the central office is here today."

3:26 p.m. Man at station 3 whistles to Pat. Moves over and checks one of the jigs on a car.

3:27 p.m. Pat steps back and watches the man work.

3:29 p.m. Pat moves into the stock area. "Don't want to overstock."

3:30 p.m. Makes a circular motion around the A, B, C, D stock area, looking at the bins and at the finished pieces.

3:31 p.m. Pat moves over to station 8. Looks inside of the trunk compartment, and hastily moves over to a bench, grabs a hammer and a spoon. Spends a few minutes hitting out spot welds on a piece not fitting properly.

3:34 p.m. After finishing the operation, Pat then feels the surface of the metal, and starts to hammer out some of the dings (dents).

3:39 p.m. Continuing same job. "I don't have to do this, but you can see what would happen if somebody didn't take this out. Would have to pull the whole car off of the pickup line later on and that would only slow things down."

3:40 p.m. Stops working on the job. Watches as the next car moves by. Operator having trouble. Moves in to hold a piece for the operator. Stands back and watches for a while. "The operator and I just saved that one from being pulled off the line."

3:42 p.m. Moves over to station 6 from station 12. Works on the job himself. Operator somewhat behind.

3:43 p.m. Talks with observer while watching 12. Has another drink. "I drink a helluva lot of water around here."

3:45 p.m. Goes to station 3, grabs a hammer and starts hitting a part near the center of post. Walks back to station 14 and picks up a part which was on the floor. Throws it in the trunk of the car going through.

3:48 p.m. Finds more parts which he puts in the trunk of the car.

3:49 p.m. Moves to a fixture holder just opposite station 8, between 8 and 14, reads the tags, and observes: "This is one of the fixtures for the new models. Notice that they are a lot bigger."

3:50 p.m. A call from operator at station 7. Pat moves over quickly into the car and holds the metal piece in place while the operator uses the gun.

3:51 p.m. Moves out of the car and back in with a hammer.

3:52 p.m. "There seems to be a lot of misformed metal coming in, and we have got to save it instead of scrapping it." Pat and operator move out of car and have a short discussion about pieces coming through out of shape.

3:53 p.m. Pat moves over to station EB and pulls the whistle three times for the jig and fixture man.

3:55 p.m. Jig and fixture man comes over. Pat walks down to station 6 and indicates that there is an overlap in the metal which is being caused by a faulty fixture. Moves over to station 4 to the fixture causing the trouble. Pat and jig and fixture man discuss it for two minutes.

3:58 p.m. Foreman and the jig and fixture man work on the faulty fixture at station 4.

3:59 p.m. Pat stands at station 4 and watches the car. Lights a cigarette.

4:04 p.m. Moves over into W area and talks with foreman about quality.

4:05 p.m. Operator comes up and tells the two foremen a joke.

4:06 p.m. Pat is hailed by inspection foreman and they move over to the arc welding booth. Discuss a problem in one of the cars. Inspection foreman informs Pat that jobs from Pat's section are coming through all right now.

4:08 p.m. Back to station 4 with jig and fixture man to check fixture. Pat jumps into the next car and puts the fixture on himself. "Still don't work."

4:09 p.m. Looks at his watch, "Well, we've got to go and get ready to shut the line down, because it's quitting time." Then moves over to his bench. Waits for buzzer.

4:12 p.m. Pat blows the whistle to close the line down. End of the work day.
Men drop their tools and within 15 seconds the jungle is entirely cleared of operators.

Next Morning

7:25 a.m. Warning whistle blows. Pat in superintendent's office. Walks to time clock near station G in sub-assembly area and waits for operators to check in.

7:30 a.m. Whistle blows as last man checks in. "Everybody's here today. Good. Pay day." Pat walks from time clock over to his bench.

7:32 a.m. Walks up to man at station H. "Watch the stock up the line." Checks some of the stock.

7:33 a.m. Continues along the line at 14, 13, 12, etc., checking each of the cars.

7:34 a.m. Passes jig and fixture man and reminds him about the bad fixture at station 4. Jig and fixture man nods.

7:35 a.m. Goes up to electrician's bench (EB). Discusses with electrician some of the welding guns. Points out one gun at station 12 and says that it should be changed because it is a bad gun and should be at the beginning of a series of welding guns. "Because if it stays where it is, the men will get into a hole."

7:37 a.m. Walks back down the line to station 4 to the faulty fixture. Jig and fixture man nods his head. Pat checks one of the jobs and says, "It looks O.K."

7:40 a.m. Man from the water test department speaks to Pat. "He's looking for something he picked up in water test, but I don't think it concerns my group. We talked about it, and I gave him an idea of where I thought it was."

7:41 a.m. Walks over to bench to speak to specifications man. Discusses the fact that someone is coming from Detroit today. Pat observes, "We need to fix the welds on these sticker plates or else there will be a complaint. I'll talk to my men and point out what it does to the finished product."

7:43 a.m. Walks over to station 1. "Waiting to see how the fixture fits." An operator signals to Pat about some trouble. Pat observes, "I guess he found time to fix it up himself, so he just called me to tell me it is O.K."

7:47 a.m. Back to station 4. Watches the fixture being put on. Works on it with the jig and fixture man.

7:49 a.m. Pat gets out of the car. "The fixture is worse than ever."

7:51 a.m. Pat watches the jig and fixture man make some readjustments.

7:52 a.m. Pat looks over at station 3 and notices a man is in trouble. Hurries over and holds metal piece while operator welds it. Stands back and watches.

7:54 a.m. Moves over to the sub-assembly area and starts checking amount of stock in the various bins.

7:55 a.m. Back to station 2 and notices a clamp on one of the bodies. Pulls the clamp off. "Sometimes they forget to take these clamps off at the gate line." Walks to the beginning of the gate line and shows the clamps to one of the operators. Both laugh. Pat walks away, "He'll correct it."

7:56 a.m. Returns to his own sub-assembly area. At B operator indicates that they are one short of a piece in stock. Pat tells him it is all right. "We could make one up from the custom style." Explains to the man that even though they are different, the missing piece can be made up all right.

7:59 a.m. Moves to point S and checks the schedule to see what is coming through. Call from operator at station 1. Moves over.

8:00 a.m. Looks at the trouble. "They're really fouled up on that piece. That did not happen in the gate line. That happened somewhere in the balloon area."

8:01 a.m. Walks over to the pickup line (W). Speaks to the foreman. Asks how the stuff looks. Nods, then turns to his repair operator, and another nod of "O.K."

8:02 a.m. Goes with his repair operator to another section of the W line.

8:04 a.m. Both work on a car with a number of inspection marks. "If we can fix that one up now, we won't have to pull it off at the end of the pickup line."

8:05 a.m. Moves over to station 2 and operates the gun momentarily.

8:06 a.m. Moves to station 1 and watches the large welding gun. Walks to station 8.

8:10 a.m. After watching a while, Pat comments. "Fouling me up on the gate line. I gotta go over and see the foreman on the gate line." Pat walks to the preceding section, checking on cars at 5, 4, and 3.

8:12 a.m. In the area of the gate line, looks around for the foreman, whom he cannot find at once. Bumps into the jig and fixture foreman and thanks him for straightening out some trouble he was having the day before.

8:14 a.m. Other foreman is found and discussion is held. Gate line foreman nods his head, and they both go down the gate line to see where the trouble is.

8:15 a.m. Both walk to the jungle area and check two of the cars, and then stand back and watch.

8:17 a.m. "He knows what it is and he'll fix it up right away." Then moves over to station 4 to the fixture which was causing the trouble the day before. "Coming through all right now."

8:18 a.m. Walks over to R at the pickup line and they have a discussion about latest jobs.

8:19 a.m. Pat walks to station E, indicates to the operator that he has been told that there are some clips missing from a piece, and the operator nods in agreement. Operator perspiring heavily. Pat said, "That man has too much to do this morning. You see we have not been running that model for a long time, and the line has been set up so that he could work it all right. But now we are getting the model in plus a lot of hard tops, which makes it tough on him and there is something I'd better do about it."

8:23 a.m. After watching the man for a moment. "We got to get an extra man to help him out for a while, before he gets into the hole. Let's go see the general foreman."

8:24 a.m. Utility man asks for a glove. Both walk over to foreman's bench where foreman takes out a set of clean gloves and hands them to utility man. Smile and a nod. Pat heads for the beginning of the body shop to look for the general foreman.

8:25 a.m. Pat observes, "Here is the spot I am in. We've only got about three more weeks to go before the line runs out, and I really don't need to ask for a man to be hired full time. It just needs a little help now and then, but for the man right there now, you can see he's overworked, and I've got to get somebody to help him out."

8:26 a.m. Spots general foreman and has a heated but friendly discussion about getting an extra man. General foreman listens and indicates that he does not have anyone to spare now, but he'll keep it in mind and let him have somebody when he can.

8:30 a.m. Pat walks back to the sub-assembly area by the jungle. Picks up small parts and observes, "I can see right now I am going to have to work about 15 minutes to get the man out of the hole. I sure do hope that the general foreman sends me an extra man."

8:31 a.m. Called by the repair man. Pat nods his head and turns back to the off-line operator and helps him to weld some of the pieces.

8:32 a.m. Approached by a man from the standards department. Talks to him while holding some of the pieces for the operator to weld. Pat walks to station 1. Called by the operator, and they discuss some faulty work.

8:35 a.m. Pat calls the repair man on the pickup line. Talks with him. Then hurries up to stations 14 and 13 and indicates a section to the operator that should be watched. Pat observes, "I thought this was going to be an easy day with everybody here and everything starting off so good at the beginning, but it's really getting fouled up now."

8:37 a.m. Goes to station E where Pat starts working himself to help out the sub-assembly operator.

8:38 a.m. After welding a couple of pieces he takes them to a station near station 2.

8:39 a.m. Comes back again to E and picks up some more parts and goes back to a stock point at the other side of station 2. Then returns back again to the bench at point E.

8:40 a.m. Picks up some more stock and quickly goes down to area near station 3.

8:41 a.m. Returns and works at bench E. Observes, "The trouble now is we are getting 70 hard-tops a day, whereas we used to get only 40. You can see what happens when the schedule goes a little bit wrong. We just about get into the rhythm of things and then we get a schedule like this which upsets everything."

8:45 a.m. He is called by an operator at station 3, and Pat drops work and goes down to station 3.

8:46 a.m. Comes back to the off-line operator at E and says, "I hope this will get you going for a while. Don't forget, now, if you need any help, just give me a call." Operator wipes his brow, smiles, and says, "O.K., but I hope I don't have to. But it sure don't look good." Pat says to observer, "He appreciated that help quite a lot. You can see that. You go up to a man, and just tell him he has got to do it whether he has the time or not, then you are sure to ruin a good operator. I could never afford to lose that boy. He's one of the best."

8:48 a.m. Starts over to station B to speak to the stock man, then turns away, because "The operator has already seen the stock man and taken care of it."

8:50 a.m. Goes over to station 2 and speaks to a man regarding the braces they were having trouble about earlier.

8:51 a.m. Walks over to station 14 and finds a small forged screw part on the floor. Picks it up, looks at it, and then looks at the overhead runners to see whether it came off one of the runners for his gun. Goes over to the tool repair crib at T and places it on the desk after notifying a repair man what he had found. The repair man nods.

8:53 a.m. Pat then goes to station R to talk to the repair man, and they both walk over to foreman's bench. Several joking remarks following which repair man asked Pat, "I'm goin' up to Maine again this year. Would you like me to bring a Christmas tree back for you?" Pat answered, "Sure, that would be good. And say, how about the lobsters? Think you can get any lobsters this year?" Repair man indicated he would try, but that lobsters were out of season.

8:55 a.m. Goes to station 14. Pat reaches the man's pocket, takes out a hammer, and starts to walk away. Operator turns around, nods his head in acknowledgment, and continues to work. Pat goes to the car at station 14 and starts hitting a section with a hammer.

8:58 a.m. Moves over to station 1 and on the way speaks to foreman in succeeding section at the end of the pickup line. Exchange a few words, and then Pat turns abruptly and starts for the trim shop.

8:59 a.m. "They tell me that some of my stuff is showing up in the trim shop, so I'd better get over there."

9:00 a.m. Pat meets general foreman in the trim shop who, in turn, explains that the clips are wrong. Pat starts to question B. about why they were wrong, and then smiles and says, "Well, you would pick that out because that's my own fault. I did them myself." Pat visits two other foremen. They discuss some of the trim shop problems. Returns back to his own sub-assembly area.

9:08 a.m. Arrives at station 1 and looks at a rack and finds that the particular pieces complained about were all right now. Moves over to sub-assembly area and checks some of the other parts.

9:14 a.m. Looks at his watch, moving around the sub-assembly area. "Looks like I'm not going to get a man after all. I guess we better look for the general foreman." Proceeds to the superintendent's office.

9:17 a.m. Meets with general foreman in the office, and is told, "No soap. Can't get a man now." General foreman then explains that other foremen need men too, and there are none available.

9:19 a.m. Starts back to his own area to station 1. "Looks bad, and I may have to work 4 men overtime."

9:20 a.m. Back at station 1, looks at braces, and finds the holes missing. These are the holes that were pointed out by the trim-shop general foreman in the recent visit.

9:21 a.m. Goes over and gets a gas weld torch and proceeds to burn holes in the braces himself.

9:23 a.m. Puts gas weld gun down and moves over to the inspector on the pickup line and tells him to keep an eye out for those braces.

9:24 a.m. Back over to station E to the man who was getting behind.

9:26 a.m. Starts to put pieces onto the frames for welding and is interrupted by someone from the office with a pay sheet and pay checks to sign. Pat moves over to electrician's bench to sign.

9:27 a.m.	Moves back to the fixture at station E and starts to work again for about six minutes.
9:33 a.m.	Approached by an office clerk. Stops working, speaks to him, and then returns to the bench.
9:34 a.m.	Continues to make up pieces at the bench for a couple of minutes.
9:37 a.m.	Picks up a bunch of the made-up parts and takes them to a rack near station 2 and returns to station E.
9:38 a.m.	Works on some more parts which go on the other side of the car. "I've had to work like this about twice a week since this model came in. We're just enough behind schedule so that this happens. Not enough to get a man full time, but too much for the man to do it himself."
9:47 a.m.	Finishes making up the number of parts and walks from station E to station 2. General foreman comes along, and Pat calls out, "I'm sinking fast. I'm sinking fast. What's the story on a man?" General foreman shakes his head slowly. "I can't see it yet."
9:50 a.m.	"I better get rid of these checks before they burn a hole in my pocket." Pat starts at station 1 at the beginning of the line and goes to each man in his section all the way through the line and hands out pay checks.
9:55 a.m.	Finishes passing out checks. Starts again at station 1 at the beginning of the line to check the braces which were in stock, which Pat had been making up. "They are going down awful fast."
9:57 a.m.	Moves over to station H and then comes back again to station 1.
9:58 a.m.	Walks over to station E to check on the progress of the operator and to check on the stock. Personnel Manager comes along and says a few words and shakes hands with Pat.
10:00 a.m.	Pat moves to station F to weld some more back light shelves. Continues this for ten minutes.
10:10 a.m.	Finishes with a number in stock and then goes to the superintendent's office. Upon arrival speaks to superintendent about getting an extra man, and also talks to general foreman. But still no apparent sign that he is going to get the man.

10:25 a.m. Takes another cigarette and leaves office back to the jungle area.

10:26 a.m. Arrives at the pickup line and is hailed by the repair man. The line has just stopped. Pat moves over quickly to bench, presses button, and starts line up.

10:28 a.m. Moves over to station H and is spoken to by the off-line man who points out that he needs a bin for some of the stock. Pat acknowledges with a nod.

10:30 a.m. Moves over to station G and starts welding a few pieces on the off-line operation.

10:31 a.m. Finishes up with a few spare pieces and walks over to station F. Stock man appears with and moves an extra bin in place. A couple of nods between Pat and the man and a wave.

10:33 a.m. Goes over to the pickup line and has a talk for a minute with his repair man. Pat picks up a hammer nearby and moves into one of the bodies and starts to hammer out a defective area.

10:34 a.m. Walks over to the end of the pickup line to a body which has been taken off the line and looks at it. A foreman trainee and some other man are using a torch on the body. Talks with them about it.

10:35 a.m. Back over to an earlier point, W, on the pickup line and talks to the inspector, asking him how his stuff is coming. Inspector says, "Your stuff from the jungle line is coming good."

10:37 a.m. Moves to station 11 where a man is having difficulty with the lead line of the gun (one of the air or water lines leading to the gun).

10:39 a.m. Hurries over to station C to check on the bench man who has been behind all morning. Pat says one or two words, and then immediately starts welding some parts on another bench himself.

10:41 a.m. Agitated whistle for the foreman. Pat stops working and goes to station 4. Takes hold of a hammer and a spoon on the way and jumps inside the car and starts hitting one of the sections. Observer asks, "Why did you do it?" Pat says that it's one of those things that was no fault of the operator because it came from the previous section, but he knew that he should fix it up himself, and he also pointed out that it was his operator who told him about "this other fouled-up part. You see the regular operator has no time. He knows that I don't want this job to go through. And somebody has to do it, so I'm it."

10:44 a.m. Back to point MH in the sub-assembly area, talks to the materials trucker.

10:45 a.m. Back over to station C to the man having trouble keeping up with the off-line operation.

10:46 a.m. Tells the man that he is trying to get him help as soon as possible and he knows he needs it.

10:47 a.m. Walks over to station 1 in response to a signal from a man, tells the operator what could be done.

10:48 a.m. Pat is signalled to by utility man at station 3 and Pat nods his head. Approached by operator at station 2. Both smile and nod their heads. Pat observes, "He and I were thinking the same thing. Both of us noticed we were almost out of stock at the same time, and he was just about to do what I was going to do, and that is go over to the sub-assembly area. The sub-assembly man himself also knows the operator is getting short because I see him making up those particular parts on that bench.

10:49 a.m. Goes to station E, picks up some parts, and takes them to station 1.

10:50 a.m. Operator nearby whistles to Pat.

10:52 a.m. Walks over to station G and starts making up a few small pieces of stock.

10:58 a.m. Starts back to station G toward a man at station 8. Operator calls and Pat turns, puts up a finger, and nods.

10:59 a.m. Returns to station G, makes up some more parts, and starts back to the beginning of the line at station 1. Delivers the parts to a rack and returns to station G.

11:00 a.m. Starts making up some more stock.

11:01 a.m. Whistle blows for foreman. Pat goes over to the pickup line.

11:02 a.m. Discusses with general foreman and another foreman a problem about a part not being put in. Fairly heated discussion about the trouble that they were having in the trim shop. The misunderstanding is cleared up. Pat then turns to foreman and says, "Say, I wish you would tell your gas welders up near my boys to stop talking to them, because it makes it tough for them to keep up." Other foreman nods his head, O.K.

11:04 a.m. Pat returns to station E and welds two more braces. Four minutes.

11:08 a.m. Takes pieces to a rack at station 2.

11:09 a.m. Returns back to bench at station D.

11:10 a.m. A loud call from a gas welder at station 15. Pat goes over and speaks to him. Tells the welder not to worry about it, that the repair man will pick up the job that is not done right. Worker nods agreement.

11:11 a.m. Pat returns to station F in the sub-assembly area. Goes around to some of the bins, picks up some parts, and begins to weld some clips.

11:14 a.m. Finished welding clips. Takes it over to the rack at station 7. Leaves them off in the rack and looks in another car. Shifts over to station 14 and then in turn goes from 14 to 13 to 12 to 11, looking at one particular place in each car.

11:15 a.m. Hurries down to gas weld line (pickup line). Asks the foreman about the possibility of a man for the afternoon. "I had more of those – models and two or three hard-tops in a row." Other foreman, says, that "with those jobs coming the way they are it's like making a new car." Pat says, "We keep telling them that, but it doesn't help out too much." Then explains that there was no need to make a big fuss over the thing, because they were soon to shut down for the new model.

11:24 a.m. Moves over to a stock area adjacent to station 14. On the way he is hailed by the foreman of the solder line. The foreman starts to say a few words when Pat hears the whistle blow for him. Rushes over to a car at station 3, checks it, turns around and continues the conversation with the solder line foreman.

11:26 a.m. Moves into the sub-assembly area by station B and is hailed back by a man at the end of the line who indicates that he is out of stock. Pat acknowledges and turns and starts again back to B, where he is about to pick up some stuff to take to station 1.

11:27 a.m. Just before picking it up, he is accosted by one of the sub-assemblers who indicates that they are out of nuts of a certain type. Stock man moves up and explains that there was a whole bag of them delivered the other day, but he has been unable to find them. Pat tells the sub-assembler to keep him posted when he gets low.

11:30 a.m. Just as Pat is about to start back to station 1, the horn blows for lunch, the line stops, and everyone in the area disappears.

(LUNCH – 11:30 to 12:12)

12:12 p.m. Pat at foreman's bench presses button and starts the line.

12:13 p.m. Operator at station 3 asks Pat what time they are going home. Pat indicates he does not know and returns to his bench, where the utility man also asks him what the story is.

12:14 p.m. Hailed by man at station B who tells Pat that they were out of bolts. In the middle of the explanation, Pat whistled for by foreman in the next section. Pat goes over to the pickup line and looks at a job, nods to foreman. Approached by a man who wants gloves.

12:15 p.m. Pat goes over to his bench and gives a pair of gloves to the man.

12:16 p.m. Back over to other foreman and talks about the rumor that closing time is going to be early today.

12:17 p.m. Other foreman says that he has a man for Pat. "I can let you have J."

12:18 p.m. Pat goes over to J. and escorts him to station E. Shows him the parts and instructs him how to do the work.

12:20 p.m. The utility man comes up and after a few short words, it is decided that the utility man will work on E because he is faster, and the parts have to be made up sooner. Pat and the utility man acknowledge that the extra man was best fitted for station F. Foreman shows the new operator some of the essentials of the job, and then stands back for a while and watches.

12:23 p.m. "Well, now that I have a man, it looks like we'll have a breather for a while." Pat walks slowly around the area. Started toward the beginning of the line at station 1.

Hailed by operator at station 5 where they discuss the condition of a welding gun.

12:26 p.m. After looking around for a while, Pat spots the electrician, and points out the trouble with the gun that he had just been discussing with an operator.

12:27 p.m. Pat and the electrician return to the electrician's bench. Pat hailed by operator at station 10. Pat jumps into the car and holds a piece of metal steady while the man operates the gun.

12:28 p.m. Pat goes by the electrician's bench and then over to F where he checks the stock and then looks at the new man breaking in. After one or two minutes of watching and making a few suggestions, Pat observes, "That's a good man. He has never been on that operation before, but he knows the operation already. You can see for yourself how handy it is to have a man who knows all of the operations. In this case he didn't know the operations too well, because I've only borrowed him from the other foreman a few times, but a fellow like that picks it up pretty good."

12:33 p.m. Moves over toward station E to check with his utility man. Remarks, "The utility man is way ahead of schedule." Pat then picks up the finished stock which the utility man had made up and takes it over to station 3 toward the beginning of the line.

12:34 p.m. Returns from station 3 back to station E for more pieces of stock and heads back again for the other side of station 3.

12:35 p.m. Goes over to station B to check on the shortage nuts. Operator at station B informs foreman that the materials handler has found the bag of nuts.

12:36 p.m. Pat in the middle of the stock area stands idle and lights a cigarette.

12:38 p.m. Moves slowly over to new man and watches him for a minute.

12:39 p.m. Over to station H at the end of line, picks up some stock and welds it in the fixture.

12:40 p.m. Whistle blows. Pat looks around, drops his welding, and goes directly to station 3, where the man points out some trouble. The man continues his work, as Pat grabs a hammer, jumps in the car, and starts to work on the defective area.

12:42 p.m. Operator at station 2 yells, "Short!" Pat hastens back to the stock area and picks up some braces and returns them immediately to the rack at station 2.

12:44 p.m. Returns to pick up some more braces, and again back to station 2.

12:45 p.m. Comes back again for more braces at station E (being made up by utility man) and again back to rack at station 2.

12:46 p.m. Called to by operator at station 4. Pat walks over, nods head, and is immediately called by operator at station 3. Climbs into car to inspect a job.

12:47 p.m. Gets out of the car and moves immediately to station 4. Observes, "Now, you're really seeing what happens when we get a bunch of hard-tops coming through in a row. In the first place those hard-tops are using up all the stock that we have been making up in this emergency, and then when you jam them all together, it's bad."

12:48 p.m. Back to station E, picks up some more stock, returns again to station 2.

12:50 p.m. Delivers the stock to the rack. Gets into the car at station 2 and out again, and observes from station 1.

12:54 p.m. After observing the cars at the beginning of his line for a minute, he moves over to the W line and looks at 3 cars. Picks up a hammer, gets into one of the cars.

12:55 p.m. Gets out, walks over to area of station 14 and looks in the trunk area of the bodies, feels around in a few places, nods to an operator.

12:56 p.m. Stands back and says, "Well, at last it's going O.K. now, but we sure had a time of it — now that we have those models back and all of the hard-tops." Walks over to station 12 and is hailed by the operator who asks, "What about the rumor that we are going to shut down early today." Pat tells him he has tried to get some word but does not know yet what it is.

12:59 p.m. Whistle for the foreman. Pat moves over to station 1 to find that the welding gun has broken down. Electrician arrives simultaneously. Discuss it momentarily.

1:00 p.m. Pat goes over to the stock area near station E, picks up more braces, and takes them down to rack at station 2.

1:03 p.m. Returns back to stock at station E, picks up an armful, and goes back to station 2. Then moves over into the large stock area by station A, on the way notices some cardboard on the floor, picks it up, and throws it away in a bin.

1:04 p.m. Proceeds to station G picking some pieces out of the stock bin and moves to the bench, and starts welding up some parts. Makes 7 of them.

1:06 p.m. Takes the parts he has made up and moves into the area of station D.

1:07 p.m. Passes utility man with a few short words and some nods. Picks up some stock made by utility man and again goes down to station 2. Utility man calls out again asking whether or not the line is going to go down. Pat indicates he does not know.

1:09 p.m. After delivering at station 2, lights a cigarette, and says, "Well, things look pretty good now. Let's go down to the office." Pat starts to walk to superintendent's office. Inside he inquires around about when they are going to shut down. No one has the answer.

1:10 p.m. Leaves the office, and spots the general foreman, and proceeds to ask if they will shut down that afternoon early. General foreman says he has no word yet.

1:16 p.m. Walks back to his sub-assembly area and looks around at the various benches. Observes, "When we go back up to 42 cars an hour, I plan to break all the men in on sub-assembly so that when the new men come in, I'll put them on the line. This allows me to have good men to draw from in the sub-assembly area to the line when there is an absenteeism on the line. It can be murder when you have a couple of men out. I'm in a better position than others because I have sub-assembly work."

1:17 p.m. Goes over to station E and tells utility man that since there is no further word about the plant shutting down early, the utility man might start on his regular afternoon relieving rounds.

1:19 p.m. Goes to station C and talks to sub-assembler who was the one having all of the difficulty keeping up in the morning. A few words and plenty of smiles from the operator. Pat says, "Thanks for sticking it out, Bill."

1:20 p.m. Pat moves from station C to station 3, looks at a job, picks up a hammer and moves into a car and gives a couple of taps to the lower part of the quarter panel.

1:21 p.m. Moves from station 3 over to the W line for a check of the cars.

1:22 p.m. Pat's utility man moves up and Pat calls the inspector over. Asks why certain things are being marked. Inspector points out why he had marked something wrong. Pat and utility man acknowledge that they understand.

1:25 p.m. Man whistles to Pat, indicates he needs gloves. Pat goes to his bench, opens it up, gets the gloves, and hands them to the man.

1:28 p.m. Approached by foreman of succeeding section. "Is my man back yet?" Pat replies, "Sure." Pat goes over to one of the W stations and checks a car.

1:29 p.m. Approached by the jig and fixture man. They talk about next year's models.

1:32 p.m. Jig and fixture man indicates that an instrument panel for the new cars has just been uncrated. Pat looks around at his section, tells utility man where he is going, and proceeds over to the tool room area, some 300 feet away. Looks over the panel completely. Says that it does not look like it is going to be too tough a job when the new cars come through.

1:39 p.m. Returns from the tool room to his own section.

1:40 p.m. Starts walking slowly down stations 14, 13, and 12.

1:41 p.m. Man at station 12 points out that a gun is not operating correctly and Pat goes over to the electrician's bench and blows for the electrician.

1:42 p.m. Points out gun to electrician. Is called by a man at station 8. Hurries over and helps man put fixture on. "He doesn't ask me for help very often, because he doesn't need it. He's another damn good boy. In fact, this whole bunch here are good boys." Takes out cigarette and observes section.

1:45 p.m. Discusses plans to use telescope booms for the welding guns when the new cars are started. Walks down to the design office to look at designs for the booms.

1:50 p.m. Back to the jungle area. Notices another foreman at station 6. Other foreman says jokingly, "Why the hell don't you run your own line, instead of me having to run it for you?" Pat, punching the foreman's arm, laughs, "Why should I if you can take care of it for me."

1:53 p.m. Pat goes over to his bench to check on the overtime chart.

1:55 p.m. Looks at chart then moves over to the W line to check one of the cars in gas welding.

1:56 p.m. Starts back, bumps into other foreman and the borrowed operator. Other foreman shoves the operator who is twice his size. Everybody around laughs.

1:58 p.m. Pat goes to the grinding booth near station S and he checks with the foreman of that line.

1:59 p.m. Upon returning Pat is stopped by a trouble-shooter. Pat asks "How are they doing in trim now?" Trouble-shooter says, "Your stuff is coming through O.K."

2:00 p.m. Pat checks two more cars at the pickup line.

2:01 p.m. Stands by watching across to his own section. "Everything's going O.K. now."

2:03 p.m. Walks toward station 14. Picks up a piece on the floor and throws it into the bin.

2:04 p.m. Stands at station 13, checking some welds in the trunk compartment.

2:06 p.m. Stands back and lights a cigarette. Watches an operator.

2:08 p.m. Signals to utility man who indicates that he is relieving the men in turn. Proceeds over by station E. Checks on some stock in this area.

2:10 p.m. Walks toward station 5. Hailed by operator at station 7. Pat acknowledges the signal with his hands.

2:12 p.m. Pat goes to station 4 and checks on a fixture and then proceeds over to his bench.

End of Observation

A SELECTED BIBLIOGRAPHY

The following list of references is intended to be helpful to readers who want to pursue further the major themes of this book. It does not pretend to include all the important books and articles in these fields, or all the works which have influenced the authors' thinking in writing this book.

1. THE FOREMAN'S ROLE

Argyris, Chris. *The Impact of Budgets on People* (New York: Controllership Foundation, Inc., 1952), Part III, "What Factory Supervisors Think of Budgets," pp. 10–14.

Gardner, B. B. and W. F. Whyte. "The Man in the Middle: Position and Problems of the Foreman," *Applied Anthropology* (*Human Organization*), vol. 4, no. 2 (Spring 1945), pp. 1–28.

Guest, R. H. "Foremen At Work – An Interim Report on Method," *Human Organization*, vol. 14, no. 2 (Summer 1955), pp. 21–24.

Mann, F. C. and J. K. Dent. "The Supervisor: Member of Two Organizational Families," *Harvard Business Review*, vol. 32, no. 6 (November-December 1954), pp. 103–112.

National Institute of Industrial Psychology. *The Foreman. A Study of Supervision in British Industry* (London and New York: Staples Press, 1951), Chapter V, "The Position, Relationships and Status of Supervisors," pp. 77–96.

Pigors, Paul and C. A. Myers. *Personnel Administration* (New York: McGraw-Hill Book Co., Inc., Second Edition, 1951), Chapter 11, "The Foreman: His Place and Function," pp. 151–172.

Roethlisberger, F. J. "The Foreman: Master and Victim of Double Talk," *Harvard Business Review*, vol. 23, no. 3 (Spring 1945), pp. 283–298. Reprinted in S. D. Hoslett (editor): *Human Factors in Managament* (New York: Harper & Bros., Revised Edition, 1951), pp. 39–59.

Selekman, B. M. *Labor Relations and Human Relations* (New York: McGraw-Hill Book Co., Inc., 1947), Chapter IV, "Building Joint Relationships," especially pp. 50–59.

Turner, A. N. "Foremen – Key to Worker Morale," *Harvard Business Review*, vol. 32, no. 1 (January-February 1954), pp. 76–86.

——— "Interaction and Sentiment in the Foreman-Worker Relationship," *Human Organization*, vol. 14, no. 1 (Spring 1955), pp. 10–16.

——— "Management and the Assembly Line," *Harvard Business Review*, vol. 33, no. 5 (September-October 1955), pp. 40–48.

Ulrich, D. N., D. R. Booz, and P. R. Lawrence. *Management Behavior and Foreman Attitude: A Case Study* (Boston: Harvard Business School, Division of Research, 1950), 56 pp.

Wray, D. F. "Marginal Men of Industry, The Foremen," *American Journal of Sociology*, vol. 54, no. 4 (January 1949), pp. 298–301.

Zaleznik, A. *Foreman Training in a Growing Enterprise* (Boston: Harvard Business School, Division of Research, 1951), 232 pp. Especially Part III, "Observation of a Foreman at Work," pp. 87–172; Part IV, "A Diagnosis of the Foreman's Behavior at Work," pp. 175–202; and "The Foreman as an Administrator," pp. 215–217.

2. WORK GROUPS AND GROUP LEADERSHIP

Argyris, Chris. "The Fusion of an Individual with the Organization," *American Sociological Review*, vol. 19, no. 3 (June 1954), pp. 267–272.

Bradford, L. P. and Ronald Lippitt. "Building a Democratic Work Group," *Personnel*, vol. 22, no. 3 (November 1945). pp. 142–152.

Cartwright, Dorwin and Alvin Zander (editors). *Group Dynamics Research and Theory* (Evanston, Illinois, and White Plains, New York: Row, Peterson and Co., 1953), Chapter 7, "Group Cohesiveness: Introduction," pp. 73–91.

Coch, Lester and J. R. P. French. "Overcoming Resistance to Change," *Human Relations*, vol. 1, no. 4 (1948), pp. 512–532. Reprinted in Cartwright and Zander (editors): *Group Dynamics Research and Theory*, pp. 257–279; in Hoslett (editor): *Human Factors in Management*, pp. 242–268; in G. E. Swanson, T. M. Newcomb, E. L. Hartley and others (editors): *Readings in Social Psychology* (New York: Henry Holt and Co., Revised Edition, 1952), pp. 474–489.

Fox, J. B. and J. F. Scott. *Absenteeism – Management's Problem*

(Boston: Harvard Business School, Division of Research Studies, Business Research Studies, no. 29, 1943).

Gordon, Thomas. "Group-Centered Leadership and Administration," in C. R. Rogers: *Client-Centered Therapy* (Boston: Houghton Mifflin Co., 1951), pp. 320–383.

Homans, George. *The Human Group* (New York: Harcourt, Brace and Co., 1950), 484 pp. Especially Chapter 16, "The Job of the Leader," pp. 415–440.

Kahn, R. L. and Daniel Katz. "Leadership Practices in Relation to Productivity and Morale," Chapter 41 of Cartwright and Zander (editors): *Group Dynamics Research and Theory*, pp. 612–628.

Katz, Daniel and R. L. Kahn. "Human Organization and Worker Motivation," Industrial Relations Research Association: *Industrial Productivity* (Champaign, Illinois: The Association, 1951), pp. 146–171.

——— "Some Recent Findings in Human Relations Research in Industry," in Swanson, Newcomb, Hartley, and others (editors): *Readings in Social Psychology*, pp. 650–665.

Marriott, R. "Size of Working Group and Output," *Occupational Psychology*, vol. 23, no. 1 (January 1949) pp. 47–57.

Mayo, Elton and G. F. F. Lombard. *Teamwork and Labor Turnover in Southern California* (Boston: Harvard Business School, Business Research Studies, no. 32, 1944).

Rice, A. K. "Productivity and Social Organization in an Indian Weaving Shed," *Human Relations*, vol. 6, no. 4 (1953), pp. 297–329.

Roethlisberger, F. J. *Management and Morale* (Cambridge: Harvard University Press, 1941), 194 pp. Especially Chapter IV, "The Social Structure of Industry," pp. 46–66.

Roethlisberger, F. J. and W. J. Dickson. *Management and the Worker* (Cambridge: Harvard University Press, 1939). Especially Part IV, "Social Organization of Employees," pp. 379–548.

Ronken, H. O. and P. R. Lawrence. *Administering Changes: A Case Study of Human Relations in a Factory* (Boston: Harvard Business School, Division of Research, 1952), 324 pp. Especially Chapter V, "A New Focus – The Relations Among Functional Groups," pp. 165–176, and Chapter IX, "Communication and Change," pp. 287–318.

Scott, J. F. and R. P. Lynton. *The Community Factor in Modern*

Techonology (Paris: UNESCO, 1952, and New York: International Documents Service, Columbia University Press). Especially Chapter IV, "Satisfactions in Industry," pp. 107–124.

Seashore, S. E. *Group Cohesiveness in the Industrial Work Group* (Ann Arbor: Survey Research Center, University of Michigan, 1954).

Trist, G. L. and K. W. Bamforth. "Some Social and Psychological Consequences of the Longwall Method of Coal-Getting," *Human Relations*, vol. 4, no. 1 (1951), pp. 3–38.

Westerlund, Gunnar. *Group Leadership: A Field Experiment* (Stockholm: Nordisk Rotogravyr, 1952). See Chapter 6, "Review of Previous Research," pp. 79–111.

Whyte, W. F. "Leadership and Group Participation," *Bulletin* 24 (Ithaca, New York: New York State School of Industrial and Labor Relations, May, 1953).

——— "Small Groups and Large Organizations." Chapter 12 of Rohrer, J. H. and Muzafer Sherif. *Social Psychology at the Crossroads* (New York: Harper & Bros., 1951), pp. 297–312.

Whyte, W. F. and others. *Money and Motivation. An Analysis of Incentives in Industry* (New York: Harper & Bros., 1955).

3. WORKERS' ATTITUDES TOWARDS THE WORK

Baldamus, W. *Incentiveness and Work Analysis* (Birmingham: Research Board, Faculty of Commerce and Social Science, The University of Birmingham, 1951).

——— "Type of Work and Motivation, "*The British Journal of Sociology*, vol. 2, no. 1 (March 1951), pp. 44–58.

Bell, Daniel. "Work in the Life of an American," Chapter 1 of W. Haber, F. H. Harbison, L. R. Klein, and G. L. Palmer (editors): *Manpower in the United States: Problems and Policies* (New York: Harper & Bros., 1954), pp. 3–22.

Cox, David and K. M. Dyce Sharp. "Research on the Unit of Work," *Occupational Psychology*, vol. 25, no. 2 (April 1951), pp. 90–108.

Davis, L. E. "Work Methods Design and Work Simplification," E. M. Mrak and G. F. Stewart (editors). *Progress in Food Research* IV (New York: Academic Press, 1953).

Davis, L. E. and R. R. Carter. "Job Design," *The Journal of Industrial Engineering*, vol. 6, no. 1 (January 1955), pp. 3–6.

Guest, R. H. "A Neglected Factor in Labour Turnover," *Occupational Psychology*, vol. 29, no. 4 (October 1955), pp. 217–231.

——— "Men and Machines. An Assembly Line Worker Looks at His Job," *Personnel*, vol. 31, no. 6 (May 1955), pp. 496–503.

——— "Work Careers and Aspirations of Automobile Workers," *American Sociological Review*, vol. 19, no. 2 (April 1954), pp. 155–163.

Marks, A. R. "An Investigation of Modifications of Job Design in an Industrial Situation and Their Effects on Some Measures of Economic Productivity" (Mimeographed Ph.D. Dissertation. Berkeley: Department of Engineering, University of California, 1954).

Mayo, Elton. "What is Monotony?" Chapter II of *The Human Problems of an Industrial Civilization* (Boston: Harvard Business School, Division of Research, 1946), pp. 28–54.

Purcell, T. V. *The Worker Speaks His Mind on Company and Union* (Cambridge: Harvard University Press, 1954), Chapter V, "The Work and the Men," pp. 102–122.

Raube, S. A. "The Problem of Boredom," *Conference Board Management Record*, vol. 10, no. 12 (December 1948), pp. 567–575.

Viteles, M. S. "Man and Machine Relationship – The Problems of Boredom," *Proceedings – 1950 Annual Fall Conference* (New York: Society for Advancement of Management, 1951), pp. 129–138.

Walker, C. R. "Adjustment, Individual and Social, to Technological Change," *Industrial Productivity* (Champaign, Illinois: Industrial Relations Research Association, 1951).

——— "The Problem of the Repetitive Job," *Harvard Business Review*, vol. 28, no. 3 (May 1950), pp. 54–58.

——— "Work Methods, Working Conditions and Morale," A. Kornhauser, R. Dubin, and A. M. Ross (editors): *Industrial Conflict* (New York: McGraw-Hill Book Co., Inc., 1954), pp. 345–358.

Walker, C. R. and R. H. Guest. "The Man on the Assembly Line," *Harvard Business Review*, vol. 30, no. 3 (May-June 1952), pp. 71–83.

——— *The Man on the Assembly Line* (Cambridge: Harvard University Press, 1952).

Walker, J. and R. Marriott. "A Study of Some Attitudes to Factory Work," *Occupational Psychology*, vol. 25, no. 3 (1951), pp. 181–191.

Wilson, A. T. M. "Some Contrasting Socio-Technical Production Systems in Industry," paper given in a symposium on "Social and Technological Organization in Industrial Production Systems" at the 14th International Congress of Psychology, Montreal, June, 1954. Abstracted in *Acta Psychologica*, vol. 11, no. 1 (1955), pp. 170–175.

Wyatt, S. and J. N. Langdon. *Fatigue and Boredom in Repetitive Work*. Great Britain. Industrial Health Research Board. Report No. 77 (London: His Majesty's Stationary Office, 1937).

——— *The Machine and the Worker, A Study of Machine-Feeding Processes*. Great Britain. Industrial Health Research Board, Report No. 82 (London: His Majesty's Stationary Office, 1938). Other reports by the Industrial Health Research Board which concern the effects of pacing and repetitiveness are Nos. 26 (1924), 30 (1925), 32 (1925), 52 (1928), 56 (1929), 69 (1934), 88 (1945), 90 (1947) and Emergency Report No. 5 (1944).

INDEX

INDEX

Lohnstatistik in Deutschland

Methodische, rechtliche und organisatorische Grundlagen seit der Mitte des 19. Jahrhunderts

Von

Dr. Wolfgang Gerß

DUNCKER & HUMBLOT / BERLIN

Gedruckt 1977 bei fotokop, wilhelm weihert, Darmstadt
Printed in Germany

ISBN 3 428 04023 6

Inhaltsverzeichnis

Seite

Vorwort

Die vorliegende Abhandlung entstand aus Erfahrungen, die in mehrjähriger Tätigkeit in der amtlichen Lohnstatistik gesammelt wurden. Eine Beurteilung der in großer Zahl veröffentlichten Auswertungen lohnstatistischer Daten ist m. E. nur aus der Kenntnis der Methoden der Lohnstatistik möglich, das heißt aus der Kenntnis der methodischen, rechtlichen und organisatorischen Grundlagen der lohnstatistischen Datenproduktion. Zu einer vollständigen Dokumentation und kritischen Würdigung der Methoden der Datenproduktion ist am ehesten jemand in der Lage, der selbst an dieser Produktion mitgearbeitet hat.

Ich danke Herrn Albert Benker, Präsident des Landesamtes für Datenverarbeitung und Statistik Nordrhein-Westfalen, für die Erlaubnis zur Auswertung von Unterlagen der amtlichen Lohnstatistik. Bei der Materialsammlung insbesondere aus der früheren Lohnstatistik konnte ich mich in starkem Maße auf die langjährigen Erfahrungen von Herrn Heinz Prill stützen, mit dem ich bis zu seiner Pensionierung in der Lohnstatistik zusammengearbeitet habe. Weiterhin danke ich den Herren Dr. Diethard B. Simmert und Diplom-Volkswirt Manfred Piecha vom Wirtschafts- und Sozialwissenschaftlichen Institut des Deutschen Gewerkschaftsbundes GmbH für die kritische Durchsicht des Textes. Schließlich danke ich Frau Irmgard Lange für ihre Bemühungen bei der Übertragung des Manuskripts in Druckvorlagen.

Dieses Buch widme ich Jutta, Cordula, Veronika und Joachim.

Heiligenhaus 1977 Wolfgang Gerß

Einleitung

Die Darstellung und Verarbeitung lohnstatistischer Daten war schon sehr oft Gegenstand von Veröffentlichungen. Die statistischen Ämter als Hauptproduzenten dieser Daten publizieren ihre Arbeitsergebnisse in zahlreichen Tabellenwerken. Über die Auswertung lohnstatistischer Daten liegt eine umfangreiche wissenschaftliche Literatur vor. Dagegen existiert bisher noch keine umfassende Dokumentation der Methoden der Lohnstatistik. Diese Abhandlung verfolgt das Ziel, die Methoden einschließlich der rechtlichen und organisatorischen Grundlagen der deutschen Lohnstatistik der vergangenen 100 Jahre zu dokumentieren. Als "roter Faden" dient dabei vor allem die Entwicklung der in der Lohnstatistik besonders vielfältigen Verfahren der Stichprobenauswahl. Neben den Methoden werden auch die Datenquellen der deutschen Lohnstatistik aufgeführt; von einer Wiedergabe der Daten selbst wird dagegen abgesehen.

Zur Lohnstatistik werden hier statistische Arbeiten von der Art gerechnet, wie sie in Deutschland üblicherweise zum Aufgabengebiet der lohnstatistischen Referate bzw. Dezernate der statistischen Ämter gehören. Damit umfaßt die Lohnstatistik alle Erhebungen bzw. Untersuchungen über die tariflichen Löhne und Gehälter der Arbeiter und Angestellten und die gesetzlichen Bezüge der Beamten und über die effektiven Verdienste der Arbeitnehmer; hinzu kommen die Erhebungen über die Personalaufwendungen der Unternehmer sowie bestimmte lohnstatistische Sonderuntersuchungen, z.B. über die Vermögensbildung der Arbeitnehmer. Gegenstand der Lohnstatistik ist somit ausschließlich die Einkommenssituation der aktiven Arbeitnehmer, d.h. nicht der Rentner bzw. Pensionäre und nicht der Selbständigen. Entsprechend der organisatorischen Gliederung der statistischen Ämter werden einige Statistiken, die ebenfalls Daten über Löhne von Arbeitnehmern liefern, nicht zur Lohnstatistik im üblichen Sinne gerechnet. Solche hier nicht berücksichtigten Statistiken sind die Lohnsteuer- und Einkommensteuerstatistik, die Sozialversicherungsstatistik (Statistiken der Rentenversicherung und der Krankenversicherung), die Statistik der gesetzlichen Unfallversicherung und verschiedene Statistiken, in denen zwar Lohnsummen erfaßt, jedoch ausschließlich von der Kostenseite her betrachtet werden (Industrieberichterstattung, Arbeitsstättenzählungen, Zensen in verschiedenen Wirtschaftsbereichen, Statistik der öffentlichen Finanzen und andere). Aus der Lohnstatistik ausgeschlossen sind ferner Statistiken, die nicht von dem Einkommen einzelner Personen, sondern von dem Einkommen von Familien bzw. Haushalten ausgehen (Erhebungen über die Wirtschaftsrechnungen von Privathaushalten, Einkommens- und Verbrauchsstichproben, Mikrozensus, Wohnungsstichproben), sowie die makroökonomischen Einkommensuntersuchungen der volkswirtschaftlichen Gesamtrechnung. Nicht berücksichtigt werden auch die in der Frühzeit der amtlichen Statistik besonders bedeutenden Statistiken über die Arbeitszeit der Arbeitnehmer, soweit sie nicht Teile lohnstatistischer Erhebungen waren oder zumindest als Nebenprodukt lohnstatistische Daten erbrachten. Da statistische Daten stets Aussagen über Gesamtheiten - d.h. nicht über einzelne Personen oder Institutionen - sind, werden die zahlreich vorliegenden Berichte einzelner Unternehmen und Verwaltungen (Militär-, Post-, Eisenbahn-, Forst-, Gemeindeverwaltungen) über die Lohnzahlungen an ihre eigenen Arbeitnehmer hier nicht zur Lohnstatistik gerechnet. Aus dem gleichen Grunde bleiben die Sammlungen einzelner tariflicher Lohn- und Gehaltssätze bzw. gesetzlicher Besoldungssätze ausgeschlossen, soweit diese Einzelsätze nicht zu Kollektivmaßzahlen verrechnet wurden. Zur Beurteilung der Einkommenssituation vor allem der Beamten werden aus den gesetzlichen Bestimmungen unter bestimmten Annahmen über das Lebens- und Dienstalter, die Familiengröße und dgl. gelegentlich Modellrechnungen aufgestellt, deren Ergebnisse zwar auch zu Aussagen über Gesamtheiten verallgemeinert werden, die jedoch mit der üblichen statistischen Datenbeschaffung nichts zu tun haben und daher hier nicht berücksichtigt werden. Im übrigen beschränkt sich die Darstellung auf die amtliche Lohnstatistik in Deutschland bis zum Ende des Zweiten Weltkrieges und danach im Gebiet der Bundesrepublik Deutschland; nicht einbezogen wird neben der vor allem von Gewerkschaften, Arbeitgeberverbänden und Industrie- und Handelskammern durchgeführten nichtamtlichen deutschen Lohnstatistik*) die Lohnstatistik der Deutschen Demokratischen Republik und die Lohnstatistik nichtdeutscher Staaten.

In den drei Kapiteln der Abhandlung wird die Lohnstatistik jeweils unter verschiedenen Aspekten und in unterschiedlicher Gliederung dargestellt. Das erste Kapitel beschreibt umfassend und detailliert die historische Entwicklung der Lohnstatistik vor dem Hintergrund der politischen und wirtschaftlich-sozialen Entwicklung. Die Gliederung dieses Kapitels wird primär nach Zeitabschnitten vorgenommen; d.h. der gesamte Untersuchungszeitraum - Mitte des 19. Jahrhunderts bis zur Gegenwart - wird in Zeitabschnitte unterteilt, die den Entwicklungsphasen der deutschen Lohnstatistik entsprechen. Das zweite Kapitel gibt einen zwar vollständigen, jedoch gedrängten Überblick über das System der deutschen Lohnstatistik. Es ist in der Weise gegliedert, daß die einzelnen lohnstatistischen Erhebungen jeweils geschlossen nacheinander abgehandelt werden, wobei besonderes Gewicht auf die Erhebungsorganisation, die Verfahren der Stichprobenziehung und die Erhebungsmerkmale gelegt wird. Das dritte Kapitel stellt die historische Entwicklung und den gegenwärtigen Stand der einzelnen methodischen Grundlagen der Lohnstatistik dar und ist zu diesem Zweck primär nach methodischen Gesichtspunkten gegliedert; d.h. die verschiedenen Aspekte der Methoden der Lohnstatistik einschließlich ihrer rechtlichen und organisatorischen Grundlagen werden nacheinander erörtert unabhängig davon, in welchem Zeitabschnitt sie von Bedeutung waren (vgl. erstes Kapitel) und auf welche lohnstatistische Erhebung sie sich beziehen (vgl. zweites Kapitel). Nach Abschluß der Abhandlung folgt eine ausführliche Zeittafel zur Entwicklung der amtlichen deutschen Lohnstatistik, die stichwortartig den Gesamtüberblick erleichtern soll und für jede wiedergegebene Jahreszahl und jedes Ereignis einen Hinweis auf den Abschnitt des ersten Kapitels enthält, in dem dieses Ereignis behandelt wird. Die Abhandlung wird außerdem durch ein umfassendes Verzeichnis der Datenquellen der amtlichen deutschen Lohnstatistik ergänzt. Dieses Verzeichnis gibt - soweit nichts anderes vermerkt ist - für die Ergebnisse der einzelnen lohnstatistischen Erhebungen die Veröffentlichungen der jeweiligen zentralen Erhebungsbehörde im Deutschen Reich (i.a. Kaiserliches Statistisches Amt bzw. Statistisches Reichsamt) und im Gebiet der Bundesrepublik

---

*) Der Anhang enthält eine kurze Darstellung der gewerkschaftlichen Lohnstatistik.

Deutschland (i.a. Statistisches Amt des Vereinigten Wirtschaftsgebietes bzw. Statistisches Bundesamt) an. Veröffentlichungen der Statistischen Landesämter werden nur in besonderen Ausnahmefällen erwähnt. Für die auf Veranlassung inter- oder supranationaler Organisationen durchgeführten Erhebungen werden neben den zentralen nationalen Veröffentlichungen auch die eigenen Veröffentlichungen dieser Organisationen aufgeführt.

Das Material zu dieser Dokumentation stammt - soweit keine anderen Quellen angegeben sind - aus amtlichen statistischen Veröffentlichungen sowie zu einem erheblichen Teil aus bisher unveröffentlichten und für Außenstehende kaum zugänglichen bzw. überschaubaren Unterlagen aus den Akten statistischer Ämter. Solche Unterlagen liegen in der Form von Erhebungsplänen, internen Arbeitsanweisungen und Richtlinien, Sitzungsprotokollen und Aktenvermerken vor. Die Möglichkeit, diese unveröffentlichten Unterlagen auszuwerten, bildete den Hauptanlaß für die besonders ausführliche Darstellung der Methoden der Lohnstatistik.

1
Die Entwicklung der amtlichen Lohnstatistik in Deutschland vor dem Hintergrund der politischen und wirtschaftlich-sozialen Entwicklung

11 Die Phase der fehlgeschlagenen Ansätze (1849 - 1891)

111 Erste vergebliche Gedanken

Die Idee einer in ganz Deutschland durchzuführenden statistischen Untersuchung der Lohnsituation tauchte bereits um die Mitte des 19. Jahrhunderts auf, als die Frankfurter Nationalversammlung sich unter anderem mit gesetzlichen Bestimmungen über den Arbeitslohn und die Arbeitszeit befaßte. Wie aus dem "Protokoll der 177. öffentlichen Sitzung der deutschen konstituierenden Nationalversammlung zu Frankfurt a. M. vom 26. Februar 1849" hervorgeht, berichtete der "volkswirtschaftliche Ausschuß" auf dieser Sitzung über den "Entwurf einer Gewerbeordnung und verschiedene diesen Gegenstand betreffende Petitionen und Anträge". Dabei wurde eine Eingabe der deutschen Buchdrucker an die Nationalversammlung erwähnt, mit der eine allgemeine Feststellung der Arbeitslöhne im ganzen Reich gefordert wurde (Beilage I zum Protokoll der 177. Sitzung, Seite 35). Die Eingabe der Buchdrucker wurde von der Nationalversammlung abgelehnt.

Nach der Gründung des Deutschen Reichs wurde das vorhandene statistische Instrumentariumdes Deutschen Zollvereins einer Bestandsaufnahme unterzogen, um Anregungen für die Gewerbestatistik des Deutschen Reichs zu sammeln. Die Zeit für den Aufbau einer Lohnstatistik war jedoch auch jetzt noch nicht reif. Zwar wurde eine Lohnstatistik grundsätzlich für sinnvoll gehalten, jedoch nicht als eine Aufgabe von hoher Priorität angesehen. Die amtliche "Kommission zur weiteren Ausbildung der Statistik des Zollvereins" erwähnte die Lohnstatistik lediglich in ihrem die Gewerbestatistik betreffenden "Bericht Nr. 18" vom 19. August 1871. "..... wie die auf die Betriebsform und die Personalverhältnisse bezüglichen Fragen (erg. der Gewerbestatistik) erkennen lassen, schlägt die Kommission auch eine Erhebung über die im Jahre 1871 gezahlten Löhne vor. Sie war sich dessen vollkommen bewusst, dass damit keine Lohnstatistik, insbesondere kein Nachweis über die Höhe der Löhne in den einzelnen Gewerben gewonnen werde. Die Kommission glaubte vielmehr eine derartige Aufnahme einer späteren Wiederholung der

Gewerbestatistik vorbehalten zu dürfen. Warum es ihr aber zu thun war: das ist die Gewinnung eines Bildes von der Summe der in einem Jahre in sämmtlichen Gewerbebetrieben überhaupt gezahlten Löhne....." (Kaiserliches Statistisches Amt: Statistik des Deutschen Reichs Band I, Berlin 1873, Seite 343). Es ging also zunächst nur um eine Lohnsummenstatistik als Kostenstatistik, während die Lohnstatistik als Einkommensstatistik in eine unbestimmte Zukunft aufgeschoben wurde.

112 Widerstand der Regierungen

Der Grund für das amtliche Desinteresse an einer Lohnstatistik lag offensichtlich darin, daß die Regierungen des Reiches und der Einzelstaaten befürchteten, daß mit statistischen Angaben über die wahre Lohnsituation und damit die soziale Lage der Arbeiter unter diesen Unruhe geschürt würde. Von sozialpolitisch engagierten Kreisen des Reichstages wurde demgegenüber wiederholt der Versuch unternommen, amtliche lohnstatistische Untersuchungen durchzusetzen. Diese Versuche blieben auf Grund der bestehenden Machtverteilung für lange Zeit ohne Erfolg, wobei kennzeichnend ist, daß der Widerstand im Reichstag selbst von den den Unternehmern nahestehenden Abgeordneten kam. Wenn in sozialpolitisch besonders brisanten Fällen wie bei der Verwendung von Kindern als billige Arbeitskräfte die Anzeichen für Mißstände so deutlich waren, daß auch die Regierungen die Notwendigkeit umfassender empirischer Untersuchungen nicht mehr übersehen konnten, wurde die Lohnfrage weitestgehend außer acht gelassen. Außerdem war die Reichsregierung bestrebt, die empirischen Untersuchungen dadurch unter ihrer unmittelbaren Kontrolle zu halten, daß sie die Bearbeitung nicht dem Kaiserlichen Statistischen Amt übertrug, sondern sich die Zusammenstellung und Auswertung der Daten selbst vorbehielt.

Am 30. April 1873 stellte der Reichstag an den Reichskanzler den Antrag, eine Erhebung über die Frauen- und Kinderarbeit in den Fabriken zu veranlassen und deren Ergebnisse dem Reichstag mitzuteilen (Stenographische Berichte über die Verhandlungen des Deutschen Reichstages, 1. Legislaturperiode, 4. Session 1873,

1. Band, Berlin 1873, Seite 405). Der Bundesrat stimmte dieser Erhebung erst am 31. Januar 1874 zu, womit die Rechtsgrundlage geschaffen war. Die Erhebung fand anschließend im ganzen Reichsgebiet nach einheitlichen Grundsätzen statt; die Durchführung oblag den Landesregierungen. Erhoben wurden unter anderem die Anzahl der Arbeiterinnen über 16 Jahre und der jugendlichen Arbeiter bis 16 Jahre, ihre durchschnittliche tatsächliche Arbeitszeit und ihr Wochenlohn in der Aufgliederung nach Gewerbezweigen. Als Wochenlohn wurde dabei ein niedrigster, ein höchster und ein durchschnittlicher Satz erfaßt. Die ermittelten Daten wurden veröffentlicht als "Ergebnisse der über die Frauen- und Kinderarbeit in den Fabriken auf Beschluß des Bundesrats ausgeführten Erhebungen, zusammengestellt im Reichskanzleramt" (Berlin 1876).

Eine weitere Veröffentlichung "Ergebnisse der über die Verhältnisse der Lehrlinge, Gesellen und Fabrikarbeiter auf Beschluß des Bundesrats angestellten Erhebungen, zusammengestellt im Reichskanzleramt" (Berlin 1876) bezieht sich auf Untersuchungen, die vor allem durch Beschwerden über Verstöße gegen die Gewerbeordnung veranlaßt wurden. Es handelt sich um keine Tabellenstatistik, sondern um eine enquêtemäßige "Vernehmung" von ausgewählten sachverständigen Arbeitgebern und Arbeitnehmern, deren Antworten - die unter anderem Angaben über die Lohnzahlung enthalten - in Protokollen festgehalten und so weit wie möglich übersichtlich geordnet und zusammengefaßt wurden.

Weitere Reichsenquêten fanden im Jahre 1878 über die Tabak-, Eisen- und Textilindustrie - mit besonderem lohnstatistischen Teil für die Textilindustrie - und im Jahre 1887 über die Lohnverhältnisse der Arbeiterinnen in der Wäschefabrikation und der Konfektionsbranche statt; die Ergebnisse wurden in den Drucksachen und Sitzungsprotokollen des Bundesrats 1878 bzw. den Drucksachen des Reichstags, Session 1887 Nr. 83, veröffentlicht. 1878 wurden durch Vermittlung der Handelskammern Unternehmer ausgewählt, die auf Fragebogen Auskunft über die durchschnittlichen Tagesverdienste und die Verdienststreuung der von ihnen beschäftigten Männer, Frauen, jugendlichen Arbeiter und Kinder gaben. 1887 wurden in mehreren

Bundesstaaten mit Hilfe der "Fabrikinspektoren", der "Gewerberäte" und der Handelskammern Meist-, Mindest- und Durchschnittsbeträge der Tagelöhne und der Akkordlöhne ermittelt.

113 Beschränkte Erfolge auf Randgebieten

Während im allgemeinen von einer echten amtlichen Lohnstatistik noch keine Rede sein konnte, gab es in zwei Teilbereichen, in denen die staatliche Verwaltung besondere Aufsichtsfunktionen und daher ein größeres Interesse an statistischen Informationen hatte, durchaus beachtenswerte und auch im weiteren Zeitablauf beständige Ansätze. Der erste Bereich war der Bergbau, der in Preußen durch das Allgemeine Berggesetz vom 24. Juni 1865 geregelt worden war und der Aufsicht der Oberbergämter unterstand. In einem mit dem 25. Juni 1872 datierten Bericht des Oberbergamtes Dortmund an den preußischen Königlichen Staatsminister für Handel, Gewerbe und öffentliche Arbeiten heißt es: "In der am 22.6.1872 zu Essen aus Anlaß des dort seit dem 17. d.Mts. ausgebrochenen Streiks der Bergarbeiter zwischen Commissarien der Königlichen Regierung zu Düsseldorf und des unterzeichneten Oberbergamts stattgefundenen Conferenz wurde es für dringend wünschenswert erachtet, seitens der Staatsbehörden in den Besitz eines fortlaufenden Nachweises über die von den Bergarbeitern des hiesigen Distrikts baar verdienten Arbeitslöhne zu gelangen."*) Daraufhin ermächtigte der Minister für Handel, Gewerbe und öffentliche Arbeiten mit Erlaß vom 22. Juli 1872 die preußischen Oberbergämter, auf Grund des § 79 des Allgemeinen Berggesetzes dauernd oder zeitweise für den ganzen Oberbergamtsbezirk oder für einzelne Teilbezirke statistische Nachweisungen über die Löhne der Bergarbeiter in den von jedem Oberbergamt selbst festzusetzenden Zeiträumen und Formen von den Bergwerksbesitzern anzufordern. Die Ergebnisse der nach diesem Erlaß von den Oberbergämtern zunächst uneinheitlich durchgeführten lohnstatistischen Erhebungen wurden laufend in der vom zuständigen preußischen Ministerium herausgegebenen "Zeitschrift für das Berg-,Hütten- und Salinenwesen im Preußischen Staate" veröffentlicht. Da die Uneinheitlichkeit die-

*) zitiert nach Unterlagen aus den Akten des ehemaligen Oberbergamtes Bonn

ser Lohnstatistik ihren Wert beeinträchtigte, wies der preußische Minister der öffentlichen Arbeiten mit Erlaß vom 28. Oktober 1887 die Oberbergämter an, in Zukunft die lohnstatistischen Erhebungen regelmäßig mit vierteljährlicher Periodizität nach einheitlichen Richtlinien durchzuführen (Zeitschrift für das Berg-, Hütten- und Salinenwesen im Preußischen Staate, herausgegeben im Ministerium der öffentlichen Arbeiten, 36. Band, Berlin 1888, Seite 43 ff.). Die bergbehördliche Lohnstatistik erfaßte sämtliche entsprechend der Art ihrer Tätigkeit nach Gruppen gegliederten Arbeiter, d. h. neben den eigentlichen Bergarbeitern auch die sonstigen im Zusammenhang mit den Bergwerken beschäftigten Arbeiter. Ermittelt wurden die Anzahl der Arbeiter, die Anzahl der Schichten und die Lohnsumme sowie die Verhältniswerte Lohnsumme pro Arbeiter und Lohnsumme pro Schicht. Die Berechnung der durchschnittlichen Anzahl der Arbeiter erfolgte zunächst, indem das arithmetische Mittel zwischen den Arbeiterbeständen am Anfang und am Ende jedes Monats und aus diesen Monatsmitteln das Mittel für Vierteljahre und für Jahre gebildet wurde. Auf Grund des Erlasses des preußischen Ministers für Handel und Gewerbe vom 16. Januar 1913 (Zeitschrift für das Berg-, Hütten- und Salinenwesen im Preußischen Staate, herausgegeben im Ministerium für Handel und Gewerbe, Jahrgang 1912, Seite 186 ff.) wurden dann Lohnsummen pro "Vollarbeiter" berechnet, wobei die Anzahl der Vollarbeiter eines Monats sich als Quotient aus der Anzahl der in dem Monat überhaupt verfahrenen Arbeitstage und der Anzahl der Arbeitstage dieses Monats ergab. Ab 1921 wurde die Anzahl der Vollarbeiter als Quotient aus der Gesamtzahl der verfahrenen Arbeitsschichten abzüglich der Schichten für Überarbeit und der Anzahl der Arbeitstage des Erhebungszeitraums berechnet. Neben den Vollarbeitern wurde ab 1921 auch die Anzahl der "angelegten Arbeiter" - d. h. der Quotient aus der Gesamtzahl der verfahrenen Arbeitsschichten abzüglich der Schichten für Überarbeit zuzüglich der entgangenen Schichten und der Anzahl der Arbeitstage des Erhebungszeitraums - der Bergarbeiterlohnstatistik zu Grunde gelegt. Die laufenden lohnstatistischen Erhebungen, die zunächst in Preußen und später als Teil der "Reichsmontanstatistik" im ganzen Reichgebiet durchgeführt wurden, gehören bis heute als "Schichten- und Lohnstatistik" zum Aufgabenbereich der Bergbehörden des Bundesgebietes. Es ist jedoch zu beachten, daß die Bergarbeiterlohnstatistik primär als Lohnkostenstatistik konzipiert wurde und in ihrer Verwendungsfähigkeit als Statistik der Arbeitsverdienste für lange Zeit gewissen Einschränkungen unterlag.

Der zweite Bereich, in dem von Behörden laufende lohnstatistische Erhebungen durchgeführt wurden, war die deutsche Handelsmarine. Auf Anregung des Reichskanzleramtes ließen die deutschen Küstenstaaten ab 1. Januar 1874 von den inländischen Seemannsämtern halbjährliche Übersichten über die Anzahl der vorgenommenen Anheuerungen von Vollmatrosen und den durchschnittlichen Geldbetrag der in den einzelnen Monaten vereinbarten effektiven Heuern aufstellen. In diese Übersichten wurden ab 1. Juli 1874 auch die Anmusterungen und Monatsheuern unbefahrener Schiffsjungen aufgenommen. Die durchschnittlichen Monatsheuern waren dabei ausdrücklich nicht auf Grund von Schätzungen, sondern durch Berechnung aus den tatsächlich erfaßten Einzelbeträgen der verabredeten Heuern zu ermitteln. Ab 1880 wurde diese Statistik der Monatsheuern von Seeleuten auf jährliche Berichterstattung umgestellt und durch genauere Anweisungen an die Seemannsämter zum Verfahren der Berechnung durchschnittlicher Heuerbeträge sowie zur Abgrenzung des Erhebungsbereichs und Definition der Erhebungsmerkmale vereinheitlicht. Nach einer weiteren Reform im Jahre 1901 wurde diese Statistik noch bis zum Jahre 1922 durchgeführt. Die Ergebnisse wurden laufend in den vom Kaiserlichen Statistischen Amt herausgegebenen "Monatsheften zur Statistik des Deutschen Reichs" (Jahrgänge 1878 bis 1891) und "Vierteljahrsheften zur Statistik des Deutschen Reichs" (Jahrgänge 1892 bis 1902) sowie im "Statistischen Jahrbuch für das Deutsche Reich" (Jahrgänge 1883 bis 1921/22) veröffentlicht.

114 Das Beispiel der Gewerkschaften

Abgesehen von den erwähnten Randgebieten hielten sich die Behörden des Reiches und der Einzelstaaten auf lohnstatistischem Gebiet weitgehend zurück. In auffallendem Gegensatz zu der amtlichen Abstinenz standen im nicht-amtlichen Bereich vor allem die lohnstatistischen Aktivitäten der Gewerkschaften, die daran interessiert waren, sich selbst und die Öffentlichkeit über die Lohnsituation und die meist schlechte soziale Lage der Arbeiter zu informieren.*) Die Hirsch-Duncker'schen Gewerkvereine führten mindestens ab 1880 periodische statistische Erhebungen über die Arbeiterlöhne durch, wobei die örtlichen Gewerkvereine der Zentralstelle des Verbandes "nach genauer Erkundigung bei den Arbeitern des Ortes" auf Fragebogen über die durchschnittlichen Wochenlöhne und Akkordlöhne sowie die höchsten und die niedrigsten Lohnsätze in der Aufgliederung nach Arbeitergruppen und Berufsgruppen berichteten. Auch die einzelnen "freien Gewerkschaften" führten zahlreiche lohnstatistische Erhebungen durch. Dabei wurden die Gewerkschaftsmitglieder - soweit diese auskunftsbereit waren, was in unterschiedlichem Maße der Fall war - nach ihren tatsächlichen Barverdiensten im Zeit- und im Stücklohn sowie nach ihren empfangenen Naturalleistungen befragt und aus diesen Angaben durchschnittliche Stunden-, Tages-, Wochen- und Jahresverdienste berechnet sowie Meist-, Mindest- und Höchstbeträge der Verdienste ermittelt. Sonntags- und Überstundenzuschläge wurden gelegentlich gesondert erfaßt. Teilweise wurden auch Häufigkeitsverteilungen der Arbeiter nach Verdienstklassen aufgestellt.

115 Methodische Lichtblicke

Während die amtliche Lohnstatistik im allgemeinen - soweit überhaupt Ansätze vorhanden waren - über sporadische und oft fehlschlagende Versuche nicht hinauskam, gab es in einigen wenigen Fällen im amtlichen bzw. halbamtlichen Bereich engbegrenzte lohnstatistische Sonderuntersuchungen mit für die weitere Zukunft richtungweisenden methodischen Elementen. Im Jahre 1887 führte die Berufsgenossenschaft der Buchdrucker eine einmalige lohnstatistische Erhebung bei ihren Mitgliedsunternehmen im Intervie-

*) vgl. Kaiserliches Statistisches Amt: Erhebungen über Arbeitslöhne in Deutschland, Uebersicht über die von Behörden und Vereinen veranstalteten Aufnahmen zur Lohnstatistik. Vierteljahrshefte zur Statistik des Deutschen Reichs, Zweiter Jahrgang 1893, Drittes Heft, Seite 1 - 6. Berlin 1893.

werverfahren durch.*) Die Interviewer, die für diesen Zweck von den unteren Verwaltungsbehörden vereidigt worden waren, ließen sich die Richtigkeit der erhaltenen Auskünfte von den Unternehmern schriftlich bestätigen. Aus den so erfaßten Lohnsummen und Arbeiterzahlen wurden durchschnittliche Tages- und Jahresverdienste nach Arbeitergruppen berechnet.

Im Jahre 1891 unternahm die "Badische Fabrikinspektion" eine Untersuchung mit fast modern anmutender Methodik über die Lage der Fabrikarbeiter im Raum Mannheim.**) Die Untersuchung beruhte auf Angaben der Arbeitgeber nach deren Lohnlisten. Dabei wurde für die einzelnen Arbeiter der Wochenverdienst in einer Reihe genau bezeichneter Wochen, die soweit wie möglich die im Laufe des Jahres vorkommenden Unterschiede in der Lohnhöhe ausgleichen sollten, ermittelt. Aus dem in den ausgewählten Wochen insgesamt gezahlten Lohnbetrag wurde der Durchschnittslohn pro Woche berechnet. Als Ergebnisse der Statistik wurden durchschnittliche Wochenverdienste der Arbeiter nach Geschlecht, Altersgruppe, Beschäftigungsart und Gewerbezweig sowie Häufigkeitsverteilungen der Arbeiter nach Wochenverdienstklassen ausgewiesen.

---

*) vgl. Kaiserliches Statistisches Amt: Erhebungen über Arbeitslöhne in Deutschland ..., a. a. O.
**) vgl. Wörishoffer: Die soziale Lage der Fabrikarbeiter in Mannheim und dessen nächster Umgebung, Karlsruhe 1891.

12 Die Phase der ersten Schritte zur Etablierung (1892 - 1919)

121 Datenbedarf für Verwaltungszwecke

Die Einsicht in die Notwendigkeit lohnstatistischer Untersuchungen setzte sich bei den Regierungen in stärkerem Maße erst durch, als die Behörden für die Ausführung bestimmter gesetzlicher Vorschriften auf Informationen über die tatsächliche Lohnsituation angewiesen waren. Nach § 8 des Krankenversicherungsgesetzes vom 15. Juni 1883 hatten die höheren Verwaltungsbehörden "ortsübliche Tagelöhne" gewöhnlicher - d. h. ungelernter - männlicher und weiblicher sowie erwachsener und jugendlicher Tagearbeiter festzusetzen. Die Festsetzung dieser Tagelöhne erfolgte nach Anhörung der Gemeindebehörden, die sich - ohne daß hierzu nähere Anweisungen zur Gewährleistung der Einheitlichkeit bestanden - ihre Informationen aus den zu diesem Zweck eingeholten Stellungnahmen der Vertreter der Arbeitgeber und der Versicherungspflichtigen beschafften. Die ortsüblichen Tagelöhne beruhten demnach nicht auf statistischen Erhebungen, sondern waren Schätzungen ortskundiger Experten bzw. Interessenvertreter. Die für die einzelnen Gemeinden vorgenommenen ersten Feststellungen der ortsüblichen Tagelöhne wurden am 24. Dezember 1892 abgeschlossen und dann jährlich fortgeschrieben. Die festgesetzten Tagelöhne wurden laufend im "Zentralblatt für das Deutsche Reich" veröffentlicht (Jahrgänge 1892 ff.). Trotz der bereits erfolgten Veröffentlichung der Einzeldaten wurde dem Kaiserlichen Statistischen Amt eine beabsichtigte Zusammenstellung und statistische Auswertung dieser Tagelöhne von der vorgesetzten Behörde - dem Reichsamt des Innern - mit Erlaß vom 19. November 1893 untersagt*); die Reichsregierung wollte offensichtlich wei-

*) vgl. Statistisches Reichsamt: Die amtliche Lohnstatistik in Deutschland. In: Lohn- und Gehaltserhebung vom Februar 1920, Statistik des Deutschen Reichs Band 293, Berlin 1921.

terhin verhindern, daß die Verbreitung lohnstatistischer Auswertungsergebnisse zu sozialpolitischen Auseinandersetzungen führte. Die ortsüblichen Tagelöhne wurden später regelmäßig unter der Bezeichnung "Ortslöhne" gemäß §§ 149-152 der Reichsversicherungsordnung von den Oberversicherungsämtern festgesetzt und bis gegen Ende des Zweiten Weltkrieges laufend im Reichsministerialblatt (Jahrgänge 1923 ff.) sowie im Reichsarbeitsblatt (Jahrgänge 1929 ff.) veröffentlicht.

Die bereits erwähnte Statistik der Monatsheuern von Seeleuten wurde ab Berichtsjahr 1901 einer Reform unterzogen, die zwar hinsichtlich der erfaßten Schiffe und Personen die Vergleichbarkeit mit den früheren Erhebungen beeinträchtigte, jedoch die Bedeutung dieser Statistik für die öffentliche Verwaltung erheblich vergrößerte. Die durchschnittliche Heuer wurde nunmehr nach § 10 des Seeunfallversicherungsgesetzes (Reichsgesetzblatt 1900 Seite 716) berechnet; die Seemannsämter reichten ihre Berichte unmittelbar dem Kaiserlichen Statistischen Amt ein. Später dienten diese Angaben zur Festsetzung der durchschnittlichen Monatsheuer gemäß §§ 1068 und 1069 der Reichsversicherungsordnung. Ab 1923 wurde die Statistik der Monatsheuern durch Erlaß des Reichsarbeitsministers mit Rücksicht auf erfolgte Änderungen der gesetzlichen Seeunfallversicherung eingestellt.*)

122 Arbeitsstatistische Institutionen

Die wiederholten Versuche des Reichstages, die Reichsregierung zur laufenden und umfassenden Untersuchung der sozialen Lage der Arbeiter zu veranlassen, führten schließlich dazu, daß die Regierung ein "Regulativ für die Errichtung einer Kommission für Arbeiterstatistik" (Nr. 802 der amtlichen Drucksachen des Reichtages, 8. Legislaturperiode, 1. Session, 1890/92) erließ. Die hiermit eingesetzte "Kommission für Arbeiterstatistik" hatte in erster Linie die Aufgabe, durch statistische Erhebungen über die Arbeitsdauer- d. h. die tägliche Arbeitszeit - in den verschiedenen Gewerbezweigen die nötigen Unterlagen für den weiteren Ausbau der

*) vgl. Statistisches Reichsamt: Vierteljahrshefte zur Statistik des Deutschen Reichs, Jahrgang 1924 Seite I.19.

Gewerbeordnung zu beschaffen. Mit einem Antrag vom 20. Januar 1892 an den Reichskanzler bemühte sich der Reichstag, die Aufgaben der Kommission dahingehend zu erweitern, daß auch laufende Erhebungen über die individuell zu erfassenden Löhne aller in den Zuständigkeitsbereich der gewerblichen Berufsgenossenschaften fallenden Arbeiter durchzuführen waren(Stenographische Berichte über die Verhandlungen des Reichstages, 8. Legislaturperiode, 1. Session, 1890/92, 6. Band, Berlin 1892, Seite 3745 ff.). Dieser Antrag des Reichstages wurde im Auftrage der Regierung in der Kommission für Arbeiterstatistik weiterbehandelt und schließlich abgelehnt (Drucksachen der Kommission für Arbeiterstatistik, Verhandlungen am 3. Juli 1893, Berlin 1893). Die Kommission bestand von 1892 bis 1902 und führte auftragsgemäß mehrere statistische Erhebungen über die Arbeitszeit in verschiedenen Gewerbezweigen durch, wobei jeweils 10 % bis 25 % der Betriebe mit Fragebogen erfaßt wurden. Die technische Abwicklung dieser Erhebungen oblag dem Kaiserlichen Statistischen Amt. In zwei Erhebungen wurde dabei auch die Lohnfrage berührt. Die erste dieser Untersuchungen war die "Erhebung über die Arbeits- und Gehaltsverhältnisse der Kellner und Kellnerinnen,veranstaltet im Jahre 1893" (Drucksachen der Kommission für Arbeiterstatistik, Erhebungen Nr. 6. Bearbeitet im Kaiserlichen Statistischen Amt, Berlin 1894.). Bei dieser Erhebung wurden Orte bzw. Bezirke von Großstädten gezielt ausgewählt, so daß alle Gemeindegrößenklassen richtig repräsentiert waren. In den ausgewählten Orten bzw. Bezirken wurden jeweils sämtliche Gast- und Schankwirtschaften mit Fragebogen erfaßt. Auf diese Weise wurde ein Auswahlsatz von 10 % der in jedem Einzelstaat vorhandenen mit Kellnerpersonal arbeitenden Wirtschaften angestrebt. An jeden Betrieb wurde ein Fragebogen verteilt, wobei die Fragebogen je zur Hälfte von Arbeitgebern und von Arbeitnehmern auszufüllen waren. "Um hierbei jede Willkür auszuschließen, wurde die Verteilung nach rein äußeren Merkmalen (z. B. abwechselnd in der alphabetischen Reihenfolge der Firmen an Arbeitgeber und Arbeitnehmer) angeordnet."*) Die Auskünfte der Arbeitgeber bzw. Arbeitnehmer waren freiwillig. Als lohnstatistische Ergebnisse wurden für die einzelnen Staaten, Gemeindegrößenklassen und Betriebsarten Häufigkeitsverteilungen des Kellnerpersonals - gegliedert nach Geschlecht und Stellung im Beruf - nach Monatsgehaltsklassen ausgewiesen. Zusätzlich angegeben wurden die empfangenen Naturalleistungen, die jedoch nicht bewertet wurden. Die zweite Untersuchung der Kommission für Arbeiterstatistik, in der die Lohnfrage berührt wurde, war die "Zusammenstellung der Ergebnisse der Ermittlungen über die Arbeitsverhältnisse in der Kleider- und Wäschekonfektion" (Drucksachen der Kommission für Arbeiterstatistik, Erhebungen Nr. 10. Bearbeitet im Kaiserlichen Statistischen Amt, Berlin 1896). Diese Untersuchung lieferte Angaben über die Brutto- und Nettoverdienste und verschiedene Abzüge von Zeit- und Stücklohnarbeitern sowie Zwischenmeistern. Es wurden jedoch nur typische Einzelfälle dargestellt; eine statistisch-tabellarische Auswertung und Berechnung von Kollektivmaßzahlen erfolgte nicht. Als Materialquellen dienten die durch die Kommission vorgenommenen mündlichen Vernehmungen von lediglich 122 Auskunftspersonen (22 Arbeitgeber, 30 Zwischenmeister, 70 Arbeiter) aus verschiedenen Orten. Ferner wurden Berichte der zuständigen Behörden über die Besichtigung ausgewählter Betriebe sowie Gewerbegerichtsakten herangezogen. Im Auftrage der Kommission für Arbeiterstatistik wurden im Kaiserlichen Statistischen Amt noch die Ergebnisse einer Sonderuntersuchung über "Gewerbliche Kinderarbeit außerhalb der Fabriken auf Grund einer Erhebung vom Jahre 1898" zusammengestellt (Kaiserliches Statistisches Amt: Vierteljahrshefte zur Statistik des Deutschen Reichs, Jahrgang 1900 Seite III.97 - 147). Bei dieser Erhebung wurden die Kinder auf Anweisung der einzelnen Staatsregierungen im allgemeinen durch die Volksschullehrer unter anderem nach der Höhe ihrer Löhne befragt. Die Erhebung verlief in den einzelnen Staaten z. T. völlig uneinheitlich und erbrachte nur sporadische lohnstatistische Angaben.

*) Kaiserliches Statistisches Amt, Abteilung für Arbeiterstatistik: Die Fortschritte der amtlichen Arbeitsstatistik in den wichtigsten Staaten; Erster Teil Vereinigte Staaten von Amerika, Großbritannien und Irland, Frankreich, Belgien, Österreich, Deutsches Reich. Beiträge zur Arbeiterstatistik Nr. 1. Berlin 1904, Seite 185.

Wegen der als unzureichend empfundenen Tätigkeit der Kommission für Arbeiterstatistik wurde im Reichstag wiederholt die Gründung eines Reichsarbeitsamts beantragt, dem die Untersuchung der Arbeitsverhältnisse einschließlich der Lohnstatistik obliegen sollte (Nr. 24 und Nr. 64 der amtlichen Drucksachen des Reichstages, 10. Legislaturperiode, 2. Session, 1900/1902). Die Reichsregierung richtete daraufhin mit Wirkung vom 1. April 1902 beim Kaiserlichen Statistischen Amt eine "Abteilung für Arbeiterstatistik" ein, auf die die Aufgaben der Kommission für Arbeiterstatistik übergingen (Denkschrift, betreffend die Errichtung einer weiteren Abteilung beim Kaiserlichen Statistischen Amt; Beilage A zur Anlage IV des Reichshaushaltsetats für 1902). Der Abteilung für Arbeiterstatistik wurde durch Reichskanzlererlaß ein "Beirat für Arbeiterstatistik" zur Seite gestellt (Bestimmungen betreffend den Beirat für Arbeiterstatistik vom 30. April 1902; Zentralblatt für das Deutsche Reich Seite 100. Nr. 638 der Drucksachen des Reichstages, 10. Legislaturperiode, 2. Session, 1900/1902). In Fortsetzung der Arbeiten der Kommission für Arbeiterstatistik führten Abteilung und Beirat für Arbeiterstatistik insgesamt neun Repräsentativerhebungen durch, deren Ergebnisse als "Drucksachen des Kaiserlichen Statistischen Amtes, Abteilung für Arbeiterstatistik, Erhebungen Nr. 1 bis 9"(Berlin 1903 bis 1912) veröffentlicht wurden. Die Erhebungen, bei denen jeweils 25 % bis 50 % der Betriebe erfaßt wurden, lieferten jedoch im allgemeinen nur Angaben über die Arbeitszeit in verschiedenen Gewerbezweigen. Die Lohnfrage wurde nur bei der Erhebung Nr. 9 über die Arbeitsverhältnisse der Angestellten der Rechtsanwälte und lediglich in der Form berührt, daß die Länge des Lohnabrechnungszeitraums erfaßt wurde; eigentliche lohnstatistische Angaben fehlten völlig.

Allgemein war die amtliche lohnstatistische Situation auch nach der Einrichtung der Abteilung für Arbeiterstatistik durch einen erheblichen Entwicklungsrückstand gegenüber der nicht-amtlichen - vor allem der gewerkschaftlichen - Lohnstatistik gekennzeichnet. So ließ z. B. der (gewerkschaftliche) Verband der Porzellanarbeiter während des ganzen Jahres 1906 von seinen Mitgliedern die verdienten Wochenlöhne fortlaufend aufzeichnen. Von der Ausfüllung der Formulare wurde die Unterstützungsberechtigung abhängig gemacht.

Neben den Wochenlöhnen war die Anzahl der wirklichen Arbeitstage und der Überstunden anzugeben. Bei der statistischen Aufbereitung wurde der Gesamtverdienst durch die Anzahl der wirklichen Arbeitstage geteilt und als durchschnittlicher Wochenverdienst das Sechsfache des auf einen Arbeitstag entfallenden Verdienstes berechnet. Ausgewiesen wurden höchste, niedrigste und durchschnittliche Wochenverdienste für 92 Berufe sowie Häufigkeitsverteilungen der Arbeiter nach Wochenverdienstklassen.*) Mit dem ausdrücklichen Ziel, den gewerkschaftlichen Lohnerhebungen amtliche Zahlen entgegenhalten zu können und darüberhinaus den Vorsprung des Auslands auf lohnstatistischem Gebiet einzuholen, nahm die Abteilung für Arbeiterstatistik mit Zustimmung des Staatssekretärs des Innern in den Jahren 1907 und 1908 Vorbesprechungen mit dem Gesamtverband deutscher Metallindustrieller auf, um die Möglichkeit einer Lohnerhebung in der Metallindustrie zu prüfen. Durch hinhaltende Stellungnahmen des offensichtlich nicht interessierten Verbandes zogen sich diese Besprechungen jedoch so lange hin, daß die Erhebung wegen des Ersten Weltkrieges nicht mehr zustandekam.**)

Wenn auch die eigenen lohnstatistischen Aktivitäten der Abteilung für Arbeiterstatistik nur sehr dürftig waren, so erlangte diese Abteilung doch dadurch Bedeutung, daß sie mit der von ihr ab 1903 herausgegebenen Monatszeitschrift "Reichsarbeitsblatt" sowie in dessen Sonderbeilagen und Sonderheften ein Forum für die laufende Verbreitung lohnstatistischer und verwandter Daten aus amtlichen und nicht-amtlichen Quellen schuf. Das Reichsarbeitsblatt war von 1903 bis 1920 das Organ der Abteilung für Arbeiterstatistik und erschien weiter als "Neue Folge" von 1920 bis gegen Ende des Zweiten Weltkrieges unter wechselnder Herausgeberschaft.

---

*) vgl. Johannes Feig: Statistik des Arbeitslohns und der Lebenshaltung. In: Die Statistik in Deutschland nach ihrem heutigen Stand, Ehrengabe für Georg von Mayr, Band II, herausgegeben von F. Zahn, München-Berlin 1911, Seite 789 - 826 (v. a. Seite 809).

**) vgl. Statistisches Reichsamt: Die amtliche Lohnstatistik in Deutschland, a. a. O.

123 Sammlung von Tarifverträgen

Mit zunehmender Mitgliederzahl der Gewerkschaften konnten diese häufiger die Arbeitgeber zum Abschluß von Tarifverträgen veranlassen. Die Tarifverträge boten daher in wachsendem Maße ein lohnendes Datenmaterial für statistische Auswertungen. Im Jahre 1913 beabsichtigte das Reichsamt des Innern, das Kaiserliche Statistische Amt mit der Sammlung und der lohnstatistischen Bearbeitung sämtlicher Tarifverträge und demnach mit der Führung eines neu zu errichtenden amtlichen Tarifarchivs zu betrauen.*) Wegen des Ersten Weltkrieges wurde dieser umfassende Plan zunächst nicht mehr verwirklicht. Das Kaiserliche Statistische Amt hatte sich jedoch bereits früher darum bemüht, von den Tarifvertragspartnern Auskünfte über die Anzahl und den Inhalt der abgeschlossenen Tarifverträge zu erhalten. Vor allem die Gewerkschaften - teilweise auch die Arbeitgeberverbände und die Gewerbegerichte - stellten daher dem Kaiserlichen Statistischen Amt seit 1906 laufend freiwillig Tarifvertragstexte zur Verfügung. Neben den Vertragstexten wurden auch schematisierte Angaben auf für diesen Zweck entwickelten Fragebogen eingeholt. Diese Sammlung von Tarifverträgen war zunächst noch sehr unvollständig; die Lücken konnten jedoch allmählich in erster Linie durch die bereitwillige Mitarbeit der Gewerkschaften weitgehend geschlossen werden. Das Kaiserliche Statistische Amt wertete die Tarifverträge zu einer jährlichen Tarifstatistik aus, die unter anderem Angaben über die Verteilung der Tarife nach verschiedenen lohnrelevanten Merkmalen - z. B. der vereinbarten Form der Entlohnung wie Zeit- oder Akkordlohn und Geld- oder Naturallohn - sowie nach tariflichen Lohnerhöhungsbetragsklassen erbrachte. Die Tarifstatistik war keine Tariflohnstatistik, sondern enthielt nur wenige lohnstatistische Ergänzungen. Die eigentlichen lohnstatistischen Angaben erfolgten nicht regelmäßig und nur in der Form von Häufigkeitsverteilungen der tarifgebundenen Betriebe und deren Arbeiter nach Tariflohnklassen - gebildet aus den jeweils niedrigsten tariflichen Stunden- und Wochenlöhnen - sowie nach Lohnzuschlagsklassen mit gesonderter Behandlung der Zuschläge für Überstunden, Sonntagsarbeit, Nachtarbeit und sonstige besondere Arbeiten. Darüber hinaus wurden nur tarifliche Einzellohnsätze - vor

*) vgl. Statistisches Reichsamt: Die amtliche Lohnstatistik in Deutschland, a. a. O.

allem die tariflichen Untergrenzen der Entlohnung bei Zeitlohn - und sehr sporadisch durchschnittliche Tariflöhne ausgewiesen. Die Ergebnisse der jährlichen Tarifstatistik wurden von der Abteilung für Arbeiterstatistik des Kaiserlichen Statistischen Amtes und später - bis zum Berichtsjahr 1931 - vom Reichsamt für Arbeitsvermittlung bzw. der Reichsarbeitsverwaltung und vom Reichsarbeitsministerium in Zusammenarbeit mit dem Statistischen Reichsamt in folgenden Publikationen veröffentlicht:

Beiträge zur Arbeiterstatistik Nr. 4 und Nr. 8 (Berlin 1906 und 1908),

Reicharbeitsblatt 1908 XII, 1909 I und II, 1918 IV, 1919 IV, 1920 I,

Sonderbeilagen zum Reicharbeitsblatt 1909 XI, 1910 VIII, 1924 Nr. 29/30,

Sonderhefte zum Reichsarbeitsblatt (4., 5., 7., 10., 12., 15., 23., 26., 27., 31., 35., 40., 43., 47., 55., 57., 58. Sonderheft, Berlin 1911 bis 1933).

124 Städte als Arbeitgeber

Ein Interesse an lohnstatistischen Daten bestand besonders in den Teilen der öffentlichen Verwaltung, die wie die Gemeinden infolge der Einrichtung von Produktions- bzw. Dienstleistungsbetrieben als Nachfrager am Arbeitsmarkt auftraten. Auf Beschluß der "Konferenz deutscher Städtestatistiker" im Oktober 1902 in Altona führte die Mehrzahl der Städte über 50 000 Einwohner - insgesamt 54 Städte - zum Stichtag 1. März 1902 eine Erhebung über die Lohnverhältnisse städtischer Arbeiter durch. Die Aufbereitung der ausgefüllten Erhebungsbogen und die Veröffentlichung der Ergebnisse wurde von den Städtestatistikern dem Kaiserlichen Statistischen Amt übertragen, das zur Aktualisierung eine Nacherhebung zum Stichtag 1. Juli 1907 bei den 34 Städten mit eigenen statistischen Ämtern veranstaltete. In beide Erhebungen wurden mit je einem Erhebungbogen sämtliche städtischen Betriebe mit mehr als 5 Arbeitern einbezogen. In diesen Betrieben wurden für alle erwachsenen männlichen Arbeiter die Lohnsätze (d. h. nicht die Arbeitsverdienste) für Normal- und Sonderarbeit (z. B. Überstundenarbeit), die Lohnformen, der Wert der Naturalleistungen, die Qualifikationsstufen und die Berufsgruppen erfaßt. Ausgewiesen wurden für die Zeitlohnarbeiter Häufigkeitsverteilungen nach Lohnklassen und für die Akkordlohnarbeiter die höchsten, mittleren und niedrigsten Akkordlöhne; daneben wurden teilweise Durchschnittslöhne und "Mehrheitslöhne" (d. h. Modalwerte) angegeben. Die Ergebnisse wurden von der Abteilung für Arbeiterstatistik des Kaiserlichen Statistischen Amtes unter dem Titel "Die Regelung des Arbeitsverhältnisses der Gemeindearbeiter in deutschen Städten, I.Erhebungen über Arbeitslohn und Arbeitszeit 1902 und 1907" veröffentlicht (Beiträge zur Arbeiterstatistik Nr. 9, Berlin 1908).

Im September 1912 wurde auf einer Tagung der Städtestatistiker in Elberfeld beschlossen, laufende jährliche Lohnerhebungen in den wichtigsten städtischen Betrieben und darüber hinaus im Juni und Dezember jedes Jahres Lohnerhebungen in einer Reihe von Privatbetrieben verschiedener Gewerbezweige durchzuführen.*) Diese Beschlüsse konnten jedoch wegen des Ersten Weltkrieges nicht mehr verwirklicht werden.

125 Beobachtung des Arbeitsmarktes

Zum Arbeitsprogramm des Kaiserlichen Statistischen Amtes gehörte es, im Reichsarbeitsblatt monatlich über die Lage des Arbeitsmarktes zu berichten. Die dazu erforderlichen Informationen wurden freiwillig von einem feststehenden Kreis von Unternehmen und Verbänden geliefert. Das Kaiserliche Statistische Amt bediente sich dieses bereits bewährten Berichtskreises, um in den Jahren 1916 (für die Berichtsjahre 1914 bis 1916) und 1917 (für die Berichtsjahre 1917 bis 1919) "Erhebungen über Lohnverhältnisse" durchzuführen bzw. einzuleiten. Die Erhebungen wurden als "Stichprobenerhebungen" bezeichnet, dürften jedoch wegen der Freiwilligkeit der Berichterstattung und bei dem geringen Stichprobenumfang - im ganzen Reichsgebiet wurden nur jeweils etwa 380 Unternehmen erfaßt - kaum repräsentative bzw. hinreichend gesicherte Ergebnisse erbracht haben. Erfragt wurden für die beiden letzten vollen Wochen der Monate März und September der Berichtsjahre summarische Angaben über die Anzahl

*) vgl. Statistisches Reichsamt: Die amtliche Lohnstatistik in Deutschland, a. a. O.

der Arbeitertagewerke (Anzahl der Arbeiter multipliziert mit der Anzahl der Arbeitsschichten), die Lohnsumme, den durchschnittlichen Tagesverdienst und die regelmäßige wochentägliche Arbeitszeit der nach Geschlecht, Arbeitergruppen und Berufsgruppen aufgegliederten "Mehrheit" der Arbeiter. Die Ergebnisse wurden, zusätzlich gegliedert nach Gewerbegruppen, unter dem Titel "Die Löhne der Arbeiterschaft während des Krieges" in den Jahrgängen 1917 (Seite 643), 1918 (Seite 297), 1919 (Seite 618) und 1920 (Seite 62) des Reichsarbeitsblattes veröffentlicht.

13 Die Phase des Aufbaus und laufenden Ausbaus (1920 - 1935)

131 Gewerkschaften als gleichberechtigte Sozialpartner

Trotz aller Bemühungen des Kaiserlichen Statistischen Amtes galt bis zum Ende des Ersten Weltkrieges im internationalen Vergleich noch die folgende negative Selbstbeurteilung der amtlichen deutschen Lohnstatistik: ".... In der Statistik der Tarifverträge dürfen die deutschen Leistungen wohl als denen der hier behandelten Staaten im ganzen überlegen bezeichnet werden. Die Bestrebungen nach Ausbau der Statistik der bestehenden Verträge finden im Ausland kein Vorbild. Um so rückständiger erscheint die deutsche Arbeitsstatistik auf dem Gebiete der Lohnerhebungen. Die bisherigen Bestrebungen der Abteilung für Arbeiterstatistik sind bisher von nur geringem Erfolge gekrönt gewesen. Irgendeine umfassende, sei es periodische, sei es einmalige Lohnstatistik, fehlt noch gänzlich, während in allen hier behandelten Ländern mehr oder minder umfangreiche Erhebungen vorliegen und sogar die schwierige Aufgabe der Ermittlung der landwirtschaftlichen Löhne fast überall angegriffen worden ist...."*) Ein merklicher Fortschritt der Lohnstatistik ergab sich erst im Zusammenhang mit den politischen und sozialen Umwälzungen, die in der Folge des Ersten Weltkrieges auftraten. Diese Umwälzungen bewirkten, daß die Gewerkschaften ihr Ansehen und ihren Einfluß bei sozialen Auseinandersetzungen erheblich vergrößern und eines ihrer Hauptziele - die tarifvertragliche Regelung der Arbeitsverhältnisse für möglichst alle Arbeitnehmer - in wesentlich stärkerem Maße durchsetzen konnten als bisher. Die Anerkennung der Gewerkschaften als gleichberechtigte Sozialpartner drückte sich unter anderem in der erstmaligen gesetzlichen Regelung des Tarifvertragsrechts durch die "Verordnung über Tarifverträge, Arbeiter- und Angestelltenausschüsse und Schlichtung von Arbeitsstreitigkeiten"

*) Johannes Feig in: Gebiete und Methoden der amtlichen Arbeitsstatistik in den wichtigsten Industriestaaten. Beiträge zur Arbeiterstatistik Nr. 12, herausgegeben vom Kaiserlichen Statistischen Amt, Abteilung für Arbeiterstatistik. Berlin 1913, S. 679.

vom 23. Dezember 1918 (Reichsgesetzblatt 1918 S. 1456) aus. Durch eine "Nachtragsverordnung" vom 31. Mai 1920 (Reichsgesetzblatt 1920 S. 1128, Reichsarbeitsblatt Neue Folge 1920 S. 9) wurden die Tarifparteien unter Androhung von Ordnungsstrafen bis zu 300 RM bei Nichterfüllung verpflichtet, innerhalb von 14 Tagen nach Abschluß eines Tarifvertrages dem Reichsamt für Arbeitsvermittlung zwei Abdrucke des Vertragstextes zu übersenden. Das Reichsamt für Arbeitsvermittlung stellte die eingesandten Tarifverträge ab 1920 zu einem amtlichen "Tarifarchiv" zusammen. Daneben wurde ab 1919 vom Reichsarbeitsministerium und ab 1922 vom Reichsamt für Arbeitsvermittlung ein "Tarifregister" als Verzeichnis der für allgemeinverbindlich erklärten Tarifverträge geführt. Im Tarifarchiv und dem Tarifregister lag nunmehr vollständiges Material für vielfältige tarifstatistische und tariflohnstatistische Auswertungen vor. Dieses Material erstreckte sich unter anderem auch auf die Angestelltentarife, die in der früheren Tarifstatistik nur vereinzelt erfaßt werden konnten. Das Reichsamt für Arbeitsvermittlung wurde durch § 31 des Arbeitsnachweisgesetzes vom 22. Juli 1922 (Reichsgesetzblatt 1922 Teil I S. 657) ausdrücklich zu regelmäßigen Berichten über die Entwicklung des Tarifwesens verpflichtet und erhielt das Recht, zur Durchführung seiner Aufgaben Erhebungen über Arbeitsbedingungen anzustellen. Die jährliche Tarifstatistik wurde als Teil dieser Berichterstattung weitergeführt. Das Reichsamt für Arbeitsvermittlung wertete für die Tarifstatistik nicht nur das Tarifarchiv bzw. Tarifregister aus, sondern holte auf besonderen statistischen Erhebungsbogen zusätzliche Angaben von den Zentralverbänden der Arbeitnehmer - für die dabei allerdings keine gesetzliche Berichtspflicht bestand - ein.

Die Führung des Tarifarchivs und die Bearbeitung der Tarifstatistik wurden später dem Statistischen Reichsamt übertragen, dem bereits die Tariflohnstatistik oblag. Nach der Tarifvertragsverordnung in der Neufassung vom 1. März 1928 (Reichsgesetzblatt 1928 Teil I S. 47) und der vom Reichsarbeitsminister erlassenen Bestimmungen über die Einsendung und Mitteilung von Tarifverträgen vom 1. März 1928 (Reichsgesetzblatt 1928 Teil I S. 48) waren die beim Abschluß von Arbeitstarifverträgen beteiligten Parteien verpflichtet, dem Statistischen Reichsamt binnen Monatsfrist von dem abgeschlossenen Tarifvertrag zwei Ausfertigungen zustellen und in gleicher Weise alle Veränderungen, Ergänzungen, Zusatzabkommen sowie das Außerkrafttreten mitzuteilen. Das Statistische Reichsamt bearbeitete die Tarifstatistik mit jährlicher Periodizität bis zu ihrer Einstellung im Jahre 1933.

132 Organisatorische Integration der Arbeitsstatistik

Die Arbeitsstatistiken und damit auch die Lohnstatistik hatten dadurch, daß die für ihre Bearbeitung zuständige "Abteilung für Arbeiterstatistik" im Kaiserlichen Statistischen Amt ein gewisses Eigenleben führte, den Charakter von nicht zum normalen Arbeitsprogramm gehörenden Sonderstatistiken. Nach dem Ersten Weltkrieg wurden organisatorische Veränderungen vorgenommen, die schließlich zu einer vollen Integration der Arbeitsstatistik in das normale Arbeitsprogramm des Statistischen Reichsamtes führten.*) Im Jahre 1920 wurde das "Reichsamt für Arbeitsvermittlung" - ab 1922 bezeichnet als "Reichsarbeitsverwaltung" - errichtet, daß mit der Tarifstatistik und der Herausgabe des Reichsarbeitsblattes einen Teil der Aufgaben der früheren Abteilung für Arbeiterstatistik des Kaiserlichen Statistischen Amtes übernahm. Beim Statistischen Reichsamt verblieb in einer neuen"Abteilung für Wirtschafts- und Sozialstatistik" die Lohnstatistik einschließlich der Tariflohnstatistik. Das Statistische Reichsamt gab als Ersatz für das Reichsarbeitsblatt nunmehr die Halbmonatsschrift "Wirtschaft und Statistik" heraus. Im Jahre 1927 wurde die Reichsarbeitsverwaltung umbenannt in "Reichsanstalt für Arbeitsvermittlung und Arbeitslosenversicherung"; die Herausgabe des Reichsarbeitsblattes wurde daraufhin dem Reichsarbeitsministerium, die Führung des Tarifarchivs einschließlich der Tarifstatistik dem Statistischen Reichsamt, und zwar der Abteilung für Wirtschafts- und Sozialstatistik, übertragen. Die Zeitschrift "Wirtschaft und Statistik" wird seit 1949 vom Statistischen Bundesamt als Monatsschrift fortgeführt.

*) vgl. Statistisches Reichsamt:
Vierteljahrshefte zur Statistik des
Deutschen Reichs, Jahrgänge 1923 S. I. 12* und
1928 S. I. 24.

133 Geldentwertung

Die Inflation nach dem Ersten Weltkrieg führte zu einem vermehrten Bedarf an solchen statistischen Daten, in denen sich die Geldwertverschlechterung unmittelbar ausdrückte. Hierzu gehörten neben den preisstatistischen unter anderem auch lohnstatistische Daten. Das Statistische Reichsamt stellte in einer Sonderarbeit die vorhandenen "Zahlen zur Geldentwertung in Deutschland 1914 - 1923" (Sonderheft 1 zu Wirtschaft und Statistik, Berlin 1925) mit einem besonderen Abschnitt über Löhne zusammen. Bei der rapiden Geldentwertung wurde es notwendig, die Verdienstentwicklung auch in Bereichen wie der Land- und Forstwirtschaft zu beobachten, in denen sich die Löhne früher verhältnismäßig wenig geändert hatten. Im Zentralblatt für das Deutsche Reich (Jahrgang 1922 Nr. 6) und im Reichsministerialblatt (Jahrgänge 1923 bis 1925, zuletzt 1925 Nr. 66) wurden erstmalig amtliche Schätzwerte über die Jahresarbeitsverdienste land- und forstwirtschaftlicher Arbeiter veröffentlicht. Darüber hinaus wurde in den Jahren der Inflation der Grundstein für eine umfassende laufende Lohnstatistik gelegt, wobei es bei dem bestehenden amtlichen Tarifarchiv nahelag, den Aufbau mit der Tariflohnstatistik zu beginnen. Im Jahre 1922 wurde eine monatliche amtliche Tariflohnstatistik eingeführt, deren Ergebnisse vom Statistischen Reichsamt laufend in "Wirtschaft und Statistik" veröffentlicht wurden.
Diese erste Tariflohnstatistik des Statistischen Reichsamtes berücksichtigte die zwischen den Arbeitgeber- und Arbeitnehmerverbänden vereinbarten oder durch Schiedsspruch festgesetzten Lohnsätze der höchsten tarifmäßigen Altersstufe der gelernten und ungelernten Arbeiter in den Hauptsitzen der wichtigsten Gewerbegruppen. Da in der Inflationszeit die Tariflöhne innerhalb eines Berichtsmonats oft mehrfach geändert wurden, wurden bis Ende 1923 die einzelnen während des Berichtsmonats in Kraft gewesenen Lohnsätze mit der Zahl der Tage, für die sie Gültigkeit hatten, vervielfältigt; die Ergebnisse wurden dann zusammengezählt und durch die Zahl der Werktage des Berichtsmonats geteilt. Später wurden die Tariflöhne jeweils nur noch zum Stichtag Monatsanfang erfaßt. Aus den zeitlich gewogenen bzw. zum Stichtag Monatsanfang erfaßten tariflichen Stunden- und Wochenlöhnen -letzere wurden er-

rechnet durch Multiplikation des tariflichen Stundenlohnes mit der regelmäßigen tariflichen Wochenarbeitszeit - der gelernten und der ungelernten Arbeiter in jeder Stadt wurde unter Berücksichtigung der Arbeiterzahlen der örtlich gewogene arithmetische Durchschnitt für jede einzelne Gewerbegruppe und schließlich für alle Gewerbegruppen berechnet. Die Tariflohnstatistik ermittelte auf diese Weise gewogene durchschnittliche Tariflöhne für Vollzeitarbeiter. Die sozialen Zulagen wurden - soweit sie in den Berichtsorten gezahlt wurden - einheitlich für die Ehefrau und zwei Kinder mit eingerechnet. Die erste monatliche Tariflohnstatistik erstreckte sich zunächst auf neun und später auf zwölf Zweige der gewerblichen Wirtschaft. Die Landwirtschaft war grundsätzlich ausgeschlossen; das Statistische Reichsamt berechnete nur einmalig für das Jahr 1925 aus den für die verschiedenen landwirtschaftlichen Vertragsgebiete festgesetzten tariflichen Einzellohnsätzen der Landarbeiter für das Reichsgebiet gewogene arithmetische Tariflohndurchschnitte, wobei als Gewichte die Anzahlen der organisierten Landarbeiter pro Vertragsgebiet dienten (Wirtschaft und Statistik Jahrgang 1926 S. 221 f.).

Im Jahre 1931 wurde die Tariflohnstatistik reformiert, wobei jedoch der Hauptzweck - die monatliche Ermittlung durchschnittlicher Tariflohnsätze - beibehalten wurde.*) Wie vorher wurden nicht alle Tariflöhne, sondern nur eine gezielte Auswahl repräsentativer Gewerbegruppen, Arbeitergruppen bzw. Berufsarten, Tarifgebiete bzw. Orte oder Ortsklassen und tariflicher Lohnzuschläge erfaßt, wobei durch Ausweitung die Repräsentation allerdings wesentlich verbessert wurde. Die Ergebnisse wurden nunmehr für 17 Gewerbegruppen, die durch Aufgliederung einzelner Gruppen in Gewerbezweige in insgesamt 33 kleinste systematische Einheiten zerfielen, ausgewiesen. Als Arbeitergruppen wurden nicht mehr nur gelernte und ungelernte Arbeiter, sondern fünf Gruppen - und zwar männliche Facharbeiter, angelernte Arbeiter und Hilfsarbeiter sowie weibliche Fach- und angelernte Arbeiter (zusammengefaßt) und Hilfsarbeiter - unterschieden; soweit in einzelnen Gewerben die vorkommenden Berufsar-

*) vgl. Statistisches Reichsamt: Die Nachprüfung und Neubearbeitung der amtlichen Tariflohnstatistik. In: Vierteljahrshefte zur Statistik des Deutschen Reichs, 40. Jahrgang 1931, Zweites Heft, Berlin 1931, S. 94-109.

ten nicht zu den fünf Gruppen zusammengesetzt werden konnten, wurden je eine oder zwei typische Berufsarten als repräsentativ für die betreffende Arbeitergruppe ausgewählt. Wie vorher wurden Zeit- und Stücklöhne (Akkordlöhne) berücksichtigt. Als tariflicher Stücklohnsatz wurde der "Akkordrichtsatz" erfaßt, d.h. der Satz, der unter normalen Betriebsverhältnissen für einen Arbeiter durchschnittlicher Leistungsfähigkeit bei entsprechend gesteigerter Arbeitsleistung in Akkordarbeit erreichbar war.*) Während früher bei den ungelernten Arbeitern nur der Zeitlohn und bei den gelernten Arbeitern entweder nur der Stück- oder nur der Zeitlohn - je nach dem Überwiegen der einen oder der anderen Lohnform - erfaßt wurde, wurde nunmehr für jede Arbeitergruppe bzw. Berufsart ein Durchschnittssatz aus beiden Lohnformen berechnet, wobei Zeit- und Stücklohnarbeiter entsprechend ihrer zahlenmäßigen Bedeutung unterschiedlich berücksichtigt wurden. In der reformierten Tariflohnstatistik wurden nur noch tarifliche Stundenlöhne ermittelt; die Berechnung tariflicher Wochenlöhne wurde eingestellt. Bei der Einbeziehung der Sozialzulagen wurden nicht mehr je Arbeiter einheitlich eine Ehefrau und zwei Kinder unterstellt, sondern eine nach Gewerbegruppen differenzierte Berechnung entsprechend den Ergebnissen der Berufszählung von 1925 vorgenommen. Die durchschnittlichen Tariflöhne wurden nach der Reform als gewogene arithmetische Mittel der Einzellohnsätze mit vorerst konstant gehaltenen Gewichten berechnet. Als Gewichte dienten die - teilweise geschätzten - Gesamtzahlen der in den einzelnen Gewerben bzw. Arbeitergruppen im Durchschnitt der Jahre 1928 bis 1930 tatsächlich beschäftigten - d.h. nicht arbeitslosen - Arbeiter. Die durchschnittlichen Tariflohnsätze wurden nach reformierter Methode erstmalig zum Stichtag 1. Januar 1931 und rückwirkend monatlich ab 1. Januar 1928 ermittelt. Die so gewonnenen Zeitreihen wurden anschließend durch Verkettung mit den Ergebnissen der früheren Tariflohnstatistik für die Monate Januar 1925 bis Dezember 1927 ergänzt.**) Das Statistische Reichsamt führte die monatliche Tariflohnstatistik nach der Reform bis gegen Ende des Zweiten Weltkrieges unverändert fort; die Ergebnisse wurden in "Wirtschaft und Stati-

---

*) Akkordrichtsätze sind die tarifvertraglich vereinbarten Lohnsätze für Akkordarbeit. Beim Stückakkord wird der Akkordsatz für eine bestimmte Arbeitsmenge unabhängig von der benötigten Ausführungszeit gezahlt.

**) Fußnote siehe folgende Seite

stik" zuletzt im Jahrgang 1944 S. 69 ff. veröffentlicht.

34 Statistische Rechtsvorschriften

Die Bedeutung der Lohnstatistik wurde nach dem Ersten Weltkrieg dadurch unterstrichen, daß für die Durchführung der Erhebungen erstmalig besondere statistische Rechtsvorschriften erlassen wurden. Die erste lohnstatistische Rechtsvorschrift war die "Verordnung (des Reichsarbeitsministers) zur Sicherung der Durchführung der Lohnstatistik für den Monat Februar 1920" vom 9. März 1920 (Reichsgesetzblatt 1920 S. 309). Diese Verordnung, die der Lohn- und Gehaltserhebung vom Februar 1920 - der ersten umfassenden amtlichen Lohnstatistik überhaupt - zugrundelag, schrieb ausdrücklich eine Auskunftspflicht - d.h. eine Pflicht zur Ausfüllung und Rücksendung der Erhebungsbogen bis zu einem bestimmten Termin - der Arbeitgeber sowie eine Verpflichtung der Arbeitgeber, der Obmänner der Arbeiter- und Angestelltenvertretungen in den Betrieben und der einzelnen Arbeitnehmer zur Unterzeichnung der Erhebungsbogen vor. Auskunftsverweigerungen oder wissentlich falsche Auskünfte wurden mit Geldstrafe bis 20 000 Mark bedroht. Eine generelle Regelung der amtlichen lohnstatistischen Erhebungen erfolgte durch das "Gesetz betreffend Lohnstatistik" vom 27. Juli 1922 (Reichsgesetzblatt 1922 Teil I S. 656). Danach konnte die Reichsregierung mit Zustimmung des Reichsrats und des Volkswirtschaftlichen Ausschusses des Reichstags nach Anhörung des zuständigen Ausschusses des Reichswirtschaftrats Erhebungen über Lohn- und Gehaltsverhältnisse der Arbeiter und Angestellten anordnen. Die Reichsregierung hatte auf Vorschlag des Reichswirtschaftsrats einen lohnstatistischen Beirat zu berufen, der unter anderem bei der Aufstellung der Erhebungsmuster hinzuzuziehen war. Bei Zuwiderhandlung gegen auf Grund dieses Gesetzes erlassene Bestimmungen war auf Anordnung der Reichsregierung eine Geldstrafe bis 100 000 Mark möglich.

Auf Grund des Gesetzes von 1922 erließ der Reichswirtschaftsminister

---

**) vgl. Statistisches Reichsamt: Zur Neubearbeitung der amtlichen Tariflohnstatistik. In: Vierteljahrshefte zur Statistik des Deutschen Reichs, 40. Jahrgang 1931, Drittes Heft, Berlin 1931, S. 116.

die "Verordnung zur Ausführung des Gesetzes, betreffend Lohnstatistik,vom 14. Juli 1927" (Reichsgesetzblatt 1927 Teil I S. 185). Nach dieser Verordnung waren im Jahre 1927 und in den darauffolgenden Jahren Erhebungen über die Lohn- und Gehaltsverhältnisse der Arbeiter und Angestellten in ausgewählten Gewerben, Orten, Betrieben und Arbeiter- bzw. Angestelltengruppen durchzuführen. Beginn und Umfang der Erhebungen und die Reihenfolge der zu erfassenden Gewerbe hatte der Reichswirtschaftsminister im Benehmen mit dem Reichsarbeitsminister - im Bergbau nur mit Zustimmung des Reichsrats - im Erlaßwege zu bestimmen. Das mit der Durchführung der Erhebungen beauftragte Statistische Reichsamt erhielt das Recht, von den auskunftspflichtigen Betriebsleitern die Vorlage der Unterlagen zur Nachprüfung der Angaben zu verlangen. Betriebsleiter, Betriebsrat und die individuell erfaßten Arbeitnehmer waren außerdem verpflichtet, die Richtigkeit der Angaben auf den Fragebogen durch ihre Unterschriften zu bestätigen. Dem stand die Verpflichtung des Statistischen Reichsamts gegenüber, Einzelangaben geheimzuhalten. Verletzungen der Auskunfts- oder der Geheimhaltungspflicht waren mit Geldstrafe bedroht.

Die Verordnung von 1927 wurde durch die "Verordnung zur Ausführung des Gesetzes betreffend Lohnstatistik vom 8. August 1938" (Reichsgesetzblatt 1938 Teil I S. 1013) abgelöst. Die Verordnung von 1938 schrieb ebenfalls ohne zeitliche Begrenzung Erhebungen über die Lohn- und Gehaltsverhältnisse der Arbeiter und Angestellten vor, über die nähere Bestimmungen - auch im Bergbau - der Reichswirtschaftsminister lediglich im Benehmen mit dem Reichsarbeitsminister zu erlassen hatte. Das Statistische Reichsamt konnte sich bei der Durchführung der Erhebungen nunmehr der Mitwirkung von Sachverständigen,anderen Behörden und Organisationen bedienen. Die Verpflichtungen zur unentgeltlichen Auskunftserteilung und zur Unterzeichnung der Fragebogen trafen nur noch die Unternehmer. Das Statistische Reichsamt konnte nach wie vor zur Nachprüfung die Vorlage der Unterlagen verlangen und war dafür zur Geheimhaltung von Einzelangaben verpflichtet. Im Falle einer Verletzung der statistischen Auskunftspflicht konnte auf Antrag des Präsidenten des Statistischen Reichsamtes eine Geldstrafe verhängt werden.

135 Untersuchung der Verdienststruktur

In der Phase des Aufbaus und Ausbaus der Lohnstatistik durch das Statistische Reichsamt wurde bereits zwischen zwei Hauptzwecken der Lohnstatistik unterschieden: der einmaligen oder gelegentlichen Untersuchung der Verdienststruktur und der laufenden Beobachtung der Verdienstentwicklung. Für die Untersuchung der Verdienststruktur sind Erhebungsverfahren notwendig, die sehr genaue und detaillierte Einblicke in das in einer bestimmten Erhebungszeit bestehende Verdienstgefüge ermöglichen; dafür wird in Kauf genommen, daß derartige Verfahren sehr arbeits- und zeitaufwendig sein müssen. Bei der Beobachtung der Verdienstentwicklung muß dagegen ein Erhebungsverfahren angewendet werden, das laufend kurzfristig nach der Erhebungszeit Ergebnisse liefert, die zugunsten der Aktualität weniger genau bzw. detailliert sein können. Das für Strukturuntersuchungen angemessene Erhebungsverfahren ist das Individualverfahren, bei dem für jeden zur Erhebungsmasse gehörenden Arbeitnehmer die Erhebungsmerkmale individuell erfaßt werden. Die erste umfassende amtliche Lohnerhebung wurde vom Statistischen Reichsamt für den Berichtsmonat Februar 1920 als Individualerhebung durchgeführt. Die Lohn- und Gehaltserhebung von 1920 wurde durch einen an die Landesregierungen gerichteten gemeinsamen Erlaß des Reichswirtschaftsministers und des Reichsarbeitsministers vom 30. Januar 1920 angeordnet und durch eine Verordnung des Reichsarbeitsministers vom 9. März 1920 (Reichsgesetzblatt 1920 S. 309) rechtlich abgesichert. Zu der Erhebung wurden insgesamt ca. 12 000 ausgewählte Betriebe (örtliche Einheiten) aller nichtlandwirtschaftlichen Gewerbegruppen mit Ausnahme des Bergbaus aus allen Größenklassen und allen Gegenden des Reichs herangezogen. Die Berichtsbetriebe wurden gezielt ausgewählt nach Vorschlägen der Reichsarbeitsgemeinschaften, zu denen sich Arbeitgeber und Arbeitnehmer der einzelnen Gewerbegruppen zusammengeschlossen hatten. Innerhalb der ausgewählten Betriebe wurden sämtliche Arbeiter und Angestellten, die am Stichtag 28. Februar 1920 beschäftigt waren, einzeln auf Fragekarten erfaßt, die vom Arbeitgeber auszufüllen und vom jeweiligen Arbeitnehmer zu unterzeichnen waren. Außerdem waren pro Betrieb je ein Arbeitersammelfragebogen und ein Angestelltensammelfragebogen vom Arbeitgeber auszufüllen und vom Obmann der Arbeiter- bzw. der Angestelltenvertretung mitzuzeichnen. Jede Reichsarbeitsgemeinschaft hatte für die Arbeiter alle typischen Berufsarten benannt, deren Durchschnittslöhne nach ihrer genauen Sachkunde für die Kenntnis der tatsächlichen Lohnverhältnisse in der gesamten Gewerbegruppe ausreichten. In die Aufbereitung der Arbeiter wurden nur diese typischen Berufsarten einbezogen; ferner für die Berechnung der durchschnittlichen Stundenlöhne nur die in der Zeit vom 16. bis 29. Februar bzw. für die Berechnung der durchschnittlichen Monatsverdienste nur die vom 2. bis 29. Februar ununterbrochen im Betrieb beschäftigten Arbeiter. Durchschnittliche Monatsverdienste wurden für solche Arbeiter berechnet, die in jeder der vier Erhebungswochen eine wenn auch beschränkte Zahl von Arbeitsstunden geleistet und dabei im Februar 1920 insgesamt eine Leistung von mindestens 150 Arbeitsstunden erreicht hatten; auf diese Weise sollten Kurzarbeiter grundsätzlich mit erfaßt werden. Erhebungsmerkmale waren der tatsächliche Verdienst während des Erhebungszeitraums (2. bis 29. Februar 1920) mit gesonderter Angabe der Überstundenzuschläge, Lohnform und Arbeitszeit bei den Arbeitern sowie Geschlecht, Familienstand, Kinderzahl, Lebensalter und Beruf. Die Erhebung wurde in den Berichtsbetrieben von den Statistischen Landesämtern durchgeführt, die nach einheitlichen Richtlinien des Statistischen Reichsamtes für jede typische Berufsart der Arbeiter aus den individuellen Verdienstangaben durchschnittliche Stunden- und Monatsverdienste aller Arbeiter für jeden einzelnen Betrieb berechneten. Diese "Betriebsdurchschnitte" wurden vom Statistischen Reichsamt unter Berücksichtigung der Arbeiterzahl pro Betrieb zu gewogenen "Ortsdurchschnitten" für jede Gemeinde zusammengezogen. Im Gegensatz zur Lohnstatistik der Arbeiter wurde die Gehaltsstatistik der Angestellten nicht zu Durchschnittsverdiensten für bestimmte Berufsarten, sondern zu einer Gehaltsklassenstatistik - d.h. zu Häufigkeitsverteilungen nach Gehaltsklassen - für die vier Hauptgruppen der Angestellten (kaufmännische Angestellte, technische Angestellte, Betriebsbeamte und Werkmeister u.ä., Büroangestellte) verarbeitet. Dabei wurden alle versicherungspflichtigen Angestellten der erfaßten Betriebe in die Erhebung einbezogen. Die Ergebnisse der Lohn- und Gehaltserhebung vom Februar 1920 wurden sowohl für Arbeiter als auch für Angestellte für die einzelnen Gemeinden als kleinste regionale Einheiten ausgewiesen.

Das Statistische Reichsamt veröffentlichte die Ergebnisse unter dem Titel "Lohn- und Gehaltserhebung vom Februar 1920" als Band 293 der "Statistik des Deutschen Reichs" (Berlin 1921).

Auf Grund der "Verordnung zur Ausführung des Gesetzes, betreffend Lohnstatistik, vom 14. Juli 1927" (Reichsgesetzblatt 1927 Teil I S. 185) ordnete der Reichswirtschaftsminister durch Erlaß vom 30. August 1927 im Einvernehmen mit dem Reichsarbeitsminister eine Individualerhebung über die tatsächlichen Arbeitsverdienste in der Textilindustrie an. Die Erhebung wurde vom Statistischen Reichsamt für die letzte vor dem 12. September 1927 liegende volle Abrechnungsperiode für Stücklohnarbeiter in 263 ausgewählten Betrieben aus 58 Orten durchgeführt, wobei in den ausgewählten Betrieben nur männliche und weibliche Facharbeiter im Stücklohn sowie Hilfsarbeiter im Zeitlohn - insgesamt 36 519 Personen, das waren 21% aller in den Erhebungsorten bei der Berufszählung von 1925 festgestellten Textilarbeiter - erfaßt wurden. Die Anzahl der erfaßten Betriebe und Arbeiter wurde als ausreichend angesehen, weil der einzelne Erhebungsort für das unter einem einheitlichen Tarifvertrag stehende Gebiet und die auf Grund von Vorschlägen der zuständigen Arbeitgeber- und Arbeitnehmerverbände gezielt ausgewählten Betriebe für den Erhebungsort typisch waren. Die methodischen Grundlagen der Erhebung wurden im Benehmen mit dem aus Vertretern der Arbeitnehmer- und Arbeitgeberverbände zusammengesetzen lohnstatistischen Beirat des Statistischen Reichsamtes festgelegt. Das Statistische Reichsamt versandte die Fragebogen daraufhin unmittelbar an die Berichtsbetriebe. Erhebungsmerkmale waren vor allem der effektive Stunden- und Wochenverdienst mit gesonderter Angabe der verschiedenen Verdienstzuschläge (Leistungs- und Sozialzuschläge), eventuelle Naturalleistungen, persönlich bedingte Verdienstminderungen (durch Krankheit, Urlaub und Ausscheiden oder Eintritt während der Erhebungszeit), der Tariflohnsatz mit Tarifgebiet und Ortsklasse, die Lohnform, die gesetzlichen Abzüge (Lohnsteuer und Arbeitnehmerbeitrag zur Sozialversicherung), der Arbeitgeberbeitrag zur Sozialversicherung, die Arbeitszeit sowie Geschlecht, Lebensalter, Qualifikation und Beruf des einzelnen Arbeiters. Ausgewiesen wurden vor allem Häufigkeitsverteilungen der Arbeiter nach Verdienstklassen und gewogene Durchschnittsverdienste. Die Individuallohnerhebung in der Textilindustrie wurde mit geringfügigen Abwandlungen im September 1930 und im September 1933 wiederholt. Ähnliche Individuallohnerhebungen fanden in ebenfalls dreijährigen Abständen in verschiedenen Erhebungszeiträumen der Jahre 1928 bis 1934 nacheinander für die wichtigsten anderen Industriezweige statt. Somit lagen weitgehend vergleichbare Ergebnisse aus Individualerhebungen über die Verdienststruktur der Arbeiter der Zweige Textilindustrie, Holzgewerbe, chemische Industrie, metallverarbeitende Industrie, eisen- und stahlerzeugende Industrie, Schuhindustrie, Buchdruckgewerbe, Steindruckgewerbe, Baugewerbe, papiererzeugende Industrie, Braugewerbe sowie Süß-, Back- und Teigwarenindustrie vor. Die Ergebnisse wurden vom Statistischen Reichsamt sukzessive in "Wirtschaft und Statistik" (Jahrgänge 1928 bis 1935) und in "Vierteljahrshefte zur Statistik des Deutschen Reichs" (Jahrgänge 1928 bis 1935) veröffentlicht.

Eine erneute Individualerhebung der Angestelltenverdienste wurde vom Statistischen Reichsamt nur noch für den Monat Februar 1934 durchgeführt, und zwar beschränkt auf die Angestellten des Bankgewerbes. Erfaßt wurden "fast alle wichtigeren"Betriebe des privaten, öffentlichen und genossenschaftlichen Bankwesens, soweit sie den Bestimmungen des Reichstarifvertrages für das Deutsche Bankgewerbe (RTV) unterlagen. In diesen Betrieben wurden sämtliche männlichen und weiblichen tariflichen und außertariflichen kaufmännischen Angestellten in die Erhebung einbezogen, deren Bezüge die Grenze der Angestelltenversicherungspflicht (600 RM monatlich) nicht überschritten. Für jeden einzelnen dieser Angestellten waren auf einer Fragekarte Angaben über den effektiven Monatsverdienst - darunter gesondert die Überstundenvergütung und die Sozialzulagen -, die gesetzlichen Abzüge, den Arbeitgeberbeitrag zur Sozialversicherung, das Tarifgehalt, die Arbeitszeit sowie über Geschlecht, Qualifikation und Lebens- und Dienstalter einzutragen. Nach der Aufbereitung ausgewiesen wurden, wie bei den Industriearbeitern, vor allem Häufigkeitsverteilungen nach Verdienstklassen und Durchschnittsverdienste. Die Ergebnisse der Individualerhebung im Bankgewerbe wurden vom Statistischen Reichsamt in "Wirtschaft und Statistik" (Jahrgänge 1934 S. 460 ff., 1935 S. 136 ff.) und in "Vierteljahrshefte zur Statistik des Deutschen Reichs" (Jahrgang 1935 S. I. 149 ff.) veröffentlicht.

136 Beobachtung der Verdienstentwicklung

Um mit verhältnismäßig geringem Kosten- und Zeitaufwand einen großen Kreis von Berichtsbetrieben laufend erfassen zu können, ging das Statistische Reichsamt in der Industriearbeiterlohnstatistik ab 1935 vom Individualverfahren zum Summenverfahren über. Beim Summenverfahren wird nicht mehr der Verdienst für jede einzelne Person, sondern nur noch die Lohnsumme für eine ganze Arbeitergruppe jeweils eines Betriebes erfragt. Auf diese Weise kann ohne merklichen Mehraufwand die Anzahl der erfaßten Arbeiter erheblich vergrößert werden. Die erhebungstechnische Vereinfachung und Beschleunigung wird durch den Verzicht auf Einsicht in die Verdienststreuung innerhalb der Arbeitergruppen erkauft. Das Summenverfahren ist demnach nicht zur detaillierten Untersuchung der Verdienststruktur und Verdienstschichtung, dafür aber um so besser zur laufenden Ermittlung wenig gegliederter aktueller Lohndaten geeignet. Das Statistische Reichsamt hatte bereits im Jahre 1934 auf Grund von Ergebnissen der Industrieberichterstattung die "Entwicklung der Lohnsummen und der Durchschnittsverdienste in der sächsischen Industrie" (Wirtschaft und Statistik Jahrgang 1934 S. 421 ff.) untersucht. Die hierbei über das Lohnsummenverfahren ermittelten Durchschnittsverdienste bezogen sich jedoch auf die unaufgegliederte und daher sehr heterogene Gesamtheit der Arbeiter in den erfaßten Betrieben. In der Industriearbeiterlohnstatistik wurde die Gesamtheit der Arbeiter dagegen in Arbeitergruppen aufgegliedert, die hinsichtlich der Tätigkeitsmerkmale und der Verdienste weitgehend homogen waren; entsprechend wurde die Gesamtlohnsumme aufgegliedert. Das Statistische Reichsamt führte derartige Verdiensterhebungen nach dem Lohnsummenverfahren zunächst für den März 1935 in der Schuhindustrie und anschließend für verschiedene Monate des Jahres 1935 in jeweils anderen Industriezweigen durch. Für Dezember 1935 fanden erstmalig Lohnsummenerhebungen in 15 Gewerben gleichzeitig statt. Diese Erhebungen wurden in den folgenden Jahren in gleichem Umfang - später in 21 Gewerbezweigen, die teilweise weiter in Fabrikationszweige untergliedert waren - mit vierteljährlicher Periodizität regelmäßig wiederholt, und zwar für die Berichtsmonate März, Juni, September und Dezember jedes Jahres. Die letzte Erhebung wurde vom Statistischen Reichsamt für März 1943 durchgeführt. Die Ergebnisse wurden laufend in "Wirtschaft und Statistik" (Jahrgänge 1935 bis 1943) veröffentlicht. Die Lohnsummenerhebungen des Statistischen Reichsamtes waren Repräsentativerhebungen, zu denen im ganzen Reichsgebiet etwa 26 000 ausgewählte Berichtsbetriebe - nur die eisenschaffende Industrie wurde total erfaßt - laufend herangezogen wurden. Um in den ausgewählten Betrieben ein repräsentatives Abbild der Gesamtheit aller Betriebe zu erhalten, wurden nicht "typische" Betriebe ausgewählt, sondern eine gezielte Auswahl in angemessenem Verhältnis aus allen Teilen der Grundgesamtheit vorgenommen. Die Betriebsauswahl erfolgte unter Mitwirkung der Organisationen der gewerblichen Wirtschaft und der Fachämter der Deutschen Arbeitsfront, wobei "besonderes Gewicht auf eine der Wirklichkeit entsprechende regionale Verteilung auch im Hinblick auf die Größe der Standorte, sowie auf die der Wirklichkeit entsprechende Heranziehung der einzelnen Betriebsgrößenklassen: Groß-, Mittel- und Kleinbetriebe gelegt"*) wurde. In den ausgewählten Betrieben, denen Fragebogen unmittelbar vom Statistischen Reichsamt übersandt wurden, wurden grundsätzlich alle männlichen und weiblichen Arbeiter summarisch erfaßt, die unmittelbar oder mittelbar für den eigentlichen Produktionsprozeß tätig waren, soweit sie nach einer Tarifordnung des betreffenden Gewerbes entlohnt wurden. Nicht erfaßt wurden Arbeiter, die während der Erhebungszeit in Urlaub oder krank waren. Die Arbeiter wurden nach fünf Arbeitergruppen - männliche Facharbeiter, angelernte Arbeiter und Hilfsarbeiter sowie weibliche Fach- und angelernte Arbeiter (zusammengefaßt) und Hilfsarbeiter - untergliedert; zur Erleichterung für die Berichtsbetriebe wurden dabei die branchentypischen Berufsbezeichnungen vorgegeben, die zu diesen Arbeitergruppen gehörten. Außer den Angaben für die fünf Arbeitergruppen wurden in den einzelnen Industriezweigen gesonderte Angaben für bestimmte typische Berufe - im allgemeinen je einen Beruf mit hoher, mittlerer und

---

*) Friedland Krause: Die deutsche Lohnstatistik. In: Die Statistik in Deutschland nach ihrem heutigen Stand, Ehrengabe für Friedrich Zahn, herausgegeben von Friedrich Burgdörfer, Band II, Berlin 1940, S. 1168 - 1179 (Zitat S. 1175).

niedriger Entlohnung - erfragt, zum Beispiel in der metallverarbeitenden Industrie für den Beruf Maschinenbauer. Die Angaben der Berichtsbetriebe bezogen sich auf eine beliebig lange Lohnabrechnungsperiode, die voll in den Erhebungsmonat fiel; die Umrechnung auf eine einheitliche Berichtsperiode wurde im Statistischen Reichsamt im Zuge der weitgehend maschinellen Aufbereitung vorgenommen. Jeder Berichtsbetrieb hatte für die jeweilige Lohnabrechnungsperiode pro Arbeitergruppe die Anzahl der Arbeiter und der insgesamt bezahlten Arbeitsstunden sowie die Bruttolohnsumme, die Nettolohnsumme und die Summe der Arbeitgeberbeiträge zur Sozialversicherung zu melden. Das Statistische Reichsamt berechnete daraus zunächst für jeden Betrieb pro Arbeitergruppe "Betriebsdurchschnitte" als Verhältniswerte, vor allem den durchschnittlichen Stundenverdienst (Lohnsumme dividiert durch Anzahl der Arbeitsstunden) und den durchschnittlichen Wochenverdienst (auf eine Woche umgerechnete Lohnsumme dividiert durch Anzahl der Arbeiter). Aus diesen Betriebsdurchschnitten wurden durch Gewichtung mit der Anzahl der Arbeitsstunden bzw. der Anzahl der Arbeiter der einzelnen Betriebe als gewogene arithmetische Mittel die zur Veröffentlichung bestimmten übergeordneten Durchschnittswerte für die Fabrikations- und Gewerbezweige berechnet.

Neben Durchschnittsverdiensten ermittelte das Statistische Reichsamt auch Verdienstindices. Der aus den vierteljährlichen Lohnsummenerhebungen der Industriearbeiter abgeleitete Effektivlohnindex war dadurch gekennzeichnet, daß die Gewichte jeweils nur für zwei unmittelbar aufeinanderfolgende Erhebungen konstant gehalten wurden, und zwar wurden die Gewichte des früheren der beiden verglichenen Erhebungsmonate für die jeweils folgende Erhebung - und nur für diese - beibehalten. Als Gewichte wurden für den Index der Stundenverdienste die Anzahl der Arbeitsstunden und für den Index der Wochenverdienste die Anzahl der Arbeiter verwendet; die Gewichtszahlen wurden dabei aus den Lohnsummenerhebungen selbst gewonnen. Die Berechnung der Indices erfolgte nach den folgenden Formeln in zwei Schritten*); zunächst wurden "Gliedziffern" ermittelt:

$$G_{(2)} = \frac{\sum_{j=1}^{k} l_{j(2)}\, g_{j(1)}}{\sum_{j=1}^{k} l_{j(1)}\, g_{j(1)}} \qquad G_{(3)} = \frac{\sum_{j=1}^{k} l_{j(3)}\, g_{j(2)}}{\sum_{j=1}^{k} l_{j(2)}\, g_{j(2)}} \quad \text{usw. bis } G_{(n)} = \frac{\sum_{j=1}^{k} l_{j(n)}\, g_{j(n-1)}}{\sum_{j=1}^{k} l_{j(n-1)}\, g_{j(n-1)}}$$

*) Fußnote siehe folgende Seite

Symbole:

G	=	Gliedziffer
(1),(2),...,(n)	=	laufende Nummern der zeitlich aufeinanderfolgenden Erhebungsmonate
j=1,..., k	=	laufende Nummern der im Index zusammengefaßten Gewerbezweige
l	=	Durchschnittslohn eines Gewerbezweiges
g	=	Anzahl der Arbeitsstunden bzw. der Arbeiter eines Gewerbezweiges

Aus den Gliedziffern wurden sodann fortlaufend die Indexzahlen (I) für die einzelnen Erhebungsmonate berechnet:

$I_{(2)} = 100\, G_{(2)}$ $\quad I_{(3)} = I_{(2)} G_{(3)}$ $\quad$ usw. bis $\quad I_{(n)} = I_{(n-1)} G_{(n)}$

Die Basis der Indexreihe $I_{(1)} = 100$ bezog sich zunächst auf den Monat Dezember 1935 und später auch auf den Jahresdurchschnitt 1936. Nach diesen Formeln wurden nur solche Indices ermittelt, die sich aus den Durchschnittslöhnen der einzelnen Gewerbezweige für übergeordnete Gewerbebereiche - z.B. Produktionsgüterindustrien oder Gewerbe insgesamt - ergaben. Die darüberhinaus vom Statistischen Reichsamt ausgewiesenen "Indices" für einzelne Gewerbezweige waren lediglich einfache Meßzahlen aus den in den beiden zu vergleichenden Erhebungsmonaten festgestellten Durchschnittsverdiensten jeweils sämtlicher Betriebe des betreffenden Gewerbezweiges ohne Ausschaltung von Gewichtsveränderungen.**) Die Entscheidung, bei den Verdienstindices keine für längere Zeit konstanten Gewichte zu verwenden, sondern die Gewichte nach jeweils zwei Erhebungsmonaten entsprechend den eingetretenen Veränderungen in den Meldungen der Berichtsbetriebe zu variieren, wurde vom Statistischen Reichsamt bewußt getroffen. "Die Indexziffern passen sich, da sie so grundsätzlich unter Benutzung variabler Gewichte gewonnen sind, den Veränderungen der Wirtschaft in stetiger Weise an. Eine Überprüfung der rechnungsmäßigen Grundlagen, wie sie bei einem mit fester Gewichtung berechneten Index von Zeit zu Zeit unerläßlich wird, ist daher bei der Indexziffer

*) vgl. Friedrich Behrens: Die amtlichen Lohnerhebungen. In: Allgemeines Statistisches Archiv, 28. Band, Jahrgang 1939, Jena 1939, S. 61-71.

**) Fußnote siehe folgende Seite

der tatsächlichen Arbeitsverdienste nicht erforderlich."***)

In die Indexberechnungen wurde auch der Kohlenbergbau einbezogen, der aus der laufenden Industriearbeiterlohnstatistik ausgeschlossen war. Das Statistische Reichsamt führte auf Grund von Nachweisungen der Zechenverbände eine besondere monatliche Statistik über die Effektivverdienste der Arbeiter im deutschen Stein- und Braunkohlenbergbau durch. Dabei wurden Verdienste, Arbeitszeiten und Belegschaftszahlen erfaßt und durchschnittliche Barverdienste pro Schicht und pro Monat je angelegten Arbeiter nach Arbeitergruppen berechnet. Der Begriff des "angelegten Arbeiters" wurde aus der parallel durchgeführten vierteljährlichen Bergarbeiterlohnstatistik der Bergbehörden übernommen. Die Monatsstatistik des Statistischen Reichsamtes unterschied sich von der den gesamten Bergbau erfassenden Vierteljahresstatistik der Bergbehörden neben ihrer Beschränkung auf den Kohlenbergbau auch durch ihren geringeren räumlichen Umfang. Die Ergebnisse der monatlichen Kohlenbergbaulohnstatistik des Statistischen Reichsamtes gingen nicht nur nach Umrechnung auf Stunden- und Wochenverdienste in die Indexberechnungen der Industriearbeiterlohnstatistik ein, sondern wurden auch als selbständige Daten laufend in "Wirtschaft und Statistik" veröffentlicht.

**) vgl. Friedrich Behrens: Neue Wege der Lohnstatistik. In: Allgemeines Statistisches Archiv, 31. Band, Jahrgang 1942/43, Jena 1943, Seite 114-138 (hier S. 127 f.).

***) Friedland Krause: Die deutsche Lohnstatistik, a.a.O. Seite 1178.

14 Die Phase der Stagnation (1936 - 1948)

141 Tarifordnung statt Tarifautonomie

Der Aufbau der nationalsozialistischen Wirtschaftsordnung brachte unter anderem eine Umgestaltung der Arbeitnehmerverbände und damit eine einschneidende Wandlung im Tarifwesen mit sich. Die früher zwischen Arbeitnehmerverbänden und Arbeitgeberverbänden frei ausgehandelten Tarifverträge wurden durch Tarifordnungen ersetzt, die den Charakter von Rechtsvorschriften hatten. Damit entfiel sowohl die Grundlage als auch die Notwendigkeit für eine statistische Beobachtung des Tarifwesens. Die Tarifstatistik wurde daher eingestellt. Zum Abschluß der Tarifstatistik fand nur noch zum Stichtag 31. Dezember 1933 eine einmalige Bestandsaufnahme sämtlicher Tarifverträge statt.*)

Im Gegensatz zur Tarifstatistik wurde die Tariflohnstatistik in dem erreichten Umfang weitergeführt. Vorrangiger als die statistische Verarbeitung zu durchschnittlichen Tariflöhnen wurde jedoch die umfassende Sammlung und amtliche Bekanntgabe der tariflichen Einzellohnsätze. Derartige Sammlungen wurden vom Statistischen Reichsamt vor allem anläßlich der Neuordnung der Tariflöhne im nationalsozialistischen Sinne in den annektierten bzw. besetzten Gebieten in den "Vierteljahrsheften zur Statistik des Deutschen Reichs" veröffentlicht, und zwar über "Die tariflichen Mindestlöhne der gewerblichen Arbeiter im Herbst 1941" (Jahrgang 1942 S. I. 3-25) und "Die tariflichen Mindestlöhne der gewerblichen Arbeiter am 1. Oktober 1942" (Jahrgang 1943 S. I/II. 25-29).

---

*) vgl. Statistisches Reichsamt: Vierteljahrshefte zur Statistik des Deutschen Reichs, Jahrgang 1934 S. I. 20.

42 Lohnstop

Der von der nationalsozialistischen Reichsregierung als Voraussetzung für die angestrebte Wiedereingliederung der Arbeitslosen in den Produktionsprozeß angeordnete Lohnstop - d.h. das Festhalten der Lohnsätze pro Zeit - bzw. Leistungseinheit - hatte zur Folge, daß die Lohnstatistik als empirische Untersuchung der Arbeitnehmerverdienste für die Wirtschaftspolitik an Bedeutung verlor. Zwar wurde die amtliche Lohnstatistik in dem erreichten Umfang fortgeführt, erhielt jedoch keine neuen Impulse mehr. Innerhalb der Lohnstatistik verlor die Beobachtung der Verdienstentwicklung - vor allem soweit sie sich auf die Stundenverdienste bezog - an Gewicht zugunsten von gelegentlichen Untersuchungen der Struktur bzw. Streuung der Verdienste. Das Statistische Reichsamt führte bis zum Ende des Zweiten Weltkrieges noch je eine Strukturerhebung im Individualverfahren in den Wirtschaftsbereichen Bäckerhandwerk, Landwirtschaft, metallverarbeitende Industrie und Forstwirtschaft durch. Für die erste Lohnwoche des Monats März 1936 fand eine "Lohnerhebung im Bäckerhandwerk des Wirtschaftsgebiets Niedersachsen" (Wirtschaft und Statistik Jahrgang 1936 S. 792) statt, bei der in 1314 ausgewählten Betrieben aus 829 Orten jeweils sämtliche Arbeiter einschließlich der Lehrlinge individuell erfaßt wurden. Die erfragten Angaben über Arbeitszeit, Bruttoverdienst sowie Menge und Wert der Sachbezüge wurden statistisch zu durchschnittlichen Bruttowochenverdiensten und Häufigkeitsverteilungen nach Verdienstklassen verarbeitet.

Für das Kalenderjahr 1937 bzw. das Wirtschaftsjahr 1936/37 wurde auf Anordnung des Reichsarbeitsministers erstmalig eine amtliche Strukturerhebung über die Effektivverdienste der Arbeiter in der Landwirtschaft durchgeführt. Die Erhebung fand unter Mitwirkung des "Reichsnährstandes" statt, der die "Kreisgefolgschaftswarte" der "Kreisbauernschaften" für die Auswahl der Berichtsbetriebe nach repräsentativen Gesichtspunkten, die Verteilung der Erhebungsbogen an die Betriebsleiter und deren Anleitung bei der Ausfüllung der Fragebogen sowie die erste Prüfung und Berichtigung der Angaben einsetzte. Im Durchschnitt des Reichsgebiets wurden etwa 5 % aller ständig beschäftigten familienfremden landwirtschaftlichen Arbeiter individuell erfaßt. Erhebungsmerkmale waren der Jahresverdienst - Bruttobarlohn nach Lohnform unter Ausgliederung besonderer Zulagen -, Arten und Mengen der Naturalleistungen, die gesetzlichen Abzüge, die Jahresarbeitszeit, die Anzahl der Urlaubstage sowie Geschlecht, Beruf, Dauer der Betriebszugehörigkeit, Lebensalter, Familienstand und Kinderzahl. Die Naturalleistungen wurden nur mengenmäßig erfaßt; ihre Bewertung erfolgte zentral im Statistischen Reichsamt vor allem mit Hilfe von Daten der amtlichen Preisstatistik. Im allgemeinen wurden Verbraucherpreise, bei Brotgetreide, Futtermitteln und Stroh Erzeuger- oder Großhandelspreise, bei Kartoffeln das arithmetische Mittel aus Erzeuger- und Verbraucherpreisen herangezogen. Die Überlassung von Land, Vieh und Gespann wurde mit landwirtschaftlichen Erfahrungssätzen, die Bereitstellung von Werkswohnungen nach der ortsüblichen freien Miete - geschätzt auf Grund der Kapitalkosten - bewertet. Bei Kost und Unterkunft erfolgte die Bewertung nach Grundsätzen der Finanzämter für die steuerliche Bewertung oder nach Richtsätzen der Heeresverwaltung für die Versorgung von Soldaten. Die für die einzelnen Arbeiter erfaßten Verdienstangaben wurden zu Durchschnittsverdiensten aufbereitet; die Verdienststreuung wurde lediglich in der Form einer Auszählung der Fälle über - bzw. unterdurchschnittlicher Lohnzahlung nachgewiesen. Die Ergebnisse über "Die amtliche Lohnerhebung in der Landwirtschaft für das Jahr 1937" wurden vom Statistischen Reichsamt in "Wirtschaft und Statistik" (Jahrgang 1941 S. 403 ff.) veröffentlicht.

An Stelle der vierteljährlichen Lohnsummenerhebung wurde einmalig für Juni 1938 in der metallverarbeitenden Industrie eine repräsentative Individuallohnerhebung mit zusätzlichen Erhebungsmerkmalen durchgeführt. Auf Erhebungslisten wurden für die einzelnen Arbeiter über das Frageprogramm der laufenden Lohnsummenerhebungen hinaus die Überstundenzuschläge, die Sozialzulagen sowie Lohnform, Familienstand, Kinderzahl und Lebensalter erfaßt.

Zur Verringerung der Belastung der Berichtsbetriebe und des Statistischen Reichsamtes wurden für die Erhebung teilweise Lohnlisten direkt abgelocht, teilweise reichten die Betriebe auch Originallochkarten oder Lochkartendoppel ein.*) Als Ergebnisse dieser Erhebung wurden lediglich Durchschnittswerte veröffentlicht (Statistisches Jahrbuch für das Deutsche Reich, Jahrgang 1939/40, S. 350-352).

Für das Forstwirtschaftsjahr vom 1. Oktober 1939 bis zum 30. September 1940 als Erhebungszeitraum veranstaltete das Statistische Reichsamt im Auftrage des Reichsarbeitsministers eine Individualerhebung über die Effektivverdienste der Arbeiter in der Forstwirtschaft. Zu der Erhebung wurde im gesamten Reichsgebiet eine gezielte repräsentative Auswahl von 1899 Betrieben der staatlichen, kommunalen und privaten Forstwirtschaft herangezogen. Von der Gesamtzahl der Betriebe ab 1000 ha Forstfläche wurden unter Mitwirkung der zuständigen Organisation des Reichsnährstandes 58 %, von den Betrieben unter 1000 ha Forstfläche 5 % als Berichtsbetriebe ausgewählt. Die Anzahl der in den einzelnen regionalen Wirtschaftsgebieten erfaßten Betriebe richtete sich im allgemeinen nach dem forstlichen Charakter der Gebiete. In kleinen Gebieten oder in solchen mit wenig Waldbesitz wurde jedoch mitunter eine im Verhältnis größere Anzahl von Betrieben herangezogen, um eine ausreichende Basis sicherzustellen. Insbesondere wurde auch wegen des besonderen Interesses an der Klarstellung der Lohnverhältnisse in den Privatforsten diese Besitzart in stärkerem Maße in die Erhebung einbezogen. In den ausgewählten Betrieben wurden sämtliche männlichen und weiblichen Waldarbeiter der höchsten tariflichen Altersstufe einschließlich der gelegentlich und vorübergehend Beschäftigten und einschließlich der Haumeister einzeln erfaßt. Erhebungsmerkmale waren vor allem der Bruttobarverdienst nach Lohnformen mit gesonderten Angaben über Sonderentschädigungen und Sozialzulagen, Arten und Mengen der Naturalleistungen - die Bewertung der Naturalien wurde analog zur Lohnerhebung in der Landwirtschaft

---

*) vgl. Friedrich Behrens: Neue Wege der Lohnstatistik, a.a.O.

für 1937 im Statistischen Reichsamt vorgenommen - und die Arbeitszeit. Die individuellen Verdienstangaben wurden ausschließlich zu durchschnittlichen Bruttostundenverdiensten aufbereitet. Die Ergebnisse über "Die Arbeitsverdienste in der Forstwirtschaft im Jahre 1940" wurden vom Statistischen Reichsamt in "Wirtschaft und Statistik" (Jahrgang 1942 S. 80-82) veröffentlicht.

Neben der Untersuchung der Verdienststruktur durch Individualerhebungen versuchte das Statistische Reichsamt, durch Sonderauswertungen der vierteljährlichen Lohnsummenerhebungen der Industriearbeiter Einblick in die Streuung der Durchschnittsverdienste nach verschiedenen Merkmalen zu gewinnen. Derartige Sonderauswertungen bezogen sich auf "Die gebietlichen Unterschiede der Arbeitsverdienste im Deutschen Reich" (Wirtschaft und Statistik Jahrgang 1942 S. 282 ff.) und "Die Abstufung der Arbeitsverdienste nach Ortsgrößenklassen" (Wirtschaft und Statistik Jahrgang 1942 S. 425 ff.). Dabei wurden jeweils für den Berichtsmonat September 1941 aus den vorliegenden Durchschnittsverdiensten für die einzelnen Gewerbezweige und die Gesamtheit der Gewerbe regionale Durchschnittsverdienste sowie Durchschnittsverdienste nach Ortsgrößenklassen - entsprechend der Einwohnerzahl der Orte - berechnet.

Unabhängig vom Statistischen Reichsamt führte die "Deutsche Arbeitsfront" in Zusammenarbeit mit dem Reichsarbeitsministerium und den Arbeitsämtern im Jahre 1940 bei 2457 Mittel- und Großbetrieben im gesamten Reichsgebiet eine als Probeerhebung bezeichnete Erhebung über die Effektiv- und die Tariflöhne von jeweils ganzen Arbeitergruppen durch.*) Die Bildung der Arbeitergruppen erfolgte in der Weise, daß jeweils Arbeiter mit gleichen Verdiensten zusammengefaßt wurden. Die Ergebnisse dieser Erhebung wurden nicht mehr veröffentlicht.

---

*) vgl. Deutsche Arbeitsfront:"Neue Wege der Lohnstatistik. Das Lohnregister." Jahrbuch des Arbeitswissenschaftlichen Instituts der DAF, 1940/41 Band II, Seite 1 ff.

143 Unklare Rechtsgrundlagen in der Nachkriegszeit

Nach dem Zweiten Weltkrieg bemühten sich die Statistischen Landesämter der Westzonen bereits ab 1946, den lohnstatistischen Bedarf der Militärregierungen und deutscher Dienststellen durch die Wiederaufnahme von statistischen Erhebungen des Deutschen Reichs zu decken. Zunächst wurden nur die vierteljährlichen Lohnsummenerhebungen der Industriearbeiter wieder aufgegriffen. Mit Erlaß vom 27. April 1946 ordnete der "Alliierte Kontrollrat" die Abgabe vierteljährlicher Berichte über die Löhne und Arbeitszeiten an. Daraufhin fand erstmalig für den Berichtsmonat Juni 1946 wieder eine Lohnsummenerhebung der Industriearbeiter statt. Auch bei den folgenden Erhebungen wurden die vom Statistischen Reichsamt eingeführten Berichtsmonate - März, Juni, September und Dezember jedes Jahres - übernommen. Als Rechtsgrundlagen der Lohnsummenerhebungen waren neben der Anordnung der Militärregierung nach wie vor das Gesetz betreffend Lohnstatistik vom 27. Juli 1922 (Reichsgesetzblatt 1922 Teil I S. 656) und die Verordnung zur Ausführung des Gesetzes betreffend Lohnstatistik vom 8. August 1938 (Reichsgesetzblatt 1938 Teil I S. 1013) in kraft. Die Rechtsvorschriften von 1922 und 1938 erwiesen sich jedoch in der Nachkriegszeit als ungeeignet, da in ihnen nicht mehr vorhandene Institutionen - Reichsregierung, Reichsrat, Reichstag, Reichswirtschaftsrat und andere - erwähnt wurden. Die Rechtsunsicherheit wurde erst durch das Gesetz über Lohnstatistik vom 22. August 1949 (Gesetzblatt der Verwaltung des Vereinigten Wirtschaftsgebietes 1949 S. 265) beseitigt, das die Vorschriften von 1922 und 1938 formell aufhob und durch neues deutsches Recht ersetzte.

144 Uneinheitliches Vorgehen der Besatzungszonen

Die vierteljährlichen Lohnsummenerhebungen der Industriearbeiter wurden ab 1946 zunächst in der britischen und der amerikanischen Besatzungszone unkoordiniert nebeneinander durchgeführt. Die französische Besatzungszone beteiligte sich vorerst gar nicht an diesen Arbeiten.

Für die Durchführung waren vor 1949 ausschließlich die Statistischen Landesämter und das Statistische Amt für die britische Besatzungszone zuständig. Die fehlende Koordinierung führte in dieser Zeit in verschiedener Hinsicht zu Uneinheitlichkeiten. So fanden nur in der britischen Zone jährliche Zusatzerhebungen statt, in denen unter anderem Nettolohnsummen ermittelt wurden, während die vierteljährlichen Erhebungen nur Bruttolohnsummen erfaßten. Die Vergleichbarkeit der Lohnsummenerhebungen wurde besonders durch das uneinheitliche Vorgehen bei der Auswahl der Berichtsbetriebe gestört. Die Auswahl wurde in der britischen Zone den Arbeitsämtern übertragen, die bei der ersten Zusammenstellung des Berichtskreises im Jahre 1946 die Repräsentation durch ausreichende Berücksichtigung von Groß-, Mittel- und Kleinbetrieben sowie regionalen Hauptsitzen der einzelnen Industriezweige gewährleisten sollten, dafür jedoch keine näheren Anweisungen erhielten. Die Amtshilfe der Arbeitsämter erstreckte sich ab 1946 zumindest in Nordrhein-Westfalen nicht nur auf die Auswahl und laufende Ergänzung des Berichtskreises, sondern auch auf den Versand, den Rücklauf und die erste Prüfung der Erhebungsbogen sowie auf Mahnungen, Rückfragen und sonstigen Schriftverkehr mit den Betrieben. Das Statistische Landesamt erhielt die Erhebungsbogen erst zur endgültigen Prüfung und statistischen Aufbereitung zurück und hatte somit nur wenig Gelegenheit, in der Vorbereitungs- und Befragungsphase durch direkten Eingriff die Einheitlichkeit sicherzustellen. Die Ergebnisse der Lohnsummenerhebungen wurden von den Statistischen Landesämtern teilweise unterschiedlich tief gegliedert. So wurden z.B. in Nordrhein-Westfalen ab 1946 regelmäßig für alle erfaßten Industriezweige gesonderte Ergebnisse für die Landesteile Nordrhein und Westfalen (ab 1947 einschließlich Lippe) ermittelt; diese Aufgliederungen wurden auch nach der Koordinierung der Lohnsummenerhebungen im Jahre 1949 als Sonderaufbereitungen bis Ende 1956 fortgesetzt. Die ab 1958 erneut aufgegriffenen Sonderaufbereitungen für die Landesteile Nordrhein und Westfalen - Lippe beschränken sich nunmehr auf ausgewählte Industriezweige (Textilindustrie, Bekleidungsindustrie, chemische Industrie, papier- und pappeverarbeitende Industrie).

15 Die Phase der Wiederbelebung (1949 - 1955)

151 Koordinierte Länderstatistiken

Die während der ersten Nachkriegsjahre in den meisten Ländern der Westzonen von den Statistischen Landesämtern unabhängig voneinander und teilweise uneinheitlich durchgeführten vierteljährlichen Lohnsummenerhebungen der Industriearbeiter wurden ab 1949 zunächst in der Weise koordiniert, daß das in der amerikanischen Zone praktizierte Verfahren dem in der britischen Zone üblichen angepaßt wurde. Die Koordinierung und methodische Leitung oblag dabei dem Statistischen Amt des Vereinigten Wirtschaftsgebietes bzw. später dessen Rechtsnachfolger, dem Statistischen Bundesamt. Die "Gemeinsame Anordnung der Verwaltungen des Vereinigten Wirtschaftsgebietes zur Durchführung von Statistiken" vom 1. Juni 1949 (Öffentlicher Anzeiger für das Vereinigte Wirtschaftsgebiet Jahrgang 2 Nr. 50 Seite 1), die die vom Statistischen Amt des Vereinigten Wirtschaftsgebietes und von den Statistischen Landesämtern einheitlich durchzuführenden Statistiken regelte, führte unter anderem die "Statistik der Arbeitsverdienste in der Industrie einschließlich Lohnindex" als vierteljährliche Erhebung auf. Die Länder der französischen Zone wurden erst auf Grund der Erstreckungsverordnung*) vom 31. März 1950 (Bundesgesetzblatt 1950 S. 81) in die gemeinsamen Statistiken einbezogen. Die vierteljährlichen Lohnerhebungen wurden bis September 1951 wie beim Statistischen Reichsamt für die Monate März, Juni, September und Dezember jedes Jahres durchgeführt. Im Dezember 1951 fiel die Erhebung mit Rücksicht auf die für November 1951 durchgeführte Gehalts- und Lohnstrukturerhebung aus. Ab Anfang 1952 wurden als Erhebungsmonate Februar, Mai, August und November verwendet. Vom Statistischen Reichsamt wurde auch das Prinzip der gezielten Auswahl eines repräsentativen Kreises von Berichtsbetrieben sowie das Summenverfah-

*) "Verordnung über die Erstreckung von Recht der Verwaltung des Vereinigten Wirtschaftsgebietes auf dem Gebiet der Statistik auf die Länder Baden, Rheinland-Pfalz, Württemberg-Hohenzollern und den bayerischen Kreis Lindau"

ren, d.h. die Erfassung von Lohnsummen und Arbeitsstundensummen für jeweils ganze Arbeitergruppen - und zwar die fünf Gruppen der männlichen Facharbeiter, angelernten Arbeiter und Hilfsarbeiter und der weiblichen Facharbeiter und angelernten Arbeiter (zusammengefaßt) und Hilfsarbeiter -,übernommen. Die Berichtsstellen hatten pro Erhebungsmonat für jede ausgewählte örtliche Niederlassung eines Unternehmens und für jede Gewerbegruppe bzw. jeden Fabrikationszweig einen besonderen Erhebungsbogen auszufüllen, in den summarische Angaben für grundsätzlich sämtliche Arbeiter des betreffenden Betriebes einzutragen waren, soweit diese zu den "produktionseigentümlichen" Arbeitskräften ihrer Branche gehörten. Die vierteljährlichen Erhebungen hatten das Ziel, den regelmäßigen effektiven Barverdienst eines vollbeschäftigten Arbeiters nachzuweisen, d.h. eines Arbeiters, der die ihm gebotenen Arbeits- und Verdienstmöglichkeiten während des ganzen Erhebungsmonats in demselben Betrieb voll wahrgenommen hat. Der erfaßte Arbeitertyp war demnach der Arbeiter, der während des ganzen Erhebungsmonats unter Arbeitsvertrag stand und nicht durch Krankheit oder Unfall an der Ausübung seiner Tätigkeit gehindert war. Die Berichtsbetriebe wurden dem Erhebungsziel entsprechend angewiesen, Lehrlinge und Anlernlinge sowie streikende Arbeiter und Arbeiter, die im Erhebungsmonat länger als drei Tage durch Krankheit ausgefallen waren, nicht zu erfassen. Kurzarbeiter wurden dagegen mit in die Erhebung einbezogen. Die von den Berichtsbetrieben gemeldeten Monatssummen wurden in den Statistischen Landesämtern für das jeweilige Landesgebiet zu durchschnittlichen Bruttostunden- und Bruttowochenverdiensten sowie zu durchschnittlich bezahlten Wochenarbeitszeiten und wöchentlichen Mehrarbeitszeiten - die als zuschlagpflichtige Über-, Sonn- und Feiertagsstunden definierten Mehrarbeitsstunden wurden dabei erst ab 1950 regelmäßig erfaßt - pro Arbeiter nach Arbeitergruppen und Industriezweigen aufbereitet. Im Falle der Wochendurchschnitte wurden die Monatsangaben im Zuge der Aufbereitung in Wochenangaben umgerechnet. Bei den Durchschnittswerten für die einzelnen Industriezweige handelte es sich um Verhältniswerte aus den erhobenen Summen, z.B. den durchschnittlichen Bruttostundenverdienst als Quotienten aus den monatlichen Summen der Bruttolöhne und der Arbeitsstunden und den durchschnittlichen

Bruttowochenverdienst als Quotienten aus der auf eine Woche umgerechneten Bruttolohnsumme und der Anzahl der erfaßten Arbeiter. Aus diesen pro Industriezweig ermittelten Verhältniswerten wurden gewogene arithmetische Mittel für übergeordnete Wirtschaftsgruppen bzw. die Gesamtheit der erfaßten Gewerbe berechnet, wobei als "Wägungszahlen" ab 1949 die Gesamtarbeiterzahlen der Industrieberichterstattung - von 1946 bis 1948 stattdessen zumindest in der britischen Zone die Beschäftigtenzahlen der von den Arbeitsämtern durchgeführten Arbeitseinsatzstatistik - dienten. Die Aufbereitung erfolgte in einigen Statistischen Landesämtern (z.B. Nordrhein-Westfalen und Hessen) teilweise maschinell mit Hollerithmaschinen, in anderen Landesämtern (z.B. Bayern) dagegen vollmanuell. Aus den für jedes Land festgestellten Durchschnittswerten wurden vom Statistischen Amt des Vereinigten Wirtschaftsgebietes bzw. dem Statistischen Bundesamt bei den Bruttostundenverdiensten durch Wägung mit der in den Lohnerhebungen ermittelten Anzahl der Arbeitsstunden und bei den Bruttowochenverdiensten durch Wägung mit den aus der Industrieberichterstattung gewonnenen Gesamtarbeiterzahlen gewogene arithmetische Mittel für das Vereinigte Wirtschaftsgebiet bzw. das Bundesgebiet berechnet. Neben Durchschnittsverdiensten wurden für das Vereinigte Wirtschaftsgebiet bzw. Bundesgebiet auch Verdienstindices ermittelt.*) Aus den Lohnsummenerhebungen des Statistischen Reichsamtes für das Jahr 1938 lagen Angaben über die durchschnittlichen Bruttostunden- und -wochenverdienste für die damaligen "Treuhänderbezirke" vor.
Die Durchschnittsverdienste dieses Basisjahres für das Vereinigte Wirtschaftsgebiet bzw. Bundesgebiet wurden als gewogene arithmetische Mittel aus den Durchschnittsverdiensten der den Ländern der Westzonen möglichst entsprechenden Treuhänderbezirke errechnet, wobei als Gewichte die Arbeiterzahlen einer "Arbeitsbucherhebung" vom 25. Juni 1938 sowie früherer Individuallohnerhebungen des Statistischen Reichsamtes verwendet wurden. Auf der Basis 1938 wurden für die Nachkriegszeit Indices der Bruttostunden- und -wochenverdienste nach den folgenden Formeln be-

*) vgl. Statistisches Amt des Vereinigten Wirtschaftsgebietes: Statistischer Bericht Arb. Nr. VI/11/1. Wiesbaden 1949, Seite 13 - 14.

rechnet:

$$G_i = \frac{\sum_{j=1}^{k} l_{j;i}\, g_{j;i}}{\sum_{j=1}^{k} l_{j;i-1}\, g_{j;i}} \qquad I_i = I_{i-1}\, G_i$$

Symbole:

G= Gliedzahl

i= 2,3,...n = laufende Nummern der zeitlich aufeinanderfolgenden Erhebungsmonate in der Nachkriegszeit (i=1= zunächst September 1938, später Jahresdurchschnitt 1938)

j= 1,.....k = laufende Nummern der im Index zusammengefaßten Gewerbezweige

l= Durchschnittslohn eines Gewerbezweiges

g= Gewichte für die Indexberechnung (bei Stundenverdiensten Anzahl der Arbeitsstunden, bei Wochenverdiensten Anzahl der Arbeiter; ermittelt aus den Lohnsummenerhebungen der Nachkriegszeit)

I= Indexzahl (I_1 = 100)

Abweichend vom Verfahren des Statistischen Reichsamtes wurden also variable Gewichte aus dem jeweiligen neuesten Berichtsmonat der Indexberechnung zugrundegelegt.

Die Ergebnisse der koordinierten vierteljährlichen Lohnsummenerhebungen über Durchschnittsverdienste und Verdienstindices für das Vereinigte Wirtschaftsgebiet bzw. Bundesgebiet wurden vom Statistischen Amt des Vereinigten Wirtschaftsgebietes bzw. dem Statistischen Bundesamt laufend in den Statistischen Berichten Arb. Nr. VI/11/1 bis VI/11/24 (Wiesbaden 1949 ff.) und später vom Statistischen Bundesamt in "Preise Löhne Wirtschaftsrechnungen Reihe 10 Arbeiterverdienste" (Stuttgart-Köln 1955 ff.) veröffentlicht.

Die Auswahl der Berichtsbetriebe der koordinierten vierteljährlichen Lohnsummenerhebung wurde nicht nach einem einheitlichen Plan vorgenommen. Als allgemeine Regel galt lediglich, daß Betriebe unter zehn Beschäftigten im allgemeinen nicht zu erfassen waren und daß "die bei den Erhebungen erfaßten Betriebe.... unter dem Gesichtspunkt einer repräsentativen Verteilung auf die einzelnen Fabrikationszweige, Betriebsgrößen, regionalen Bezirke und Ortsgrößenklassen ausgewählt" *) werden sollten. Innerhalb dieses Rahmens wurden die Berichtsbetriebe von den einzelnen Ländern nach deren Belieben gezielt ausgewählt, wobei willkürliche Auswahlsatzdifferenzierungen in den verschiedenen Industriezweigen und Bundesländern vorkamen. Der Kreis der Berichtsbetriebe blieb nicht konstant, sondern wurde - vor allem durch die Heranziehung von Ersatzbetrieben für ausgefallene Betriebe - von den Ländern laufend nach deren Gutdünken geändert. Bei der Vorbereitung und Durchführung der Erhebungen arbeiteten die Statistischen Landesämter eng mit den Arbeitsämtern zusammen. Den Arbeitsämtern wurde nicht nur die erstmalige Gewinnung "geeigneter"Berichtsbetriebe, sondern auch die laufende Auswahl von Ersatzbetrieben übertragen. Das Statistische Landesamt Nordrhein-Westfalen erteilte bei der Auswahl von Ersatzbetrieben den Arbeitsämtern außer der Angabe des Arbeitsamtsbezirkes, des Wirtschaftzweiges und der Anzahl der auszuwählenden Ersatzbetriebe keine weiteren Anweisungen. Von Zeit zu Zeit nahm das Statistische Landesamt Nordrhein-Westfalen in Zusammenarbeit mit dem Landesarbeitsministerium Nordrhein-Westfalen in dessen Eigenschaft als "Hauptabteilung Landesarbeitsamt" eine "Überprüfung der Repräsentation" durch fachmännische Betrachtung von geordneten Verzeichnissen der Berichtsbetriebe vor. In einem Schreiben des nordrhein-westfälischen Arbeitsministeriums vom 21. Januar 1949 an das Statistische Landesamt Nordrhein-Westfalen heißt es: "....... Eine Reihe von Industrien....... werden m. E. in einem zu großen Umfange erfaßt. Ich möchte darum bitten, den Kreis der Berichtsfirmen hier etwas einzuschränken. In der Metallverarbeitenden Industrie kann man sich des Eindrucks nicht erweh-

*) Statistisches Amt des Vereinigten Wirtschaftsgebietes: Statistischer Bericht Arb. Nr. VI/11/1. Wiesbaden 1949, Seite 3.

ren, als ob hier zu viele Großbetriebe berücksichtigt worden sind. Hier müßte m.E. ausgetauscht werden. ......" Die Berichtsbetriebe konnten auch auf ihren besonderen Antrag gegen bisher nicht berichtende Betriebe ausgetauscht werden. Das Statistische Landesamt Nordrhein-Westfalen wies die Arbeitsämter an, eventuellen Anträgen von Berichtsbetrieben auf Freistellung grundsätzlich stattzugeben, sofern es sich um bisher korrekt und pünktlich berichtende Betriebe handelte, eine längere Berichterstattung vorlag und ein nach Gewerbegruppe, Betriebsgrößenklasse und Ortsklasse vergleichbarer Ersatzbetrieb aus demselben Arbeitsamtsbezirk zur Erhebung herangezogen werden konnte. Die Freistellung und der Austausch gegen einen Ersatzbetrieb wurden zunächst selbständig von den einzelnen Arbeitsämtern, später vom Statistischen Landesamt Nordrhein-Westfalen selbst nach Beratung durch die Arbeitsämter vorgenommen. Die Amtshilfe der Arbeitsämter ging noch weit über die Auswahl von Berichtsbetrieben hinaus. In den ersten Jahren der koordinierten Lohnsummenerhebungen liefen der Versand und der Rücklauf der Erhebungsbogen zumindest in Nordrhein-Westfalen über die Arbeitsämter, die zunächst auch die Mahnungen, ersten Prüfungen der Erhebungsbogen, Rückfragen bei den Betrieben, Terminsetzungen, Beratungen der Betriebe und sämtlichen sonstigen Schriftwechsel selbstverantwortlich übernahmen. Ab 1950 wurde die Amtshilfe der Arbeitsämter in Nordrhein-Westfalen stark eingeschränkt; der Grund dafür lag darin, daß die Arbeitsämter bei der Vermittlung von Arbeitsplätzen an Arbeitslose auf ein gutes Verhältnis zu den Betrieben angewiesen waren und dieses Verhältnis insbesondere nicht durch Mahnungen wegen ausstehender statistischer Meldungen belasten wollten. Ab November 1954 führte das Statistische Landesamt Nordrhein-Westfalen die Lohnsummenerhebungen schließlich ganz ohne die Amtshilfe der Arbeitsämter durch.

Trotz der Koordinierungsbemühungen des Statistischen Amtes des Vereinigten Wirtschaftsgebietes bzw. des Statistischen Bundesamtes blieb den Ländern Raum für eigene lohnstatistische Aktivitäten. So führte das Statistische Landesamt Schleswig-Holstein eine als Experiment bezeichnete "Repräsentativerhebung über die Einkommensschichtung in Schleswig-Holstein im Jahre 1949" durch, die sich durch eine ungewöhnliche Methodik auszeichnete. Zu der Erhebung wurden nach den Unterlagen der Einwohnermeldeämter der Gemeinden alle im Erwerbsalter stehenden Personen ausgewählt, die an einem 11. November geboren worden waren. Die Stichprobe umfaßte insgesamt etwa 4 000 Personen, was einem Auswahlsatz von einem Vierhundertstel entsprach. Damit wurde erstmalig in der amtlichen Lohnstatistik ein Auswahlverfahren angewendet, das eine Modifikation der reinen Zufallsauswahl war. Die einzelnen ausgewählten Personen wurden direkt nach ihrem Individualeinkommen - d.h. nicht ihrem Haushaltseinkommen - befragt. Da keine gesetzliche Auskunftspflicht bestand, wurde ein Anreiz zur Teilnahme an der Erhebung durch die Verlosung zweier Geldpreise in Höhe von 60 DM bzw. 40 DM gegeben.

152 Vereinigtes Wirtschaftsgebiet

Nachdem mit dem "Gesetz über die Errichtung eines Statistischen Amtes des Vereinigten Wirtschaftsgebietes" vom 21. Januar 1948 (Gesetzblatt der Verwaltung des Vereinigten Wirtschaftsgebietes 1948 S. 19) der Wiederaufbau eines zentralen statistischen Amtes eingeleitet worden war, übernahm das Statistische Amt des Vereinigten Wirtschaftsgebietes ab Anfang 1949 nicht nur die Koordinierung der bereits eingeführten vierteljährlichen Lohnsummenerhebungen der Länder, sondern führte in Zusammenarbeit mit den Statistischen Landesämtern auch neue lohnstatistische Erhebungen durch, die primär Zwecken der Verwaltungen des Vereinigten Wirtschaftsgebietes dienten. Nach der "Gemeinsamen Anordnung der Verwaltungen des Vereinigten Wirtschaftsgebietes zur Durchführung von Statistiken" vom 1. Juni 1949 (Öffentlicher Anzeiger für das Vereinigte Wirtschaftsgebiet Jahrgang 2 Nr. 50 Seite 1) waren die vierteljährlichen Erhebungen über die Arbeiterverdienste in der Industrie einmal jährlich durch eine erweiterte Erhebung zu ersetzen. Diese erweiterte Erhebung wurde jedoch nach ihrer erstmaligen Durchführung für den Berichtsmonat September 1949 nie wiederholt. Die erweiterte Lohnerhebung vom September 1949 beruhte wie die vierteljährlichen Erhebungen auf dem Summenverfahren, wobei jedoch zusätzliche Merkmale erfaßt wurden. Erhebungsmerkmale waren der Brutto- und Nettoverdienst nach Lohnform (Zeit- und Stücklohn) mit gesonderter Angabe der Zuschläge für Über-, Sonntags- und Feiertagsarbeit, die gesetzlichen Abzüge (Lohnsteuer und Arbeitnehmerbeitrag zur Sozialversicherung) und die Arbeitszeit sowie die Arbeitergruppe (nach Geschlecht und Qualifikation) und die tarifliche Altersstufe; außerdem hatten die Betriebe anzugeben, wie viele Arbeiter jeweils bestimmten vorgegebenen Monatsverdienstklassen angehörten. Ausgewiesen wurden Durchschnittsverdienste je Arbeiter pro Stunde, Woche und Monat sowie die auf den summarischen Angaben der Betriebe beruhenden Häufigkeitsverteilungen nach 16 Lohnklassen. Die Ergebnisse der erweiterten Lohnerhebung wurden in der vom Statistischen Amt des Vereinigten Wirtschaftsgebietes bzw. später (ab Juni 1950) vom Statistischen Bundesamt herausgegebenen "Neuen Folge" der Monatszeitschrift "Wirtschaft und Statistik" (Jahrgänge 1949 und 1950) veröffentlicht.

Aufgrund einer Anordnung des Direktors der Verwaltung für Arbeit des Vereinigten Wirtschaftsgebietes vom 8. April 1949 fand für den Berichtsmonat Mai 1949 eine einmalige statistische Erhebung über die tatsächlichen Verdienste der Angestellten in den wichtigeren Zweigen der Industrie, im Handel sowie im Bank- und Versicherungsgewerbe statt, zu der gezielt ausgewählte Betriebe herangezogen wurden. "Die Auswahl der Betriebe in regionaler und sachlicher Hinsicht (Betriebsgröße, Produktionszweig bzw. Handelsbranche) erfolgte - in den einzelnen Ländern verschieden - im Einvernehmen mit den Arbeitsverwaltungen, den Industrie- und Handelskammern, den Fachverbänden und entsprechenden Organisationen durch die Statistischen Landesämter mit der Maßgabe, daß eine ausreichende Berücksichtigung der Ortsgrößenklassen, der Betriebsgrößenklassen und der in den Wirtschaftsgruppen zusammengefaßten Wirtschaftszweige (Branchen) gesichert ist. Von der Festlegung eines Repräsentationsgrades mußte dabei abgesehen werden, da die Berücksichtigung der angeführten Merkmale und die Erfassung der Gehaltsverhältnisse jeweils für den ganzen Betrieb die gleichmäßige Einhaltung eines Auswahlsatzes nicht zuläßt." *) Allgemein wurde lediglich angestrebt, pro Ge-

---

*) Fußnote siehe folgende Seite

werbegruppe mindestens 10 % der Betriebe und 20 % der zum Erhebungsbereich gehörenden Angestellten zu erfassen. In den ausgewählten Betrieben wurden nach dem Summenverfahren jeweils sämtliche erwachsenen Angestellten mit einem Bruttogehalt bis zu 600 DM monatlich erfaßt. Die summarischen Angaben bezogen sich auf "Leistungsgruppen", d.h. Angestelltengruppen, zu denen die Angestellten nach ihrer Qualifikation entsprechend ihrer Berufsausbildung und ihren Tätigkeitsmerkmalen von den Betrieben selbst zusammenzufassen waren. Es wurden vier Leistungsgruppen unterschieden: ohne berufliche Ausbildung, Berufsausbildung für einfache Tätigkeit, Berufsausbildung für qualifizierte Tätigkeit, Berufsausbildung für besonders verantwortliche und selbständige Tätigkeit. Die Angestellten waren ferner summarisch nach Altersklassen und der Beschäftigungsart - kaufmännische Angestellte, technische Angestellte, Meister im Angestelltenverhältnis - aufzugliedern. Erhebungsmerkmale waren vor allem der Bruttoverdienst (aufgegliedert nach Grundgehalt, übertariflichen Zulagen, Sozialzulagen und Mehrarbeitsvergütungen), die gesetzlichen Abzüge und der Nettoverdienst sowie die betriebsüblichen Jahreszuwendungen. Ausgewiesen wurden in erster Linie Durchschnittsverdienste je Angestellten, wobei bei der Zusammenfassung von Durchschnitten kleinerer Teilgruppen zu Durchschnitten für übergeordnete Gruppen unterstellt wurde, daß jede Teilgruppe in der Erhebungsmasse relativ genauso stark wie in der Grundgesamtheit repräsentiert war. Daneben wurden auch Häufigkeitsverteilungen nach Verdienstklassen ausgewiesen, wobei jeweils die ganze Angestelltengruppe derjenigen Verdienstklasse zugeordnet wurde, in die sie nach ihrem Durchschnittsverdienst fiel. Die Ergebnisse der Angestelltenverdiensterhebung von 1949 wurden in "Wirtschaft und Statistik" (Jahrgang 1950) veröffentlicht.

Nach einer Anordnung des Direktors der Verwaltung für Arbeit des Vereinigten Wirtschaftsgebietes vom 12. Februar 1949 war eine einmalige statistische Erhebung über die Tariflöhne der Industriearbeiter durchzuführen, durch die die tariflichen Lohn-

---

*) Peter Deneffe: Die Angestelltenverdienste im Vereinigten Wirtschaftsgebiet im Mai 1949. In: Wirtschaft und Statistik Jahrgang 1950, Seite 68.

sätze für die einzelnen Arbeitergruppen und Ortsklassen sowie die Anzahl der auf sie entfallenden Arbeiter erfaßt werden sollten. Die Erhebung fand durch Befragung sämtlicher Industriebetriebe als Zusatzerhebung zur Industrieberichterstattung vom April 1949 statt. Die Ergebnisse dieser Erhebung bildeten die Grundlage für die Wiederaufnahme der Tariflohnstatistik, die daraufhin mit vierteljährlicher Periodizität - jeweils für die Monate März, Juni, September und Dezember - in der Weise durchgeführt wurde, daß die Statistischen Landesämter für ihr Gebiet in Anlehnung an das Verfahren des Statistischen Reichsamtes tarifliche Durchschnittslöhne berechneten und diese dem Statistischen Amt des Vereinigten Wirtschaftsgebietes bzw. dem Statistischen Bundesamt zur Zusammenfassung zu Gesamtdurchschnitten zur Verfügung stellten. Die Ergebnisse wurden nur im Statistischen Jahrbuch für die Bundesrepublik Deutschland (Jahrgang 1952 Seite 440 f.) veröffentlicht. Die Rechtsgrundlage für diese vierteljährliche "Fortschreibung" der tariflichen Durchschnittslöhne wurde erst nachträglich durch einen Erlaß der Verwaltung für Arbeit des Vereinigten Wirtschaftsgebietes vom 17. November 1949 in Verbindung mit dem Gesetz über Lohnstatistik vom 22. August 1949 (Gesetzblatt der Verwaltung des Vereinigten Wirtschaftsgebietes 1949 Seite 265) geschaffen. Als Durchschnittslöhne wurden lediglich durchschnittliche tarifliche Stundenlohnsätze einschließlich der Sozialzulagen - für jeden Arbeiter wurde dabei der Satz für die Ehefrau und ein Kind zugrundegelegt - und sonstiger tariflicher Zulagen für Arbeiter der höchsten tarifmäßigen Altersstufe nach Industriezweigen und fünf Arbeitergruppen (gegliedert wie bei der vierteljährlichen Lohnsummenerhebung) ermittelt. Die Durchschnittsberechnung erfolgte in der Weise, daß zunächst für jede tarifliche Lohngruppe ein "Ortsklassendurchschnitt" als gewogenes arithmetisches Mittel aus den Lohnsätzen der einzelnen Ortsklassen - als Gewichte wurden dabei im allgemeinen die in der Erhebung vom April 1949 ermittelten Besetzungszahlen der Arbeiter in den einzelnen Ortsklassen unverändert weiterverwendet - berechnet wurde. Aus den Ortsklassendurchschnitten der einzelnen Lohngruppen wurden dann analog als gewogene arithmetische Mittel tarifliche Durchschnittslöhne für die Gesamtheit der Lohngruppen einer Arbeitergruppe gebildet. Die Berechnung tariflicher Durchschnittslöhne wurde Ende 1951 eingestellt; bei der späteren Wiederaufnahme der Tariflohnstatistik, die dann gemäß § 2 Ziffer 7 des Gesetzes über die Statistik für Bundeszwecke vom 3. September 1953 (Bundesgesetzblatt 1953 Teil I Seite 1314) ohne Beteiligung der Statistischen Landesämter vom Statistischen Bundesamt zentral durchgeführt wurde,*) wurden neben der Registrierung tariflicher Einzellohnsätze lediglich Tariflohnindices aufgestellt. Das Material für die laufende Bearbeitung der Tariflohnstatistik wird seit 1949 den bei den obersten Arbeitsbehörden geführten amtlichen Tarifarchiven entnommen. Nach dem Tarifvertragsgesetz vom 9. April 1949 (Gesetzblatt der Verwaltung des Vereinigten Wirtschaftsgebietes 1949 Seite 55) in Verbindung mit der zugehörigen Durchführungsverordnung vom 7. Juni 1949 (Gesetzblatt der Verwaltung des Vereinigten Wirtschaftsgebietes 1949 Seite 89) waren die Tarifvertragsparteien verpflichtet, dem Direktor der Verwaltung für Arbeit des Vereinigten Wirtschaftsgebietes und den obersten Arbeitsbehörden der Länder, auf deren Gebiet sich der jeweilige Tarifvertrag erstreckte, innerhalb eines Monats nach Vertragsabschluß kostenfrei Abschriften des Tarifvertrages und seiner Änderungen - einschließlich des Außerkrafttretens - zu übersenden. Bei Nichteinhaltung dieser Verpflichtungen konnten Ordnungsstrafen in Geld bis zu 300 DM festgesetzt werden. Das Tarifvertragsgesetz wurde erst am 25. August 1969 (Bundesgesetzblatt 1969 Teil I Seite 1323) neu gefaßt, wobei der Wortlaut redaktionell überarbeitet - vor allem "Bundesminister für Arbeit und Sozialordnung" statt "Direktor der Verwaltung für Arbeit" -,der Inhalt der Durchführungsverordnung vom 7. Juni 1949 mit in das Gesetz eingebaut und die "Ordnungsstrafe" durch eine "Geldbuße wegen Ordnungswidrigkeit" ersetzt wurde.

Nachdem das Gesetzgebungsrecht auf dem Gebiete der amtlichen Statistik von den Militärregierungen an deutsche Stellen zurückgegangen war, erfolgten nach und nach rechtliche Neuregelungen

*) In einigen Bundesländern - z.B. Bayern - wird vom Statistischen Landesamt daneben eine laufende landeseigene Tariflohnstatistik nach dem Verfahren des Statistischen Bundesamtes durchgeführt.

der verschiedenen statistischen Arbeitsbereiche. Im Bereich der Lohnstatistik trat das vom "Wirtschaftsrat" beschlossene "Gesetz über Lohnstatistik" vom 22. August 1949 (Gesetzblatt der Verwaltung des Vereinigten Wirtschaftsgebietes 1949 Seite 265) in kraft. Danach waren Erhebungen der statistischen Ämter des Vereinigten Wirtschaftsgebietes und der Länder über Lohn- und Gehaltsverhältnisse und sonstige Arbeitsbedingungen der Arbeitnehmer, Heimarbeiter und anderen arbeitnehmerähnlichen Personen durchzuführen. Der Direktor der Verwaltung für Arbeit des Vereinigten Wirtschaftsgebietes wurde generell ermächtigt, unter Mitwirkung der obersten Arbeitsbehörden der Länder sowie der Spitzenorganisationen der Gewerkschaften und der Vereinigungen der Arbeitgeber im Benehmen mit dem Statistischen Amt des Vereinigten Wirtschaftsgebietes Zeitpunkt, Art und Umfang der lohnstatistischen Erhebungen zu bestimmen. Im übrigen wurden die unentgeltliche Auskunftspflicht der Befragten, die Verpflichtung der Befragten und ggf. des Betriebsrates zur Unterzeichnung der Erhebungsbogen und die Verpflichtung, den statistischen Ämtern die notwendigen Unterlagen zur Nachprüfung der Angaben vorzulegen, vorgeschrieben. Bei einer Verletzung der Auskunftspflicht konnte auf Antrag des Leiters eines statistischen Amtes eine Geldstrafe bis zu 1 000 DM verhängt werden. Die statistischen Ämter durften die erfragten Angaben nur zu statistischen Zwecken verarbeiten und waren verpflichtet, Angaben über einzelne Befragte geheimzuhalten.

Auf Grund des Gesetzes über Lohnstatistik vom 22. August 1949 erließ der Direktor der Verwaltung für Arbeit des Vereinigten Wirtschaftsgebietes am 17. November 1949 Bestimmungen über die Durchführung einmaliger lohnstatistischer Erhebungen in der Landwirtschaft und in der Forstwirtschaft. Daraufhin fanden für das Berichtsjahr vom 1. Januar bis zum 31. Dezember 1950 eine Lohnstrukturerhebung in der Landwirtschaft und für das Berichtsjahr vom 1. Oktober 1949 bis zum 30. September 1950 eine Lohnstrukturerhebung in der Forstwirtschaft statt. Bei der Lohnstrukturerhebung in der Landwirtschaft wurden mit Hilfe von Interviewern repräsentativ ausgewählte Betriebe und in diesen Betrieben jeweils alle ständig beschäftigten familienfremden Arbeiter im Individualverfahren erfaßt. Während des Erhebungszeitraums fanden sechs Teilerhebungen für jeweils zwei Monate statt, in denen Angaben für jeden Arbeiter und jeden einzelnen Monat zu machen waren. Die Angaben waren in einen Betriebsbogen - soweit es sich um allgemeine Daten für den ganzen Betrieb bzw. für alle Arbeiter des Betriebes handelte- und in einen Arbeiterbogen oder eine Arbeiterliste - soweit es sich um Angaben für die einzelnen Arbeiter handelte - einzutragen. Als Interviewer wurden vorzugsweise Mitarbeiter der Landwirtschaftskammern und der Landwirtschaftsschulen eingesetzt. Hinsichtlich der Arbeitsteilung zwischen den statistischen Ämtern galt die nach dem Zweiten Weltkrieg allgemein übliche Regelung, daß die Statistischen Landesämter die Arbeiten von der Betriebsauswahl bis zur Erstellung der Landesergebnisse ausführten und das Statistische Amt des Vereinigten Wirtschaftsgebietes bzw. das Statistische Bundesamt für die methodische Vorbereitung einschließlich der Ausarbeitung von Erhebungs- und Aufbereitungsrichtlinien und die Zusammenfassung der Ländererergebnisse zum Gesamtergebnis zuständig war. Die Auswahl der Berichtsbetriebe der Lohnstrukturerhebung in der Landwirtschaft wurde nach einem organisatorisch aufwendigen Verfahren vorgenommen. In jedem Land wurde unter dem Vorsitz des Statistischen Landesamtes ein "Landesausschuß" aus Vertretern des Landwirtschaftsministeriums, der Landwirtschaftskammern und der landwirtschaftlichen Arbeitnehmer- und Arbeitgeberverbände gebildet. Der Landesausschuß wählte zunächst für jeden Landkreis gezielt durchschnittlich 75 "geeignete" Betriebe aus, wobei sich die Eignung nach der Repräsentation und der Berichtswilligkeit richtete. Von diesen Betrieben wurden pro Landkreis als Berichtsbetriebe durchschnittlich 15 (mindestens 10) Betriebe sowie drei Reservebetriebe zufällig ausgewählt. Für jeden Stadtkreis bzw. jede kreisfreie Stadt wurden vom Landesausschuß direkt durchschnittlich fünf Berichtsbetriebe gezielt ausgewählt. Die Berichtsbetriebe sollten sich im Durchschnitt aller Länder - in den einzelnen Ländern unterschiedlich - wie folgt auf Betriebsgrößenklassen nach der landwirtschaftlichen Nutzfläche verteilen: 20 % Betriebe unter 10 ha, 20 % Betriebe 10 bis unter 20 ha, 40 % Betriebe 20 bis unter 50 ha, 20 % Betriebe ab 50 ha. Insgesamt wurden durch dieses Auswahlverfahren etwa 2,5 % aller land-

wirtschaftlichen Arbeiter erfaßt. Erhebungsmerkmale der Lohnstrukturerhebung in der Landwirtschaft waren vor allem der Brutto- und Nettobarverdienst nach Lohnform mit gesonderter Erfassung der Sozialzuschläge und sonstigen Zulagen, die gesetzlichen Abzüge, Arten und Mengen der empfangenen Naturalleistungen, die Arbeitszeit sowie Angaben über die Person des Arbeiters (Geschlecht, Lebensalter, Qualifikation, Beruf, Zugehörigkeit zur Hausgemeinschaft des Betriebsinhabers u.a.). Die individuellen Verdienstangaben wurden lediglich zu Durchschnittsverdiensten pro Stunde und pro Jahr aufbereitet. Die Bewertung der Naturalleistungen wurde nach einheitlichen Richtlinien von den Statistischen Landesämtern vor allem auf Grund von Ergebnissen der amtlichen Preisstatistik - in der Regel Erzeugerpreise, teilweise Großhandelspreise, in besonderen Fällen Verbraucherpreise, die durch Angaben der Interviewer über "ortsübliche Ladenpreise" ergänzt wurden - vorgenommen. Die Ergebnisse der Lohnstrukturerhebung wurden vom Statistischen Bundesamt unter dem Titel "Die Arbeiterverdienste in der Landwirtschaft 1950" als Statistischer Bericht Arb. Nr. VI/16/1 (Wiesbaden 1952) veröffentlicht.

Bei der Lohnstrukturerhebung in der Forstwirtschaft für das Berichtsjahr 1949/50 wurden ebenfalls mit Hilfe von Interviewern - die vor allem von den forstwirtschaftlichen Verwaltungsbehörden gestellt wurden - repräsentativ ausgewählte staatliche, kommunale, körperschaftliche und private Forstbetriebe und in diesen Betrieben jeweils alle Arbeiter im Individualverfahren erfaßt. Während des Erhebungszeitraums fanden zwei Teilerhebungen für jeweils drei Monate und eine Teilerhebung für sechs Monate statt, in denen Angaben für jeden Arbeiter und jeden einzelnen Monat zu machen waren. Neben anderen Bereichen der Methodik und Erhebungstechnik war auch die Auswahl der Berichtsbetriebe ähnlich organisiert wie bei der gleichzeitigen Lohnstrukturerhebung in der Landwirtschaft. Von einem sachverständigen "Landesausschuß", in dem außer dem den Vorsitz führenden jeweiligen Statistischen Landesamt die Landwirtschaftskammern, die Forstdezernate der Regierungspräsidenten, die Forstämter und die forstwirtschaftlichen Gewerkschaften und Arbeitgeberverbände vertreten waren, wurden die Berichtsbetriebe gezielt ausgewählt. Als allgemeine Richtlinie galt dabei, daß durchschnittlich 10 % der Betriebe mit 5 % bis 10 % aller Forstarbeiter so auszuwählen waren, daß die erfaßten Arbeiter zur Hälfte privaten Betrieben und zu je einem Viertel kommunalen und staatlichen Betrieben angehörten; außerdem war bei privaten Betrieben eine Größenklassengliederung - unter 50 ha, 50 bis unter 100 ha, ab 100 ha Forstfläche - mit höheren Auswahlsätzen (bis zu 30 %) für die Kleinbetriebe zu berücksichtigen. Die Auswahlsätze wurden in den Ländern teilweise variiert; in Nordrhein-Westfalen wurden die Staatsbetriebe total, die Kommunalbetriebe zu 10 % und die Privatbetriebe zu 0,25 % (insgesamt 360 Betriebe) erfaßt. Erhebungsmerkmale der Lohnstrukturerhebung in der Forstwirtschaft waren vor allem der nach verschiedenen Kriterien aufgegliederte Brutto- und Nettobarverdienst, die gesetzlichen Abzüge, Arten und Mengen der empfangenen Naturalleistungen - die Bewertung dieser Leistungen erfolgte nach dem gleichen Verfahren wie bei der Lohnstrukturerhebung in der Landwirtschaft -, die Arbeitszeit sowie die in derartigen Strukturerhebungen üblichen Angaben über die Person des Arbeiters, vor allem zur Bestimmung seiner Qualifikation. Die als Ergebnisse ausgewiesenen durchschnittlichen Stunden- und Jahresverdienste wurden berechnet, nachdem die Angaben über die in der Erhebung erfaßten Arbeiter gesondert für die einzelnen Qualifikationsgruppen auf jeweils 100 % aller Forstarbeiter hochgerechnet worden waren; die dazu notwendigen Totalzahlen der Forstarbeiter waren in den zentralen forstwirtschaftlichen Verwaltungsbehörden der Länder größtenteils bekannt. Die Ergebnisse der Lohnstrukturerhebung wurden vom Statistischen Bundesamt unter dem Titel "Die Verdienste der Forstarbeiter im Jahre 1950" als Statistischer Bericht Arb. Nr. VI/17/1 (Wiesbaden 1952) veröffentlicht.

Auf Grund von Rechtsvorschriften des Vereinigten Wirstschaftsgebietes wurde auch eine Gehalts- und Lohnstrukturerhebung im öffentlichen Dienst als organisatorisch unselbständiger Teil der Personalstandserhebung der öffentlichen Verwaltung zum 2. September 1950 durchgeführt. Diese Erhebung galt zusammen mit der Personalstandserhebung als Annex zur jährlichen Rechnungsstatistik der öffentlichen Haushalte und war daher mit dieser durch die "Gemeinsame Anordnung der Verwaltungen des Vereinigten Wirtschaftsgebietes zur Durchführung von Statistiken" vom 1. Juni 1949 (Öffentlicher Anzeiger für das Vereinigte Wirtschaftsgebiet Jahrgang 2 Nr. 50 Seite 1) rechtlich fundiert. Da die Gehalts- und Lohnstrukturerhebung jedoch in der "Gemeinsamen Anordnung" nicht ausdrücklich erwähnt war, weigerte sich das Land Bayern, die Erhebung durchzuführen. Die Erhebung fand in den übrigen Ländern des Vereinigten Wirtschaftsgebietes für den Berichtsmonat September 1950 bei sämtlichen in die Personalstandserhebung einbezogenen Dienststellen - Gebietskörperschaften (Hoheits- bzw. Kämmereiverwaltungen, Schulen und Hochschulen, Polizei; dabei Gemeinden nur ab 1 000 Einwohner), Eigenbetriebe und Eigengesellschaften von Gebietskörperschaften, der Aufsicht einer Gebietskörperschaft unterstehende Körperschaften bzw. Anstalten oder Stiftungen des öffentlichen Rechts, Verwaltungen der Grund- und Sondervermögen der öffentlichen Hand, Bundesbahn, Bundespost, Sparkassen - statt. Bei diesen Dienststellen wurden im Individualverfahren diejenigen während des ganzen Erhebungsmonats vollbeschäftigten Bediensteten (Beamte, Angestellte, Arbeiter, Personen in Ausbildung) und Versorgungsempfänger erfaßt, deren Familiennamen mit den Buchstaben D, L, R oder T begannen; das entsprach einem Auswahlsatz von 15 % aller Personen der Grundgesamtheit. Für die einzelnen ausgewählten Personen wurden bei den für die Lohn- und Gehaltszahlung zuständigen Behörden auf Individualzählblättern vor allem der Brutto- und Nettomonatsverdienst - die Monatsangaben für die Arbeiter wurden bei der Aufbereitung in Wochenangaben umgerechnet -, die gesetzliche Besoldungs- bzw. tarifliche Vergütungsgruppe und die Laufbahngruppe der Beamten und Angestellten, die Qualifikationsgruppe der Arbeiter -entsprechend den Arbeitergruppen der vierteljährlichen Lohnsummenerhebungen in der Industrie - sowie weitere in den Strukturerhebungen übliche persönliche Angaben erfragt. Die individuellen Verdienstangaben wurden zu durchschnittlichen Monatsverdiensten bzw. bei den Arbeitern auch zu durchschnittlichen Wochen- und Stundenverdiensten aufbereitet. Das Statistische Bundesamt schrieb die in der Erhebung ermittelten Durchschnittsverdienste nachträglich fort, indem es darauf die zum 1. April 1951 in kraft getretenen Erhöhungen der Grundvergütungen um mindestens 20 % pauschal aufschlug. Die Ergebnisse der Erhebung einschließlich der Fortschreibung wurden vom Statistischen Bundesamt unter dem Titel "Die Verdienste der Beschäftigten im öffentlichen Dienst 1950" als Statistischer Bericht Arb. Nr. VI/13/1 (Wiesbaden 1953) veröffentlicht.

153 Organisationen des Kohlenbergbaus

Vor 1945 hatte das Statistische Reichsamt neben der den gesamten Bergbau als Totalerhebung erfassenden vierteljährlichen Bergarbeiterlohnstatistik der Bergbehörden auf Grund von Angaben der Zechenverbände eine monatliche Statistik über die Arbeiterverdienste im Kohlenbergbau durchgeführt. Nach 1945 wurde die Bergarbeiterlohnstatistik als nunmehr monatliche Schichten- und Lohnstatistik von den Oberbergämtern der Westzonen bzw. des Bundesgebietes weitergeführt; dabei wurde jedoch in der britischen Zone der Kohlenbergbau statt von den Bergbehörden von der neugeschaffenen Institution "Deutsche Kohlenbergbauleitung" erfaßt. Die die vierteljährliche Lohnsummenerhebung der Industriearbeiter - die den Bergbau ausschloß - bearbeitenden statistischen Ämter waren bemüht, durch Verhandlungen mit den Oberbergämtern und der Deutschen Kohlenbergbauleitung zu erreichen, daß vergleichbare lohnstatistische Daten über die Industrie und den Bergbau ermittelt werden konnten. Während die Vergleichbarkeit mit dem Nichtkohlenbergbau zunächst nicht zu erreichen war, konnten die Lohnerhebungen im Kohlenbergbau und in der Industrie methodisch einander schrittweise angenähert werden. In der amerikanischen Zone erhielten die Statistischen Landesämter bereits ab 1947 Kopien der Meldungen der Kohlenbergwerke zur Bergarbeiterlohnstatistik, um sie für ihre Zwecke selbst aufzubereiten. In der britischen Zone übernahm die Deutsche Kohlenbergbauleitung ab 1949 die Aufbereitung zu Landesergebnissen, die dann den Statistischen Landesämtern und dem Statistischen Amt des Vereinigten Wirtschaftsgebietes bzw. dem Statistischen Bundesamt zum Einbau in die Ergebnisse der Industriearbeiterlohnstatistik und zur Veröffentlichung zur Verfügung gestellt wurden. In "Wirtschaft und Statistik" wurden zunächst in Sondertabellen für den Steinkohlenbergbau monatliche Angaben über die durchschnittlichen Bruttobarverdienste und Gesamteinkommen (einschließlich Naturalleistungen) je angelegten Arbeiter und je verfahrene bzw. vergütete Schicht nach Arbeitergruppen entsprechend der Qualifikation veröffentlicht. Ab Jahrgang 1953 von "Wirtschaft und Statistik" bezogen sich die nunmehr vierteljährlichen Angaben auf den Stein- und den Braunkohlenbergbau und wurden in die Ergebnistabellen der Industriearbeiterlohnerhebungen eingefügt. Nach Auflösung der Deutschen Kohlenbergbauleitung wurde im Jahre 1954 die "Statistik der Kohlenwirtschaft e.V." als ein in Bonn eingetragener Verein mit Geschäftsstellen in Essen (für den Steinkohlenbergbau) und Köln (für den Braunkohlenbergbau) gegründet. Der Statistik der Kohlenwirtschaft e.V. wurde - teilweise gegen den Widerstand der Oberbergämter - die Aufgabe übertragen, die Bergarbeiterlohnstatistik im Kohlenbergbau durchzuführen und weiterhin fertig aufbereitete Landesergebnisse den statistischen Ämtern zum Einbau in die vierteljährlichen Lohnsummenerhebungen zu liefern. Die Einschaltung der Statistik der Kohlenwirtschaft e.V. als Erhebungs- und Aufbereitungsstelle, bei der persönliche Beziehungen zum Statistischen Bundesamt und dem Statistischen Landesamt Nordrhein-Westfalen eine wesentliche Rolle spielten, ließ sich nicht überall durchsetzen; so lehnte das niedersächsische Statistische Landesamt die Zusammenarbeit mit dem privatrechtlichen Verein ab und zog es vor, im Kohlenbergbau wie später auch im Nichtkohlenbergbau ausschließlich mit dem zuständigen Oberbergamt zusammenzuarbeiten. Die Statistik der Kohlenwirtschaft e.V. wird seit ihrer Gründung nicht nur bei den vierteljährlichen Lohnsummenerhebungen, sondern auch bei den Gehalts- und Lohnstrukturerhebungen eingeschaltet, soweit diese den Kohlenbergbau betreffen.

154 Bundesstatistik

Eine lohnstatistische Rechtsvorschrift der Bundesrepublik Deutschland wurde erstmalig mit der "Verordnung zur Durchführung einer Statistik der Gehalts- und Lohnverhältnisse" vom 22. Dezember 1951 (Bundesanzeiger 1951 Nr. 249) geschaffen. Diese Verordnung ermächtigte den Bundesminister für Arbeit, den

Zeitpunkt der Erhebung und die zu erfassenden Wirtschaftszweige zu bestimmen. Der Bundesminister für Arbeit erließ daraufhin insgesamt dreimal "Bestimmungen zur Verordnung zur Durchführung einer Statistik der Gehalts- und Lohnverhältnisse", und zwar am 29. Dezember 1951 (Bundesanzeiger 1952 Nr. 9) zu einer Erhebung in der gewerblichen Wirtschaft für den Berichtsmonat November 1951, am 30. September 1952 (Bundesanzeiger 1952 Nr. 193) zu einer Erhebung in der Forstwirtschaft für das Berichtsjahr vom 1. Oktober 1952 bis zum 30. September 1953 und am 2. Januar 1953 (Bundesanzeiger 1953 Nr. 3) zu einer Erhebung in der Landwirtschaft für das Berichtsjahr vom 1. Februar 1953 bis zum 31. Januar 1954. Die Erhebungen in diesen drei Wirtschaftsbereichen wurden als repräsentative Gehalts- und Lohnstrukturerhebungen im Individualverfahren durchgeführt. Auf Grund der Verordnung vom 22. Dezember 1951 sollte auch noch eine Gehalts- und Lohnstrukturerhebung im öffentlichen Dienst durchgeführt werden, die jedoch bis zur Aufhebung dieser Verordnung durch das "Gesetz über die Lohnstatistik" vom 18. Mai 1956 (Bundesgesetzblatt 1956 Teil I S. 429) nicht mehr stattfand.

Die Gehalts- und Lohnstrukturerhebung in der gewerblichen Wirtschaft für November 1951 erfaßte gleichmäßig in allen Bundesländern sowie in allen Wirtschaftszweigen des Erhebungsbereichs auf Grund von Anschriftenverzeichnissen der Arbeitsstättenzählung 1950 sämtliche Betriebe ab zehn Beschäftigten und von den Betrieben mit weniger als zehn Beschäftigten nach dem "systematischen Auswahlverfahren" jeden siebten Betrieb. Erhebungseinheiten waren neben Betrieben als örtliche Einheiten ggf. auch fachlich unterschiedliche Betriebsteile. Die erfaßten Betriebe mit weniger als zehn Beschäftigten hatten auf Erhebungsbogen individuelle Angaben für alle Arbeiter und Angestellten zu machen, die Betriebe ab zehn Beschäftigten nur für die Arbeiter und Angestellten, deren Familiennamen mit den Buchstaben D, L, R oder T begannen. Mit diesem Auswahlplan wurde ein gleichmäßiger Auswahlsatz von etwa 15 % der Arbeitnehmer in allen Wirtschaftszweigen, Betriebsgrößenklassen und tariflichen Vergütungs- bzw. Lohngruppen angestrebt. Erstmalig in der amtlichen Lohnstatistik wurde als Maßstab für die Qualifikation aller Arbeitnehmer ein Leistungsgruppenschema aufgestellt, das seitdem ein wesentliches Kennzeichen der lohnstatistischen Erhebungen ist. Die Leistungsgruppen wurden nach der Berufsausbildung und Berufserfahrung sowie nach den tatsächlichen Tätigkeitsmerkmalen (vor allem im Hinblick auf Verantwortung und Selbständigkeit) gebildet. Bei den Arbeitern wurden drei Leistungsgruppen unterschieden, die mit den arabischen Ziffern 1 (hohe Qualifikation, vor allem Facharbeiter), 2 (mittlere Qualifikation, vor allem angelernte Arbeiter) und 3 (niedrige Qualifikation, vor allem Hilfsarbeiter) bezeichnet wurden. Bei den Angestellten wurden die mit römischen Ziffern bezeichneten fünf Leistungsgruppen I (leitende Stellung mit voller Aufsichts- und Dispositionsbefugnis), II (besondere Erfahrungen und selbständige Leistungen in verantwortlicher Tätigkeit mit eingeschränkter Aufsichts- und Dispositionsbefugnis), III (mehrjährige Berufserfahrung oder besondere Fachkenntnisse und Fähigkeiten sowie selbständige Leistungen nach allgemeinen Anweisungen), IV (einfache Tätigkeit ohne eigene Entscheidungsbefugnis auf Grund einer abgeschlossenen Berufsausbildung oder in mehrjähriger Berufstätigkeit erworbener Fachkenntnisse) und V (einfache schematische oder mechanische Tätigkeit ohne Berufsausbildung) eingeführt. Die Zuordnung der einzelnen Arbeiter und Angestellten zu den Leistungsgruppen wurde nicht den Betrieben überlassen, sondern nach einheitlichen Gesichtspunkten in den Statistischen Landesämtern vorgenommen. Zu diesem Zweck wurden vom Statistischen Bundesamt - teilweise auch von den Statistischen Landesämtern selbst - im allgemeinen im Einvernehmen mit den Tarifvertragsparteien Richtlinien über die Eingliederung der Lohn- und Gehaltsgruppen der verschiedenen vorkommenden Tarifverträge in die statistischen Leistungsgruppen ausgearbeitet. Das Einvernehmen mit den Tarifparteien konnte vor allem bei den Angestelltentarifen nicht immer erzielt werden; in diesen Fällen entschied das Statistische Bundesamt allein über die Eingliederung. Die nicht nach einem Tarifvertrag bezahlten Arbeitnehmer wurden von den Statistischen Landesämtern nach den Angaben im Erhebungsbogen so gut wie möglich den Leistungsgruppen zugeordnet. Als Erhebungsmerkmale wurden - bei den Angestellten für den ganzen Monat November 1951, bei den Arbeitern für eine betriebliche Lohnabrechnungsperiode von mindestens vier überwiegend in den Erhebungsmonat fallenden Wochen - vor allem der Bruttoverdienst nach Lohnform mit gesonderter Angabe der Mehrarbeits- bzw. Sonn- oder Feiertagsbezahlung, die gesetzlichen Abzüge, der Arbeitgeberbeitrag zur Sozialversicherung, die Jahressonderzuwendung für das Jahr 1951, die Arbeitszeit der Arbeiter sowie Geschlecht, Lebensalter, Familienstand, Kinderzahl und Beruf individuell erfaßt. Als Ergebnisse wurden in erster Linie durchschnittliche Stunden-, Wochen- und Monatsverdienste - unter anderem auch nach Gemeindegrößenklassen sowie nach Beschäftigungsarten der Angestellten (kaufmännische Angestellte, technische Angestellte, Meister im Angestelltenverhältnis) - sowie Häufigkeitsverteilungen nach Verdienstklassen ausgewiesen. Die Ergebnisse wurden vom Statistischen Bundesamt als Bände 90 (Die Verdienste der Arbeiter in der gewerblichen Wirtschaft im November 1951) und 91 (Die Verdienste der Angestellten in der gewerblichen Wirtschaft im November 1951) der "Statistik der Bundesrepublik Deutschland" (Stuttgart-Köln 1954) veröffentlicht.

Die Lohnstrukturerhebung in der Forstwirtschaft für 1952/53 erfaßte auf Grund von Verzeichnissen der landwirtschaftlichen Betriebszählung 1949 sämtliche staatlichen und kommunalen Forstbetriebe ab 100 ha Waldfläche und in diesen Betrieben mit Ausnahme der zu 100 % erfaßten Haumeister nur diejenigen im Hauptberuf als Waldarbeiter beschäftigten und ausschließlich forstwirtschaftliche Arbeiten verrichtenden männlichen und weiblichen Arbeiter, deren Familiennamen mit den Buchstaben D, G, L, R, T oder W begannen; das waren etwa 25 % der Grundgesamtheit dieser Arbeiter. Das Erhebungsjahr wurde in vier Berichtsquartale aufgeteilt, wobei auf den Erhebungsbogen jedoch Angaben pro Arbeiter für jeden einzelnen Monat zu machen waren. Berichtsstellen waren die für die Lohnabrechnung zuständigen Stellen, d.h. die Forstämter bzw. Forstbetriebe. Die Erhebungsbogen wurden den Berichtsstellen von den Statistischen Landesämtern über die Forstdezernate der Regierungspräsidenten bzw. die entsprechenden vorgesetzten Behörden postalisch übersandt und gelangten auf dem gleichen Wege zur Aufbereitung in die Statistischen Landesämter zurück. Erhebungsmerkmale waren vor allem der Bruttobarverdienst nach Lohnform mit gesonderter Angabe der Urlaubsvergütung und des Lohnfortzahlungsbetrages bei Krankheit sowie verschiedener Zulagen, die gesetzlichen Abzüge, der Arbeitgeberbeitrag zur Sozialversicherung, Gratifikationen und Treuegelder, Arten und Mengen der Naturalleistungen - die Bewertung wurde nachträglich mit Hilfe von Verbraucher- oder Erzeugerpreisen der amtlichen Preisstatistik durch die Statistischen Landesämter vorgenommen -, die Arbeitszeit sowie weitere in den Strukturerhebungen übliche persönliche Merkmale (unter anderem auch die Qualifikation bzw. Art der Tätigkeit und die Dauer der Betriebszugehörigkeit). Aus den individuellen Verdienstangaben wurden durchschnittliche Stunden- und Jahresverdienste sowie Häufigkeitsverteilungen nach Verdienstklassen berechnet. Da die Haumeister zu 100 % und die übrigen Arbeiter nur zu 25 % erfaßt wurden, erfolgte für die Berechnung von Durchschnittsverdiensten für die Gesamtheit der Arbeiter eine "Reduktion" der erfaßten Lohnsummen der Haumeister auf ein Viertel und damit auf das Niveau der Lohnsummen der übrigen Arbeiter. Die Ergebnisse der Erhebung wurden vom Statistischen Bundesamt als Band 92 Heft 1 (Verdienste der Arbeiter in der Forstwirtschaft, Ergebnisse der Lohnstrukturerhebung in der Forstwirtschaft 1952/53) der "Statistik der Bundesrepublik Deutschland" (Stuttgart 1957) veröffentlicht.

Die Gehalts- und Lohnstrukturerhebung in der Landwirtschaft für 1953/54 erfaßte eine repräsentative Stichprobe von Betrieben ab fünf ha landwirtschaftlicher Nutzfläche, die aus dem Anschriftenmaterial der landwirtschaftlichen Betriebszählung 1949 in einem zweistufigen Auswahlverfahren zufällig ausgewählt wurden."Da die Streuung der Verdienste der Landarbeiter in den einzelnen Arbeitergruppen nach Betriebsgrößenklassen und Ländern nicht bekannt war, vielmehr erst durch diese Erhebung ermittelt werden sollte, war für die Auswahl eine echte Quotenbestimmung unter Verwendung einer Zuverlässigkeitsgrenze nicht möglich. Die Repräsentationsquote wurde daher in der Weise festgelegt, daß unter Berücksichtigung der für aussagefähige Ergebnisse notwendigen Mindestbesetzung der Arbeitergruppen eine im Rahmen der finanziellen Möglichkeiten vertretbare Zahl von Betrieben bestimmt wurde."*) Die Auswahl wurde gesondert für drei Betriebsgrößenklassen nach der landwirtschaftlichen Nutzfläche (5 bis unter 20 ha, 20 bis unter 50 ha, ab 50 ha) vorgenommen. In der ersten Stufe des Auswahlverfahrens wurde je Bundesland aus den in eindimensionale Ordnung gebrachten kreisangehörigen Gemeinden für die Auswahl in der unteren und der mittleren Betriebsgrößenklasse jede achte und für die Auswahl in der oberen Betriebsgrößenklasse jede vierte Gemeinde ausgewählt. In der zweiten Stufe des Auswahlverfahrens wurde dann innerhalb der einzelnen ausgewählten kreisangehörigen Gemeinden für die Auswahl in der unteren Betriebsgrößenklasse jeder dritte, in der mittleren Betriebsgrößenklasse jeder zweite und in der oberen Betriebsgrößenklasse jeder Betrieb als Berichtsbetrieb ausgewählt. Wenn in einer ausgewählten kreisangehörigen Gemeinde keine Betriebe der gewünschten Größenklasse vorhanden waren, wurde entweder eine benachbarte Gemeinde erfaßt oder eine Ersatzgemeinde zufällig ausgewählt. In den kreisfreien Städten bzw. Stadtkreisen, die sämtlich in die Erhebung einbezogen wurden, wurde für die untere Größenklasse jeder einundzwanzigste, für die mittlere Größenklasse jeder vierzehnte und für die obere Größenklasse jeder vierte Betrieb als Berichtsbetrieb ausgewählt. Insgesamt wurden durch das Auswahlverfahren 6,3 % aller Betriebe mit etwa 10 % aller familienfremden Arbeitskräfte der Grundgesamtheit erfaßt. Die Berichtsbetriebe hatten Angaben für jeden der bei ihnen beschäftigten Arbeiter und Angestellten - letztere wurden jedoch nur in Betrieben ab 50 ha landwirtschaftlicher Nutzfläche erfaßt - individuell auf Erhebungsbogen zu melden. Dabei wurden alle vorkommenden Qualifikations- und Berufsgruppen - mit Ausnahme der Arbeiter, die wie z.B. Forst- und Weinbauarbeiter nicht als eigentliche landwirtschaftliche Arbeiter gelten - sowie auch vorübergehend erkrankte Arbeitnehmer und geistig behinderte Arbeiter - deren Beschäftigung ausdrücklich als für die Landwirtschaft typisch bezeichnet wurde! - einbezogen. Die Berichtsbetriebe der oberen Größenklasse und diejenigen Berichtsbetriebe der mittleren Größenklasse, in denen im Jahr vor der Erhebung

*) Statistisches Bundesamt: Statistik der Bundesrepublik Deutschland Band 92 Heft 2, Stuttgart 1958, S. 5 - 6.

außer den in der Hausgemeinschaft des Betriebsinhabers lebenden Monatslöhnern noch weitere familienfremde Arbeitskräfte länger als zwei Monate beschäftigt worden waren, hatten die erfragten Angaben für jeden Monat des ganzen Erhebungsjahres zu machen. Die übrigen Berichtsbetriebe hatten nur für die Monate Februar, Mai, September und November des Erhebungsjahres Meldungen abzugeben. Die Saisonarbeiter wurden in jedem Fall nur in den Monaten Mai bis November, die Aushilfskräfte nur in den Monaten Mai und September erfaßt. Die Erhebungsbogen wurden den Berichtsbetrieben von den Statistischen Landesämtern postalisch über die Gemeindeverwaltungen zugesandt; auf dem gleichen Wege liefen die Erhebungsbogen an die Statistischen Landesämter zur Aufbereitung zurück. Die letzten auskunftssäumigen Betriebe wurden - zumindest in Nordrhein-Westfalen - von Vertretern der Kreisstellen, Landwirtschaftsschulen und Wirtschaftsberatungsstellen der Landwirtschaftskammern zum Zwecke der "Beratung" aufgesucht. Bei besonders ausgeprägter Berichtsunwilligkeit wurden teilweise nachträglich Ersatzbetriebe erfaßt. Zu diesem Zweck wurden von den Statistischen Landesämtern vor allem solche Gemeinden gezielt ausgewählt, in denen im allgemeinen gut berichtet worden war; diese Gemeinden hatten dann ohne nähere Anweisung selbst eine vorgegebene Anzahl von Ersatzbetrieben zu benennen. Größenmäßig vergleichbare Ersatzbetriebe wurden auch ausgewählt, wenn ein Betrieb, der zur Zeit der landwirtschaftlichen Betriebszählung 1949 noch existierte, im Erhebungsjahr nicht mehr vorhanden war oder inzwischen seine landwirtschaftliche Nutzfläche erheblich geändert hatte. Die von den Betrieben gemeldeten Angaben wurden bei der Aufbereitung in den Statistischen Landesämtern in einigen Fällen geändert. Die Angaben mußten grundsätzlich für einen vollen Monat oder für einen Lohnabrechnungszeitraum von vier Wochen gemacht werden; im zweiten Fall wurde eine "Umrechnung" in Monatswerte vorgenommen. Wenn bei einem Arbeitnehmer wegen Krankheit oder Einstellung bzw. Entlassung während eines Erhebungsmonats nur ein verringerter Verdienst angegeben war, wurde eine "Hochrechnung" auf den vollen erreichbaren Monatsverdienst vorgenommen. Als "Hochrechnung" wurde auch bezeichnet, wenn bei Arbeitnehmern, die nur in vier Monaten erfaßt worden waren, aus den Verdienstangaben dieser Monate eine Schätzung des gesamten Jahresverdienstes abgeleitet wurde. Schließlich war wegen der unterschiedlichen Auswahlsätze in den Betriebsgrößenklassen auch eine echte "Hochrechnung" der Stichprobendaten auf 100 % der Grundgesamtheit erforderlich. Wenn die Angaben für einen Arbeitnehmer in einem einzelnen Erhebungsmonat ganz fehlten, erfolgte eine "Ergänzung" durch Einsetzen der entsprechenden Daten aus einem benachbarten Erhebungsmonat oder durch Interpolation zwischen den beiden benachbarten Monaten. Als Erhebungsmerkmale wurden vor allem der Barverdienst und gesondert die Barprämien, die gesetzlichen Abzüge, der Arbeitgeberbeitrag zur Sozialversicherung, Arten und Mengen der Naturalleistungen - die Bewertung wurde in den Statistischen Landesämtern wie bei der Lohnstrukturerhebung in der Forstwirtschaft für 1952/53 vorgenommen -, die Arbeitszeit der im Stundenlohn stehenden Arbeiter sowie weitere persönliche Merkmale (unter anderem auch die Dauer der Tätigkeit in der Landwirtschaft und die Dauer der Betriebszugehörigkeit) erfaßt. Als Ergebnisse ausgewiesen wurden in erster Linie durchschnittliche Stunden-, Monats- und Jahresverdienste und Häufigkeitsverteilungen nach Verdienstklassen. Das Statistische Bundesamt veröffentlichte die Ergenisse der Erhebung als Band 92 Heft 2 (Verdienste der Arbeiter und Angestellten in der Landwirtschaft, Ergebnisse der Gehalts- und Lohnstrukturerhebung in der Landwirtschaft 1953) der "Statistik der Bundesrepublik Deutschland" (Stuttgart 1958).

Der Begriff "Bundesstatistik" wurde durch das Gesetz über die Statistik für Bundeszwecke vom 3. September 1953 (Bundesgesetzblatt 1953 Teil I Seite 1314) als offizielle Bezeichnung für Statistiken festgelegt, die auf Grund von Rechtsvorschriften der Bundesrepublik Deutschland für Zwecke von Institutionen des Bundes durchgeführt werden. Das Gesetz von 1953 regelte zwar allgemein - d.h. nicht auf die einzelnen Bereiche der amtlichen Statistik wie z.B. die Lohnstatistik eingehend -, jedoch umfassend das gesamte Organisations- und Verfahrensrecht sowie das materielle Recht der Bundesstatistik. Insbesondere legte das Gesetz von 1953 die Aufgaben des Statistischen Bundesamtes und die Zusammensetzung und Befugnisse des beim Statistischen Bundesamt neu zu bildenden Statistischen Beirats sowie die für die Bundesstatistik geltenden Grundsätze der Gesetzmäßigkeit, Auskunftspflicht und Geheimhaltungspflicht fest. Die Rechtsgrundlagen der einzelnen Bereiche der Statistik brauchen seitdem keine besonderen Bestimmungen über diese Grundsätze mehr zu enthalten. Der Grundsatz der Gesetzmäßigkeit besagt, daß die Statistiken durch Gesetze, die hinsichtlich der zu erfassenden Tatbestände und des Kreises der Befragten hinreichend spezifiziert sind, angeordnet werden müssen; Erhebungen geringeren Umfangs dürfen auch durch befristete Rechtsverordnungen der Bundesregierung angeordnet werden. Nach dem Grundsatz der Auskunftspflicht sind die Befragten verpflichtet, die statistischen Auskünfte wahrheitsgemäß, vollständig, fristgemäß und grundsätzlich unentgeltlich zu erteilen und die Richtigkeit der Angaben durch Unterschrift zu bestätigen. Eine Verletzung der Auskunftspflicht kann als Ordnungswidrigkeit mit einer Geldbuße bis zu 10 000 DM geahndet werden. Nach dem Grundsatz der Geheimhaltungspflicht sind von den statistischen Ämtern Einzelangaben der Befragten über persönliche oder sachliche Verhältnisse geheimzuhalten; d.h. die Angaben dürfen nur nach Zusammenfassung bekanntgegeben werden. Eine Verletzung der Geheimhaltungspflicht wird auf Antrag des Verletzten mit Freiheitsstrafe oder Geldstrafe bestraft. Die Verletzung der Geheimhaltungspflicht wurde durch § 203 Absatz 2 des Strafgesetzbuches in der Neufassung vom 2. Januar 1975 (Bundesgesetzblatt 1975 Teil I Seite 1) in das allgemeine Strafrecht übernommen.

155 Internationale Anregungen

Durch das Ratifikationsgesetz vom 15. April 1954 (Bundesgesetzblatt 1954 Teil II Seite 437) trat für die Bundesrepublik Deutschland das "Übereinkommen Nr. 63 der Internationalen Arbeitsorganisation vom 20. Juni 1938 über Statistiken der Löhne und der Arbeitszeit in den hauptsächlichsten Zweigen des Bergbaus und des verarbeitenden Gewerbes, einschließlich des Baugewerbes, sowie in der Landwirtschaft" in kraft. Mit diesem Übereinkommen wurden völkerrechtliche Verpflichtungen übernommen, die in den darauffolgenden Jahren eine Erweiterung der deutschen Lohnstatistik vor allem durch laufende Erhebungen im verarbeitenden Handwerk und in der Landwirtschaft notwendig machten.

Die Internationale Arbeitsorganisation veranstaltete für das Berichtsjahr 1955 in neun europäischen Staaten (Bundesrepublik Deutschland, Belgien, Frankreich, Griechenland, Großbritannien, Italien, Jugoslawien, Österreich, Türkei) eine einmalige eigene Erhebung über die Aufwendungen der Unternehmen für ihre Arbeitnehmer. Form und Inhalt des Erhebungsbogen, Erhebungsrichtlinien, Begriffsdefinitionen und die zu erfassenden Wirtschaftszweige wurden zentral von der Internationalen Arbeitsorganisation festgelegt; die Durchführung der Erhebung oblag den Behörden der neun Staaten, in der Bundesrepublik Deutschland ausschließlich dem Statistischen Bundesamt ohne Beteiligung der Statistischen Landesämter. Nach dem Erhebungsplan waren acht Wirtschaftszweige zu erfassen; da die Angaben für den Bergbau und die Eisen- und Stahlindustrie von der Europäischen Gemeinschaft für Kohle und Stahl geliefert wurden und da die Deutsche Bundesbahn ihre Teilnahme verweigerte, hatte das Statistische Bundesamt nur fünf Wirtschaftszweige (Maschinenbau, Schiffbau, Elektroindustrie, Textilindustrie, Schuhindustrie) in die Erhebung einzubeziehen. In diesen Wirtschaftszweigen wurden zunächst sämtliche Unternehmen ab 20 Beschäftigten zur Mitarbeit aufgefordert. Um trotz der Freiwilligkeit der Teilnahme einen Anreiz zur Mitarbeit zu geben, wurde denjenigen Unternehmen, die sich an dieser Erhebung beteiligten, die Freistellung von der Ausfüllung eines entsprechenden Fragebogens im Rahmen einer für das Jahr 1956 vorgesehenen nationalen Gehalts- und Lohnstrukturerhebung in der gewerblichen Wirtschaft zugesagt. Diese Zusage wurde bei der später auf das Jahr 1957 verschobenen Gehalts- und Lohnstrukturerhebung nicht eingehalten. Bei der internationalen Erhebung für 1955 beteiligten sich in den fünf genannten Wirtschaftszweigen nur gut 50 % der angeschriebenen Unternehmen; die erfaßten Angaben wurden jedoch als hinreichend repräsentativ befunden.*) Die Ergebnisse der Erhebung - sämtliche Personalkosten und Personalnebenkosten gegliedert nach Aufwands-

---

*) Fußnote siehe folgende Seite

arten - wurden unter dem Titel "Die Arbeitskosten in der europäischen Industrie" als Nr. 52 der Neuen Folge der Studien und Berichte des Internationalen Arbeitsamtes (Genf 1959) veröffentlicht.

Nach der Gründung der Europäischen Gemeinschaft für Kohle und Stahl (Montanunion) fanden vom Berichtsjahr 1953 an jährliche Personalkostenerhebungen in den"EGKS-Industrien" (Steinkohlenbergbau, Eisenerzbergbau, Eisen- und Stahlindustrie) statt, wobei die Hohe Behörde der Montanunion ohne Einschaltung der nationalen statistischen Ämter in Zusammenarbeit mit den zuständigen nationalen Unternehmensverbänden die Aufwendungen nur für die Arbeiter in sämtlichen Betrieben (örtliche Einheiten) - bzw. Betriebsteilen (fachliche Einheiten), wenn nur ein Teil des Betriebes zu den EGKS-Industrien gehörte - erfaßte. Diese Erhebungen werden nach wie vor als jährliche Totalerhebungen durchgeführt, nunmehr vom Statistischen Amt der Europäischen Gemeinschaften und in der Bundesrepublik Deutschland in Zusammenarbeit mit der Statistik der Kohlenwirtschaft e.V., dem Betriebswirtschaftlichen Institut der Eisenhüttenindustrie bzw. der Wirtschaftsvereinigung Eisen- und Stahlindustrie und dem Unternehmensverband Eisenerzbergbau.

*) vgl. Peter Deneffe, Siegfried Guckes: Die Aufwendungen der Unternehmen für die Arbeitnehmer im Jahr 1955. In Wirtschaft und Statistik Jahrgang 1958, Seite 269 ff.

16 Die Phase der Reform und Systematisierung (1956 - 1959)

161 Integration des Bergbaus

Nach mehrjährigen Verhandlungen zwischen den statistischen Ämtern und den Behörden und Organisationen des Bergbaus gelang es, ab Anfang 1956 den gesamten Bergbau voll vergleichbar in die vierteljährlichen Lohnsummenerhebungen in der Industrie einzubeziehen. Während der Kohlenbergbau, der schon früher den statistischen Ämtern lohnstatistische Daten geliefert hatte, nunmehr die allgemein angewandte lohnstatistische Methode übernahm, wurde der Nichtkohlenbergbau in der laufenden Industriearbeiterlohnstatistik neu erfaßt. Die volle Vergleichbarkeit bezog sich allerdings nur auf die üblichen Ergebnisse der Erhebungen - durchschnittliche Bruttostunden- und Bruttowochenverdienste und durchschnittliche Wochenarbeitszeiten nach Qualifikationsgruppen der Arbeiter, wobei die anzahlmäßig unbedeutenden weiblichen Arbeiter im Bergbau nicht erfaßt wurden, sowie ab Anfang 1957 auch durchschnittliche Bruttomonatsverdienste nach Beschäftigungsarten, Qualifikationsgruppen und Geschlecht der Angestellten -; in der Erhebungs- und Aufbereitungsorganisation bestanden dagegen auch nach 1956 erhebliche Abweichungen von dem normalen Verfahren. Die Grundlage für die Datenerfassung in den Bergbaubetrieben bildete nach wie vor grundsätzlich die als monatliche Totalerhebung durchgeführte Schichten- und Lohnstatistik (Bergarbeiterlohnstatistik). Im Kohlenbergbau wurde weiterhin von dem Angebot der "Statistik der Kohlenwirtschaft e.V." Gebrauch gemacht, die Aufbereitung der Einzelmeldungen zur Schichten- und Lohnstatistik für Zwecke der vierteljährlichen Lohnsummenerhebung in deren Berichtsmonaten zu Durchschnittsergebnissen für die in Frage kommenden Bundesländer vorzunehmen. Die Statistischen Landesämter erhielten also nicht die Einzelmeldungen der Betriebe des Kohlenbergbaus, sondern lediglich ihr aggregiertes Landesergebnis. Die ab 1957 vorgenommene Erfassung und Aufbereitung der Verdienstangaben für die Angestellten des Kohlenbergbaus erfolgte in gleicher Weise wie bei den Arbeitern.

Im Nichtkohlenbergbau lieferten die zuständigen Oberbergämter - z.B. für Nordrhein-Westfalen die Oberbergämter Bonn und Dortmund bzw. nach deren Auflösung seit Anfang 1970 das in Dortmund ansässige "Landesoberbergamt Nordrhein-Westfalen" - den Statistischen Landesämtern für die Arbeiter in gleicher Weise aggregierte Verdienst- und Arbeitszeitangaben als Landesdurchschnitte wie im Kohlenbergbau. Die Angaben für die Angestellten im Nichtkohlenbergbau wurden dagegen nicht der Schichten- und Lohnstatistik entnommen, sondern eigens für Zwecke der vierteljährlichen Summenerhebung ermittelt; und zwar verteilten die Oberbergämter die ihnen von den Statistischen Landesämtern gesammelt zur Verfügung gestellten Erhebungsbogen zur Ausfüllung an die einzelnen Bergbaubetriebe und sandten die ausgefüllten Erhebungsbogen gesammelt wieder an die Statistischen Landesämter zur Aufbereitung zurück. Durch die Einschaltung der Oberbergämter und der Statistik der Kohlenwirtschaft e.V. und die Ausnutzung der totalen Schichten- und Lohnstatistik wurde erreicht, daß der gesamte Bergbau in der Bundesrepublik Deutschland - mit Ausnahme lediglich der niedersächsischen Torfgewinnung - in den vierteljährlichen Summenerhebungen total erfaßt werden konnte, während die Erhebungen in den übrigen Wirtschaftsbereichen repräsentativ durchgeführt wurden.

Neben der organisatorischen Sonderstellung weist der Bergbau dadurch Besonderheiten auf, daß die amtliche Lohnstatistik über den für die anderen Wirtschaftsbereiche üblichen Merkmalskatalog hinaus als bergbauspezifische Merkmale den Wert der den Arbeitnehmern gewährten Kohlendeputate und die auf Grund gesetzlicher Bestimmungen*) an die unter Tage beschäftigten Arbeitnehmer gezahlte Bergmannsprämie erfaßt. Außerdem wird die seit Anfang 1970 im Steinkohlenbergbau des Ruhrreviers gezahlte tarifliche Treueprämie in der vierteljährlichen Summenerhebung neben dem Bruttoverdienst gesondert erfaßt und als Durchschnittsbetrag in Form einer Fußnote in den Veröffentlichungen des Statistischen Bundesamtes und des Statistischen Landesamtes (bzw. des Landesamtes für

---

*) vgl. Gesetz über Bergmannsprämien in der Fassung vom 12. Mai 1969 (Bundesgesetzblatt 1969 Teil I Seite 434).

Datenverarbeitung und Statistik) Nordrhein-Westfalen ausgewiesen. Eine aufbereitungstechnische Besonderheit des Steinkohlenbergbaus und des oberbayerischen Pechkohlenbergbaus besteht darin, daß in der vierteljährlichen Summenerhebung der Berechnung der Stundenverdienste, der Wochenverdienste und der bezahlten Wochenarbeitszeit seit 1965 eine angenommene gleichmäßige Verteilung der gesetzlichen Wochenfeiertage im Jahr zugrundegelegt wird. Diese "ratierliche Berechnung" bedeutet, daß die gesetzlichen Wochenfeiertage nicht mit ihrer zufälligen Anzahl im Erhebungsmonat, sondern mit einem angenäherten Jahreszwölftel angesetzt werden. Das Verfahren der ratierlichen Berechnung wurde von 1967 bis 1969 auch auf die im rheinisch-westfälischen Steinkohlenbergbau tariflich vereinbarten "zusätzlichen Ruhetage" angewendet, entfällt hier jedoch seit 1970, da nunmehr alle Samstage als Ruhetage im Sinne des Tarifvertrages gelten.

Bei den Gehalts- und Lohnstrukturerhebungen in der gewerblichen Wirtschaft wurde ebenfalls die Statistik der Kohlenwirtschaft e.V. eingeschaltet, die die Erhebungsbogen an die auf jeden Fall total erfaßten Betriebe des Kohlenbergbaus verteilte, nach der Ausfüllung wieder einsammelte und nach Überprüfung zur Aufbereitung an die Statistischen Landesämter zurücksandte. Der Nichtkohlenbergbau wurde in den Gehalts- und Lohnstrukturerhebungen wie die anderen Wirtschaftsbereiche unmittelbar von den Statistischen Landesämtern erfaßt.

162 Das lohnstatistische Grundgesetz

Das Gesetz über die Lohnstatistik vom 18. Mai 1956 (Bundesgesetzblatt 1956 Teil I Seite 429) brachte eine grundlegende Reform der amtlichen deutschen Lohnstatistik und legte in groben Zügen das seitdem gültige System der nationalen Effektivverdienststatistik fest. Nach diesem Gesetz waren zunächst weiterhin vierteljährliche Lohnsummenerhebungen in repräsentativ ausgewählten Betrieben durchzuführen, und zwar nunmehr für Arbeiter und Angestellte in den Wirtschaftsbereichen verarbeitende Industrie, Bergbau, Bauhauptgewerbe (einschließlich Bauhandwerk) und Energiewirtschaft und Wasserversorgung sowie für Angestellte in den

Wirtschaftsbereichen Handel, Kreditwirtschaft und Versicherungsgewerbe. Diese Summenerhebungen wurden im Sprachgebrauch der statistischen Ämter nach der Reform als "vierteljährliche Verdiensterhebung in Industrie und Handel" bezeichnet. Neu eingeführt wurde eine seitdem als Summenerhebung mit ergänzenden Individualangaben für Arbeiter in Betrieben mit weniger als zehn Beschäftigten durchgeführte "halbjährliche Verdiensterhebung im Handwerk", die Arbeiter, Angestellte und Lehrlinge bzw. Anlernlinge in repräsentativ ausgewählten Betrieben bestimmter Zweige des produzierenden Handwerks (ohne handwerkliches Bauhauptgewerbe) erfaßte. Ebenfalls neu eingeführt wurden laufende Individuallohnerhebungen bei repräsentativ ausgewählten Betrieben - die Auswahl war so zu bemessen, daß im Durchschnitt bis zu 10 % der Arbeiter der Grundgesamtheit erfaßt wurden - in der Landwirtschaft, die sich auf in die Hausgemeinschaft des Betriebsinhabers aufgenommene ständig beschäftigte männliche und weibliche landwirtschaftliche Arbeiter im Monatslohn und nicht in die Hausgemeinschaft aufgenommene männliche landwirtschaftliche Arbeiter im Stundenlohn erstreckten. Die laufenden lohnstatistischen Erhebungen in der Landwirtschaft fanden bis Ende 1958 mit halbjährlicher Periodizität und danach als "jährliche Verdiensterhebung in der Landwirtschaft" statt. Das Gesetz von 1956 bestimmte ferner, daß in Abständen von drei bis fünf Jahren als "Sondererhebungen" bezeichnete Gehalts- und Lohnstrukturerhebungen mit umfangreichem Merkmalskatalog im Individualverfahren - lediglich die nicht einzelnen Arbeitnehmern zuzurechnenden sozialen Nebenleistungen waren im Summenverfahren zu erfassen - durchzuführen waren. Die Bundesregierung wurde ermächtigt, durch Rechtsverordnungen mit Zustimmung des Bundesrates die von den Sondererhebungen zu erfassenden Wirtschaftsbereiche zu bestimmen; dabei war lediglich der öffentliche Dienst ausgeschlossen. Bei sämtlichen durch das Gesetz über die Lohnstatistik von 1956 vorgeschriebenen Erhebungen waren ausschließlich die Arbeitgeber auskunftspflichtig.

Das Gesetz von 1956 stellt nach wie vor die Grundlage für die amtliche deutsche Effektivverdienststatistik dar; es wurde lediglich in einigen Punkten durch das Gesetz zur Änderung des Gesetzes über die Lohnstatistik vom 4. August 1971 (Bundesgesetzblatt 1971 Teil I Seite 1217) neuen Erfordernissen angepaßt.

Die ab Anfang 1957 in reformierter Form durchgeführte vierteljährliche Verdiensterhebung in Industrie und Handel knüpfte an die frühere laufende Lohnsummenerhebung der Industriearbeiter an. Beibehalten wurden neben dem Summenverfahren und den Erhebungsmonaten - Februar, Mai, August und November jedes Jahres - vor allem das Erhebungsziel - Nachweis des regelmäßigen Verdienstes des vollbeschäftigten Arbeitnehmers - und das Verfahren der Verhältniswertberechnung. Der durchschnittliche Bruttostundenverdienst eines Arbeiters wurde nach wie vor als Quotient aus monatlicher Bruttolohnsumme und monatlicher Summe der bezahlten Arbeitsstunden aller Arbeiter der betreffenden Arbeitergruppe und der durchschnittliche Bruttowochenverdienst als Quotient aus wöchentlicher Bruttolohnsumme und Anzahl der Arbeiter berechnet; zusätzlich wurde der durchschnittliche Bruttomonatsverdienst eines Angestellten als Quotient aus monatlicher Bruttogehaltssumme und Anzahl aller Angestellten der betreffenden Angestelltengruppe ermittelt. Erhebungseinheiten waren weiterhin grundsätzlich Betriebe als örtliche Einheiten; von Betrieben mit unterschiedlichen Fertigungsprogrammen war für jeden Betriebsteil als fachliche Einheit ein eigener Fragebogen auszufüllen. Der Kreis der Berichtsbetriebe wurde für die reformierte Verdiensterhebung neu ausgewählt. Auswahlgrundlagen waren für die Industrie und das Bauhauptgewerbe die jeweils letzten Totalerhebungen zur Industrieberichterstattung und zur Bauberichterstattung, für die Bereiche Handel, Kreditwirtschaft und Versicherungsgewerbe die Arbeitsstättenzählung 1950 und für die Energiewirtschaft und Wasserversorgung private bzw. verbandseigene Anschriftenverzeichnisse; der Bergbau wurde durch die Statistik der Kohlenwirtschaft e.V. und die Oberbergämter total erfaßt. Aus den Auswahlgrundlagen wurden zunächst die Betriebe mit im allgemeinen weniger als zehn bzw. ausnahmsweise (in Bauhauptgewerbe, Handel, Kreditwirtschaft und Versicherungsgewerbe) weniger als fünf Beschäftigten ausgesondert. Die verbleibenden Betriebe der Auswahlgesamtheit wurden in jedem einzelnen Wirtschaftszweig nach mehreren Betriebsgrößenklassen entsprechend der Beschäftigtenzahl gegliedert. In jedem Wirtschaftszweig und jeder Größenklasse wurden dann so viele Betriebe als Berichtsbetriebe ausgewählt, daß etwa 25 % - in Bauhauptgewerbe, Handel, Kreditwirtschaft und Versicherungsgewerbe

etwa 10 % - der Arbeitnehmer der Grundgesamtheit erfaßt wurden. Das angewandte Auswahlverfahren war das Prinzip der gezielten Auswahl. "Die Betriebe wurden so ausgewählt, daß innerhalb jeder ..... Wirtschaftsgruppe oder jedes Wirtschaftszweiges eine richtige Zusammensetzung der Berichtsbetriebe nach den die Verdiensthöhe hauptsächlich bestimmenden Faktoren (Betriebsgröße und Ortsklasse) gewährleistet ist, so daß die für die Berichtsbetriebe ermittelten Durchschnittswerte praktisch als für alle Betriebe zutreffend angesprochen werden können."*)
Die Bestimmung der einzelnen Berichtsbetriebe blieb den Statistischen Landesämtern ohne weitere Anweisung überlassen. Bei der Auswahl wurden Abweichungen von der angestrebten Erfassungsquote der Arbeitnehmer in den einzelnen Schichten (Größenklassen innerhalb der Wirtschaftszweige) in gewissen Grenzen vernachlässigt; so wurden bei beabsichtigter 25 %iger Erfassung 20 bis 30 % und bei beabsichtigter 10 %iger Erfassung 7 bis 13 % akzeptiert. In den Wirtschaftszweigen mit etwa 10 %iger Erfassung wurden die erfaßten Summenangaben bei der Aufbereitung in den Statistischen Landesämtern auf die allgemeine Erfassungsquote von 25 % hochgerechnet, wobei der Hochrechnungsfaktor in jedem Fall 2,5 betrug. Wenn in einer Schicht durch einen einzigen Betrieb bereits die beabsichtigte Erfassungsquote überschritten wurde, erfolgte bei der Aufbereitung eine Rückrechnung der Summenangaben dieses Betriebes auf das angestrebte Niveau durch Multiplikation mit einem "Reduktionsfaktor". Die Summenangaben des total erfaßten Bergbaus wurden für die Zusammenfassung mit den Angaben der übrigen Wirtschaftsbereiche zu einem Viertel in die Verdiensterhebung übernommen. Bei der Betriebsauswahl von 1957 diente das Modell der geschichteten proportionalen Auswahl mit - abgesehen von der erwähnten Differenzierung - gleichen Auswahlsätzen in allen Schichten als Leitmotiv, wobei sich die Auswahlsätze allerdings nicht auf die Auswahleinheiten (Betriebe), sondern auf die Arbeitnehmer bezogen.

*) Peter Deneffe, Wolf v.d. Decken: Die methodischen Grundlagen der laufenden Verdiensterhebungen in Industrie und Handel. In Wirtschaft und Statistik Jahrgang 1957, S. 522 ff. (Zitat S. 524).

Wegen der einheitlichen bzw. rechnerisch vereinheitlichten Erfassungsquote der Arbeitnehmer konnte bei der Verhältniswertberechnung sowohl für die einzelnen Wirtschaftszweige als auch für übergeordnete Wirtschaftsbereiche auf eine besondere Gewichtung bzw. Hochrechnung der Summenangaben auf 100 % der Arbeitnehmer der Grundgesamtheit verzichtet werden, wodurch das Aufbereitungsverfahren verhältnismäßig einfach blieb. Der 1957 festgelegte Kreis der Berichtsbetriebe blieb grundsätzlich so lange unverändert erhalten, bis auf Grund neuerer Auswahlgrundlagen eine generelle Neuauswahl vorgenommen wurde; dies geschah erst wieder im Jahre 1964. Nach den Richtlinien des Statistischen Bundesamtes sollten sogenannte unechte Antwortausfälle - Erlöschen eines Berichtsbetriebes infolge Geschäftsaufgabe, Konkurs usw. - laufend durch andere Betriebe des gleichen Wirtschaftszweiges und der gleichen Größenklasse ersetzt werden. Im Statistischen Landesamt Nordrhein-Westfalen bestanden gegen dieses Verfahren methodische Bedenken; hier wurden daher ab 1957 unechte Antwortausfälle ersatzlos gestrichen. Für eventuelle echte Antwortausfälle - Auskunftsverweigerung bzw. unbrauchbare oder zu späte Auskunftserteilung - wurden zumindest in Nordrhein-Westfalen von vornherein Reservebetriebe miterfaßt, jedoch nur bei Bedarf aufbereitet. Da der Hauptzweck der vierteljährlichen Verdiensterhebung darin bestand, die Verdienstentwicklung über einen längeren Zeitraum zu verfolgen, ergab sich das Bedürfnis, die Ergebnisse der früheren Lohnsummenerhebungen der Industriearbeiter so weit wie möglich mit den Ergebnissen der reformierten Verdiensterhebung vergleichbar zu machen, um so durchlaufende bruchfreie Zeitreihen bilden zu können. Zu diesem Zweck wurde vom Statistischen Bundesamt ein einfaches Verfahren zur Umrechnung der Ergebnisse der früheren Lohnsummenerhebungen auf das Niveau der Ergebnisse der reformierten Verdiensterhebung entwickelt.*) Für den Berichtsmonat Februar 1957 wurden sowohl letztmalig die Betriebe des alten Berichtskreises als auch erstmalig die Betriebe des neuen Berichtskreises erfaßt.

---

*) vgl. Peter Deneffe: Die Arbeiterverdienste im Mai 1957. In Wirtschaft und Statistik Jahrgang 1957, S. 528 ff.

Beide Kreise wurden gesondert aufbereitet, so daß den Ergebnissen des alten Kreises Ergebnisse des neuen Kreises gegenübergestellt werden konnten, die denselben Bezugszeitraum betrafen. Die Ergebnisse des neuen Kreises wurden sodann in Prozenten der entsprechenden Ergebnisse des alten Kreises ausgedrückt. Diese Prozentzahlen wurden als "Umrechnungsfaktoren" bezeichnet. Unter der Annahme, daß die in den Umrechnungsfaktoren ausgedrückten Verdienstunterschiede, die im Februar 1957 zwischen dem alten und dem neuen Berichtskreis bestanden, in relativ gleicher Höhe auch in allen Erhebungsmonaten vor dem Berichtskreiswechsel festzustellen gewesen wären, konnten die Ergebnisse der früheren Lohnsummenerhebungen seit deren Wiederbeginn im Jahre 1946 durch Multiplikation mit den Umrechnungsfaktoren weitgehend mit den Ergebnissen der reformierten Verdiensterhebung vergleichbar gemacht werden. Das Verfahren der Bildung bruchfreier Zeitreihen mit Hilfe derartiger Umrechnungsfaktoren wurde analog auch bei den späteren Berichtskreiswechseln - in den Jahren 1964 und 1972 - der vierteljährlichen Verdiensterhebung angewendet.*)

Die Berichtsbetriebe der vierteljährlichen Verdiensterhebung in Industrie und Handel hatten für die Erhebungsmonate entsprechend dem Lohnsummenverfahren grundsätzlich monatliche Verdienstsummen und Arbeitsstundensummen für ganze Arbeitnehmergruppen zu melden. Im Gegensatz zu den früheren Lohnsummenerhebungen waren auch die für die jeweiligen Betriebe nicht produktionseigentümlichen Arbeitskräfte (Kraftfahrer, Kantinenpersonal usw.) einzubeziehen. Die Arbeitnehmergruppen wurden wie bereits bei der Gehalts- und Lohnstrukturerhebung in der gewerblichen Wirtschaft 1951 (vgl. Seite 78) neu als "Leistungsgruppen" gebildet - drei Leistungsgruppen der Arbeiter und fünf Leistungsgruppen der Angestellten, wobei allerdings die Leistungsgruppe I der Angestellten in der vierteljährlichen Verdiensterhebung nicht erfaßt wur-

---

*) vgl. W. Gerß: Neuauswahl der Berichtsbetriebe zur laufenden Verdiensterhebung und ihre methodischen Konsequenzen. In: Statistische Rundschau für das Land Nordrhein-Westfalen, herausgegeben vom Statistischen Landesamt Nordrhein-Westfalen, Heft 8/1973 Seite 348 ff.

de -, und auch die Definitionen der Leistungsgruppen und die nach Konsultation der Tarifvertragsparteien in der Regel vom Statistischen Bundesamt und ausnahmsweise von den Statistischen Landesämtern aufgestellten Richtlinien über die Zuordnung der tariflichen Lohn- und Gehaltsgruppen zu den statistischen Leistungsgruppen stimmten in vierteljährlicher Verdiensterhebung und Gehalts- und Lohnstrukturerhebung überein. Im Gegensatz zur Gehalts- und Lohnstrukturerhebung konnten die Arbeitnehmer jedoch in der vierteljährlichen Verdiensterhebung nicht von den Statistischen Landesämtern den Leistungsgruppen zugeordnet werden, sondern mußten wegen der summarischen Erfassung von den Berichtsbetrieben selbst nach Leistungsgruppen gegliedert werden. Während die Berichtsbetriebe aber für die Abgrenzung der Arbeitergruppen der früheren Lohnsummenerhebung (vgl. Seite 60) nur kurzgefaßte allgemeine Erläuterungen auf den Erhebungsbogen erhalten hatten, konnten sie sich bei der Bildung der Leistungsgruppen der reformierten Verdiensterhebung auf die Zuordnungsrichtlinien und die detaillierten Beschreibungen der Tätigkeitsmerkmale in den Definitionen stützen.

Da die von den Berichtsbetrieben der vierteljährlichen Verdiensterhebung gelieferten Summenangaben sich immer auf einen ganzen Lohnabrechnungszeitraum - bei Angestellten immer und bei Arbeitern in der Regel einen Monat - bezogen, mußte für die Berechnung von Wochendurchschnitten bei der Aufbereitung in den Statistischen Landesämtern für jeden einzelnen Betrieb eine Umrechnung in Summenangaben pro Woche vorgenommen werden. Der hierzu verwendete "Umrechnungsfaktor" war im Normalfall - das heißt wenn der Lohnabrechnungszeitraum einen Monat betrug - der Quotient aus der Differenz zwischen der Zahl der regelmäßigen betrieblichen Arbeitsstunden pro Arbeiter im Erhebungsmonat und der Zahl der regelmäßigen betrieblichen Arbeitsstunden pro Arbeiter an denjenigen Tagen des Erhebungsmonats, die außerhalb des Zeitraums von vier vollen Wochen - das heißt nach den ersten 28 Kalendertagen des Erhebungsmonats - lagen, im Zähler und dem Vierfachen der Zahl der regelmäßigen betrieblichen Arbeitsstunden pro Arbeiter im Erhebungsmonat im Nenner.

Im Ausnahmefall - das heißt bei einem ein-, zwei-, drei-, vier-, fünf- oder sechswöchigen Lohnabrechnungszeitraum - mußten die gemeldeten Summenangaben für Arbeiter bei der Aufbereitung durch die Anzahl der Wochen des Berichtszeitraumes dividiert werden.

Als Ergebnisse der vierteljährlichen Verdiensterhebung wurden neben den durchschnittlichen Bruttostunden- und Bruttowochenverdiensten der Arbeiter und Bruttomonatsverdiensten der Angestellten nach Wirtschaftszweigen, Geschlecht, Leistungsgruppen und Beschäftigungsarten (kaufmännische und technische Angestellte) der Angestellten für die Arbeiter auch durchschnittliche wöchentliche bezahlte Arbeitszeiten, tatsächlich geleistete Arbeitszeiten und Mehrarbeitszeiten - definiert als über die betriebsübliche Arbeitszeit hinaus geleistete und nicht durch Gewährung von Freizeit an anderen Tagen ausgeglichene Arbeitsstunden - ausgewiesen. Die Ergebnisse der reformierten Verdiensterhebung wurden vom Statistischen Bundesamt laufend in "Preise Löhne Wirtschaftsrechnungen" (seit 1962 "Fachserie M") Reihe 15 I. Arbeiterverdienste und II. Angestelltenverdienste (Stuttgart 1958 ff bzw. Stuttgart-Mainz 1962 ff.) veröffentlicht.

Bereits bei der erweiterten Industriearbeiterlohnerhebung für September 1949 (vgl. Seite 65) waren die Berichtsbetriebe nach ihrer Zugehörigkeit zu einer Handwerksinnung befragt worden, um die Zweckmäßigkeit einer laufenden Lohnstatistik im Handwerk zu prüfen. In Schleswig-Holstein hatte die Handwerkskammer im Jahre 1949 eine Lohnstatistik bei ihren Mitgliedsbetrieben durchgeführt, die eine zeitlang in vierteljährlichen Abständen wiederholt und deren Aufbereitung vom Statistischen Landesamt Schleswig-Holstein übernommen wurde. Die "halbjährliche Verdiensterhebung im Handwerk" als Bundesstatistik fand erstmalig erst für November 1957 und seitdem für Mai und November jedes Jahres statt. Die Erhebung beschränkte sich auf die zehn Handwerkszweige Kraftfahrzeugreparatur, Schlosserei, Tischlerhandwerk, Herrenschneiderei, Damenschneiderei, Bäckerhandwerk, Fleischerei, Klempnerei einschließlich Gas- und Wasserinstallation, Elektroinstallation und Malerhandwerk.

In der Damenschneiderei wurden nur weibliche, in der Herrenschneiderei männliche und weibliche und in den übrigen Handwerkszweigen nur männliche Arbeiter erfaßt; in sämtlichen Handwerkszweigen wurden männliche und weibliche Angestellte, Lehrlinge und Anlernlinge in die Erhebung einbezogen. Das Erhebungsziel entsprach dem der vierteljährlichen Verdiensterhebung in Industrie und Handel; nachzuweisen war demnach der regelmäßige Verdienst des vollbeschäftigten Arbeitnehmers. Für die Auswahl der Berichtsbetriebe wurden in jedem Bundesland die totalen Betriebsauflistungen der Auswahlgrundlage (Handwerkszählung 1956) nach Schichten (Beschäftigtengrößenklassen innerhalb der zu erfassenden Handwerkszweige) sortiert, wobei die Betriebe mit weniger als drei Arbeitnehmern ausgesondert wurden. In jeder Schicht wurden dann so viele Betriebe als Berichtsbetriebe ausgewählt, daß die Erfassung von 10 % der Arbeitnehmer der Grundgesamtheit pro Land, Handwerkszweig und Größenklasse auf Dauer gesichert war. Sofern ein Statistisches Landesamt glaubte, mit dem Satz von 10 % nicht auszukommen, um aussagefähige Landesergebnisse zu gewinnen, konnte dieser Repräsentationssatz überschritten werden, die erfaßten Summenangaben mußten dann jedoch bei der Aufbereitung auf den einheitlichen Satz von 10 % umgerechnet werden. In der Praxis der Betriebsauswahl wurde zunächst pro Schicht grundsätzlich jeder sechste Betrieb der Grundgesamtheit nach dem systematischen Auswahlverfahren ausgewählt. Anschließend wurden die handwerklichen Nebenbetriebe und die Betriebe mit ausschließlich mithelfenden Familienangehörigen als Arbeitnehmer ausgesondert. Für die verbleibenden ausgewählten Betriebe wurde die Anzahl der abhängig Beschäftigten nach dem Stand der Meldungen zur Handwerkszählung 1956 festgestellt. Diese Anzahl sollte als Vorsorge gegen spätere Ausfälle in jeder Schicht um mindestens ein Viertel über der nach dem Auswahlplan zu erfassenden Arbeitnehmerzahl liegen; soweit diese Mindestzahl nicht erreicht wurde, wurden zusätzliche Berichtsbetriebe ausgewählt. In der obersten Betriebsgrößenklasse - Betriebe mit 50 oder mehr Beschäftigten - wurden die Berichtsbetriebe unter Einhaltung des einheitlichen Repräsentationssatzes nicht zufällig, sondern gezielt ausgewählt. In Nordrhein-Westfalen wurde über den Auswahlplan hinaus eine zunächst 100 %ige und dann 50 %ige Reserve an Berichtsbetrieben laufend miterfaßt und bei Bedarf in die Aufbereitung einbezogen; diese Erfassung von Reservebetrieben wurde ab 1966 eingestellt. Andererseits wurde der Berichtskreis in Nordrhein-Westfalen nachträglich dadurch verkleinert, daß ein Teil der Berichtsbetriebe, die für November 1957 trotz zweimaliger Mahnung keine Meldung abgegeben hatten, bis auf weiteres von der Auskunftspflicht entbunden wurden. Außerdem wurden in Nordrhein-Westfalen entsprechend einer den Handwerkskammern gegebenen Zusage diejenigen Berichtsbetriebe der amtlichen Verdiensterhebung freigestellt, die freiwillig an der nichtamtlichen Handwerksberichterstattung der Kammern teilnahmen. Der ausgewählte Berichtskreis der Verdiensterhebung im Handwerk blieb bis zur generellen Neuauswahl auf Grund einer neueren Auswahlgrundlage - die Neuauswahl erfolgte im Jahre 1966 - grundsätzlich unverändert; nur beim Erlöschen eines Berichtsbetriebes war ein Ersatzbetrieb desselben Handwerkszweiges und derselben Größenklasse heranzuziehen. Darüber hinaus sollte ursprünglich die Repräsentation an jedem Jahresende anhand der Veränderungen des Betriebsbestandes der von den Handwerkskammern geführten Handwerksrolle überprüft und die Anzahl der Berichtsbetriebe entsprechend erhöht oder verringert werden; dieser Plan wurde jedoch nicht verwirklicht. Als Ergebnisse der halbjährlichen Verdiensterhebung im Handwerk wurden durchschnittliche Bruttostunden- und Bruttowochenverdienste und durchschnittliche Wochenarbeitszeiten der nach drei Arbeitergruppen (Vollgesellen, Junggesellen, übrige Arbeiter) gegliederten Arbeiter sowie Bruttoverdienstsummen - d.h. keine Durchschnittsverdienste - der Angestellten, Lehrlinge und Anlernlinge ausgewiesen; ferner wurde angegeben, wieviele Arbeiter von ihren Arbeitgebern volle Kost bzw. Unterkunft erhielten. Den Berichtsbetrieben wurden für die Zuordnung der Arbeiter nach Arbeitergruppen vom Statistischen Bundesamt aufgestellte Richtlinien über die Eingliederung der handwerklichen Tarifgruppen in die statistischen Arbeitergruppen zur Verfügung gestellt. Die Ergebnisse der Verdiensterhebung im Handwerk wurden vom Statistischen Bundesamt laufend in "Preise Löhne Wirtschaftsrechnungen" (seit 1962 "Fachserie M") Reihe 16 (Stuttgart-Mainz 1959 ff.) veröffentlicht.

Die laufende Verdiensterhebung in der Landwirtschaft wurde in den Jahren 1957 und 1958 für die Monate März und September und ab 1959 jährlich einmal für September durchgeführt. Erfaßt wurden in nach zwei Größenklassen (20 bis unter 50 ha und ab 50 ha landwirtschaftlicher Nutzfläche; Betriebe unter 20 ha blieben ausgeschlossen) gegliederten ausgewählten Betrieben jeweils sämtliche Arbeiter der höchsten tarifmäßigen Altersstufe - Stundenlöhner dabei nur in Betrieben ab 50 ha landwirtschaftlicher Nutzfläche -, soweit sie zu den im Gesetz über die Lohnstatistik von 1956 angeführten Arbeiterkategorien gehörten. Für die einzelnen Arbeiter waren von den Berichtsbetrieben die Berufsbezeichnungen und ggf. die tariflichen Lohngruppen anzugeben; die Statistischen Landesämter faßten danach bei der Aufbereitung die Arbeiter zu Qualifikationsgruppen zusammen. Bei der ersten Erhebung für März 1957 wurden insbesondere zur Erledigung von Rückfragen bei den Berichtsbetrieben teilweise Interviewer eingesetzt, die von den Landwirtschaftsschulen und Wirtschaftsberatungsstellen der Landwirtschaftskammern gestellt wurden. Die späteren Erhebungen wurden nur noch postalisch durchgeführt. Die Verdiensterhebung in der Landwirtschaft erfaßte ausschließlich die Barverdienste. Bei den Erhebungen für 1957 bis 1959 ermittelte das Statistische Bundesamt außerdem Schätzwerte für die Gesamtverdienste, indem der Wert gewährter Kost und Wohnung unter Verwendung der von den Länderfinanzministern festgelegten Sätze für Zwecke der Berechnung von Lohnsteuer und Sozialversicherungsbeiträgen und der Wert der übrigen Naturalleistungen nach den mit der zwischenzeitlichen Preisentwicklung fortgeschriebenen Ergebnissen der Gehalts- und Lohnstrukturerhebung in der Landwirtschaft 1953/54 auf die Barverdienste aufgeschlagen wurde. Die Angaben der Berichtsbetriebe konnten sich statt auf den vollen Erhebungsmonat auch auf einen Zeitraum von vier Wochen beziehen, der dann bei der Aufbereitung in den Statistischen Landesämtern auf einen Monat umgerechnet wurde.

Die Aufbereitung führte nur zu Verhältniswerten, die wie in der amtlichen Lohnstatistik üblich als Durchschnittsverdienste bzw. durchschnittliche Arbeitszeiten bezeichnet wurden; Häufigkeitsverteilungen nach Verdienstklassen wurden trotz des Individualverfahrens nicht gebildet. Bei der Auswahl der Berichtsbetriebe wurde angestrebt, in den einzelnen Bundesländern so viele Betriebe zu erfassen, daß jedes Land proportional zu der Anzahl seiner landwirtschaftlichen Arbeitskräfte im Bundesergebnis vertreten war. Anzahl und Quoten der auszuwählenden Betriebe wurden für die einzelnen Bundesländer und Betriebsgrößenklassen unterschiedlich festgelegt. Als Auswahlgrundlage wurden die Ergebnisse der auf Grund einer Rechtsverordnung vom 18. Juni 1956 (Bundesanzeiger 1956 Nr. 117) für Juli 1956 durchgeführten repräsentativen Erhebung über die Arbeitskräfte in der Landwirtschaft verwendet. Aus dieser Auswahlgesamtheit wurden die Berichtsbetriebe der Verdiensterhebung nach dem systematischen Auswahlverfahren unter Einhaltung vorgegebener und in der angeführten Weise differenzierter Auswahlabstände von den Statistischen Landesämtern ausgewählt, wobei diejenigen Betriebe ausgelassen wurden, die als Unterstichprobe innerhalb der Arbeitskräfteerhebung zu einer monatlichen Berichterstattung herangezogen wurden. Die ursprünglich festgelegten Auswahlquoten wurden nachträglich pauschal um 10 % - in einigen Bundesländern noch stärker, zum Beispiel in Nordrhein-Westfalen um 100 % - erhöht, um den seit Juli 1956 eventuell eingetretenen Ausfällen zu begegnen. Trotzdem wurden bei der ersten Erhebung im März 1957 weit weniger Arbeiter erfaßt, als man sich auf Grund des Auswahlplans erhofft hatte. Daher wurde bei den Erhebungen ab September 1957 die Anzahl der Berichtsbetriebe der Größenklasse von 20 bis unter 50 ha landwirtschaftlicher Nutzfläche weiter erhöht, indem vor allem Betriebe mit annähernd 50 ha Nutzfläche zusätzlich gezielt ausgewählt wurden. Als Ergebnisse der Verdiensterhebung in der Landwirtschaft wurden durchschnittliche Bruttostunden- und Bruttomonatsverdienste (1957 bis 1959 Barverdienste und geschätzte Gesamtverdienste, ab 1960 nur noch Barverdienste) und durchschnittliche Arbeitszeiten sowie ab 1965 durchschnittliche gesetzliche Abzüge ausgewiesen. Das Statistische Bundesamt veröffentlichte die Ergebnisse laufend in "Preise Löhne Wirtschaftsrechnungen" (seit 1962 "Fachserie M") Reihe 14 (Stuttgart-Mainz 1958 ff.). Die Ergebnisse der Verdiensterhebung in der Landwirtschaft wurden amtlicherseits vor allem für die jährlichen "Grünen Berichte" der Bundesregierung, insbesondere für Zwecke des Lohnniveauvergleichs zwischen landwirtschaftlichen Arbeitern und Industriearbeitern, ausgewertet.

Die erste vom Gesetz über die Lohnstatistik von 1956 vorgeschriebene Gehalts- und Lohnstrukturerhebung fand auf Grund der "Ersten Verordnung über die Durchführung einer Sondererhebung zur Lohnstatistik" vom 7. Februar 1957 (Bundesanzeiger 1957 Nr. 30) für den Berichtsmonat Oktober 1957 bzw. das Berichtsjahr 1957 als Repräsentativerhebung in der gewerblichen Wirtschaft statt. Dabei wurden für Oktober 1957 in ausgewählten Betrieben (örtliche Einheiten) vor allem die Verdienste ausgewählter Arbeiter und Angestellter im Individualverfahren sowie für das Jahr 1957 in ausgewählten Unternehmen (rechtliche Einheiten) die sozialen Nebenleistungen für sämtliche Arbeitnehmer im Summenverfahren erfaßt. Im Gehalts- und Lohnstrukturteil der Erhebung (Individualverfahren) wurde durch den Auswahlplan die gleichmäßige Repräsentation von ca. 15 % der Arbeitnehmer in allen Gewerbezweigen, tariflichen Gehalts- und Lohngruppen und Betriebsgrößenklassen angestrebt. Die Auswahl erfolgte nach einem zweistufigen Auswahlverfahren. In der ersten Stufe wurden aus den nach drei Beschäftigtengrößenklassen - Größenklasse I grundsätzlich 10 bzw. in einigen Wirtschaftszweigen 5 oder 2 bis 19 Beschäftigte (kleinere Betriebe blieben ausgeschlossen), Größenklasse II 20 bis 99 Beschäftigte, Größenklasse III 100 oder mehr Beschäftigte - geschichteten Auswahlgrundlagen - Betriebsauflistungen früherer Totalerhebungen wie Arbeitsstättenzählung, Industrie- und Bautotalerhebung - die Berichtsbetriebe nach dem systematischen Auswahlverfahren ausgewählt. In der zweiten Stufe wurden die von den Berichtsbetrieben zu erfassenden Arbeitnehmer nach bestimmten Anfangsbuchstaben der Familiennamen ausgewählt; fakultativ wurde Betrieben mit maschineller Datenverarbeitung für die Arbeitnehmerauswahl das systematische Auswahlverfahren angeboten.

Die Auswahlsätze waren in allen Bundesländern und allen Wirtschaftszweigen einheitlich, und zwar wurde in der Größenklasse I jeder siebte Betrieb mit seinen sämtlichen Arbeitnehmern, in der Größenklasse II jeder zweite Betrieb mit etwa 30 % seiner Arbeitnehmer und in der Größenklasse III jeder Betrieb mit etwa 15 % seiner Arbeitnehmer erfaßt. Die Arbeitnehmerauswahl nach Anfangsbuchstaben der Familiennamen beruhte auf der Überlegung, daß nach Beobachtungen über die Häufigkeit der Namensanfänge eine bestimmte Buchstabengruppe mit bestimmter Wahrscheinlichkeit einem Auswahlsatz entspricht, der innerhalb eines bestimmten Vertrauensbereichs um den laut Auswahlplan angestrebten Auswahlsatz liegt. Um zu vermeiden, daß infolge regionaler Häufung der Familiennamen eine gewisse Einseitigkeit bei der Arbeitnehmerauswahl entstand, wurden bei der Gehalts- und Lohnstrukturerhebung 1957 erstmalig in der amtlichen Lohnstatistik die Arbeitnehmer nicht nach konstanten Anfangsbuchstaben, sondern nach dem Verfahren der alternierenden Buchstabenauswahl mit rotierenden Alphabetabschnitten ausgewählt. Das Statistische Bundesamt legte zu diesem Zweck zentral einen Katalog von verschiedenen Alphabetabschnitten fest, die den angestrebten Auswahlsätzen entsprachen. Die Statistischen Landesämter teilten dann selbständig jedem Berichtsbetrieb in regelmäßigem Turnus eine der in Frage kommenden Buchstabengruppen zu. Der Auswahlsatz für die Arbeitnehmerauswahl wurde für jeden Berichtsbetrieb auf Grund seiner Größenklasse zur Zeit der Erstellung der Auswahlgrundlage festgelegt; spätere Änderungen der Beschäftigtenzahl blieben hinsichtlich des Auswahlsatzes unberücksichtigt. Da keine Ergebnisse nach Größenklassen ermittelt werden sollten, die Schichtung vielmehr nur für Zwecke der Auswahl vorgenommen wurde, konnte auch bei der Aufbereitung die Größenklasse der Auswahlgrundlage für jeden Berichtsbetrieb beibehalten werden. In den Größenklassen I und II wurden für eventuelle "echte Antwortausfälle" (Auskunftsverweigerung u.a.) von vornherein zufällig ausgewählte Reservebetriebe miterfaßt und bei Bedarf in die Aufbereitung einbezogen. Die Gehalts- und Lohnstrukturerhebung 1957 erfaßte grundsätzlich monatliche Verdienstangaben für die vollbeschäftigten und vollbezahlten Arbeiter und Angestellten, die bei der Aufbereitung durch die Statistischen Landesämter zu Leistungsgruppen zusammengefaßt wurden.

Auch die nicht betriebseigentümlichen Arbeitskräfte wurden einbezogen. Die von den Betrieben gemeldeten Angaben, die sich nicht genau auf den Erhebungsmonat bezogen, wurden bei der Aufbereitung betriebsweise auf einen Zeitraum von der Länge des Oktober 1957 umgerechnet. Als "Umrechnungsfaktor" diente der Quotient aus der Anzahl der normalen betrieblichen Arbeitsstunden des Monats Oktober und der Anzahl der normalen betrieblichen Arbeitsstunden des abweichenden Berichtszeitraums. Bei kleineren Betrieben konnte zur Vereinfachung der Umrechnungsfaktor gleich 1 gesetzt werden, wenn der vom Oktober 1957 abweichende Berichtszeitraum die gleiche Anzahl von kalendermäßigen Arbeitstagen hatte. Die monatlichen Verdienstangaben für die Arbeiter wurden bei der Aufbereitung unter anderem je Wirtschaftszweig mit Hilfe eines "Reduktionsfaktors" zu durchschnittlichen Wochenangaben verrechnet. Der Reduktionsfaktor (Rf) ergab sich nach folgender Formel:

$$Rf = \frac{\sum_{i=1}^{n} \frac{WSt_i}{MSt_i} A_i}{\sum_{i=1}^{n} A_i}$$

Symbole:

i = 1,2,....,n = laufende Nummern der Betriebe

n = Anzahl der Betriebe in einem Wirtschaftszweig

WSt = (ggf. durchschnittliche) Anzahl der betriebsüblichen Wochenarbeitsstunden in den Wochen des Berichtsmonats Oktober 1957

MSt = Anzahl der betriebsüblichen Arbeitsstunden im Monat Oktober 1957

A = Anzahl der erfaßten Arbeiter

Erhebungsmerkmale des Gehalts- und Lohnstrukturteils der Sondererhebung von 1957 waren vor allem der effektive Bruttoverdienst (ggf. nach Lohnform) unter Ausgliederung der Bezahlung für Mehrarbeit und der Familienzuschläge, der Tariflohn bzw. das Tarifgehalt, die gesetzlichen Abzüge, die Arbeitszeit der Arbeiter sowie weitere persönliche Merkmale (Geschlecht, Lebensalter, Beruf, Qualifikation, Kinderzahl, Dauer der Firmenzugehörigkeit).

Die individuellen Verdienstangaben wurden zu durchschnittlichen Stunden-, Wochen- und Monatsverdiensten sowie zu Häufigkeitsverteilungen nach Verdienstklassen aufbereitet.

Im Erhebungsteil "soziale Nebenleistungen" der Sondererhebung von 1957 wurden in den Wirtschaftsbereichen Industrie, Baugewerbe und Handel sämtliche Unternehmen mit mindestens 20 Arbeitnehmern erfaßt, deren Betriebe - das heißt mindestens einer ihrer Betriebe - zum Gehalts- und Lohnstrukturteil ausgewählt worden waren. Bei der Aufbereitung wurde angenommen, daß von den Unternehmen mit 20 bis 99 Arbeitnehmern die Hälfte und von den Unternehmen mit 100 oder mehr Arbeitnehmern alle erfaßt worden wären. Infolgedessen wurden die von den Unternehmen mit 20 bis 99 Arbeitnehmern gemeldeten Summenangaben allgemein mit dem Hochrechnungsfaktor 2 hochgerechnet. In diesem Erhebungsteil erhielten die Berichtsunternehmen die Fragebogen von den Statistischen Landesämtern und sandten sie nach Ausfüllung wieder an die Statistischen Landesämter zurück; die Prüfung und Aufbereitung der Erhebungsbogen erfolgte zentral im Statistischen Bundesamt. Die Berichtsunternehmen lieferten im Summenverfahren für sämtliche bei ihnen beschäftigten Arbeitnehmer - getrennt nach Arbeitern und Angestellten - vor allem Angaben über die Personalkosten und Personalnebenkosten einschließlich der Naturalleistungen in sehr detaillierter Gliederung nach Aufwandsarten. Die Ergebnisse beider Erhebungsteile der Sondererhebung von 1957 wurden vom Statistischen Bundesamt als Band 246 (Heft 1 Verdienste der Arbeiter in der Industrie im Oktober 1957, Heft 2 Verdienste der Angestellten in der gewerblichen Wirtschaft im Oktober 1957, Heft 3 Aufwendungen der Unternehmen für ihre Arbeitnehmer im Jahre 1957) der "Statistik der Bundesrepublik Deutschland" (Stuttgart-Mainz 1960/61) veröffentlicht.

Auf Grund der "Zweiten Verordnung über die Durchführung einer Sondererhebung zur Lohnstatistik" vom 8. August 1961 (Bundesanzeiger 1961 Nr. 153) fand für den Berichtsmonat Oktober 1962 abermals eine repräsentative Gehalts- und Lohnstrukturerhebung in der gewerblichen Wirtschaft im Individualverfahren statt, die methodisch weitestgehend mit dem Gehalts- und Lohnstrukturteil der Sondererhebung von 1957 übereinstimmte; auf eine Wiederholung des Erhebungsteiles "soziale Nebenleistungen" wurde dagegen verzichtet. Die amtliche Begründung zur "Zweiten Verordnung" vom 8. August 1961 (Bundesratsdrucksache Nr. 243/61) sah für die Arbeitnehmerauswahl als Regelfall den Auswahlsatz von 7,5 % vor, stellte jedoch den einzelnen Bundesländern die Entscheidung über die Höhe des für sie gültigen Auswahlsatzes ausdrücklich frei. Bei der Entscheidung der Bundesländer über die Höhe des Auswahlsatzes wurden teilweise statistisch-methodische Gesichtspunkte gegenüber Kostengesichtspunkten zurückgestellt. So ergab sich die Kuriosität, daß einige kleinere Länder (Schleswig-Holstein, Bremen, Rheinland-Pfalz, Saarland) für die Arbeitnehmerauswahl mit 7,5 % einen niedrigeren Auswahlsatz verwendeten als die übrigen Länder (darunter die großen Flächenstaaten) mit 15 %. Im Gegensatz zu der Erhebung von 1957 waren die Auswahlsätze also bei der Erhebung von 1962 nicht in allen Bundesländern einheitlich; und zwar wurde der im übrigen aus der Erhebung von 1957 übernommene Auswahlplan für die Länder mit dem niedrigeren Auswahlsatz in der Weise modifiziert, daß hier in der Größenklasse I jeder siebte Betrieb mit etwa 50 % seiner Arbeitnehmer, in der Größenklasse II jeder zweite Betrieb mit etwa 15 % seiner Arbeitnehmer und in der Größenklasse III jeder Betrieb mit etwa 7,5 % seiner Arbeitnehmer erfaßt wurde. Im Gegensatz zu der Erhebung von 1957 wurden bei der Erhebung von 1962 neben Ergebnissen nach Wirtschaftszweigen auch Ergebnisse nach Beschäftigtengrößenklassen ermittelt; daher mußten bei der Aufbereitung die Betriebe eventuell abweichend von der Auswahlgrundlage nach Wirtschaftszweigen und Größenklassen entsprechend den tatsächlichen Verhältnissen im Erhebungsmonat zugeordnet werden. Über die erhobenen bzw. als Ergebnisse ausgewiesenen Merkmale der Erhebung von 1957 hinaus wurden in der Erhebung von 1962 die Lohnabrechnungsform der Arbeiter (Stundenlohn, fester Wochenlohn oder fester Monatslohn) und summarisch die betriebliche Arbeitszeiteinteilung (Fünf- oder Sechstagewoche) erfaßt. Die Ergebnisse der Gehalts- und Lohnstrukturerhebung in der gewerblichen Wirtschaft 1962 wurden vom Statistischen Bundesamt in der Fachserie M Reihe 17 I (Band 1 Arbeiterverdienste, Band 2 Angestelltenverdienste) veröffentlicht (Stuttgart-Mainz 1966).

Zur Vervollständigung des Systems der amtlichen Effektivverdienststatistik ordnete die "Zweite Verordnung über die Durchführung einer Sondererhebung zur Lohnstatistik" vom 8. August 1961 als repräsentative Individualerhebungen auch eine Gehalts- und Lohnstrukturerhebung in der Landwirtschaft für das Berichtsjahr vom 1. Februar 1962 bis zum 31. Januar 1963, eine Lohnstrukturerhebung in der Forstwirtschaft für das Berichtsjahr vom 1. Oktober 1961 bis zum 30. September 1962 und eine Gehalts- und Lohnstrukturerhebung im Erwerbsgartenbau für den Berichtsmonat Mai 1962 an. Die Gehalts- und Lohnstrukturerhebung in der Landwirtschaft erfaßte in ausgewählten Betrieben ab 20 ha landwirtschaftlicher Nutzfläche, bei denen das Schwergewicht der Produktion auf landwirtschaftlichen Erzeugnissen (Getreide, Hackfrüchte, Vieh, Milch, Eier usw.) lag, grundsätzlich jeweils sämtliche familienfremden Arbeitskräfte, die als typische landwirtschaftliche Arbeitskräfte vollwertige Arbeit leisteten. Die einzelnen Arbeiter wurden bei der Aufbereitung in den Statistischen Landesämtern nach ihrer Qualifikation und ihren Tätigkeitsmerkmalen zu Arbeitergruppen zusammengefaßt, wobei als Grundlage die jeweilige Angabe des Betriebes über die tarifliche Lohngruppe, die ausgeübte Tätigkeit und die Fachausbildung diente. Von den Angestellten wurden nur männliche Inspektoren und Verwalter als ausgewählte Angestelltengruppen in die Erhebung einbezogen. Die Berichtsbetriebe hatten in vier Teilerhebungen zu je drei Monaten für jeden Monat des Berichtsjahres individuelle Angaben zu liefern, und zwar über die im Stundenlohn stehenden Arbeiter für alle zwölf Monate, über die im Monatslohn stehenden Arbeiter sowie die Angestellten dagegen nur für einen Monat. Die Erhebung sollte ursprünglich im Interviewerverfahren durchgeführt werden; da zu den gebotenen Bedingungen jedoch keine geeigneten Interviewer gewonnen werden konnten, mußten die Statistischen Landesämter die Angaben von den Berichtsbetrieben postalisch einholen. Lediglich die trotz mehrfacher Mahnung ausstehenden Meldungen wurden teilweise durch Einschaltung von Gemeindebediensteten eingeholt. Zur Erleichterung des geplanten Interviewereinsatzes und zur Abschwächung von Unregelmäßigkeiten, die in einem einzigen Erhebungsmonat auftreten konnten, sollten die Monatslöhner (Arbeiter und Angestellte) ursprünglich in je einer Hälfte der Betriebe im August und im September 1962 erfaßt werden; da der Interviewereinsatz entfiel, beschränkte man sich jedoch für die Monatslöhner auf den September 1962 als Berichtsmonat. Als Auswahlgrundlage für die Betriebsauswahl dienten die Ergebnisse der landwirtschaftlichen Betriebszählung 1960. Die Betriebe der Auswahlgesamtheit wurden nach ihrer landwirtschaftlichen Nutzfläche entweder einer unteren Größenklasse (20 bis unter 50 ha) oder einer oberen Größenklasse (50 oder mehr ha) zugeordnet. In der unteren Größenklasse sollten nach dem Auswahlplan als Berichtsbetriebe 15 % derjenigen Betriebe ausgewählt werden, die bei der landwirtschaftlichen Betriebszählung 1960 ständig beschäftigte familienfremde Arbeitskräfte hatten. In der oberen Größenklasse waren als Berichtsbetriebe 30 % derjenigen Betriebe auszuwählen, die bei der landwirtschaftlichen Betriebszählung 1960 mindestens nichtständige Arbeitskräfte hatten. Während in der oberen Größenklasse die Arbeiter im Stundenlohn und im Monatslohn sowie die Angestellten erfaßt wurden, beschränkten sich die Meldungen der Betriebe der unteren Größenklasse auf die Arbeiter im Monatslohn. Wegen der unterschiedlichen Auswahlsätze in den beiden Größenklassen mußte bei der Ermittlung von Durchschnittsergebnissen für die Gesamtheit der Betriebe eine Hochrechnung der erfaßten Angaben mit unterschiedlichen Hochrechnungsfaktoren auf 100 % der Grundgesamtheit vorgenommen werden. Für die Realisierung des Auswahlplans wurden den Statistischen Landesämtern nach deren Belieben vom Statistischen Bundesamt mehrere alternative Auswahlverfahren angeboten. Nach dem in Nordrhein-Westfalen angewendeten Verfahren wurde die Betriebsauswahl in den beiden Größenklassen unabhängig voneinander vorgenommen. Zunächst wurden gesondert in jeder Größenklasse die Betriebe der Grundgesamtheit regional nach Gemeinden sortiert, wobei die Reihenfolge der Gemeinden einer "Anordnung in Serpentinenlinie" entsprach, das heißt die Gemeinden wurden in einem zwei bis drei Gemeinden breiten Band von der Westgrenze zur Ostgrenze Nordrhein-Westfalens, dann wieder von der Ostgrenze zur Westgrenze usw. angeordnet. Den Ausgangspunkt dieser Anordnung bildeten die nördlichsten, den Endpunkt die südlichsten Gemeinden Nordrhein-Westfalens. Innerhalb der Gemeinden blieb die Anordnung der Betriebe der Grundgesamtheit je

Größenklasse so erhalten, wie sie in den Auflistungen der landwirtschaftlichen Betriebszählung 1960 vorgegeben war. Aus den auf diese Weise von Gemeinde zu Gemeinde einer geographischen Serpentinenlinie folgenden Auflistungen der Betriebe der Auswahlgesamtheit wurden nach dem systematischen Auswahlverfahren - d.h. ausgehend von einer Zufallsstartzahl unter Einhaltung fester Auswahlabstände - bestimmte Betriebe ausgewählt, und zwar in der unteren Größenklasse jeder achtzigste und in der oberen Größenklasse jeder zwanzigste Betrieb. Als Berichtsbetriebe wurden dann außer den systematisch ausgewählten Betrieben die in der Anordnung der Auswahlgesamtheit darauffolgenden elf Betriebe (untere Größenklasse) bzw. fünf Betriebe (obere Größenklasse) bestimmt. Die auf diese Berichtsbetriebe folgenden sechs Betriebe (untere Größenklasse) bzw. zwei Betriebe (obere Größenklasse) wurden als bei Bedarf in die Aufbereitung einzubeziehende Reservebetriebe ausgewählt. In die Stichprobe gelangten demnach nicht isoliert ausgewählte Betriebe, sondern ganze Klumpen regional benachbarter Betriebe. Diese Klumpenauswahl wurde ursprünglich lediglich im Hinblick auf den geplanten Interviewereinsatz vorgenommen, jedoch dann trotz des Verzichts auf den Interviewereinsatz beibehalten, obwohl bei postalischen Erhebungen eine reine Zufallsauswahl vorzuziehen ist. Erhebungsmerkmale der Gehalts- und Lohnstrukturerhebung in der Landwirtschaft 1962/63 waren vor allem der Barverdienst mit gesonderter Angabe der Bezahlung für Über-, Sonn- und Feiertagsstunden bei Stundenlöhnern und der Jahrestantiemen und -barprämien bei Angestellten, die Naturalleistungen, die gesetzlichen Abzüge, die Arbeitszeit der Arbeiter sowie weitere in Gehalts- und Lohnstrukturerhebungen übliche persönliche Merkmale. Die unentgeltlich gewährten Naturalleistungen wurden nur nach Arten und Mengen erfaßt und bei der Aufbereitung in den Statistischen Landesämtern nach den für Zwecke der Sozialversicherung von den zuständigen obersten Landesbehörden festgelegten Sätzen bewertet. Bei den gegen Entgelt gewährten Naturalleistungen wurden die an die Arbeitgeber gezahlten bzw. von diesen einbehaltenen Beträge dem Barverdienst der Arbeitnehmer zugerechnet. Für den Berichtsmonat Oktober 1962 wurde auf besonderen Erhebungsbogen für die einzelnen Arbeitnehmer - und zwar nur für die im Stundenlohn stehenden Arbeiter - die zu zahlende Miete für eventuell bereitgestellte Werkswohnungen erfaßt. Diese Wohnungsbogen wurden zentral im Statistischen Bundesamt aufbereitet; dabei wurde durch Gegenüberstellung mit vergleichbaren Einzelangaben aus der Einkommens- und Verbrauchsstichprobe 1962 der jeweilige "Mietvorteil" als Differenz zwischen der niedrigeren Miete für die Werkswohnung und dem tatsächlichen Mietwert der Wohnung berechnet. Als Ergebnisse der Gehalts- und Lohnstrukturerhebung in der Landwirtschaft wurden vor allem durchschnittliche Stunden-, Monats- und Jahresverdienste sowie Häufigkeitsverteilungen nach Verdienstklassen ausgewiesen. Die Ergebnisse wurden vom Statistischen Bundesamt in der Fachserie M Reihe 17 II (Arbeiter- und Angestelltenverdienste) veröffentlicht (Stuttgart-Mainz 1964).

Die Lohnstrukturerhebung in der Forstwirtschaft 1961/62 stellte in methodischer und organisatorischer Hinsicht weitestgehend eine Wiederholung der bereits für 1952/53 durchgeführten Strukturerhebung (vgl. Seite 79) dar. Erfaßt wurden wieder - diesmal auf Grund von Verzeichnissen der landwirtschaftlichen Betriebszählung 1960 - alle staatlichen und kommunalen Forstbetriebe ab 100 ha Waldfläche und in diesen Betrieben im Individualverfahren sämtliche Haumeister sowie diejenigen sonstigen Arbeiter, deren Familiennamen mit den Buchstaben D, G, L, R, T oder W begannen. Allerdings beschränkte sich die Erhebung für 1961/62 neben den Haumeistern auf die ständig beschäftigten männlichen Waldarbeiter der höchsten tarifmäßigen Altersstufe. Ferner ergab sich dadurch eine Vereinfachung, daß das Erhebungsjahr nicht mehr in Berichtsquartale aufgeteilt wurde; die Betriebe wurden vielmehr nur zu einer einmaligen Berichterstattung für das gesamte Forstwirtschaftsjahr herangezogen. Die Naturalleistungen wurden nicht mehr erfaßt; darüber hinaus wurde der Katalog der Erhebungsmerkmale noch weiter verkürzt. Erhebungsmerkmale waren vor allem der Bruttoverdienst nach Lohnform mit gesonderter Angabe des Lohnfortzahlungsbetrages bei Krankheit sowie verschiedener Zulagen, die gesetzlichen Abzüge, die Arbeitszeit sowie weitere in den Strukturerhebungen übliche persönliche Merkmale. Die Ergebnisse der Lohnstrukturerhebung in der Forstwirtschaft 1961/62 wurden vom Statistischen Bundesamt in der Fachserie M Reihe 17 III (Arbeiterverdienste) veröffentlicht (Stuttgart-Mainz 1963).

Zu der Gehalts- und Lohnstrukturerhebung im Erwerbsgartenbau 1962 wurden aus Auflistungen der Gartenbauerhebung 1961 nach dem systematischen Auswahlverfahren einheitlich in allen Bundesländern 50 % der Erwerbsgartenbaubetriebe mit familienfremden Arbeitskräften unabhängig von der Betriebsgröße als Berichtsbetriebe ausgewählt. Zum Erwerbsgartenbau im Sinne der Erhebung gehörten Betriebe, in denen die Gartenbauerzeugnisse - Gemüse, Obst u.a. - mindestens 90 % der Verkaufserlöse aus eigenem Anbau auf sich vereinigten und die nach eigenen Angaben nicht als Hauptbetriebszweig Landschaftsgärtnerei, Ladengeschäft, Blumen- und Kranzbinderei, Obstwein- und -saftherstellung oder -brennerei oder Herstellung von Konserven betrieben. Die Berichtsbetriebe hatten Individualangaben für jeweils sämtliche mit gärtnerischen Arbeiten beschäftigten familienfremden Arbeiter und Angestellten, die den ganzen Erhebungsmonat über voll beschäftigt waren, zu melden. Neben den Barverdiensten wurden auch die unentgeltlich gewährten Naturalleistungen nach Arten und Mengen erfaßt und bei der Aufbereitung in den Statistischen Landesämtern mit Hilfe der von den obersten Landesbehörden für Zwecke der Sozialversicherung festgelegten Sätze bewertet; soweit Deputate wie Obst und Gemüse in den Bewertungsrichtlinien der obersten Landesbehörden nicht aufgeführt waren, erfolgte die Bewertung nach dem Landesdurchschnitt des jeweiligen Verbraucherpreises. Erhebungsmerkmale waren vor allem der Bruttoverdienst mit gesonderter Angabe der Bezahlung für Mehrarbeit, die gesetzlichen Abzüge, die Arbeitszeit der Arbeiter sowie weitere verdienstbestimmende persönliche Merkmale (u.a. Qualifikation, ausgeübte Tätigkeit und Anzahl der Berufsjahre). Die individuellen Verdienstangaben wurden zu durchschnittlichen Stunden- und Monatsverdiensten und Häufigkeitsverteilungen nach Verdienstklassen aufbereitet. Die Ergebnisse wurden vom Statistischen Bundesamt in der Fachserie M Reihe 17 IV (Arbeiter- und Angestelltenverdienste) veröffentlicht (Stuttgart-Mainz 1963).

163 Maschinelle Datenverarbeitung

Bereits im Statistischen Reichsamt wurden die vierteljährlichen Lohnsummenerhebungen und teilweise auch die Individuallohnerhebungen mit Hilfe von Lochkartenmaschinen aufbereitet. Als sich nach dem Zweiten Weltkrieg das Schwergewicht der statistischen Aufbereitung auf die Statistischen Landesämter verlagerte, wurden zunächst unterschiedliche Aufbereitungsverfahren angewendet. Dabei war besonders das Statistische Landesamt Nordrhein-Westfalen führend auf dem Gebiet der maschinellen Datenverarbeitung. Bereits in der ersten Nachkriegszeit wurden die vierteljährlichen Lohnsummenerhebungen der Industriearbeiter in Nordrhein-Westfalen mit Hilfe von Lochkartenmaschinen aufbereitet. Es handelte sich zunächst um eine teilmaschinelle Aufbereitung, bei der nur die Summen und Durchschnittswerte für die einzelnen Wirtschaftszweige maschinell ermittelt, die Zusammenfassung der Einzelzweigdurchschnitte zu Durchschnitten für übergeordnete Wirtschaftsgruppen sowie die Plausibilitätskontrollen dagegen ausschließlich manuell durchgeführt wurden. Das Vertrauen in die maschinelle Datenverarbeitung war offensichtlich noch nicht sehr groß, denn die maschinell ermittelten Durchschnittswerte wurden zur Kontrolle manuell nachgerechnet. Auch die Gehalts- und Lohnstrukturerhebungen und sonstigen Sondererhebungen der Nachkriegszeit bis zur Mitte der fünfziger Jahre wurden in Nordrhein-Westfalen bereits teilmaschinell - d.h. hinsichtlich der Ergebnisberechnung maschinell, hinsichtlich der Plausibilitätskontrolle vorwiegend manuell - mit Lochkartenmaschinen aufbereitet; bei der Gehalts- und Lohnstrukturerhebung in der Landwirtschaft 1953/54 wurde darüber hinaus die Auswahl der Berichtsbetriebe maschinell vorgenommen. Das Reformjahr 1957 brachte in der maschinellen Datenverarbeitung der Lohnstatistik insoweit einen Fortschritt, als von diesem Zeitpunkt an das Verfahren der teilmaschinellen Lochkartenaufbereitung mit maschineller Ergebnisberechnung und vorwiegend manueller Plausibilitätskontrolle sowohl bei den laufenden Verdiensterhebungen in Industrie und Handel und im Handwerk als auch bei den Gehalts- und Lohnstrukturerhebungen in allen Bundesländern angewendet wurde. Anfang der sechziger

Jahre erfolgte in der amtlichen Statistik der Übergang vom konventionellen Lochkartenverfahren zur elektronischen Datenverarbeitung, und zwar wurden bis 1962 im Statistischen Bundesamt und in allen Statistischen Landesämtern einheitlich Datenverarbeitungsanlagen von Typ IBM 1401 eingerichtet. Mit Hilfe der elektronischen Datenverarbeitung war es möglich, neben der Betriebsauswahl, Ergebnisberechnung und Tabellierung auch die Plausibilitätskontrolle weitgehend maschinell durchzuführen. Diese vollmaschinelle Aufbereitung wurde im Verlauf der sechziger Jahre für das gesamte System der laufenden und einmaligen lohnstatistischen Erhebungen die Regel. Die vollmaschinelle Aufbereitung wurde in der vierteljährlichen Verdiensterhebung in Industrie und Handel im Jahre 1964, in der halbjährlichen Verdiensterhebung im Handwerk im Jahre 1966 und in den Gehalts- und Lohnstrukturerhebungen ebenfalls ab 1966 eingeführt. Nur in Ausnahmefällen - bei Erhebungen mit besonders geringer Erhebungsmasse wie der jährlichen Verdiensterhebung in der Landwirtschaft - wurde die Aufbereitung weiterhin manuell vorgenommen; für die Ermittlung der Summen wurden teilweise - zum Beispiel in einigen Ländern bei der Gehalts- und Lohnstrukturerhebung im Erwerbsgartenbau 1962 - auch Buchungsautomaten eingesetzt. Für die maschinelle Betriebs- bzw. Unternehmensauswahl wurde allgemein ein vom Statistischen Bundesamt unter der Bezeichnung "Stichprobenauswahl-Standardprogramm STIA" entwickeltes Programm für die maschinelle Zufallsauswahl aus geschichteten Gesamtheiten verwendet. In den Jahren 1966 bis 1968 rüsteten das Statistische Bundesamt und die Statistischen Landesämter ihre Maschinenausstattung auf leistungsfähigere EDV-Anlagen (vor allem Typ IBM 360) um, wobei teilweise unterschiedliche Typen und Größen eingesetzt wurden. Mit Hilfe dieser Anlagen konnte die maschinelle Plausibilitätskontrolle bei den lohnstatistischen Erhebungen in den darauffolgenden Jahren nach und nach erheblich erweitert und verfeinert werden; in den siebziger Jahren wurde außerdem in erhöhtem Maße dazu übergegangen, für den Datentransport zwischen den statistischen Ämtern statt der herkömmlichen Liefertabellen Datenträger - in der Regel Magnetbänder - zu verwenden. Durch die Uneinheitlichkeit der Maschinenausstattung in den Statistischen Landesämtern

- verstärkt dadurch, daß das Statistische Landesamt Nordrhein-Westfalen für die Bearbeitung von Statistiken ab 1972 eine neue Anlage vom Typ Siemens 7.750-J einsetzte - wurde andererseits die Verwendung gemeinsamer Programme für die maschinelle Aufbereitung erschwert.

Im Zuge der im Jahre 1957 durchgeführten Reform der Effektivverdienststatistik wurden auch die Indexberechnungen auf eine neue methodische Grundlage gestellt. Die neuen Indices - es handelte sich um Effektivverdienstindices und Indices der Tariflöhne und -gehälter - wurden nach dem Modell des Preisindex von Laspeyres unter Verwendung von Gewichten berechnet, die mehrere Jahre lang konstant gehalten wurden. Das Statistische Bundesamt ermittelte nunmehr vierteljährlich und jährlich die folgenden lohnstatistischen Indices:

Index der durchschnittlichen Bruttostundenverdienste der Arbeiter in der Industrie

Index der durchschnittlichen Bruttowochenverdienste der Arbeiter in der Industrie

Index der durchschnittlichen Bruttomonatsverdienste der Angestellten in Industrie und Handel

Index der tariflichen Stundenlöhne der Arbeiter in der gewerblichen Wirtschaft und bei Gebietskörperschaften

Index der tariflichen Wochenlöhne der Arbeiter in der gewerblichen Wirtschaft und bei Gebietskörperschaften

Index der tariflichen Monatsgehälter der Angestellten in der gewerblichen Wirtschaft und bei Gebietskörperschaften

Index der Tariflöhne in der Landwirtschaft

Die Indices der Effektivverdienste wiesen die Verdienstentwicklung auf Grund der Ergebnisse der "vierteljährlichen Verdiensterhebung in Industrie und Handel" aus. Als erste dieser Indices wurden die Indices der Arbeiterverdienste berechnet.*) Die in jedem Bundesland, jedem Wirtschaftszweig und jeder Arbeitergruppe - differenziert nach Geschlecht und Leistungsgruppe - konstant gehaltenen Gewichte wurden zunächst ermittelt, indem die Arbeiterzahlen der Gehalts- und Lohnstrukturerhebung in der gewerblichen Wirtschaft 1951 mit Hilfe anderer Statistiken (vor allem Industrie- und Bauberichterstattung) auf den Stand des Jahres

*) vgl. Kurt Horstmann, Wolf v.d. Decken: Neuberechnung der Indices über die Verdienste und die bezahlten Wochenstunden der Industriearbeiter. In Wirtschaft und Statistik Jahrgang 1959. Seite 184 ff.

1954 fortgeschrieben und anschließend mit den jahresdurchschnittlichen Bruttostunden- bzw. Bruttowochenverdiensten der Verdiensterhebung für 1954 multipliziert wurden. Diesen Indices lag also die Struktur des Jahres 1954 zugrunde. Die auf der Basis des "Wägungsjahres" 1954 berechneten Indices wurden allerdings auf den Jahresdurchschnitt 1950 umbasiert,so daß der gleich 100 gesetzte Beginn der veröffentlichten Indexreihen nicht mit dem Basiszeitraum des Laspeyres-Modells zusammenfiel. In mehrjährigen Abständen wurden die Gewichte der Verdienstindices durch Vergleich mit neueren Strukturdaten überprüft und gegebenenfalls neu festgelegt. Als nächstes Wägungsjahr wurde das Jahr 1958 verwendet; die neuen Gewichte wurden durch Multiplikation der Arbeiterzahlen der Gehalts- und Lohnstrukturerhebung in der gewerblichen Wirtschaft 1957 - auf eine Fortschreibung auf den Stand des Jahres 1958 wurde verzichtet - mit den Jahresdurchschnittsverdiensten der Verdiensterhebung für 1958 gewonnen. Bei dieser Gelegenheit wurde analog auch mit der Berechnung von Indices der effektiven Angestelltenverdienste begonnen.*) Als Basis der veröffentlichten Indexreihen diente nunmehr ebenfalls der Jahresdurchschnitt 1958. Einige Jahre später wurden die Indexreihen auf den Jahresdurchschnitt 1962 umbasiert, als Wägungsjahr wurde jedoch weiterhin das Jahr 1958 verwendet. Eine Neubestimmung der Gewichte erfolgte erst zusammen mit der abermaligen Umbasierung auf den Jahresdurchschnitt 1970. Die neuen Gewichte wurden durch Multiplikation der Arbeitnehmerzahlen der Gehalts- und Lohnstrukturerhebung in der gewerblichen Wirtschaft 1966 - von einer Fortschreibung auf den Stand des Jahres 1970 wurde wiederum abgesehen - mit den Jahresdurchschnittsverdiensten der vierteljährlichen Verdiensterhebung für 1970 ermittelt. Sämtliche Indices der Effektivverdienste wurden nach der folgenden Formel berechnet:

$$_{o}I_{t} = \frac{\sum_{i=1}^{n} \frac{v_{it}}{v_{io}} v_{io} z_{io}}{\sum_{i=1}^{n} v_{io} z_{io}} \cdot 100$$

*) vgl. Hans-Gustav Kloß: Index der Bruttomonatsverdienste der Angestellten in Industrie und Handel auf der Basis 1958. In Wirtschaft und Statistik Jahrgang 1962, Seite 84 ff.

Symbole:

$_{o}I_{t}$ = Index für den Berichtszeitraum t bezogen auf den Basiszeitraum o

i=1,2....,n = laufende Nummern der einzelnen Verdienstreihen (d.h. der einzelnen Wirtschaftszweige bzw. Leistungsgruppen), die im Index zusammengefaßt werden

n = Anzahl der Verdienstreihen

v = Durchschnittlicher Bruttostundenverdienst (bzw. durchschnittlicher Bruttowochen- oder Bruttomonatsverdienst) pro Arbeiter bzw. pro Angestellten (nach vierteljährlicher Verdiensterhebung)

z = Anzahl der Arbeiter bzw. der Angestellten (nach - eventuell fortgeschriebenen - Gehalts- und Lohnstrukturerhebungen)

Die Indexreihen der Effektivverdienste wurden vom Statistischen Bundesamt laufend in "Preise Löhne Wirtschaftsrechnungen" (seit 1962 "Fachserie M") Reihe 15 I. Arbeiterverdienste (ab Heft 1/1959) und II. Angestelltenverdienste (ab Heft 4/1961) veröffentlicht (Stuttgart 1958 ff. bzw. Stuttgart-Mainz 1962 ff.).

Die Materialgrundlage für die Indices der Tariflöhne und -gehälter bildeten die bei den obersten Arbeitsbehörden des Bundes und der Länder geführten amtlichen Tarifarchive. Die Indices der Tariflöhne und -gehälter in der gewerblichen Wirtschaft und bei Gebietskörperschaften wurden nach einheitlicher Methode ermittelt.*) Diese Indices wiesen die Entwicklung der tariflichen Grundlohn- und Grundgehaltssätze ohne Berücksichtigung der verschiedenen Zulagen und Zuschläge aus. In die Berechnung wurden grundsätzlich nur Zeitlohnsätze einbezogen, lediglich für die Tabakindustrie wurde stattdessen auf den tariflichen "Akkordstundenlohnsatz" zurückgegriffen. Für die Indices wurden gezielt ausgewählte Verbandstarifverträge - abgeschlossen jeweils zwischen einer Arbeitgebervereinigung und einer Gewerkschaft - und Firmentarifverträge - abgeschlossen zwischen einem einzelnen Arbeitgeber

*) vgl. Peter Deneffe, Ursula Schulz: Zur Berechnung von Indices der Tariflöhne und Tarifgehälter. In: Wirtschaft und Statistik Jahrgang 1958, Seite 494 ff.

und einer Gewerkschaft -, jedoch keine tarifähnlichen Betriebsvereinbarungen - früher als "Haustarife" bezeichnet - zwischen einzelnen Arbeitgebern und ihren Betriebsräten ausgewertet. Die Auswahl der Tarifverträge wurde nach ihrer Bedeutung - gemessen an der Anzahl der betroffenen Arbeitnehmer - vorgenommen. In jedem einzelnen Wirtschaftszweig wurden die Tarifverträge mit der größten Arbeiter- bzw. Angestelltenzahl ausgewählt, solange bis 75 % der in dem betreffenden Wirtschaftszweig beschäftigten Arbeiter bzw. Angestellten durch die Verträge repräsentiert waren. Aus jedem ausgewählten Tarifvertrag wurden zunächst nur die oberste und die unterste Lohn- bzw. Gehaltsgruppe sowie einige dazwischenliegende stark besetzte Gruppen in die Indexberechnung einbezogen. Für die ausgewählten Tarifverträge und Tarifgruppen wurden Zeitreihen tariflicher Stundenlohnsätze bzw. tariflicher Monatsgehaltssätze gebildet, wobei nur die Sätze der höchsten tarifmäßigen Altersstufe - d.h. für die Angestellten die sogenannten Endgehälter - und der höchsten tariflichen Ortsklasse verwendet wurden. Die konstant gehaltenen Gewichte für diese Zeitreihen wurden zunächst wie bei den Effektivverdienstindices berechnet, in dem die Arbeiter - bzw. Angestelltenzahlen der Gehalts- und Lohnstrukturerhebung in der gewerblichen Wirtschaft 1951 mit Hilfe der Industrie- und Bauberichterstattung und anderer Statistiken auf den Stand des Jahres 1954 fortgeschrieben und anschließend mit den jahresdurchschnittlichen Tariflohn- bzw. -gehaltssätzen für 1954 multipliziert wurden. Die nicht zu den ausgewählten Tarifgruppen gehörenden Arbeitnehmer wurden bei der Gewichtung dadurch mitberücksichtigt, daß sie den nächstliegenden in die Indexberechnung einbezogenen Lohn- bzw. Gehaltsgruppen zugeordnet wurden. In die Gewichte ging jeweils die Gesamtzahl der Arbeiter bzw. Angestellten eines Wirtschaftszweiges ein, das heißt nicht nur die Anzahl der gewerkschaftlich organisierten Arbeitnehmer der tarifgebundenen Unternehmen. Abweichend vom Wägungsjahr 1954 wurde die zeitliche Basis der veröffentlichten Indexreihen auf den gleich 100 gesetzten November 1950 gelegt. Nach dem hier geschilderten Verfahren wurde neben den Indices der tariflichen Stundenlöhne der Arbeiter und der tariflichen Monatsgehälter der Angestellten analog auch ein Index der tariflichen Wochenarbeitszeit der Arbeiter berechnet. Der Index der tariflichen Wochenlöhne der Arbeiter ergab sich dann durch Multiplikation des Index der tariflichen Stundenlöhne mit dem Index der tariflichen Wochenarbeitszeit. Als nächstes Wägungsjahr wurde wie bei den Effektivverdienstindices das Jahr 1958 verwendet; die Gewichte wurden durch Multiplikation der Arbeitnehmerzahlen der Gehalts- und Lohnstrukturerhebung in der gewerblichen Wirtschaft 1957 - teilweise ergänzt durch Daten des Mikrozensus und der Industrieberichterstattung - mit den jahresdurchschnittlichen Tariflohn- bzw. -gehaltssätzen für 1958 ermittelt. Auch die zeitliche Basis der neuen Indexreihen war der Jahresdurchschnitt 1958. Bei der Umbasierung auf den Jahresdurchschnitt 1962 wurde das Wägungsschema von 1958 beibehalten, bei der Umbasierung auf den Jahresdurchschnitt 1970 dagegen ein neues Wägungsschema durch Multiplikation der Arbeitnehmerzahlen der Gehalts- und Lohnstrukturerhebung in der gewerblichen Wirtschaft 1966 mit den jahresdurchschnittlichen Tariflohn - bzw. -gehaltssätzen für 1970 verwendet. Anläßlich der Umbasierung auf 1970 wurde die Datengrundlage der Tariflohn- und -gehaltsindices in der Weise erweitert, daß nunmehr in den ausgewählten Tarifverträgen jeweils sämtliche Lohn- und Gehaltsgruppen in die Berechnung einbezogen sowie zu den Lohn- und Gehaltssätzen eventuelle laufend gezahlte vermögenswirksame Leistungen und im öffentlichen Dienst die Ortszuschläge addiert wurden. Die Berechnung der Indices der Tariflöhne und -gehälter in der gewerblichen Wirtschaft und bei Gebietskörperschaften wurde im übrigen nach der gleichen Formel wie bei den Effektivverdienstindices vorgenommen.

Die Methodik des Index der Tariflöhne in der Landwirtschaft wich in einigen Punkten von der der anderen Tarifindices ab.*) In diesen Index wurden ausgewählte Arbeiterlohngruppen aus sämtlichen landwirtschaftlichen Tarifverträgen einbezogen. Als Lohnsätze wurden Zeitlohnsätze für alle Ortsklassen verwendet, und zwar die tariflich festgesetzten Monatslöhne für die im Monatslohn stehen-

---

*) vgl. Ursula Schulz: Zur Berechnung eines Index der Tariflöhne in der Landwirtschaft. In: Wirtschaft und Statistik Jahrgang 1958, Seite 596 ff.

den und Stundenlöhne für die im Stundenlohn stehenden Arbeiter der höchsten tarifmäßigen Altersstufe. Soweit unentgeltliche Naturalleistungen tariflich vorgesehen waren, wurden sie für die Jahre ab 1957 nach den jeweiligen amtlichen Sätzen bewertet, die für Zwecke der Berechnung der Lohnsteuer und der Sozialversicherungsbeiträge gültig waren. Für die Jahre vor 1957 wurden zur Bewertung der Naturalleistungen die amtlichen Sätze von 1957 mit der Entwicklung des Preisindex für die Lebenshaltung zurückgeschrieben. Der Index der Tariflöhne in der Landwirtschaft wurde gesondert als Index der Stundenlöhne, als Index der Monatsbarlöhne (diese Reihe wurde später eingestellt), als Index der Gesamtmonatslöhne (Monatsbarlöhne zuzüglich Naturalleistungen) und als Gesamtlohnindex (Durchschnitt aus Stunden- und Monatslöhnen) aufgestellt. Die zeitlichen Basen dieser Indexreihen wurden wie bei den nichtlandwirtschaftlichen Tarifindices zunächst auf den November 1950 und später auf die Jahresdurchschnitte 1958, 1962 und 1970 gelegt. In das Wägungsschema ging im Gegensatz zu den nichtlandwirtschaftlichen Tarifindices nicht der durchschnittliche Tariflohn, sondern ausschließlich die Anzahl der Arbeiter des Wägungsjahres ein. Als konstante Gewichte dienten zunächst die Arbeiterzahlen - unter Einschluß der nicht gewerkschaftlich organisierten Arbeiter sowie der in nicht-tarifgebundenen Betrieben beschäftigten Arbeiter -, die nach den Ergebnissen der landwirtschaftlichen Betriebszählung 1949 und der Statistik der Arbeitsverwaltung im Durchschnitt der Wirtschaftsjahre 1950/51 bis 1952/53 bestanden hatten. Bei der Umbasierung auf das Jahr 1958 wurde kein neues Wägungsschema aufgestellt. Bei den späteren Umbasierungen auf die Jahre 1962 und 1970 wurden als neue Gewichte Arbeiterzahlen der jeweils letzten landwirtschaftlichen Betriebszählung(für 1960 bzw. 1971) der Indexberechnung zugrundegelegt. Die Formel für die Berechnung des Index der Tariflöhne in der Landwirtschaft lautet:

$$ {}_{o}I_{t} = \frac{\sum_{i=1}^{n} \frac{v_{it}}{v_{io}} z_{io}}{\sum_{i=1}^{n} z_{io}} \cdot 100 $$

Symbole:

$_oI_t$ = Index für den Berichtszeitraum t bezogen auf den Basiszeitraum 0

i=1,2,..,n = laufende Nummern der einzelnen Lohnreihen (d.h. der einzelnen Lohngruppen), die im Index zusammengefaßt werden

n = Anzahl der Lohnreihen

v = gewogener durchschnittlicher Tariflohn je Lohngruppe im Bundesgebiet (gewogen mit den jeweiligen Arbeiterzahlen über alle Ortsklassen und alle Bundesländer bzw. Tarifgebiete)

z = Anzahl der Arbeiter

Sämtliche Indices der Tariflöhne und -gehälter wurden vom Statistischen Bundesamt laufend in "Preise Löhne Wirtschaftsrechnungen" (seit 1962 "Fachserie M") Reihe 11 III veröffentlicht (Stuttgart-Mainz 1959 ff.), und zwar als Vierteljahresindices zum Ende der jeweiligen Berichtsmonate der vierteljährlichen Verdiensterhebung in Industrie und Handel sowie als Jahresindices, die als Durchschnitte aus den vier Vierteljahresindices jedes Jahres gebildet wurden. Diese Veröffentlichungen enthielten auch Angaben über die vierteljährlichen und jährlichen prozentualen Erhöhungen der tariflichen Stundenlöhne bzw. Monatsgehälter der Arbeiter bzw. Angestellten in der gewerblichen Wirtschaft und bei Gebietskörperschaften nach Erhöhungsklassen. Darüber hinaus wurden in der Fachserie M Reihe 11 I und II nur Einzelangaben aus Tarifverträgen (Lohn- und Gehaltssätze sowie sonstige tarifliche Regelungen) wiedergegeben, ohne statistisch verarbeitet zu werden.

Unabhängig vom Statistischen Bundesamt wurde von der Deutschen Bundesbank seit 1957 mit monatlicher Periodizität ein "Index des Tariflohn- und -gehaltsniveaus" auf Stunden- und auf Wochenverdienstbasis - später auf Stunden- und auf Monatsverdienstbasis - berechnet, der Arbeiter, Angestellte und Beamte zusammenfaßte und damit die Tariflohnentwicklung von ca. 85 % aller Arbeitnehmer repäsentierte. In die Berechnung wurden nur die tariflichen Grundlohn- und -gehaltssätze ohne Berücksichtigung der Zulagen einbezogen. Neben der Indexreihe für die Gesamtwirtschaft wurde eine besondere Indexreihe für den Wirtschaftsbereich Industrie aufgestellt. Der Index der Deutschen Bundesbank "stellt eine durch laufende Verkettung gewonnene Meßziffer des gesamten Tariflohnniveaus, nicht dagegen eine aus Einzelreihen für eine Anzahl von Wirtschaftszweigen gewonnene Durchschnittsziffer dar. Die Verkettung erfolgt dabei in der Weise, daß jede nach einem bestimmten Indexstand in Kraft getretene Tariflohn- bzw. -gehaltserhöhung dem Index hinzugerechnet wird, und zwar mit dem Gewicht, das den davon betroffenen Arbeitnehmern im Verhältnis zur Gesamtzahl der in der Tariflohnstatistik erfaßten Beschäftigten entspricht. Diese Hinzurechnung wird jeweils am Ende eines Monats vorgenommen, so daß die Meßziffern stets Monatsendstände sind. Die Zahl der tarifstatistisch erfaßten Beschäftigten, die zur Gewichtung bei der Ermittlung der durchschnittlichen Erhöhungssätze dient, wird innerhalb eines Jahres konstant gehalten, jedoch von Jahr zu Jahr der Beschäftigtenentwicklung angepaßt. Im Gegensatz zum Tariflohnindex des Statistischen Bundesamtes, der mit konstanten Gewichten errechnet wird, kommen daher in dem Index der Bundesbank bei mehrjährigen Vergleichen auch Verschiebungen in der Beschäftigtenstruktur zum Ausdruck".*) Der Index des Tariflohn- und -gehaltsniveaus wird erst seit 1967 - rückwirkend für die Jahre ab 1958 - laufend veröffentlicht (Monatsberichte der Deutschen Bundesbank, Frankfurt am Main 1967 ff.).

*) zitiert nach unveröffentlichten Unterlagen der Deutschen Bundesbank.

165 Rentenreform

Die im Jahre 1957 vollzogene Reform der gesetzlichen Rentenversicherung brachte insbesondere für Zwecke der Rentendynamisierung einen erheblichen Mehrbedarf an laufenden lohnstatistischen Daten und damit eine weitere Zunahme der Bedeutung der amtlichen Lohnstatistik mit sich. Für die Berechnung der Renten und der Versicherungsbeiträge hatte die Bundesregierung nunmehr jährlich nach Anhören des Statistischen Bundesamtes eine "allgemeine Bemessungsgrundlage" festzusetzen, die sich nach dem durchschnittlichen Bruttoarbeitsentgelt aller Versicherten "im Mittel des dreijährigen Zeitraumes vor dem Kalenderjahr, das dem Eintritt des Versicherungsfalles voraufgegangen ist", richtete (Artikel 1 § 1255 des Gesetzes zur Neuregelung des Rechts der Rentenversicherung der Arbeiter vom 23. Februar 1957, Bundesgesetzblatt 1957 Teil I S. 45; Artikel 1 § 32 des Gesetzes zur Neuregelung des Rechts der Rentenversicherung der Angestellten vom 23. Februar 1957, Bundesgesetzblatt 1957 Teil I S. 88; Artikel 1 § 54 des Gesetzes zur Neuregelung der knappschaftlichen Rentenversicherung vom 21. Mai 1957, Bundesgesetzblatt 1957 Teil I S. 533). Die laufenden Renten wurden bei Veränderungen der allgemeinen Bemessungsgrundlage jährlich angepaßt. Nach der "Verordnung über die Feststellung von Leistungen aus den gesetzlichen Rentenversicherungen bei verlorenen, zerstörten, unbrauchbar gewordenen oder nicht erreichbaren Versicherungsunterlagen" vom 3. März 1960 (Bundesgesetzblatt 1960 Teil I S. 137) waren die betroffenen Arbeitnehmer in Leistungsgruppen einzustufen, deren Gliederung, Bezeichnungen und Definitionen weitestgehend aus der amtlichen Effektivverdienststatistik übernommen wurden.

Auch für die Kriegsopferversorgung wurden laufend lohnstatistische Daten benötigt. Nach § 30 des Bundesversorgungsgesetzes in der Neufassung des Gesetzes zur Änderung und Ergänzung des Kriegsopferrechts vom 27. Juni 1960 (Bundesgesetzblatt 1960 Teil I S. 453) war ein "Berufsschadensausgleich" zu gewähren, der sich nach dem Durchschnittseinkommen der betreffenden Berufsgruppe richtete. Allgemeine Vergleichsgrundlage zur laufenden Ermittlung des Durchschnittseinkommens waren die Ergebnisse der amtlichen lohnstatistischen Erhebungen des Statistischen Bundesamtes. Die "Verordnung zur Durchführung des § 30 Abs. 3 und 4 des Bundesversorgungsgesetzes" vom 28. Februar 1968 (Bundesgesetzblatt 1968 Teil I S. 194) definierte das Durchschnittseinkommen ausdrücklich als durchschnittlichen Bruttoverdienst, wie er in den laufenden Verdiensterhebungen in Industrie und Handel, Handwerk und Landwirtschaft für die einzelnen Wirtschaftszweige und Leistungs- bzw. Arbeitnehmergruppen ermittelt wurde. Die Kriegsopferrenten werden nunmehr wie die Renten aus der gesetzlichen Rentenversicherung jährlich angepaßt.

Für Zwecke der gesetzlichen Unfallversicherung und der gesetzlichen Krankenversicherung mußten nach der Reichsversicherungsordnung nach wie vor sogenannte Ortslöhne sowie für landwirtschaftliche Arbeitnehmer durchschnittliche Jahresarbeitsverdienste festgesetzt werden. Die Festsetzungen, für die die Oberversicherungsämter unter Mitwirkung von Vertretern der Unternehmer und der Arbeitnehmer zuständig waren, erfolgten nach dem Zweiten Weltkrieg zunächst auf Grund der "Ersten Verordnung über Ortslöhne und Jahresarbeitsverdienste in der Sozialversicherung" vom 9. August 1950 (Bundesgesetzblatt 1950 S. 369). Die Festsetzungen wurden seitdem entsprechend der Einkommensentwicklung von Zeit zu Zeit aktualisiert. Auch bei der Reform der gesetzlichen Unfallversicherung (Gesetz zur Neuregelung des Rechts der gesetzlichen Unfallversicherung vom 30. April 1963, Bundesgesetzblatt 1963 Teil I S. 241) wurde die Bestimmung aufrechterhalten, daß gewisse Renten sich nach den Ortslöhnen bzw. durchschnittlichen Jahresarbeitsverdiensten zu richten haben. Mit dem Inkrafttreten des Vierten Buches Sozialgesetzbuch vom 23. Dezember 1976 (Bundesgesetzblatt 1976 Teil I S. 3845) entfallen zum 1. Juli 1977 die Festsetzungen in der bisherigen Form; stattdessen gibt nunmehr der Bundesminister für Arbeit und Sozialordnung laufend die für die Sozialversicherung jeweils maßgebende einheitliche Bezugsgröße bekannt.

17 Die Phase der Internationalisierung (1960 - 1970)

171 Supranationale Rechtsvorschriften

Der Ausbau der Europäischen Wirtschaftsgemeinschaft hatte einen wachsenden Bedarf an vergleichbaren statistischen Daten für alle Mitgliedsländer der Gemeinschaft zur Folge. Die EG-Kommission war daher bemüht, durch das "Statistische Amt der Europäischen Gemeinschaften" sowohl die bestehenden nationalen Statistiken vereinheitlichen als auch die nationalen statistischen Programme durch eigene europäische Erhebungen ergänzen zu lassen. Auf dem Gebiet der Lohnstatistik wurden seit dem Berichtsjahr 1959 zunächst jährliche und später in dreijährigen Abständen wiederholte Erhebungen über die Personalkosten und Personalnebenkosten im produzierenden Gewerbe durchgeführt. Diese Erhebungen beruhten als supranationale Erhebungen auf Verordnungen des "Rates der Europäischen Wirtschaftsgemeinschaft" - bzw. später des "Rates der Europäischen Gemeinschaften" -, die auf den Vertrag zur Gründung der Europäischen Wirtschaftsgemeinschaft - insbesondere auf Artikel 213 - gestützt waren und unmittelbar in jedem Mitgliedstaat galten. Danach war es das Ziel der Erhebungen, der EG-Kommission die notwendigen Informationen über Arbeitskosten und Einkommen der Arbeitnehmer zu liefern, die sie zur Erfüllung der ihr nach dem Vertrag obliegenden Aufgaben benötigte. Die Verordnungen legten ferner als Berichtszeitraum jeweils ein volles Jahr fest und bestimmten, daß die Arbeitgeber auskunftspflichtig und die statistischen Ämter zur Geheimhaltung von Einzelauskünften verpflichtet waren. Form und Inhalt der Erhebungsbogen und die sonstigen Einzelheiten der Erhebungen einschließlich der Stichprobenpläne wurden von der EG-Kommission festgelegt; die Befragung und Aufbereitung wurde von den nationalen statistischen Ämtern - in der Bundesrepublik Deutschland in Zusammenarbeit zwischen dem Statistischen Bundesamt und den Statistischen Landesämtern - durchgeführt. Die in den statistischen Ämtern anfallenden Kosten der Erhebungen gingen nach den Verordnungen "zu Lasten der in den Haushaltsplänen der Europäischen Gemeinschaften für diesen Zweck bereitgestellten Mittel", die jedoch im allgemeinen nicht ausgereicht haben. Als erste dieser supranationalen Rechtsverordnungen wurde die Verordnung Nr. 10 vom

25. August 1960 (Amtsblatt der Europäischen Gemeinschaften 1960 Nr. 56 S. 1199) erlassen, wonach für das Berichtsjahr 1959 eine Personalkostenerhebung in 14 Industriezweigen durchzuführen war. Erfaßt wurden in diesen Zweigen sämtliche Betriebe als örtliche Einheiten - in Ausnahmefällen auf besonderen Antrag auch Unternehmen als rechtliche Einheiten -, die im Jahresdurchschnitt 1959 mindestens 50 Arbeitnehmer beschäftigt hatten. Auf Grund der Verordnung Nr. 14 vom 24. Juli 1961 (Amtsblatt der Europäischen Gemeinschaften 1961 Nr. 55 S. 1054) wurden für das Berichtsjahr 1960 acht weitere Industriezweige erfaßt; nunmehr wurden in der Bundesrepublik Deutschland sämtliche Unternehmen als rechtliche Einheiten - in den anderen EG-Ländern Betriebe als örtliche Einheiten - in die Erhebung einbezogen, die im Durchschnitt des Berichtsjahres mindestens 50 Arbeitnehmer beschäftigt hatten. Unter Beibehaltung dieses Abgrenzungskriteriums wurde nach der Verordnung Nr. 28 vom 14. Mai 1962 (Amtsblatt der Europäischen Gemeinschaften 1962 Nr. 41 S. 1277) für das Berichtsjahr 1961 eine Erhebung bei Unternehmen in 13 weiteren Industriezweigen durchgeführt; dabei wurde in zwei Zweigen - Bekleidungsindustrie und Herstellung von Metallerzeugnissen - statt einer partiellen Totalerhebung von den Unternehmen mit 50 bis 99 Arbeitnehmern nur jedes zweite erfaßt und bei der Aufbereitung eine entsprechende Hochrechnung vorgenommen. Auf Grund der Verordnung Nr. 151 vom 13. Dezember 1962 (Amtsblatt der Europäischen Gemeinschaften 1962 Nr. 133 S. 2841) wurde die Erhebung von 1959 für das Berichtsjahr 1962 - nunmehr bei Unternehmen als Erhebungseinheiten -, die Erhebung von 1960 für das Berichtsjahr 1963 und die Erhebung von 1961 für das Berichtsjahr 1964 wiederholt. Die Verordnung Nr. 101 vom 14. Juli 1966 (Amtsblatt der Europäischen Gemeinschaften 1966 Nr. 134 S. 2540) schrieb für das Berichtsjahr 1966 eine repräsentative Personalkostenerhebung in sämtlichen Zweigen des produzierenden Gewerbes einschließlich des Baugewerbes und des produzierenden Handwerks mit Ausnahme der Energiewirtschaft und Wasserversorgung vor, bei der ausgewählte Unternehmen - deren Angaben bei der Aufbereitung zu Totalwerten hochgerechnet wurden - mit mindestens 50 Arbeitnehmern im Durchschnitt des Berichtsjahres erfaßt wurden. Eine weitere Ausweitung des Erhebungsbereichs brachte die Verordnung Nr. 1899 vom 26. November 1968 (Amtsblatt

der Europäischen Gemeinschaften 1968 Nr. L 289 S. 4), die die Rechtsgrundlage einer Personalkostenerhebung im gesamten produzierenden Gewerbe einschließlich der Energiewirtschaft und Wasserversorgung für das Berichtsjahr 1969 bildete. Bei dieser Repräsentativerhebung war auskunftspflichtige Auswahleinheit das Unternehmen, Erhebungseinheit dagegen der Betrieb. Die ausgewählten Unternehmen hatten grundsätzlich für jeden ihrer Betriebe unabhängig von deren Größe und Produktionsrichtung einen besonderen Erhebungsbogen auszufüllen, sofern das Unternehmen im Durchschnitt des Berichtsjahres mindestens 50 Arbeitnehmer hatte. Aufbereitungseinheiten waren sowohl der Betrieb (für Zwecke der Europäischen Gemeinschaften) als auch das Unternehmen (für deutsche Zwecke). Die Erhebung von 1969 wurde auf Grund der Verordnung Nr. 2259 vom 19. Oktober 1971 (Amtsblatt der Europäischen Gemeinschaften 1971 Nr. L 238 S. 1) mit gleicher Methodik für das Berichtsjahr 1972 wiederholt, wobei nunmehr Unternehmen mit mindestens zehn Arbeitnehmern einbezogen wurden. Nach der Verordnung Nr. 328 vom 10. Februar 1975 (Amtsblatt der Europäischen Gemeinschaften 1975 Nr. L 37 S. 1) wurde in der gleichen Art wie für 1972 bei repräsentativ ausgewählten Unternehmen ab zehn Arbeitnehmern eine Erhebung für das Berichtsjahr 1975 durchgeführt. In der Verordnung Nr. 328 wurde zur Regelung der in den statistischen Ämtern anfallenden Erhebungskosten erstmalig eine klarere Formulierung verwendet: "Die Mitgliedstaaten erhalten für die Durchführung der Erhebung einen der Zahl der befragten Betriebe oder Unternehmen entsprechenden Pauschalbetrag. Dieser Betrag geht zu Lasten der im Haushaltsplan der Europäischen Gemeinschaften für diesen Zweck bereitgestellten Mittel". Die Personalkostenerhebungen der Europäischen Gemeinschaften im produzierenden Gewerbe werden weiterhin in dreijährigen Abständen wiederholt.

Die Personalkostenerhebungen waren von Anfang an durch eine besondere erhebungstechnische Problematik gekennzeichnet. Ungewöhnlich viele Unternehmen konnten die sehr vielfältigen und detaillierten Fragen angeblich entweder gar nicht oder nur mit unzumutbar großem Aufwand beantworten bzw. mußten auf Schätzungen zurückgreifen, weil ihre Buchhaltungsaufzeichnungen nicht ausreichten. Die Rechtsverordnungen schrieben demgegenüber lediglich vor, daß die Arbeitgeber die erforderlichen Auskünfte "auf der Grundlage des Zahlenmaterials der Buchhaltung" zu erteilen hatten. Eine weitere rechtliche Schwierigkeit ergab sich dadurch, daß die Statistischen Landesämter bei den Repräsentativerhebungen bemüht waren, zur Erhaltung einer hinreichend großen Stichprobe auch Unternehmen zu erfassen, die laut Auswahlgrundlage mindestens 50 bzw. 10 Arbeitnehmer hatten, jedoch im Durchschnitt des Erhebungsjahres mit ihrer Arbeitnehmerzahl unter dieser Erfassungsgrenze lagen; diese Unternehmen konnten wegen der engen Bestimmungen der Rechtsverordnungen nicht zur Berichterstattung gezwungen werden.

Hinsichtlich der Erhebungsorganisation wiesen die Personalkostenerhebungen einige Besonderheiten auf. Die Befragung der Berichtsunternehmen oblag grundsätzlich den Statistischen Landesämtern. Die zum Zuständigkeitsbereich der Europäischen Gemeinschaft für Kohle und Stahl gehörenden Unternehmen wurden dagegen - im Falle des Steinkohlenbergbaus und des Eisenerzbergbaus immer, im Falle der Eisen- und Stahlindustrie teilweise - unter Umgehung der nationalen statistischen Ämter von den zuständigen Unternehmensverbänden in direkter Zusammenarbeit mit dem Statistischen Amt der Europäischen Gemeinschaften erfaßt. Die übrigen Unternehmen waren für alle ihre Betriebe demjenigen Statistischen Landesamt gegenüber berichtspflichtig, in dessen Gebiet die Unternehmensleitung ihren Sitz hatte. Da seit der Erhebung für 1969 neben der Unternehmensaufbereitung auch eine Aufbereitung nach Betrieben vorgenommen wurde, mußten die Statistischen Landesämter für die Ermittlung von regionalen Betriebsergebnissen die Angaben für in anderen Bundesländern liegende Zweigbetriebe untereinander austauschen. In die Unternehmensaufbereitung wurden alle erfaßten Unternehmen ab 50 bzw. ab 10 Arbeitnehmern mit sämtlichen (auch kleineren) Zweigbetrieben, in die Betriebsaufbereitung nur die Betriebe mit mindestens 50 bzw. 10 Arbeitnehmern einbezogen. Die Unternehmen bzw. Betriebe wurden dabei - unabhängig von ihrer Kennzeichnung in der Auswahlgrundlage - der Größenklasse und dem Wirtschaftszweig zugeordnet, denen sie nach ihrer Arbeitnehmerzahl und nach ihrer wirtschaftlichen Tätigkeit im Erhebungsjahr tatsächlich angehörten. Der Gliederung und Bezeichnung der Wirtschaftszweige wurden europäische Systematiken zugrundegelegt, und zwar zunächst die NICE (Nomenclature des Industries établies dans les Communautés européennes) und seit der Erhebung für 1972 die NACE (Nomenclature générale des activités économiques dans les Communautés européennes).

Bei den Repräsentativerhebungen wurden die Berichtsunternehmen aus Auflistungen früherer Totalerhebungen - jährliche Unternehmenserhebungen in der Industrie und im Bauhauptgewerbe, Handwerkszählung, Totalerhebungen der Betriebe im Bauhauptgewerbe, Zensus im produzierenden Gewerbe, Arbeitsstättenzählung - als geschichtete Stichproben mit pro Schicht festgelegten Zufallsstartzahlen und prinzipiell unterschiedlichen Auswahlabständen nach dem systematischen Auswahlverfahren ausgewählt. Die Schichten wurden innerhalb jedes einzelnen Wirtschaftszweiges als Unternehmensgrößenklassen nach der Beschäftigtenzahl oder der Arbeitnehmerzahl gebildet. Eine Schichtung der Auswahlgesamtheiten nach Bundesländern wurde wegen der teilweise zu geringen Besetzungszahlen nicht vorgenommen, so daß der für eine Schicht berechnete Auswahlabstand einheitlich für alle Bundesländer galt; dadurch ergaben sich für die Bundesländer unterschiedliche Genauigkeiten in den aus den Stichproben geschätzten Totalergebnissen. Der Berechnung der Auswahlabstände - bzw. der Auswahlsätze als deren Kehrwerte - im Auswahlplan wurden Variationskoeffizienten zugrunde gelegt, die aus früheren Personalkostenerhebungen für das Merkmal "Personalnebenkosten insgesamt je Arbeiter eines Unternehmens" geschätzt wurden. Die Auswahlabstände wurde dann pro Schicht nach einer vorgegebenen Genauigkeitsabstufung (Exponent 0,10) so bestimmt, daß für alle Schichten vergleichbare relative Standardfehler zu erwarten waren. Alle Schichten, die in dem der Berechnung des Auswahlplans zugrunde gelegten Datenmaterial - in der Regel der Auswahlgesamtheit selbst - nicht besetzt waren, wurden im Auswahlplan formal mit dem Auswahlabstand 1 berücksichtigt. Außerdem wurde der Auswahlabstand 1 in allen Wirtschaftszweigen für die oberste Größenklasse vorgegeben, auch wenn im Auswahlplan ein höherer Abstand berechnet worden war. Wenn einzelne ausgewählte Unternehmen bei der Befragung ausfielen, wurde zwischen unechten und echten Antwortausfällen unterschieden. Bei "unechten Ausfällen" - das sind zum Zeitpunkt der Befragung nicht mehr bestehende bzw. nicht mehr zu den erfaßten Wirtschaftszweigen gehörende Unternehmen - wurden die Unternehmen als Berichtsunternehmen ersatzlos gestrichen, bei "echten Ausfällen" - das sind bestehende Unternehmen, die die Antwort verweigern oder so schlecht erteilen, daß sie nicht verwertet werden kann - wurden die ausgefallenen Angaben bei der Aufbereitung durch Dopplung der Angaben eines Berichtsunternehmens desselben Wirtschaftszweiges, derselben Größenklasse und seit der Erhebung für 1969 nach Möglichkeit auch mit derselben Anzahl von Zweigbetrieben ergänzt. Die in den Stichproben erfaßten Angaben wurden bei der Aufbereitung zu Totalwerten hochgerechnet. Der dem Auswahlabstand des Auswahlplans entsprechende Hochrechnungsfaktor wurde für jedes Stichprobenunternehmen unveränderbar festgelegt. Da die Unternehmen unabhängig von ihrer Zuordnung im Auswahlplan den Wirtschaftszweigen und Größenklassen nach den tatsächlichen Verhältnissen im Erhebungsjahr gegebenenfalls neu zugeordnet wurden und dann ihre Hochrechnungsfaktoren in die neuen Schichten mitnahmen, konnten im Gegensatz zum Auswahlplan bei der Aufbereitung in eine Schicht Unternehmen mit verschiedenen Hochrechnungsfaktoren gelangen. Die Hochrechnung konnte daher nicht "pro Schicht", sondern mußte "pro Unternehmen" vorgenommen werden.

Als Ergebnisse der Personalkostenerhebungen der Europäischen Gemeinschaften wurden in erster Linie hochgerechnete Summenangaben - zur Ergänzung auch Durchschnittsangaben pro Arbeiter und pro Angestellten - über sämtliche nach Aufwandsarten tiefgegliederten Personalkosten und Personalnebenkosten einschließlich der Naturalleistungen ausgewiesen. Bei den späteren Erhebungen wurden auch Fallauszählungen vorgenommen, die Aufschluß darüber gaben, wie viele Unternehmen jeweils Personalkosten bestimmter Aufwandsarten hatten und welche Beträge diese Unternehmen dafür aufwendeten. Im Rahmen der Fallauszählungen wurde unter anderem ermittelt, in wie vielen Unternehmen Arbeitnehmer nach dem Dritten Vermögensbildungsgesetz zulagebegünstigte vermögenswirksame Leistungen erhielten oder Teile des Arbeitseinkommens vermögenswirksam anlegten, wie hoch diese Leistungen bzw. angelegten Einkommensteile waren und wie viele Arbeitnehmer davon begünstigt wurden. Die EG-Kommission behielt sich laut vertraglicher Vereinbarung zwischen den Europäischen Gemeinschaften und den Mitgliedstaaten stets das Recht vor, die Ergebnisse der Erhebungen nach eigenem Ermessen zu verwenden und zu veröffentlichen. Die nationalen statistischen Ämter durften erst nach ausdrücklicher Zustimmung der EG-Kommission die Ergebnisse für ihr Land veröffentlichen. Die Veröffentlichung der Ergebnisse aller Erhebungen für die Bundesrepublik Deutschland erfolgte durch das Statistische Bundesamt in "Preise Löhne Wirtschaftsrechnungen" (seit 1962 "Fachserie M") Reihe 15 in der Form von "Sonderbeiträgen" (Stuttgart - Mainz 1961 ff.).

172 Geplante Zufallsstichproben

Im Lauf der sechziger Jahre wurden in verstärktem Maße neuere Erkenntnisse der Theorie der Stichprobenziehung in die Praxis der amtlichen Lohnstatistik übernommen. Für die laufenden Verdiensterhebungen wurden auf Grund detaillierter Stichprobenpläne neue Berichtskreise als Zufallsstichproben aufgestellt. In der vierteljährlichen Verdiensterhebung in Industrie und Handel wurde Anfang 1964 ein derartiger Berichtskreiswechesl vorgenommen.*) Ziel des neuen Auswahlplans war es, die alten Berichtsbetriebe so weit wie möglich gegen bisher noch nicht erfaßte Betriebe auszutauschen und die Zufallsfehler berechenbar und bei vorgegebenem Gesamtstichprobenumfang möglichst klein und in allen Wirtschaftszweigen etwa gleich groß zu machen. Auswahlgrundlagen waren Betriebsauflistungen früherer Totalerhebungen (Totalerhebungen zur Industrie- und zur Bauberichterstattung sowie Arbeitsstättenzählung). Auswahleinheit war der ganze Betrieb als örtliche Einheit; Erhebungseinheit war ebenfalls grundsätzlich der Betrieb, jedoch ausnahmsweise auch der Betriebsteil als fachliche Einheit, wenn eine örtliche Einheit verschiedene Produktionsrichtungen in sich vereinigte und gleichzeitig verschiedene Tarifregelungen anwandte. Aus den Auswahlgrundlagen wurden zunächst die nicht zu erfassenden Betriebe mit weniger als zehn - in Bauhauptgewerbe, Handel, Kreditwirtschaft und Versicherungsgewerbe mit weniger als fünf - Beschäftigten ausgesondert. Die verbleibenden Betriebe wurden innerhalb jedes Bundeslandes erst nach Wirtschaftszweigen und dann nach Beschäftigtengrößenklassen geschichtet; innerhalb der einzelnen Schichten (Größenklassen) wurden die Betriebe nach der Anzahl ihrer Beschäftigten in aufsteigender Reihenfolge angeordnet. Aus der auf diese Weise geschichteten Grundgesamtheit wurden die Berichtsbetriebe nach dem systematischen Auswahlverfahren mit gesondert für jede Schicht

*) vgl. Wolf v.d. Decken, Hans-Joachim Schulz: Reform der laufenden Verdiensterhebung in Industrie und Handel 1964. In: Wirtschaft und Statistik Jahrgang 1964, S. 712 ff.

festgelegten Zufallsstartzahlen und festen - jedoch von Schicht zu Schicht grundsätzlich unterschiedlichen - Auswahlabständen ausgewählt. Der Auswahlabstand 1 - d.h. Totalerfassung - wurde für die oberste Größenklasse jedes Wirtschaftszweiges, für Schichten, die im Auswahlplan nicht berechnet werden konnten, aber in der endgültigen Auswahlgrundlage besetzt waren, und für sonstige Schichten mit sehr geringer Besetzungszahl festgelegt. Im übrigen erfolgte die Aufteilung des Gesamtstichprobenumfangs auf die Schichten - das heißt die Bestimmung der unterschiedlichen Auswahlsätze in den einzelnen Schichten - tendenziell "optimal" im Sinne des Satzes von Tschuprow und Neyman. In einigen Wirtschaftszweigen wurden die Betriebe der Grundgesamtheit innerhalb der Schichten noch nach Untergruppen sortiert. Diese Untergruppen bildeten sogenannte "Anordnungsgruppen", das heißt sie wurden nacheinander so angeordnet, daß durch das systematische Auswahlverfahren jede Untergruppe proportional zu ihrem Umfang erfaßt wurde. Die Betriebe wurden dann innerhalb jeder Untergruppe nach aufsteigender Beschäftigtenzahl geordnet. Die Untergruppen waren jeweils Teilbereiche von Wirtschaftszweigen - zum Beispiel im Wirtschaftszweig Textilindustrie die Teilbereiche Spinnerei, Weberei und sonstige Textilindustrie -, für die gesonderte Ergebnisse ausgewiesen werden sollten, die jedoch in der Auswahlgrundlage - zumindest zum Zeitpunkt der Erstellung des Auswahlplans - nicht getrennt vorlagen. Bei der Stichprobenziehung wurde das systematische Auswahlverfahren in der Weise modifiziert, daß dann nicht immer der bei der Anwendung des vorgegebenen Auswahlabstands zu erfassende Betrieb ausgewählt wurde, wenn dieser Betrieb bereits zum alten Berichtskreis gehört hatte. In diesen Fällen wurde statt des zunächst bestimmten der nächstfolgende bisher nicht erfaßte Betrieb ausgewählt, falls ein solcher in der betreffenden Schicht innerhalb des Auswahlabstandes vorhanden war. Durch diese "Rotation" - die selbstverständlich nur in nicht total erfaßten Schichten möglich war - wurde erreicht, daß die bisherigen Berichtsbetriebe weitgehend von der Berichterstattung entbunden und durch neue Berichtsbetriebe ersetzt werden konnten. Bei der Auswahl von 1964 wurden aus dem Rest der Auswahlgesamtheit Ersatzbetriebe - das waren Betriebe, die nach abgeschlossener Auswahl der Stichprobe in besonderen auf ein sehr geringes Maß beschränkten Einzelfällen einen vorgesehenen Stichprobenbetrieb ersetzen sollten - zufällig ausgewählt. Die Ersatzbetriebe blieben zunächst in Reserve, bis sie gegebenenfalls zum Austausch herangezogen wurden. Auf die Verwendung von Ersatzbetrieben wurde später ganz verzichtet.

Die ausgewählten Berichtsbetriebe hatten weiterhin nach dem Summenverfahren Verdienst- und Arbeitsstundensummen für Arbeitnehmergruppen zu melden. Die von den Stichprobenbetrieben gemeldeten Summen wurden bei der Aufbereitung in den Statistischen Landesämtern in jeder Schicht addiert und auf 100 % der Grundgesamtheit hochgerechnet. Die Hochrechnung wurde nicht mehr wie früher nach der Anzahl der erfaßten Beschäftigten, sondern nach der Anzahl der erfaßten Betriebe vorgenommen. Als Hochrechnungsfaktoren wurden nicht einfach die Auswahlabstände bzw. die Kehrwerte der Auswahlsätze laut Auswahlplan verwendet; die endgültigen Hochrechnungsfaktoren wurden vielmehr jeweils als Quotienten aus der Anzahl der Betriebe in einer Schicht der Grundgesamtheit und der Anzahl der Stichprobenbetriebe in derselben Schicht erst nach vollzogener Auswahl auf Grund der tatsächlichen Besetzungszahlen bestimmt. Die Hochrechnungsfaktoren blieben während der ganzen Laufzeit der Stichprobe - das heißt bis zur nächsten Neuauswahl des Berichtskreises - konstant. Innerhalb einer Schicht galt für alle Betriebe derselbe Hochrechnungsfaktor; die maschinelle Aufbereitung konnte daher so eingerichtet werden, daß nicht jeder Betrieb einzeln, sondern die Schichtsummen aller erfaßten Betriebe zusammen hochzurechnen waren. Diese "Hochrechnung pro Schicht" hatte jedoch zur Folge, daß für Betriebe, die aus besonderen Gründen aus ihrer ursprünglichen Schicht zusammen mit ihrem ursprünglichen Hochrechnungsfaktor in eine andere Größenklasse oder einen anderen Wirtschaftszweig mit möglicherweise anderen Hochrechnungsfaktoren umgesetzt wurden, in jedem in Frage kommenden Wirtschaftszweig eine "Sonderschicht" gebildet werden mußte. In die Sonderschichten kamen fachliche Einheiten, die als eigene Erhebungseinheiten von örtlichen Auswahleinheiten abgespalten wurden (sie erhielten denselben Hochrechnungsfaktor wie die jeweilige ursprüngliche örtliche Einheit), ferner Betriebe, die gegenüber der Auswahlgrundlage ihren Wirtschaftszweig gewechselt hatten (sie nahmen ihren Hochrechnungsfaktor in den neuen Wirtschaftszweig mit), sowie Unternehmen, denen ausnahmsweise die Abgabe gemeinsamer Meldungen für mehrere in der Stichprobe erfaßte Zweigbetriebe zugestanden wurde (für diese Unternehmen wurde jeweils ein neuer Hochrechnungsfaktor auf Grund der Auswahlchance sämtlicher erfaßten Zweigbetriebe berechnet). Die Sonderschichten enthielten somit Erhebungseinheiten mit unterschiedlichen Hochrechnungsfaktoren; daher wurde in den Sonderschichten jede Einheit einzeln hochgerechnet ("Hochrechnung pro Betrieb"). Da die Hochrechnungsfaktoren im Zeitablauf konstant blieben, konnten die pro Schicht hochgerechneten Summen im Falle von Antwortausfällen von den zu schätzenden wahren Summen der Grundgesamtheit über den Stichprobenfehler hinaus abweichen. Bei "unechten Antwortausfällen" (Betriebsschließungen u.a.) wurden die betreffenden Betriebe ersatzlos aus dem Berichtskreis gestrichen. Bei "echten Antwortausfällen" (Auskunftsverweigerung u.a.) wurde pro Schicht eine Ergänzung der Hochrechnung durch Multiplikation der Schichtsummen mit einem "Ergänzungsfaktor" vorgenommen. Der Ergänzungsfaktor ergab sich für jede Schicht - lediglich in den Sonderschichten entfiel die Ergänzung - als Quotient aus der Differenz zwischen der Anzahl der für den Erhebungsmonat angeschriebenen - das heißt zur Berichterstattung aufgeforderten - Betriebe und der Anzahl der seit dem letzten Erhebungsmonat erloschenen Berichtsbetriebe im Zähler und der Summe der Anzahl der Betriebe, die für den Erhebungsmonat tatsächlich berichtet hatten, und der Anzahl der im Erhebungsmonat ruhenden Berichtsbetriebe im Nenner. Aus den hochgerechneten, ergänzten und über alle Schichten eines Wirtschaftszweiges addierten Summenangaben der Berichtsbetriebe - für die Arbeiter wurden außerdem wie früher zur Berechnung von Wochendurchschnitten die gemeldeten monatlichen Verdienst- und Arbeitsstundensummen pro Betrieb in Wochensummen umgerechnet - wurden für jeden Wirtschatszweig - analog auch für zusammengefaßte Wirtschaftsbereiche - als Verhältniswerte durchschnittliche Bruttostundenverdienste, Bruttowochenverdienste und Wochenarbeitszeiten pro Arbeiter sowie durchschnittliche Bruttomonatsverdienste pro Angestellten berechnet, die als Schätzwerte für die entsprechenden Durchschnittswerte der Grundgesamtheit dienten. Bei diesem Schätzverfahren handelte es sich um die sogenannte "kombinierte Verhältnisschätzung".*)

*) vgl.Statistisches Bundesamt: Stichproben in der amtlichen Statistik, Stuttgart - Mainz 1960, S. 551.

Im übrigen wurde die vierteljährliche Verdiensterhebung in Industrie und Handel nach dem Berichtskreiswechsel von 1964 mit dem gleichen Erhebungsziel - Nachweis des regelmäßigen Verdienstes des vollbeschäftigten Arbeitnehmers - fortgeführt. Dem Erhebungsziel entsprechend wurden zunächst weiterhin unter anderem Arbeiter nicht erfaßt, die im Erhebungsmonat länger als drei Tage durch Krankheit ausgefallen waren. Als durch das "Gesetz über die Fortzahlung des Arbeitsentgelts im Krankheitsfalle und über Änderungen des Rechts der gesetzlichen Krankenversicherung" vom 27. Juli 1969 (Bundesgesetzblatt 1969 Teil I S. 946) die erkrankten Arbeiter den Angestellten gleichgestellt wurden, wurden dagegen ab 1970 einheitlich alle Arbeiter und Angestellten aus der Erhebung ausgeschlossen, die wegen Krankheit, Einstellung oder Entlassung während der Erhebungszeit nicht für den ganzen Erhebungsmonat Lohn oder Gehalt bezogen hatten.

Ende 1972 wurde für die vierteljährliche Verdiensterhebung in Industrie und Handel nach grundsätzlich dem gleichen Verfahren wie 1964 abermals ein neuer Kreis von Berichtsbetrieben ausgewählt.*) Der Auswahlplan sah dabei eine verstärkte Differenzierung der durchschnittlichen Auswahlsätze in den Bundesländern vor, und zwar erhielten die kleineren Länder höhere, die größeren Länder niedrigere durchschnittliche Auswahlsätze als nach dem Plan von 1964, während der durchschnittliche Auswahlsatz für das Bundesgebiet mit 10,3 % etwa gleich hoch blieb. Da die Schichtung nach Beschäftigtengrößenklassen (Schichten) nur zur Verbesserung der Genauigkeit in den einzelnen Wirtschaftszweigen (Schichtgruppen) dienen sollte, wurde der Auswahlplan von 1972 so berechnet, daß der Stichprobenumfang innerhalb der Schichtgruppen auf die Schichten nach dem Satz von Tschuprow und Neyman, der Gesamtstichprobenumfang auf die Schichtgruppen dagegen nach der sogenannten Genauigkeitsabstufung - als Richtmerkmal diente dabei der Bruttostundenverdienst - aufgeteilt wurde; außerdem wurde in einigen Wirtschaftszweigen eine höhere

*) vgl. W. Gerß: Neuauswahl der Berichtsbetriebe zur laufenden Verdiensterhebung und ihre methodischen Konsequenzen. In: Statistische Rundschau für das Land Nordrhein-Westfalen, herausgegeben vom Statistischen Landesamt Nordrhein-Westfalen, Heft 8/1973 S. 348 ff.

Genauigkeit - d.h. ein niedrigeres Niveau des relativen Standardfehlers - vorgegeben, sofern die zur Verfügung stehenden Auswahlgrundlagen nicht so tief nach Teilbereichen von Wirtschaftszweigen gegliedert vorlagen, wie sie für die Nachweisung der Ergebnisse der vierteljährlichen Verdiensterhebung benötigt worden wären. Innerhalb der Schichten wurden die Betriebe der Auswahlgesamtheit im Gegensatz zu dem Auswahlplan von 1964 regional angeordnet. Im übrigen wurde bei dem Berichtskreiswechsel von 1972 neben dem Auswahlverfahren auch das bisherige Aufbereitungsverfahren in der Verdiensterhebung beibehalten. Die Erhebung wurde nur insoweit geringfügig geändert, daß nunmehr die bisher ausgeschlossenen Meister im Angestelltenverhältnis einschließlich der Poliere und Schachtmeister in die Gruppe der technischen Angestellten einbezogen und neben den bezahlten Arbeitsstunden und den Mehrarbeitsstunden die tatsächlich geleisteten Arbeitsstunden der Arbeiter nicht mehr erfaßt wurden. Ferner wurden Arbeiter, die aus persönlichen Gründen länger als drei Tage unbezahlt gefehlt hatten, im Gegensatz zu früher nicht mehr in die Erhebung einbezogen.

Für die jährliche Verdiensterhebung in der Landwirtschaft wurde ab September 1964 ein neuer Berichtskreis herangezogen. Die Auswahlgesamtheit bestand aus sämtlichen in der landwirtschaftlichen Betriebszählung 1960 erfaßten Betrieben - mit Ausnahme der Forst-, Gartenbau- und Weinbaubetriebe - ab 20 ha landwirtschaftlicher Nutzfläche einschließlich der Betriebe ohne familienfremde Arbeitskräfte. Die Auswahlgesamtheit wurde in jedem Bundesland nach drei Größenklassen (Schichten) entsprechend der landwirtschaftlichen Nutzfläche geschichtet. Innerhalb der Schichten wurden die Betriebe regional angeordnet. Die Auswahl der Berichtsbetriebe wurde gesondert in jeder Schicht nach dem systematischen Auswahlverfahren vorgenommen; dabei wurden in jeder Größenklasse die Zufallsstartzahlen von Land zu Land unterschiedlich, die Auswahlabstände dagegen gleich groß festgesetzt. In der unteren Größenklasse (20 bis unter 50 ha) wurde jeder zwanzigste, in der mittleren Größenklasse (50 bis unter 100 ha) jeder zehnte und in der oberen Größenklasse (100 oder mehr ha) jeder vierte Betrieb ausgewählt. Zur Entlastung der bisherigen Berichtsbetriebe wurde wie bei der vierteljährlichen Verdiensterhebung in Industrie und Handel bei der Auswahl eine

"Rotation" vorgenommen, und zwar wurden soweit wie möglich diejenigen Betriebe nicht ausgewählt, die bereits früher zur Verdiensterhebung in der Landwirtschaft oder zur Gehalts- und Lohnstrukturerhebung in der Landwirtschaft 1962/63 herangezogen worden waren. Die erfaßten individuellen Verdienst- und Arbeitszeitangaben der Berichtsbetriebe wurden bei der Aufbereitung in den Statistischen Landesämtern innerhalb jeder Schicht addiert und anschließend pro Schicht auf den einheitlichen Satz von 10 % der Grundgesamtheit hochgerechnet bzw. reduziert. Antwortausfälle wurden wie bei der vierteljährlichen Verdiensterhebung in Industrie und Handel behandelt; das heißt bei "unechten Antwortausfällen" wurden die betreffenden Betriebe ersatzlos gestrichen, während bei "echten Antwortausfällen" die fehlenden Angaben pro Schicht mit Hilfe eines "Ergänzungsfaktors" hinzugeschätzt wurden. Die Berechnung von Verhältniswerten als Ergebnisse der Verdiensterhebung in der Landwirtschaft - Durchschnittsverdienste und durchschnittliche Arbeitszeiten - erfolgte ebenfalls analog zur Verdiensterhebung in Industrie und Handel. Anläßlich des Berichtskreiswechsels von 1964 wurde in der Verdiensterhebung in der Landwirtschaft noch eine geringfügige Änderung in der Weise vorgenommen, daß die Betriebe nicht mehr wie bisher die Berufsbezeichnungen und tariflichen Lohngruppen ihrer Arbeiter anzugeben hatten, sondern für jeden Arbeiter von vier im Erhebungsbogen vorgegebenen verbal beschriebenen Kategorien der ausgeübten Tätigkeit die zutreffende ankreuzen mußten. Diese Kategorien entsprachen bereits den bei der Verdiensterhebung unterschiedenen Qualifikationsgruppen.

In der halbjährlichen Verdiensterhebung im Handwerk wurde ab Mai 1966 ein neuer Berichtskreis befragt. Auswahlgrundlage waren Betriebsauflistungen der Handwerkszählung 1963, aus denen die nicht zu erfassenden handwerklichen Nebenbetriebe, Betriebe mit weniger als drei Arbeitnehmern und Betriebe mit ausschließlich mithelfenden Familienangehörigen als Arbeitnehmer ausgesondert wurden. Die verbleibenden Betriebe der Auswahlgesamtheit wurden innerhalb jedes Bundeslandes erst nach den zehn zu erfassenden Handwerkszweigen (vgl. Seite 96) und dann nach Betriebsgrößenklassen (Schichten) entsprechend der Beschäftigtenzahl geschichtet. Für die Berechnung des Auswahlplans wurde eine Genauigkeitsabstufung zwischen den Handwerkszweigen vorgegeben; und zwar sollten innerhalb jedes Landes die Erhebungsergebnisse in den am schwächsten besetzten Handwerkszweigen einen höchstens doppelt so großen relativen Standardfehler haben wie die Ergebnisse in den am stärksten besetzten Zweigen. Die Vorgabe einer Fehlerabstufung zwischen den Bundesländern erübrigte sich, da jedes Land von vorn herein die maximale Anzahl von Berichtsbetrieben festgelegt hatte, zu deren Erfassung es bereit war. Die auf diese Weise für die einzelnen Handwerkszweige jedes Landes sich ergebenden Stichprobenumfänge wurden jeweils "optimal" nach dem Satz von Tschuprow und Neyman auf die Schichten verteilt. Die Auswahlsätze in den einzelnen Schichten waren also unterschiedlich; der durchschnittliche Auswahlsatz betrug 13,5 %. Die Berichtsbetriebe wurden aus der Auswahlgesamtheit nach dem systematischen Auswahlverfahren ausgewählt, wobei außer den Auswahlabständen auch die Zufallsstartzahlen gesondert für jede Schicht festgelegt wurden. Das systematische Auswahlverfahren wurde wie bei der vierteljährlichen Verdiensterhebung in Industrie und Handel durch "Rotation" modifiziert, um die bisherigen Berichtsbetriebe so weit wie möglich gegen neue Berichtsbetriebe auszutauschen. Ferner wurden aus dem Berichtskreis der Verdiensterhebung im Handwerk alle Betriebe ersatzlos gestrichen, die als handwerklich-industrielle Kombinationsbetriebe bereits eine Auswahlchance für den Berichtskreis der Verdiensterhebung in Industie und Handel gehabt hatten. Die von den Stichprobenbetrieben nach dem Summenverfahren gemeldeten Summenangaben wurden bei der Aufbereitung schichtweise addiert und anschließend pro Schicht auf 100 % der Grundgesamtheit hochgerechnet. Die Hochrechnungsfaktoren wurden wie bei der vierteljährlichen Verdiensterhebung in Industrie und Handel erst nach vollzogener Betriebsauswahl auf Grund der tatsächlichen Besetzungszahlen endgültig festgelegt. Auch die Behandlung von Antwortausfällen erfolgte wie bei der Verdiensterhebung in Industrie und Handel; während bei "unechten Antwortausfällen" die betreffenden Betriebe ersatzlos im Berichtskreis gestrichen wurden, wurden bei "echten Antwortausfällen" die fehlenden Angaben mit Hilfe eines "Ergänzungsfaktors" pro Schicht hinzugeschätzt. Ebenfalls von der Verdiensterhebung in Industrie und Handel übernommen wurde das Verfahren, mit Hilfe von "Umrechnungsfaktoren" -

die für den Erhebungsmonat Mai 1966 ermittelt wurden - die Ergebnisse des alten Berichtskreises mit denen des neuen Berichtskreises in durchlaufenden bruchfreien Zeitreihen zu verknüpfen (vgl. Seite 93). Im übrigen wurden Inhalt, Umfang, Methodik und Zweck der halbjährlichen Verdiensterhebung im Handwerk auch nach dem Berichtskreiswechsel von 1966 beibehalten.

Die Bemühungen der staatlichen Sozialpolitik zur Förderung der Vermögensbildung der Arbeinehmer brachten für die amtliche Lohnstatistik über das herkömmliche Erhebungsprogramm hinaus den Auftrag mit sich, statistische Daten zur Erfolgskontrolle der verschiedenen Vermögensbildungsgesetze zu liefern. Zusammen mit der Personalkostenerhebung der Europäischen Wirtschaftsgemeinschaft in ausgewählten Industriezweigen für das Jahr 1961 wurde in der Bundesrepublik Deutschland ohne besondere Rechtsgrundlage auf Wunsch des Bundesministeriums für Arbeit und Sozialordnung als Probeerhebung mit freiwilliger Teilnahme der Berichtsunternehmen eine Zusatzbefragung über die im Jahre 1961 angefallenen Aufwendungen der Arbeitgeber nach dem "Gesetz zur Förderung der Vermögensbildung der Arbeitnehmer" vom 12. Juli 1961 (Bundesgesetzblatt 1961 Teil I S. 909) vorgenommen. Eine umfassende Erhebung mit gesetzlicher Auskunftspflicht fand dann für das Berichtsjahr 1963 auf Grund der "Verordnung zur Durchführung einer Erhebung über die Anwendung des Gesetzes zur Förderung der Vermögensbildung der Arbeitnehmer" vom 22. April 1964 (Bundesanzeiger 1964 Nr. 80) statt. Zu dieser Erhebung wurden repräsentativ ausgewählte Unternehmen herangezogen; dabei waren die Auswahlsätze bereits in der Rechtsverordnung festgelegt. In der Energiewirtschaft und Wasserversorgung, dem Bergbau, dem verarbeitenden Gewerbe, dem Baugewerbe und dem Kredit- und Versicherungsgewerbe war im Durchschnitt höchstens jedes zehnte Unternehmen mit 2 bis 9 Beschäftigten und jedes dritte Unternehmen mit 10 oder mehr Beschäftigten, im Einzelhandel jedes dritte Unternehmen mit 50 oder mehr Beschäftigten, im Straßenverkehrsgewerbe jedes dritte Unternehmen mit 10 oder mehr Beschäftigten und in der Binnenschiffahrt jedes Unternehmen mit 10 oder mehr Beschäftigten zu erfassen. Ausgeschlossen wurden Unternehmen, in denen außer den Inhabern nur mithelfende Familienangehörige als

Arbeitnehmer beschäftigt waren. Als Auswahlgrundlage dienten Auflistungen der Arbeitsstättenzählung 1961. Nach dem ursprünglichen Auswahlplan des Statistischen Bundesamtes war eine zweiphasige Auswahl vorgesehen. In der ersten Phase sollten die Unternehmen einheitlich für jeweils den gesamten Wirtschaftsbereich nach den in der Verordnung genannten Auswahlsätzen ausgewählt und mit einer Postkarte befragt werden, ob das Vermögensbildungsgesetz überhaupt angewendet würde. Auf Grund des Ergebnisses dieser Vorbefragung sollten dann für die zweite Phase der Auswahl die endgültigen - unter Umständen innerhalb der Wirtschaftsbereiche nach Wirtschaftszweigen differenzierten - Auswahlsätze festgelegt werden. Fragebogen sollten nur an die in der zweiten Phase ausgewählten Unternehmen versandt werden. Dieser zweiphasige Auswahlplan - der nachträglich durch die Erhebungsergebnisse gerechtfertigt wurde, nach denen nur etwa 2 % der Unternehmen den Arbeitnehmern vermögenswirksame Leistungen angeboten hatten, also 98 % der Unternehmen in den Fragebogen keine Angaben machen konnten - wurde von den meisten Statistischen Landesämtern wegen der zusätzlichen Kosten des Versands der Postkarten abgelehnt und daher nicht realisiert. Stattdessen wurde eine einphasige Auswahl in der Weise vorgenommen, daß die Auswahlgesamtheit zuerst nach zwei Beschäftigtengrößenklassen - Unternehmen mit 2 bis 9 bzw. mit 10 oder mehr Beschäftigten - und dann nach Wirtschaftszweigen geschichtet wurde; in diesen Schichten wurden die Berichtsunternehmen unter Anwendung der in der Verordnung genannten nicht weiter differenzierten Auswahlsätze nach dem systematischen Auswahlverfahren bestimmt. Bei der Aufbereitung wurden die Berichtsunternehmen nach Wirtschaftszweigen und nunmehr sieben Größenklassen - für die gesonderte Ergebnisse zu ermitteln waren - entsprechend den tatsächlichen Verhältnissen im Erhebungsjahr und damit unter Umständen abweichend vom Auswahlplan neu geordnet. Aus der Aufbereitung ausgeschlossen wurden die Unternehmen, die in der Auswahlgrundlage noch zu den zu erfassenden Größenklassen gehört hatten, bis zum Erhebungsjahr jedoch mit ihrer Beschäftigtenzahl unter die untere Erfassungsgrenze gesunken waren. Die Angaben der Berichtsunternehmen wurden auf 100 % der Grundgesamtheit hochgerechnet; die Hochrechnungsfaktoren wurden dabei für jedes einzelne Unternehmen als Kehrwert des Auswahlsatzes durch den Auswahlplan festgelegt und blieben auch unverändert, wenn das Unternehmen einem neuen Wirtschaftszweig oder einer neuen Größenklasse zugeordnet wurde. Als Ergebnisse der Erhebung wurden vor allem Angaben über die Anzahl der vermögenswirksame Leistungen anbietenden Unternehmen, die Anzahl der begünstigten Arbeitnehmer und die Durchschnittsbeträge der vermögenswirksamen Leistungen pro Arbeiter und pro Angestellten ausgewiesen. Die Ergebnisse wurden vom Bundesministerium für Arbeit und Sozialordnung im "Bundesarbeitsblatt" (Jahrgang 1965 Seite 186 ff.) veröffentlicht.*) Eine entsprechende amtliche Erhebung über die Anwendung des "Zweiten Gesetzes zur Förderung der Vermögensbildung der Arbeitnehmer" vom 1. Juli 1965 (Bundesgesetzblatt 1965 Teil I S. 585) wurde für das Jahr 1967 geplant, jedoch nicht durchgeführt. Statistische Angaben über die Anwendung des "Dritten Gesetzes zur Förderung der Vermögensbildung der Arbeitnehmer" in der Fassung vom 27. Juni 1970 (Bundesgesetzblatt 1970 Teil I S. 930) bzw. vom 15. Januar 1975 (Bundesgesetzblatt 1975 Teil I S. 258) werden seit dem Berichtsjahr 1972 in den Personalkostenerhebungen der Europäischen Gemeinschaften im produzierenden Gewerbe ermittelt (vgl. Seite 129).

Das Gesetz über die Lohnstatistik vom 18. Mai 1956 (Bundesgesetzblatt 1956 Teil I S. 429) hatte insofern eine Lücke im System der amtlichen Effektivverdienststatistik gelassen, als von den in mehrjährigen Abständen vorgesehenen Sondererhebungen (Gehalts- und Lohnstrukturerhebungen) der öffentliche Dienst ausdrücklich ausgeschlossen war. In der amtlichen Begründung zum Gesetz über die Lohnstatistik (Bundestagsdrucksache Nr. 1994 vom 30. Dezember 1955) hieß es dazu: "Der öffentliche Dienst ist aus diesen Erhebungen deswegen ausgeschlossen, weil für die Erfassung der Verdienste in diesem Bereich mit dem Finanzstatistischen Gesetz eine gesetzliche Grundlage geschaffen werden soll. Der Entwurf des Gesetzes über die Finanzstatistik sieht u.a. vor, daß in Verbindung mit den Personalstrukturerhebungen auch Erhebungen über die Löhne und Gehälter der im öffentlichen Dienst Beschäftigten durchgeführt werden."

*) vgl. Hermann Berié: Die Anwendung des Vermögensbildungsgesetzes. In: Bundesarbeitsblatt Jahrgang 1965, S. 186 ff.

Diese Bestimmung wurde jedoch später nicht in den Text des Gesetzes über die Finanzstatistik vom 8. Juni 1960 (Bundesgesetzblatt 1960 Teil I S. 322) übernommen. Die offen gebliebene Lücke wurde erstmalig erst durch das "Gesetz über eine Statistik des Personals, der Dienstbezüge, Vergütungen und Löhne im öffentlichen Dienst" vom 15. Mai 1968 (Bundesgesetzblatt 1968 Teil I S. 385) geschlossen. Danach war einmalig neben einer totalen Personalstrukturerhebung für den Berichtsmonat September 1968 im Individualverfahren eine repräsentative Gehalts- und Lohnstrukturerhebung durchzuführen. Dabei wurden sämtliche Dienststellen (Behörden und Einrichtungen bzw. Verwaltungsstellen einschließlich Schulen und Hochschulen) des Bundes, der Länder, der Gemeinden und der Gemeindeverbände, ihre nicht rechtsfähigen Wirtschaftsunternehmen, Bundesbahn und Bundespost, die Deutsche Bundesbank, die Sozialversicherungsträger und ihre öffentlich-rechtlichen Verbände, die Bundesanstalt für Arbeitsvermittlung und Arbeitslosenversicherung sowie die jeweils zugehörigen Sondervermögen total erfaßt. Ausgeschlossen blieben alle Gemeinden mit weniger als 1 000 Einwohnern und in Nordrhein-Westfalen darüberhinaus die amtsangehörigen Gemeinden mit weniger als 10 000 Einwohnern. Miterfaßt wurden die Dienststellen der Polizei, jedoch nicht das militärische Personal der Bundeswehr und der Vollzugsdienst des Bundesgrenzschutzes. In diesen Berichtsstellen waren nach dem Gesetz vom 15. Mai 1968 höchstens 30 % der im ganzen Erhebungsmonat vollbeschäftigten und vollbezahlten Bediensteten - Beamte, Richter, DO-Angestellte der Sozialversicherungsträger, Angestellte, Arbeiter - unter Ausschluß der Versorgungsempfänger, der Personen in Ausbildung, der Beamten der Besoldungsordnung B und der übertariflich bezahlten Angestellten individuell auf Erhebungsbogen zu erfassen. Auswahl- und Erhebungseinheit war somit der einzelne Bedienstete, die Auskunftspflicht oblag dagegen ausschließlich den Beschäftigungs- oder Abrechnungsstellen. In Nordrhein-Westfalen wurden über die gesetzliche Erfassungsquote hinaus sämtliche Landesbeamten und Richter in die Erhebung einbezogen, und zwar nicht auf Individualzählblättern, sondern durch Auswertung der im Statistischen Landesamt Nordrhein-Westfalen - das im Auftrage des Landesamtes für Besoldung und Versorgung Nordrhein-Westfalen für die maschinelle Berechnung der Bezüge zuständig war - auf Datenträgern vorliegenden Besoldungsunterlagen. Auch von einigen kommunalen Berichtsstellen wurden dem Statistischen Landesamt Nordrhein-Westfalen statt der Individualzählblätter maschinell zu verarbeitende Datenträger (Individuallochkarten) eingereicht.

Für die Auswahl der Bediensteten wurden Schichten gebildet, indem zuerst nach Beschäftigungsbereichen (Behörden und Einrichtungen, Wirtschaftsunternehmen, Sozialversicherungsträger) und dann nach Dienstherren (Bund, die einzelnen Länder, die Gesamtheit der Gemeinden und Gemeindeverbände jedes Landes) geschichtet wurde. Eine Schicht bildeten also zum Beispiel die Bediensteten bei sämtlichen kommunalen Behörden und Einrichtungen in Nordrhein-Westfalen. Die Auswahlsätze für die Bedienstetenauswahl wurden für alle Berichtsstellen innerhalb einer Schicht einheitlich, von Schicht zu Schicht jedoch grundsätzlich unterschiedlich nach einer vorgegebenen Genauigkeitsabstufung festgelegt. Die sich aus der Genauigkeitsabstufung zunächst ergebenden Auswahlsätze wurden zur Vereinfachung der Aufbereitung so weit gerundet, daß im endgültigen Auswahlplan nur noch die Auswahlsätze 14,3 % (Auswahlabstand 7), 20,0 % (Auswahlabstand 5) und 33,3 % (Auswahlabstand 3) vorkamen. Die Berichtsstellen wählten dann selbst die von ihnen zu erfassenden Bediensteten in einigen Fällen nach dem systematischen Auswahlverfahren - unter Anwendung der genannten Auswahlabstände ausgehend von Zufallsstartzahlen, die von den Statistischen Landesämtern vorgegeben wurden -, in der Regel jedoch nach bestimmten Anfangsbuchstaben der Familiennamen aus. Zu diesem Zweck wurden konstante Buchstabengruppen festgelegt, die zu den genannten Auswahlsätzen führten. Beim Auswahlabstand 7 galten in jedem Fall die Buchstaben M, R und T, beim Auswahlabstand 5 die Buchstaben E, K, R und T und beim Auswahlabstand 3 die Buchstaben B, C, D, H und K. Auf die bei den Gehalts- und Lohnstrukturerhebungen in der gewerblichen Wirtschaft übliche "alternierende Buchstabenauswahl" (vgl. Seite 102) mußte verzichtet werden, weil die Verteilung der Erhebungsbogen an die Berichtsstellen nicht immer unmittelbar von den Statistischen Landesämtern vorgenommen werden konnte. Bei den Beamten der Deutschen Bundesbahn wurde von dem allgemeinen Auswahlplan in der Weise abgewichen, daß in einigen gezielt ausgewählten Bundesbahndirektionen jeweils sämtliche Beamten erfaßt wurden. Dieses Verfahren wurde für vertretbar gehalten, weil bei allen Bundesbahndirektionen eine etwa gleiche Beschäftigtenstruktur unterstellt werden konnte.

Die von den Berichtsstellen für die erfaßten Bediensteten gemeldeten Individualangaben über Verdienste und Arbeitszeiten wurden bei der Aufbereitung auf 100 % der Grundgesamtheit hochgerechnet, wobei als Hochrechnungsfaktor der jeweilige Auswahlabstand laut Auswahlplan diente. Die Berichtsstellen konnten die Angaben für die Arbeiter statt für den Monat September 1968 auch für einen anderen überwiegend in den Erhebungsmonat fallenden Zeitraum von mindestens vier Wochen machen; in diesem Fall wurde bei der Aufbereitung eine Umrechnung auf einen Zeitraum von der Länge des Erhebungsmonats vorgenommen. In jedem Fall wurden die Monatsangaben für die Arbeiter zur Berechnung von Wochenergebnissen auf durchschnittliche Wochenangaben reduziert. Der verwendete "Umrechnungsfaktor" bzw. der "Reduktionsfaktor" wurde wie bei den Gehalts- und Lohnstrukturerhebungen in der gewerblichen Wirtschaft ermittelt (vgl. Seite 103). Für die einzelnen Bediensteten wurden unter anderem die gesetzlichen Besoldungs- bzw. tariflichen Vergütungs- oder Lohngruppen erfaßt, nach denen bei der Aufbereitung eine Zuordnung zu den in der amtlichen Effektivverdienststatistik üblichen Leistungsgruppen der Angestellten und der Arbeiter vorgenommen wurde. Für die Beamten wurden dabei die gleichen Leistungsgruppen gebildet wie für die Angestellten. Erhebungsmerkmale der Gehalts- und Lohnstrukturerhebung im öffentlichen Dienst 1968 waren vor allem der Bruttoverdienst (bei Arbeitern nach Lohnform) in der Aufgliederung nach Grundgehalt bzw. Grundlohn, Orts- bzw. Sozialzuschlag, Kinderzuschlag, Mehrarbeitszuschlag, Nacht- bzw. Sonn- oder Feiertagszuschlag und sonstigen steuerpflichtigen Zuschlägen, die gesetzlichen Abzüge, die Arbeitszeit der Arbeiter sowie weitere in den Strukturerhebungen übliche persönliche Merkmale. Als Ergebnisse wurden vor allem durchschnittliche Stunden-, Wochen- und Monatsverdienste sowie Häufigkeitsverteilungen nach Verdienstklassen ausgewiesen. Die Ergebnisse wurden vom Statistischen Bundesamt in der Fachserie M Reihe 17 V (Dienstbezüge, Vergütungen und Löhne) veröffentlicht (Stuttgart - Mainz 1971).

173 Europäische Harmonisierung

Um die Entwicklung der Arbeiterverdienste im gesamten Gebiet der Europäischen Wirtschaftsgemeinschaft in kürzeren Abständen laufend beobachten zu können, stellte das Statistische Amt der Europäischen Gemeinschaften seit 1964 für alle Mitgliedstaaten vergleichbare statistische Angaben über die durchschnittlichen Bruttostundenverdienste der "manuell beschäftigten" Arbeiter im produzierenden Gewerbe einschließlich Bergbau und Baugewerbe für die Berichtsmonate April und Oktober jedes Jahres zusammen. Die Angaben wurden nach Wirtschaftszweigen und nach dem Geschlecht der Arbeiter sowie im Steinkohlen- und Eisenerzbergbau nach über und unter Tage beschäftigten Arbeitern, jedoch nicht nach Leistungsgruppen gegliedert. Ein Nebenzweck dieser international harmonisierten Verdienststatistik bestand darin, die Ergebnisse der seit 1966 in dreijährigen Abständen wiederholten Personalkostenerhebungen der Europäischen Gemeinschaften im produzierenden Gewerbe für die zwischen jeweils zwei Erhebungen liegenden Jahre behelfsmäßig fortzuschreiben. Für die Beschaffung der Ausgangsdaten der harmonisierten Verdienststatistik wurden keine eigenen Erhebungen durchgeführt; vielmehr wurden die in den Mitgliedsländern bestehenden nationalen laufenden Verdiensterhebungen den Wünschen der Europäischen Gemeinschaften so weit angepaßt, daß die Ergebnisse neben nationalen Zwecken gleichzeitig den Zwecken der EG-Kommission dienen konnten. Als Datenquelle der harmonisierten Verdienststatistik wurde in der Bundesrepublik Deutschland die vierteljährliche Verdiensterhebung in Industrie und Handel verwendet. Die für die Harmonisierung erforderlichen Anpassungsmaßnahmen bestanden in erster Linie darin, daß die vierteljährliche Verdiensterhebung wegen der von den Europäischen Gemeinschaften festgelegten Berichtsmonate April und Oktober ab 1964 nicht mehr wie früher im Februar, Mai, August und November, sondern im Januar, April, Juli und Oktober jedes Jahres durchgeführt wurde; ferner wurden die bisher nicht erfaßten Montagearbeiter mit ihren nunmehr zum Bruttoverdienst gerechneten lohnsteuerpflichtigen Auslösungen in die Erhebung einbezogen. Die harmonisierte Verdienststatistik wurde ab Oktober 1972 auf die durchschnittlichen Bruttomonatsverdienste der Angestellten in Industrie, Handel, Kreditwirtschaft und Versicherungsgewerbe ausgedehnt.

Die nationale vierteljährliche Verdiensterhebung sollte seit ihrer Einführung nicht nur Durchschnittsverdienste und durchschnittliche Arbeitszeiten für die vier Erhebungsmonate jedes Jahres, sondern auch jahresdurchschnittliche Mittelwerte der Verdienste und Arbeitszeiten liefern. Dabei bestand seit 1964 die doppelte Schwierigkeit, daß erstens wie früher nur für vier der zwölf Monate des Jahres Daten vorlagen und zweitens infolge der Verlegung der Erhebungsmonate diese nun nicht mehr symmetrisch zur Jahresmitte lagen. Bei der Schätzung der fehlenden Daten für die übrigen acht Monate wurde angenommen, daß im Falle der Verdienste sämtliche - tatsächlich ermittelten oder hypothetischen - Monatsmittelwerte während eines Kalenderjahres einem linearen Trend mit im allgemeinen positiver Steigung folgten. Im Falle der Arbeitszeiten wurde angenommen, daß die Monatsmittelwerte während eines Kalenderjahres keine Trendveränderung aufwiesen bzw. einem linearen Trend mit der Steigung Null folgten. Unter diesen Voraussetzungen war die zur Jahresmitte asymmetrische Lage der neuen Erhebungsmonate lediglich bei den Verdiensten, jedoch nicht bei den Arbeitszeiten für die Berechnung von Jahresmittelwerten von Bedeutung. Jahresmittelwerte der Arbeitszeiten ergaben sich ab 1964 genau wie früher als einfach - das heißt lediglich nach der hochgerechneten und ergänzten Anzahl der Arbeitnehmer in den einzelnen Erhebungsmonaten - gewichtete arithmetische Mittel der vier Monatsmittelwerte; dies Verfahren wurde vor 1964 auch für die Berechnung der jahresdurchschnittlichen Verdienste angewendet. Ab 1964 waren die ausgewiesenen Jahresmittelwerte der Verdienste dagegen doppelt - das heißt außer nach der Anzahl der Arbeitnehmer auch nach der relativen Lage der einzelnen Erhebungsmonate zur Jahresmitte - gewichtete arithmetische Mittel der vier Monatsmittelwerte. Der Bestimmung der Gewichte für die Ermittlung der neuen Jahresmittelwerte der Verdienste lag die Schätzung der Daten für die fehlenden acht Monate nach der Gauß'schen Methode der kleinsten Quadrate zugrunde. Nach dieser Methode wurde aus den bekannten Daten der vier Erhebungsmonate eine Regressionsgerade bestimmt, die sich über das ganze Jahr erstreckte. Als Jahresmittelwert galt dann der nach dem sechsten Monat des betreffenden Kalenderjahres - das heißt der in der Mitte der für das Jahr bestimmten Regressionsgeraden - liegende theoretische Wert.*)

174 Doppelte Rechtsgrundlagen

Das Bestreben der Kommission der Europäischen Gemeinschaften, international vergleichbare lohnstatistische Erhebungen in allen Mitgliedstaaten anzuordnen, und der Wunsch der Mitgliedstaaten, die Mehrbelastung durch die zusätzlichen statistischen Anforderungen der EG-Kommission in Grenzen zu halten, führten dazu, daß gleichartige europäische und nationale Statistiken in der Erhebungs- und Aufbereitungsphase so weit wie möglich zusammengelegt wurden. Diese Erhebungen beruhten dann sowohl auf einer europäischen als auch auf einer nationalen Rechtsgrundlage.
Als erste Erhebung mit doppelter Rechtsgrundlage wurde für Oktober 1966 eine Gehalts- und Lohnstrukturerhebung in der gewerblichen Wirtschaft durchgeführt. Rechtsgrundlagen dieser repräsentativen Individualerhebung waren sowohl die "Dritte Verordnung über die Durchführung einer Sondererhebung zur Lohnstatistik" vom 20. Mai 1966 (Bundesanzeiger 1966 Nr. 98) in Verbindung mit dem Gesetz über die Lohnstatistik vom 18. Mai 1956 (Bundesgesetzblatt 1956 Teil I Seite 429) als auch die vom Rat der Europäischen Wirtschaftsgemeinschaft erlassene "Verordnung Nr. 188 zur Durchführung einer Erhebung über Struktur und Verteilung der Löhne in Industrie und Handwerk" vom 12. Dezember 1964 (Amtsblatt der Europäischen Gemeinschaften 1964 Nr. 214 S. 3634). Für die Erhebung wurde ein Erhebungsplan aufgestellt, nach dem durch Erfassung der gleichen Erhebungseinheiten und unter Verwendung der gleichen Erhebungsformulare mit einer einzigen Befragung sowohl die Informationsbedürfnisse der Bundesrepublik Deutschland als auch die der Europäischen Gemeinschaften befriedigt werden konnten. Die EG-Verordnung stützte sich auf den Vertrag zur Gründung der Europäischen Wirtschaftsgemeinschaft vom 27. Juli 1957 (Bundesgesetzblatt 1957 Teil II S. 753)

*) vgl. W. Gerß: Laufende Fehlerrechnungen in der Verdiensterhebung - Methodische Grundlagen und Auswertungsmöglichkeiten. In: Statistische Rundschau für das Land Nordrhein-Westfalen, herausgegeben vom Landesamt für Datenverarbeitung und Statistik Nordrhein-Westfalen, Jahrgang 1975, Seite 379 ff.

- insbesondere auf Artikel 213 - und galt unmittelbar in jedem Mitgliedstaat. Außerdem war in Zusammenhang mit der "Entschließung der Konferenz der Mitgliedstaaten vom 30. Dezember 1961 über die Durchführung des Grundsatzes des gleichen Entgelts für Männer und Frauen" eine Lohnstrukturerhebung vereinbart worden. Die EG-Verordnung bestimmte, daß für einen Erhebungszeitraum von mindestens vierzehn Tagen ausschließlich im Oktober 1966 Arbeiter in Betrieben (örtliche Einheiten) des verarbeitenden Gewerbes und des Baugewerbes mit mindestens zehn Arbeitnehmern zu erfassen waren; auskunftspflichtig waren die Arbeitgeber. Die technischen Einzelheiten der Erhebung - insbesondere eine Rahmenregelung für den Stichprobenplan - waren von der EG-Kommission festzulegen, die Befragung oblag den nationalen statistischen Ämtern, in der Bundesrepublik Deutschland vor allem den Statistischen Landesämtern nach allgemeinen Anweisungen des Statistischen Bundesamtes. Die in der Befragung angefallenen Einzelauskünfte waren ohne namentliche Angabe der Auskunftspflichtigen dem Statistischen Amt der Europäischen Gemeinschaften zur Verfügung zu stellen, wo die für die EG-Kommission bestimmten Ergebnistabellen - unter anderem auch mit Daten für einzelne Bundesländer - zentral aufgestellt wurden; im übrigen galt für die Einzelangaben die übliche statistische Geheimhaltungspflicht. Die Kosten der EG-Erhebung gingen nach der EG-Verordnung "zu Lasten der in den Haushaltsplänen der Europäischen Gemeinschaften für diesen Zweck bereitgestellten Mittel".

Die nationale "Dritte Verordnung" bestimmte, daß für den Erhebungsmonat Oktober 1966 die Arbeitsverdienste bzw. Arbeitszeiten und für das Erhebungsjahr 1966 die gesamten Jahresverdienste einschließlich der einmaligen bzw. unregelmäßigen Zahlungen von Arbeitern und Angestellten in Betrieben der gewerblichen Wirtschaft - dabei wurde mit Rücksicht auf die EG-Erhebung erstmalig in einer Gehalts- und Lohnstrukturerhebung im verarbeitenden Gewerbe das Handwerk mit einbezogen - zu erfassen waren. Auf Wunsch der EG-Kommission war bei der Aufbereitung erstmalig eine Unterscheidung zwischen vollbeschäftigten und teilzeitbeschäftigten Arbeitnehmern vorzunehmen. Während die Angaben für den

Erhebungsmonat für alle zur Stichprobe gehörenden Arbeitnehmer zu machen waren, die Ende Oktober 1966 unter Arbeitsvertrag standen - in die Aufbereitung der Monatserhebung wurden allerdings nur die Arbeitnehmer einbezogen, die während des ganzen Erhebungsmonats unter Arbeitsvertrag standen und ihren vollen vertragsgemäßen Verdienst erhielten -, bezogen sich die Angaben für das Erhebungsjahr auf Arbeitnehmer, die während des ganzen Jahres 1966 bei demselben Unternehmen unter Arbeitsvertrag standen. Im Gegensatz zu der EG-Erhebung wurde bei der Aufbereitung der nationalen Erhebung der in der amtlichen deutschen Lohnstatistik übliche Arbeitsschnitt zwischen den statistischen Ämtern - Tabellierung von Landesergebnissen durch die Statistischen Landesämter, Zusammenfassung zu Bundesergebnissen durch das Statistische Bundesamt - beibehalten.

Die von der EG-Kommission für den Stichprobenplan der EG-Erhebung von 1966 festgelegte Rahmenregelung war so flexibel, daß sie ohne besondere Schwierigkeiten mit dem Stichprobenplan der nationalen Erhebung in Einklang gebracht werden konnte. Die Richtlinien der EG-Kommission besagten lediglich, daß im Durchschnitt aller Wirtschaftszweige kleine Betriebe repräsentativ mit jeweils sämtlichen Arbeitern, mittlere Betriebe repräsentativ mit jeweils einem Teil der Arbeiter und große Betriebe total mit jeweils einem Teil der Arbeiter zu erfassen waren. Die relativen Stichprobenfehler der für die einzelnen Wirtschaftszweige ermittelten Gesamtergebnisse sollten nach Möglichkeit gleich groß sein; das bedeutete eine tendenziell "optimale" Aufteilung der Gesamtstichprobe auf die Wirtschaftszweige mit annähernd gleichen Stichprobenumfängen und gegebenenfalls unterschiedlichen Auswahlsätzen pro Wirtschaftszweig. Die EG-Richtlinien legten ferner auf Grund einer Schätzung des Variationskoeffizienten innerhalb jeder zu erfassenden Untergruppe von Arbeitern für jeden Mitgliedstaat die mindestens zu erfassende Gesamtarbeiterzahl fest, wonach sich für die Bundesrepublik Deutschland ein Gesamtstichprobenumfang von 500 000 Arbeitern und damit Stichprobenumfänge von 10 000 Arbeitern pro Wirtschaftszweig ergaben. Für die Bestimmung der in die Stichprobe einzubeziehenden Arbeiter galt der Grundsatz, "daß jeder Arbeiter ein und derselben Branche die gleiche Wahrscheinlichkeit haben soll, in die Stichprobe aufgenommen zu werden". Darüberhinaus war das Verfahren der Arbeiterauswahl den Mitgliedstaaten freigestellt; die Bundesrepublik Deutschland, die Niederlande und Belgien nahmen die Arbeiterauswahl nach den Anfangsbuchstaben der Familiennamen, Frankreich nach den Geburtsmonaten der Arbeiter vor, während in Italien für diesen Zweck Zufallszahlentafeln verwendet wurden.

Nach dem nationalen Stichprobenplan von 1966 wurden die Betriebe der Auswahlgesamtheit - als Auswahlgrundlagen dienten die letzten Totalerhebungen zur Industrieberichterstattung und zur Bauberichterstattung sowie totale Großzählungen wie Handwerkszählung, Verkehrszensus und Arbeitsstättenzählung - unter Ausschluß der nicht zu erfassenden Kleinbetriebe - diese wurden wie bei den Gehalts- und Lohnstrukturerhebungen in der gewerblichen Wirtschaft für 1957 und 1962 abgegrenzt - erst nach Wirtschaftszweigen und dann nach drei Größenklassen (Schichten) sortiert. Zur unteren Größenklasse gehörten Betriebe mit höchstens 19 Beschäftigten, zur mittleren Größenklasse Betriebe mit 20 bis 99 Beschäftigten und zur oberen Größenklasse Betriebe mit mindestens 100 Beschäftigten. Innerhalb der Größenklassen wurden die Betriebe der Auswahlgesamtheit erst regional und dann nach der Beschäftigtenzahl angeordnet. Die Auswahl der Berichtsbetriebe erfolgte nach dem systematischen Auswahlverfahren mit pro Schicht festgelegten Auswahlabständen und vorgegebenen Zufallsstartzahlen. In der unteren Größenklasse wurden im Durchschnitt aller Wirtschaftszweige 15 % der Betriebe, in der mittleren Größenklasse 50 % der Betriebe und in der oberen Größenklasse sämtliche Betriebe als Berichtsbetriebe ausgewählt. Die Auswahlsätze für die Betriebsauswahl waren in allen Bundesländern gleich, dagegen in den beiden unteren Größenklassen von Wirtschaftszweig zu Wirtschaftszweig unter Berücksichtigung einer vorgegebenen Genauigkeitsabstufung - die Ergebnisse in den schwach besetzten Wirtschaftszweigen sollten höchstens doppelt so große Stichprobenfehler haben wie die Ergebnisse in den stark besetzten Zweigen - in der Weise unterschiedlich, daß in den schwach besetzten Wirtschaftszweigen höhere und in den stark besetzten Zweigen niedrigere Auswahlsätze festgelegt wurden. Der Gesamtauswahlsatz für die in die Stichprobe aufzunehmenden Arbeitnehmer - d.h. das Produkt aus dem Auswahlsatz der ersten Stufe (Betriebsauswahl) und dem Auswahlsatz der zweiten Stufe (Arbeitnehmerauswahl) - sollte in allen drei Größenklassen im Durchschnitt aller Wirtschaftszweige gleich sein, so daß die Stichprobe innerhalb eines Wirtschaftszweiges selbstgewichtend wurde. Daraus folgte, daß in den Betrieben, die von Größenklasse zu Größenklasse und von Wirtschaftszweig zu Wirtschaftszweig nach unterschiedlichen Auswahlabständen ausgewählt wurden, auch unterschiedliche - und zwar im Vergleich zur Betriebsauswahl in umgekehrter Richtung abgestufte - Auswahlsätze für die Auswahl der Arbeitnehmer in Ansatz zu bringen waren. Im Durchschnitt aller Wirtschaftszweige ergaben sich somit für die Arbeitnehmerauswahl Auswahlsätze von 100 % in der unteren, 30 % in der mittleren und 15 % in der oberen Größenklasse. Die für die einzelnen Wirtschaftszweige festgelegten Gesamtauswahlsätze - Produkte aus den Auswahlsätzen der ersten und der zweiten Stufe - wurden zur Vereinfachung der Hochrechnung so weit gerundet, daß nur Sätze von 50 %, 25 %, 12,5 % und 6,25 % vorkamen. Der durchschnittliche Gesamtauswahlsatz betrug in jedem Bundesland wie in jeder Größenklasse 15 %. Die Bestimmung der von den Berichtsbetrieben in die Stichprobe aufzunehmenden Arbeitnehmer erfolgte wie bei den Gehalts- und Lohnstrukturerhebungen in der gewerblichen Wirtschaft für 1957 und 1962 nach dem Verfahren der "alternierenden Buchstabenauswahl" (vgl. S. 102). Bei der Aufbereitung in den Statistischen Landesämtern wurden im Falle "echter Antwortausfälle" (Auskunftsverweigerung u.a.) die fehlenden Angaben durch Dopplung der Angaben eines Berichtsbetriebes aus derselben Schicht geschätzt; im Falle "unechter Antwortausfälle" (Betriebsschließung u.a.) wurden die betreffenden Betriebe ersatzlos aus dem Berichtskreis gestrichen. Die wegen der von Wirtschaftszweig zu Wirtschaftszweig unterschiedlichen Auswahlsätze im Gegensatz zu den früheren Gehalts- und Lohnstrukturerhebungen in der gewerblichen Wirtschaft erforderliche Hochrechnung der Stichprobenergebnisse auf 100 % der Grundgesamtheit wurde vorgenommen, indem die individuellen Verdienst- und Arbeitszeitangaben jedes einzelnen erfaßten Arbeitnehmers mit einem ganzzahligen Hochrechnungsfaktor multipliziert wurden, der sich als Produkt aus den reziproken Auswahlsätzen der ersten Stufe (Betriebsauswahl) und der zweiten Stufe (Arbeitnehmerauswahl) des Auswahlverfahrens ergab. Die Hochrechnungsfaktoren wurden vor der Erhebung durch den Auswahlplan festgelegt und blieben auch dann unverändert, wenn sich bei einem Berichtsbetrieb zwischen dem Zeitpunkt der Erstellung der Auswahlgrundlage und dem Zeitpunkt der Befragung der Wirtschaftszweig oder die Größenklasse änderte. Wenn ein Berichtsbetrieb nach der Erstellung der Auswahlgrundlage ausnahmsweise in mehrere einzeln zu erfassende Teilbetriebe aufgespalten wurde, wurde jeder Teilbetrieb im Auswahlplan und bei der Hochrechnung wie der ursprüngliche Gesamtbetrieb behandelt, behielt also dieselbe Buchstabengruppe für die Arbeitnehmerauswahl und denselben Hochrechnungsfaktor, auch wenn er einer anderen Größenklasse oder einem anderen Wirtschaftszweig zuzuordnen war. Im übrigen entsprach die Gehalts- und Lohnstrukturerhebung 1966 in der Aufbereitung den Gehalts- und Lohnstrukturerhebungen in der gewerblichen Wirtschaft für 1957 und 1962, insbesondere hinsichtlich der Bildung von Leistungsgruppen sowie der "Umrechnung" in Monatsangaben und der "Reduktion" zu Wochenangaben (vgl. Seite 103). Erhebungsmerkmale der Gehalts- und Lohnstrukturerhebung 1966 waren vor allem der Bruttoverdienst im Erhebungsmonat (bei Arbeitern nach Lohnform mit gesonderter Angabe der Bezahlung für Mehrarbeit), der Gesamtbruttojahresverdienst unter Ausgliederung der Weihnachtsgratifikation, die gesetzlichen Abzüge, die Arbeitszeit der Arbeiter sowie weitere persönliche Merkmale wie Geschlecht, Familienstand, Lebensalter, Kinderzahl, Beruf, Qualifikation und Dauer der Unternehmenszugehörigkeit. Die individuellen Verdienstangaben wurden zu durchschnittlichen Stunden-, Wochen-, Monats- und Jahresverdiensten sowie zu Häufigkeitsverteilungen nach Verdienstklassen aufbereitet. Die Ergebnisse der Gehalts- und Lohnstrukturerhebung 1966 wurden vom Statistischen Bundesamt in der Fachserie M Reihe 17 I (Band 1 Arbeiterverdienste, Band 2 Angestelltenverdienste) veröffentlicht (Stuttgart - Mainz 1970).

In weitgehender methodischer Übereinstimmung mit der Erhebung von 1966 wurde für Oktober 1972 abermals eine Gehalts- und Lohnstrukturerhebung in der gewerblichen Wirtschaft mit doppelter Rechtsgrundlage als repräsentative Individualerhebung durchgeführt, die auf der "Vierten Verordnung über die Durchführung einer Sondererhebung zur Lohnstatistik" vom 24. April 1972 (Bundesgesetzblatt 1972 Teil I S. 729) und auf der vom Rat der Europäischen Gemeinschaften erlassenen "Verordnung Nr. 2395 zur Durchführung einer Erhebung über Struktur und Verteilung von Löhnen und Gehältern in der Industrie" vom 8. November 1971 (Amtsblatt der Europäischen Gemeinschaften 1971 Nr. L 249 S. 52) beruhte. Nach der EG-Verordnung waren die Löhne und Gehälter von Arbeitern, Angestellten, Meistern und Führungskräften im gesamten verarbeitenden Gewerbe einschließlich des Handwerks, im industriellen und handwerklichen Baugewerbe und in der Energiewirtschaft und Wasserversorgung zu erfassen, wobei als Erhebungszeitraum für die Arbeiter der Oktober 1972 und für die übrigen Arbeitnehmer hinsichtlich der Monatsangaben der Oktober 1972 und hinsichtlich der Jahresangaben - gesamte Bruttojahresverdienste mit gesonderter Angabe der einmaligen bzw. unregelmäßigen Zahlungen - das Jahr 1972 galt. Nach der nationalen "Vierten Verordnung" waren für den Oktober 1972 die Arbeitsverdienste bzw. Arbeitszeiten und für das Jahr 1972 die gesamten Jahresverdienste von Arbeitern und Angestellten in Betrieben der gewerblichen Wirtschaft zu erfassen. Neben der Unterscheidung der Arbeitnehmer nach Vollbeschäftigten und Teilzeitbeschäftigten wurde dabei erstmalig in einer Gehalts- und Lohnstrukturerhebung auch eine gesonderte Erfassung der Lehrlinge und ihrer Ausbildungsvergütungen vorgenommen. Dagegen fiel die bei den früheren Gehalts- und Lohnstrukturerhebungen in der gewerblichen Wirtschaft übliche Unterscheidung der Angestellten nach kaufmännischen und technischen Angestellten weg. Der Auswahlplan der Erhebung von 1972 wich in einigen Punkten von dem Auswahlplan der Erhebung von 1966 ab. Die Auswahlsätze für die Betriebsauswahl wurden nicht nur von Größenklasse zu Größenklasse und von Wirtschaftszweig zu Wirtschaftszweig, sondern auch von Bundesland zu Bundesland unterschiedlich festgelegt, so daß der durchschnittliche relative Standardfehler der Ergebnisse für das kleinste Land etwa doppelt so groß wurde wie für das größte Land. Als Auswahlgrundlage für die Betriebsauswahl diente ausschließlich die Arbeitsstättenzählung 1970. Die Betriebe der Auswahlgesamtheit wurden nunmehr in den meisten Wirtschaftszweigen nach vier Größenklassen - höchstens 19 Beschäftigte, 20 bis 99 Beschäftigte, 100 bis 499 Beschäftigte, mindestens 500 Beschäftigte -, in einigen Wirtschaftszweigen auch nach fünf oder drei Größenklassen sortiert. Die Festlegung der unterschiedlichen Auswahlsätze für die Betriebsauswahl in den einzelnen Größenklassen erfolgte nach vorgegebener Genauigkeitsabstufung, so daß sich in den Größenklassen mit größerer Gesamtzahl der Beschäftigten ein niedrigerer relativer Standardfehler ergab als in den Größenklassen mit kleinerer Gesamtzahl der Beschäftigten. Die Auswahlsätze für die Arbeitnehmerauswahl waren innerhalb jeder Größenklasse grunsätzlich für alle Wirtschaftszweige und alle Bundesländer gleich, und zwar waren von den einzelnen Berichtsbetrieben in der untersten Größenklasse 100 %, in der zweituntersten Größenklasse 50 %, in der zweitobersten Größenklasse 25 % und in der obersten Größenklasse 12,5 % der Arbeitnehmer zu erfassen. Abweichungen von diesen einheitlichen Auswahlsätzen für die Arbeitnehmerauswahl ergaben sich in einigen Wirtschaftszweigen vor allem durch die zusätzlich zu berücksichtigende Forderung des Statistischen Amtes der Europäischen Gemeinschaften, daß in jedem Wirtschaftszweig im Bundesgebiet mindestens 10 000 Arbeitnehmer zu erfassen waren. Im übrigen entsprach der Auswahlplan von 1972 dem von 1966; auch der durchschnittliche Gesamtauswahlsatz - Produkt aus dem Auswahlsatz für die Betriebsauswahl und dem Auswahlsatz für die Arbeitnehmerauswahl - betrug im Bundesgebiet 1972 wie bei der Erhebung von 1966 etwa 15 %. Erhebungsmerkmale der Gehalts- und Lohnstrukturerhebung 1972 waren vor allem der Bruttoverdienst im Erhebungsmonat (bei Arbeitern nach Lohnform und Art der Lohnberechnung sowie bei Arbeitern und Angestellten mit gesonderter Angabe der Bezahlung für Mehrarbeit), der Gesamtbruttojahresverdienst unter Ausgliederung der einmaligen bzw. unregelmäßigen Zahlungen, die gesetzlichen Abzüge, die Arbeitszeit und Urlaubsdauer der Arbeiter und Angestellten sowie weitere persönliche Merkmale (Geschlecht, Lebensalter, Beruf, Qualifikation, Dauer der Unternehmenszugehörigkeit, Hochschulstudium bei Angestellten). Als Ergebnisse wurden in erster Linie durchschnittliche

Stunden-, Wochen-, Monats- und Jahresverdienste sowie Häufigkeitsverteilungen nach Verdienstklassen ausgewiesen. Die Ergebnisse der Erhebung von 1972 wurden vom Statistischen Bundesamt in der Fachserie M Reihe 17 I (Band 1 Arbeiterverdienste, Band 2 Angestelltenverdienste) veröffentlicht (Stuttgart - Mainz 1976).

175 Fortgesetzte Ausweitung für die Europäischen Gemeinschaften

Auf Veranlassung der Europäischen Gemeinschaften wurde in den sechziger Jahren damit begonnen, in allen Mitgliedstaaten gleichzeitige und vergleichbare Erhebungen über die Personalkosten und Personalnebenkosten auch außerhalb des produzierenden Gewerbes durchzuführen. Das Statistische Bundesamt veranstaltete zunächst für das Jahr 1962 zum Testen der Fragebogen eine Probeerhebung bei Unternehmen des Straßenverkehrsgewerbes - Personenbeförderung mit Omnibussen im Überlandverkehr sowie Möbeltransport und sonstige Güterbeförderung mit Kraftfahrzeugen mit Ausnahme des werkseigenen Kraftverkehrs - mit mindestens fünf Arbeitnehmern. Da die Teilnahme an der Probeerhebung freiwillig war, gingen von den 429 angeschriebenen Unternehmen nur 77 Meldungen ein. Eine umfassendere Personalkostenerhebung mit gleicher Abgrenzung des Erhebungsbereichs und Auskunftspflicht der Arbeitgeber wurde auf Grund der vom Rat der Europäischen Wirtschaftsgemeinschaft erlassenen "Verordnung Nr. 100 zur Durchführung einer Lohnerhebung im Straßenverkehrsgewerbe" vom 14. Juli 1966 (Amtsblatt der Europäischen Gemeinschaften 1966 Nr. 134 S. 2538) durchgeführt. Berichtszeitraum dieser Repräsentativerhebung war das ganze Jahr 1967; zu erfassen waren Betriebe oder Unternehmen - in der Bundesrepublik Deutschland war Auswahl-, Erhebungs- und Aufbereitungseinheit nur das Unternehmen als rechtliche Einheit -, die im Jahresdurchschnitt 1967 mindestens fünf Arbeitnehmer beschäftigt hatten. Im übrigen entsprach die Personalkostenerhebung im Straßenverkehrsgewerbe 1967 nach dem Inhalt der EG-Verordnung, der Erhebungs- und Aufbereitungsorganisation, den Erhebungsmerkmalen und der Form der Ergebnisse weitgehend den Personalkostenerhebungen im produzierenden Gewerbe (vgl. S. 124). Der Plan für die Unternehmensauswahl, nach dem in der Bundesrepublik Deutschland rund 1 000 Unternehmen in die Stichprobe einzubeziehen waren, sah eine geschichtete Stichprobe mit systematischem Auswahlverfahren vor. Die Schichten waren definiert als Beschäftigtengrößenklassen innerhalb der einzelnen Zweige des Straßenverkehrsgewerbes. Auswahlgrundlage war der Verkehrszensus 1962. Die Auswahlsätze waren in den einzelnen Schichten tendenziell unterschiedlich; der Stichprobenumfang wurde dabei pro Schicht so bestimmt, daß die relativen Standardfehler der Bundesergebnisse nach Größenklassen in den einzelnen Zweigen bei den wichtigsten Durchschnittsmerkmalen unter 5 % lagen. Die Auswahlabstände waren innerhalb einer Schicht in allen Bundesländern gleich, die Zufallsstartzahlen wurden jedoch für jedes Land gesondert festgelegt. Im Durchschnitt aller Schichten wurden 10 % der Unternehmen der Grundgesamtheit für die Stichprobe ausgewählt. Der im Auswahlplan pro Schicht festgelegte Auswahlabstand wurde bei der Aufbereitung unverändert als Hochrechnungsfaktor übernommen, auch wenn sich bei einem Unternehmen der Verkehrszweig oder die Größenklasse zwischen der Erstellung der Auswahlgrundlage und dem Erhebungszeitraum geändert hatten. Wenn in diesem Zeitraum ein Berichtsunternehmen in mehrere rechtlich selbständige Teilunternehmen aufgespalten wurde, wurden alle Teilunternehmen einzeln erfaßt und erhielten jeweils denselben Hochrechnungsfaktor wie das ursprüngliche Gesamtunternehmen. Die nachträgliche Änderung des Verkehrszweiges oder der Größenklasse mußte jedoch bei der Aufbereitung für die Zuordnung der Unternehmen zur Ermittlung von Ergebnissen nach Zweigen und Größenklassen berücksichtigt werden. Dabei wurden allerdings Unternehmen, die nach der Erstellung der Auswahlgrundlage unter die Erfassungsgrenze von fünf Arbeitnehmern gesunken waren, nicht ausgesondert, sondern bei der Aufbereitung der untersten erfaßten Größenklasse zugeordnet; gestrichen wurden lediglich Unternehmen, die inzwischen ganz ohne Arbeitnehmer arbeiteten. Ersatzlose Streichungen aus dem Berichtskreis wurden auch bei Unternehmen vorgenommen, bei denen es sich um "unechte Antwortausfälle" (Liquidation u.a.) handelte. "Echte Antwortausfälle" (Auskunftsverweigerung u.a.) wurden dagegen durch Dopplung der Angaben eines Unternehmens aus derselben Schicht ersetzt. Die Personalkostenerhebung im Straßenverkehrsgewerbe 1967 war durch eine ungewöhnliche Art der bei der Aufbereitung vorzunehmenden Plausibilitätskontrolle gekennzeichnet. Die zu diesem Zweck festzusetzenden Grenzwerte wurden dabei nicht wie sonst in der Lohnstatistik üblich nach bereits vorliegenden Erfahrungswerten, sondern aus der Erhebung selbst nach folgendem Beispiel ermittelt:

Jahres-verdienst-klassen (DM)	7000 bis unter 8000	8000 bis unter 9000	9000 bis unter 10 000	10 000 bis unter 11 000	11 000 bis unter 12 000	12 000 bis unter 13 000	13 000 bis unter 14 000	14 000 bis unter 15 000	15 000 bis unter 16 000
Anzahl der Unternehmen (Zuordnung nach dem Durchschnitts-verdienst der Angestellten)	1	1	0	5	17	4	0	1	1

Das Produkt aus der Gesamtzahl der Berichtsunternehmen (hier 30) und dem konstanten Faktor 0,05 ergibt die rohe Prüfgröße 1,5, die durch Rundung auf die nächstgrößere ganze Zahl zu der endgültigen Prüfgröße 2 führt. Grenzwerte für die Plausibilitätskontrolle sind dann diejenigen Klassengrenzen, oberhalb bzw. unterhalb derer höchstens so viele Fälle liegen, wie die Prüfgröße angibt, im Beispiel also 9 000 DM und 14 000 DM. Wenn unplausible oder fehlende Angaben im Erhebungsbogen nicht durch Rückfrage bei dem Berichtsunternehmen geklärt werden konnten, wurde statt dessen das gewogene arithmetische Mittel der entsprechenden Angaben aller anderen Erhebungsbogen derselben Schicht eingesetzt, wobei als Gewichte die Arbeitnehmerzahlen der einzelnen Unternehmen dienten. Während in der Bundesrepublik Deutschland die Erhebungs- und Aufbereitungsarbeiten bis zur Plausibilitätskontrolle den Statistischen Landesämtern oblagen, wurden die Ergebnisse - mit Ausnahme von Sondertabellen für Bayern nur Tabellen mit Bundesergebnissen nach Verkehrszweigen und Größenklassen - zentral vom Statistischen Bundesamt zusammengestellt. Die Ergebnisse der Personalkostenerhebung im Straßenverkehrsgewerbe 1967 wurden vom Statistischen Bundesamt in "Wirtschaft und Statistik" (Jahrgang 1969) veröffentlicht.

Um die Möglichkeit von Personalkostenerhebungen im Handel, Bank- und Versicherungsgewerbe zu testen, führte das Statistische Bundesamt unter freiwilliger Beteiligung von 28 Unternehmen des Einzelhandels, 10 Unternehmen des Bankgewerbes und 11 Unternehmen des Versicherungsgewerbes für das Jahr 1966 eine Probeerhebung durch. Eine umfassende Erhebung dieser Art in den gleichen Wirtschaftsbereichen mit Auskunftspflicht der Arbeitgeber fand dann für das Berichtsjahr 1970 auf Grund der vom Rat der Europäischen Gemeinschaften erlassenen "Verordnung Nr. 2053 über die Durchführung einer Lohnerhebung im Einzelhandel, im Bank- und im Versicherungsgewerbe" vom 17. Oktober 1969 (Amtsblatt der Europäischen Gemeinschaften 1969 Nr. L 263 S. 8) statt. Danach waren im Einzelhandel, im Versicherungsgewerbe und bei genossenschaftlichen Kreditinstituten Unternehmen mit mindestens 20 - voll- oder teilzeitbeschäftigten - Arbeitnehmern (in die Erhebung einbezogen wurden allerdings nur die vollbeschäftigten Arbeitnehmer) und im übrigen Bankgewerbe sämtliche Unternehmen zu erfassen; ausgeschlossen blieben lediglich die öffentlich-rechtlichen Bank- und Versicherungsunternehmen. Die EG-Verordnung sah für die Unternehmen des Einzelhandels mit 20 bis 49 Arbeitnehmern die Möglichkeit der Repräsentativerhebung - von dieser Möglichkeit wurde in der Bundesrepublik Deutschland Gebrauch gemacht -, für die übrigen zu erfassenden Unternehmen nur die Totalerhebung vor. Die Arbeitsteilung zwischen dem Statistischen Bundesamt und den Statistischen Landesämtern entsprach der in der amtlichen deutschen Lohnstatistik allgemein üblichen Regelung, wonach die Statistischen Landesämter zunächst die Landesergebnisse und das Statistische Bundesamt anschließend das Bundesergebnis erstellten. Das Statistische Amt der Europäischen Gemeinschaften erhielt vom Statistischen Bundesamt nur die Gesamtergebnisse für das Bundesgebiet. Bei den repräsentativ zu erfassenden Unternehmen betrug der Auswahlsatz einheitlich 50 %, in einigen Einzelhandelszweigen - z.B. Apotheken - wurden allerdings auch die Unternehmen mit 20 bis 49 Arbeitnehmern total erfaßt. Die Stichprobendaten wurden jeweils auf 100 % der Grundgesamtheit hochgerechnet. Auswahlgrundlage für den Einzelhandel war die Handels- und Gaststättenzählung

1968. Für das Bank- und Versicherungsgewerbe wurden die Unternehmensanschriften vorwiegend nichtstatistischen Quellen wie Nachschlagewerken und Mitgliederverzeichnissen von Verbänden entnommen. Die Einzelheiten der Aufbereitung - wie Bestimmung der Hochrechnunsfaktoren, Zuordnung zu Größenklassen und Wirtschaftszweigen, Behandlung von Antwortausfällen und dgl. - sowie die Erhebungsmerkmale und Form der Ergebnisse entsprachen dem Verfahren, das auch bei den EG-Personalkostenerhebungen in den anderen Wirtschaftsbereichen angewandt wurde. Die Ergebnisse der Personalkostenerhebung 1970 für das Bundesgebiet - gegliedert nach Wirtschaftszweigen und Beschäftigtengrößenklassen - wurden vom Statistischen Bundesamt in der Fachserie M Reihe 15 als Sonderbeitrag (Stuttgart - Mainz 1973) veröffentlicht.

Zur Aktualisierung der Ergebnisse der Personalkostenerhebung 1970 erließ der Rat der Europäischen Gemeinschaften die "Verordnung Nr. 3192 über eine Arbeitskostenerhebung im Groß- und Einzelhandel, im Bank- und im Versicherungsgewerbe" vom 22. November 1973 (Amtsblatt der Europäischen Gemeinschaften 1973 Nr. L 326 S. 1). Danach waren für das Berichtsjahr 1974 Unternehmen mit mindestens zehn Arbeitnehmern nunmehr allgemein im Stichprobenverfahren zu erfassen. Die Aufbereitung der Erhebung bis zur Erstellung von Ergebnissen für die Mitgliedstaaten oblag den nationalen statistischen Ämtern. Das Statistische Amt der Europäischen Gemeinschaften erhielt die aufbereiteten Ergebnisse vom Statistischen Bundesamt nach Bundesländern, Wirtschaftszweigen und Beschäftigtengrößenklassen. Im Gegensatz zu der Erhebung von 1970 wurden auch die öffentlichrechtlichen Bank- und Versicherungsunternehmen mit Ausnahme der Deutschen Bundesbank erfaßt. Die Erhebung von 1974 erfuhr ferner dadurch eine Erweiterung, daß neben den vollbeschäftigten auch die teilzeitbeschäftigten Arbeitnehmer einbezogen und mit ihren Merkmalen bei der Aufbereitung in den Statistischen Landesämtern auf Vollbeschäftigte umgerechnet wurden. Nach dem Plan der EG-Kommission waren in der Bundesrepublik Deutschland insgesamt 12 000 Unternehmen in der Stichprobe zu erfassen. Auswahlgrundlage war für alle Wirtschaftsbereiche die Arbeitsstättenzählung 1970. Die Unternehmen der Auswahlgesamtheit wurden vor der Auswahl innerhalb jedes Bundeslandes erst nach Wirtschaftszweigen und dann nach Beschäftigtengrößen - klassen

(Schichten) sortiert. Der für das Bundesgebiet vorgesehene Gesamtstichprobenumfang wurde zunächst auf die einzelnen Bundesländer verteilt, indem die Auswahlsätze pro Land prinzipiell unterschiedlich nach vorgegebener Genauigkeitsabstufung (Exponent 0,3) nur unter Berücksichtigung der Besetzungszahlen in den einzelnen Ländern in der Auswahlgrundlage bestimmt wurden; auf diese Weise wurde der durchschnittliche relative Standardfehler der Ergebnisse für das kleinste Land etwas mehr als doppelt so groß wie für das größte Land. Der sich damit ergebende Gesamtstichprobenumfang pro Land wurde anschließend ebenfalls nach einer vorgegebenen Genauigkeitsabstufung (Exponent 0,2) und entsprechend differenzierten Auswahlsätzen auf die Wirtschaftszweige und Größenklassen verteilt, wobei als Richtmerkmal die teils aus der Personalkostenerhebung 1970 und teils aus der Gehalts- und Lohnstrukturerhebung 1966 geschätzten Personalkosten je Unternehmen zugrundegelegt wurden, während der Variationskoeffizient in den einzelnen Schichten einheitlich angenommen wurde. Für die obersten Größenklassen aller Wirtschaftszweige wurde regelmäßig die Totalerfassung vorgesehen. Die Bestimmung der Stichprobenunternehmen erfolgte nach dem Zufallsprinzip unter Anwendung des üblichen systematischen Auswahlverfahrens in den einzelnen Schichten. Die Stichprobendaten mußten bei der Aufbereitung auf 100 % der Grundgesamtheit hochgerechnet werden, indem die Angaben jedes einzelnen Berichtsunternehmens mit dem jeweiligen Auswahlabstand laut Auswahlplan als Hochrechnungsfaktor multipliziert wurden. Der Hochrechnungsfaktor blieb auf jeden Fall unverändert, auch wenn das Unternehmen zum Erhebungszeitpunkt einem anderen Wirtschaftszweig oder einer anderen Größenklasse angehörte als in der Auswahlgrundlage oder wenn es inzwischen seinen Sitz in ein anderes Bundesland verlegt hatte. Wenn ein ausgewähltes Unternehmen inzwischen in rechtlich selbständige Teilunternehmen aufgespalten worden war, verblieben alle Teilunternehmen in der Erhebung und erhielten denselben Hochrechnungsfaktor wie das ursprüngliche Gesamtunternehmen. Für die Ergebniserstellung wurden die Unternehmen u. U. abweichend von der Auswahlgrundlage nach den tatsächlichen Verhältnissen im Berichtszeitraum den Wirtschaftszweigen, Größenklassen sowie den Bundesländern neu zugeordnet. Ausgewählte Unternehmen, die nach der Auswahlgrundlage mindestens zehn, im Berichtsjahr jedoch weniger als zehn Arbeitnehmer hatten, konnten nicht mehr zur Berichterstattung gezwungen werden; die von diesen Unternehmen trotzdem eingegangenen Meldungen verblieben jedoch in der Aufbereitung und wurden dann den untersten Größenklassen zugeordnet. Die Behandlung von Antwortausfällen erfolgte wie bei den EG-Personalkostenerhebungen im produzierenden Gewerbe, das heißt "echte Ausfälle" wurden gedoppelt und "unechte Ausfälle" ersatzlos gestrichen. Die Erhebungsmerkmale einschließlich der Form der Ergebnisse entsprachen ebenfalls denen der Personalkostenerhebungen im produzierenden Gewerbe. Die Ergebnisse der Personalkostenerhebung 1974 für die Bundesrepublik Deutschland wurden vom Statistischen Bundesamt in der Fachserie 16 als Einzelveröffentlichung (Stuttgart - Mainz 1977) veröffentlicht. Derartige Erhebungen in den Wirtschaftsbereichen Handel, Bank- und Versicherungsgewerbe finden nach den Plänen der EG-Kommission weiterhin in dreijährigen Abständen statt.

In zeitlichem Zusammenhang mit der Personalkostenerhebung 1974 wurde auf Grund der vom Rat der Europäischen Gemeinschaften erlassenen "Verordnung Nr. 178 zur Durchführung einer Erhebung über Struktur und Verteilung der Löhne und Gehälter im Groß- und Einzelhandel, im Bank- und Versicherungsgewerbe" vom 21. Januar 1974 (Amtsblatt der Europäischen Gemeinschaften 1974 Nr. L 21 S. 2) eine Gehalts- und Lohnstrukturerhebung als repräsentative Individualerhebung mit von der EG-Kommission festgelegten Erhebungsbogen durchgeführt, die erstmalig organisatorisch nicht mit einer gleichartigen nationalen Erhebung verbunden wurde. Danach waren die Löhne und Gehälter von voll- und teilzeitbeschäftigten Arbeitern und Angestellten in einfacher, gehobener und leitender Stellung zu erfassen. Sämtliche Arbeitnehmer wurden bei der Aufbereitung einheitlich nach sechs "Qualifikationsgruppen" aufgegliedert, die aus den in der amtlichen deutschen Lohnstatistik üblichen Leistungsgruppen der Arbeiter bzw. der Angestellten gebildet werden konnten. Als Erhebungszeiträume sah die EG-Verordnung für die auf einen Monat bezogenen Verdienstangaben einen beliebigen Monat des Jahres 1974 - vorzugsweise den Oktober (dieser Monat wurde daraufhin in der Bundesrepublik Deutschland als Erhebungsmonat verwendet) - und für die Jahresangaben - Bruttojahresverdienste mit gesondertem Nachweis der einmaligen oder unregelmäßigen Zahlungen - das Jahr 1974 vor. Auskunftspflichtig waren Unternehmen (rechtliche Einheiten) mit mindestens zehn Arbeitnehmern. Die bei der Erhebung ermittelten Einzelangaben wurden wie bei den Gehalts- und Lohnstrukturerhebungen in der gewerblichen Wirtschaft von 1966 und 1972 dem Statistischen Amt der Europäischen Gemeinschaften zur Verfügung gestellt, das daraus die für die Zwecke der EG-Kommission bestimmten Ergebnistabellen - unter anderem auch mit Daten für einzelne Bundesländer - zentral aufstellte. Von einer eigenen nationalen Tabellierung wurde dagegen abgesehen. Die Auswahl der Erhebungseinheiten erfolgte nach dem bei den Gehalts- und Lohnstrukturerhebungen üblichen zweistufigen Verfahren. Die erste Stufe (Unternehmensauswahl) wurde im Auswahlplan und bei der praktischen Ziehung der Stichprobe mit der Unternehmensauswahl der Personalkostenerhebung 1974 gekoppelt. Auswahlgrundlage, Schichtung, Auswahlsätze bzw. Auswahlabstände und praktiziertes Auswahlverfahren für die Unternehmensauswahl waren bei der Gehalts- und Lohnstrukturerhebung und bei der Personalkostenerhebung identisch. Um die Berichtsunternehmen nach Möglichkeit jedoch nicht mit zwei verhältnismäßig arbeitsaufwendigen Erhebungen gleichzeitig zu belasten, wurden durch die Festlegung jeweils unterschiedlicher Zufallsstartzahlen in den nicht total erfaßten Schichten bei den beiden Erhebungen verschiedene Unternehmen in die Stichprobe einbezogen, die in der Auswahlgrundlage maschinell in einem einzigen Arbeitsgang bestimmt wurden. In der zweiten Auswahlstufe der Gehalts- und Lohnstrukturerhebung 1974 hatten die Berichtsunternehmen nach dem üblichen Verfahren der alternierenden Buchstabenauswahl bestimmte Arbeitnehmer auszuwählen. Nach der Rahmenregelung der EG-Kommission waren in der Bundesrepublik Deutschland insgesamt maximal 240 000 Arbeitnehmer zu erfassen. Zur Ermittlung der Auswahlsätze für die Arbeitnehmerauswahl wurde dieser Gesamtstichprobenumfang zuerst nach einer vorgegebenen Genauigkeitsabstufung (Exponent 0,3) unter alleiniger Berücksichtigung der Besetzungszahlen in der Auswahlgrundlage auf die Bundesländer und anschließend ebenfalls nach vorgegebener Genauigkeitsabstufung (Exponent 0,05) auf die einzelnen Unternehmensschichten je Land verteilt, wobei als Richtmerkmal der teils aus der Personalkostenerhebung 1970 und teils aus der Gehalts- und Lohnstrukturerhebung 1966 geschätzte Bruttomonatsverdienst je Arbeitnehmer diente. Die Auswahlsätze für die Arbeitnehmerauswahl wurden unter Berücksichtigung des zusätzlichen Wunsches der EG-Kommission, in jedem nachzuweisenden Wirtschaftszweig mindestens 10 000 Arbeitnehmer zu erfassen - dieser Wunsch führte zu dem o.a. sehr niedrigen Exponenten der Genauigkeitsabstufung -, festgelegt. Die Gesamtauswahlsätze ergaben sich schließlich als Produkte aus den Auswahlsätzen der ersten Stufe (Unternehmensauswahl) und der zweiten Stufe (Arbeitnehmerauswahl); diese Gesamtauswahlsätze wurden so weit gerundet, daß im endgültigen Auswahlplan nur noch Sätze von 100 %, 50 %, 25 %, 12,5 %, 6,25 % und 3,125 % vorkamen. Der bundesdurchschnittliche Gesamtauswahlsatz betrug rund 10 %. Die Hochrechnung, Behandlung von Antwortausfällen, Zuordnung zu Wirtschaftszweigen und Unternehmensgrößenklassen und die sonstigen Einzelheiten der Aufbereitung wurden analog zu den Gehalts- und Lohnstrukturerhebungen 1966 und 1972 bzw. zur Personalkostenerhebung 1974 vorgenommen. Auch hinsichtlich der Erhebungsmerkmale hielt sich die Gehalts- und Lohnstrukturerhebung 1974 in dem Rahmen der früheren Strukturerhebungen.

18 Die Phase der Konsolidierung und Bereinigung (ab 1971)

181 Wandlungen in der Entlohnung

Das System der amtlichen deutschen Lohnstatistik wurde auch in den siebziger Jahren grundsätzlich beibehalten, jedoch hinsichtlich der Erhebungsprogramme in einigen Punkten durch Ergänzungen oder Kürzungen neuen wirtschaftlich-sozialen Entwicklungstendenzen angepaßt. Ferner wurde das Bestreben deutlich, durch Änderungen in der Erhebungsorganisation und der Aufbereitungstechnik eine Senkung der Kosten bzw. eine Beschleunigung des Arbeitsablaufs zu erreichen. Daneben sollten durch die stärkere Berücksichtigung theoretisch-statistischer Modelle die Auswertungsmöglichkeiten verbessert werden.

Zunächst wurde das Gesetz über die Lohnstatistik vom 18. Mai 1956 (Bundesgesetzblatt 1956 Teil I S. 429) durch das "Gesetz zur Änderung des Gesetzes über die Lohnstatistik" vom 4. August 1971 (Bundesgesetzblatt 1971 Teil I S. 1217) in einigen Punkten reformiert. Das Gesetz von 1971 brachte neben einigen Änderungen in anderen Bereichen der Lohnstatistik vor allem die Einführung einer neuen "Bruttojahresverdiensterhebung in Industrie und Handel", wodurch inzwischen eingetretenen Wandlungen in der Entlohnung Rechnung getragen werden sollte. In der amtlichen Begründung des Gesetzes von 1971 (Bundesratsdrucksache Nr. 700/70 vom 18. Dezember 1970) wurde dazu ausgeführt, daß die zunehmende Bedeutung der in der vierteljährlichen Verdiensterhebung in Industrie und Handel nicht erfaßten einmaligen oder unregelmäßigen Zahlungen die Novellierung des lohnstatistischen Gesetzes von 1956 notwendig machte. Die vierteljährliche Verdiensterhebung sollte als kurzfristiger Indikator die Entwicklung der Bruttoverdienste der vollbeschäftigten Arbeitnehmer aufzeigen und mußte sich daher auf die laufend - d. h. die der Art nach in jedem Lohn- und Gehaltsabrechnungszeitraum anfallenden - gezahlten Beträge beschränken, weil die nur einmal im Jahr oder in unregelmäßigen Abständen gezahlten Beträge wegen ihres zufälligen Anfalls die aufgezeigte Verdienstentwicklung eventuell verfälscht hätten und weil andererseits die vier Erhebungsmonate der vierteljährlichen Erhebung - Januar, April, Juli, Oktober - kein vollständiges Bild dieser Zahlungen vermitteln könnten. Demgegenüber hatten die nicht-laufenden Zahlungen vor allem in der Form des zusätzlichen Urlaubsgeldes, des Weihnachtsgeldes und zusätzlicher Monatsgehälter an Bedeutung gewonnen, so daß die Ergebnisse der vierteljährlichen Verdiensterhebung in ständig verringertem Maße die Gesamtverdienste wiedergaben. Von einer Änderung des Verdienstbegriffs der vierteljährlichen Erhebung mußte aus den genannten Gründen zur Vermeidung von Brüchen in den vierteljährlichen Verdienstreihen abgesehen werden. Eine laufende Ermittlung der Gesamtverdienste war daher nur durch eine neue Bruttojahresverdiensterhebung möglich, die alle im ganzen Berichtsjahr angefallenen laufenden und nicht-laufenden Zahlungen umfaßte. Die Bruttojahresverdiensterhebung in Industrie und Handel wurde erstmalig für das Berichtsjahr 1971 durchgeführt und seitdem jährlich wiederholt. Sie erfaßte in repräsentativ ausgewählten Betrieben gegliedert nach dem Geschlecht jeweils sämtliche vollbeschäftigten Arbeiter und Angestellten (mit Ausnahme der Angestellten der Leistungsgruppe I), die das ganze Jahr hindurch dem Betrieb angehörten, sowie deren Bruttojahresarbeitsverdienste, d. h. sämtliche laufenden und nicht-laufenden Verdienstbeträge in jeweils einer Summe. Die Angaben waren von den Betrieben auf Fragebogen nicht für die einzelnen Arbeitnehmer, sondern für die vorgesehenen Arbeitnehmergruppen nach dem Summenverfahren zu machen. Bei der Bildung dieser Arbeitnehmergruppen wurde im Gegensatz zur vierteljährlichen Verdiensterhebung keine Aufgliederung nach Leistungsgruppen vorgenommen. Im übrigen schloß sich die Bruttojahresverdiensterhebung eng an die vierteljährliche Verdiensterhebung an. In beiden Erhebungen wurde jeweils derselbe Kreis von Berichtsbetrieben erfaßt, wodurch sich bei der Plausibilitätskontrolle zusätzliche Möglichkeiten der Abstimmung boten, indem pro Betrieb die Einzelmeldungen zur Jahreserhebung einerseits und zur vierteljährlichen Erhebung andererseits zusammengeführt wurden. In beiden Erhebungen war der Betrieb als örtliche Einheit Erhebungseinheit; gehörte ein Betrieb mehreren Wirtschaftszweigen an, wurde er grundsätzlich als Ganzes demjenigen Wirtschaftszweig zugeordnet, in dem der überwiegende Teil seiner Arbeitnehmer beschäftigt war. Auch die Hochrechnung und die Behandlung von Antwortausfällen entsprachen dem bei der vierteljährlichen Erhebung praktizierten Verfahren (vgl. Seite 132). Entsprechend dem Berichtskreiswechsel der vierteljährlichen Erhebung vom Oktober 1972 wurde auch in der Jahreserhebung ab Berichtsjahr 1972 ein neuer Kreis von Berichtsbetrieben erfaßt; die Ermittlung von "Umrechnungsfaktoren" zur rechnerischen Verknüpfung der Ergebnisse für den alten und den neuen Berichtskreis war jedoch bei der Jahreserhebung nicht möglich. Ein geringfügiger Unterschied bestand in den beiden Erhebungen dadurch, daß bei der Jahreserhebung erkrankte Arbeitnehmer auf jeden Fall miterfaßt wurden, auch wenn sie länger als sechs Wochen krank waren und somit keinen Lohn bzw. kein Gehalt mehr bezogen, während bei der vierteljährlichen Erhebung nur die vollbezahlten Arbeitnehmer einbezogen wurden. Die summarisch erfaßten Angaben der Jahreserhebung wurden bei der Aufbereitung in den Statistischen Landesämtern nach der Hochrechnung und Ergänzung von echten Antwortausfällen für die einzelnen Wirtschaftszweige und Bundesländer zu Verhältniswerten verrechnet, und zwar ergab sich der durchschnittliche Bruttojahresverdienst der Arbeiter bzw. der Angestellten als Quotient aus der Bruttojahreslohn- bzw. -gehaltssumme und der Anzahl der Arbeiter bzw. Angestellten. Die Ergebnisse der Bruttojahresverdiensterhebung in Industrie und Handel wurden vom Statistischen Bundesamt für die Berichtsjahre ab 1971 laufend in "Wirtschaft und Statistik" (Jahrgang 1975 ff.) veröffentlicht.

Die zunehmende Bedeutung privatrechtlicher Pensionsansprüche der Arbeitnehmer gegen ihre Arbeitgeber als besondere Form der indirekten Entlohnung war der Ausgangspunkt für die von der Bundesregierung erlassene "Verordnung zur Durchführung einer Erhebung über Arten und Umfang der betrieblichen Altersversorgung" vom 11. März 1974 (Bundesgesetzblatt 1974 Teil I Seite 681). Die Verordnung schrieb für das Berichtsjahr 1973 bzw. für den Erhebungsstichtag 31. Dezember 1973 eine statistische Erhebung über die betriebliche Altersversorgung als Repräsentativerhebung vor. Auskunftspflichtige Auswahl- und Erhebungseinheit war das Unternehmen als rechtliche Einheit. Erfaßt wurden Unternehmen mit mindestens zehn Beschäftigten der gewerblichen Wirtschaft mit

Ausnahme des Baugewerbes; ausgeschlossen blieben neben Körperschaften, Anstalten und Stiftungen des öffentlichen Rechts auch privatrechtliche Unternehmen der öffentlichen Hand, deren Arbeitnehmer bei einer öffentlich-rechtlichen Zusatzversorgungseinrichtung - z. B. der Versorgungsanstalt des Bundes und der Länder - gemeldet waren. Die Berichtsunternehmen hatten summarische Angaben für alle vollbeschäftigten Arbeiter und Angestellten zu machen, die am 31. Dezember 1973 im Unternehmen unter Arbeitsvertrag standen. Dabei waren die "Leitenden Angestellten" gemäß § 5 Absatz 3 des Betriebsverfassungsgesetzes gesondert zu erfassen. Die von den Berichtsunternehmen ausgefüllten Erhebungsbogen wurden von den Statistischen Landesämtern geprüft und anschließend dem Statistischen Bundesamt zur zentralen Aufstellung der Ergebnistabellen zugeleitet; neben den Tabellen für das Bundesgebiet fielen dabei lediglich für die Länder Nordrhein-Westfalen, Baden-Württemberg und Bayern Sondertabellen mit Landesergebnissen an. Im übrigen wurden die Ergebnisse nicht nach Wirtschaftszweigen, sondern nur nach Unternehmensgrößenklassen entsprechend der Beschäftigtenzahl gegliedert. Bei der Erhebung über die betriebliche Altersversorgung von 1973 wurden im Erhebungsbogen teilweise für die amtliche Lohnstatistik ungewöhnliche Fragen gestellt. So sollten die Unternehmen durch eine Modellrechnung die für ihre Arbeitnehmer theoretisch erreichbare Altersversorgung ermitteln; ferner sollten sie ihre Arbeitnehmer selbst schwerpunktmäßig den einzelnen Typen der Altersversorgung zuordnen. Der Plan für die Unternehmensauswahl ging davon aus, daß im Bundesgebiet insgesamt höchstens 10 000 Unternehmen zu erfassen waren. Die Unternehmen der Auswahlgesamtheit wurden erst nach Wirtschaftszweigen und dann nach Beschäftigtengrößenklassen (Schichten) sortiert; eine Schichtung nach Bundesländern wurde nicht vorgenommen. Die Aufteilung des Gesamtstichprobenumfangs auf die Schichten erfolgte optimal im Sinne des Satzes von Neyman und Tschuprow mit prinzipiell unterschiedlichen Auswahlsätzen in den einzelnen Schichten. Da in den Ergebnissen nur Anzahlen und keine quantitativen Merkmale nachgewiesen werden sollten, wurden die Mittelwerte und Varianzen, die zur Berechnung des Auswahlplans je Schicht erforderlich waren, über die Binomialverteilung unter Berücksichtigung des Klumpeneffekts

(Anzahl der Beschäftigten je Unternehmen) geschätzt. Die Bestimmung der Berichtsunternehmen erfolgte nach dem systematischen Auswahlverfahren gesondert in den einzelnen Schichten; dabei wurden zwar die Auswahlabstände bundeseinheitlich verwendet, dagegen die Zufallsstartzahlen nicht nur nach vorkommenden Auswahlabständen, sondern auch nach Bundesländern entsprechend deren Größe differenziert. Die sich für die einzelnen Schichten ergebenden Auswahlsätze wurden soweit gerundet, daß nur die Auswahlabstände 1, 2, 3 und 4 auftraten. Auswahlgrundlagen waren für das produzierende Gewerbe die Personalkostenerhebung der Europäischen Gemeinschaften für das Jahr 1972 und für die übrigen Wirtschaftsbereiche die Arbeitsstättenzählung 1970. Da die Personalkostenerhebung selbst eine Repräsentativerhebung war, ergab sich in diesem Bereich eine zweiphasige Unternehmensauswahl. Von den in der ersten Phase - d. h. zur Stichprobe für die Personalkostenerhebung - ausgewählten Unternehmen wurden zunächst diejenigen aussortiert, die nach ihren Angaben zur Personalkostenerhebung keine betriebliche Altersversorgung hatten. Auf die verbleibenden Unternehmen wurde dann in der zweiten Phase der o.a. Auswahlplan der Erhebung über die betriebliche Altersversorgung angewendet. Bei der Aufbereitung wurden für die im Anschluß an die erste Phase aussortierten Unternehmen die benötigten Daten nach den aus der Personalkostenerhebung bereits vorliegenden Angaben übernommen und mit den neu ermittelten Daten der bei der Erhebung über die betriebliche Altersversorgung erfaßten Unternehmen in den Ergebnissen zusammengefaßt. Bei der erforderlichen Hochrechnung der Stichprobenergebnisse auf 100 % der Grundgesamtheit wurde für jedes Berichtsunternehmen als unveränderlicher Hochrechnungsfaktor der Auswahlabstand laut Auswahlplan festgelegt. Für die Unternehmen, die aus der totalen Arbeitsstättenzählung gezogen wurden, entsprach der Hochrechnungsfaktor unmittelbar dem bei der Ziehung der Stichprobe verwendeten Auswahlabstand. Für die Unternehmen, die aus der repräsentativen Personalkostenerhebung gezogen wurden, ergab sich der Gesamthochrechnungsfaktor als Produkt aus den Auswahlabständen der ersten Phase (Auswahlabstand laut Auswahlplan der Personalkostenerhebung) und der zweiten Phase (Auswahlabstand laut Auswahlplan der Erhebung über die betriebliche Altersversorgung). Für die Ergebniserstellung wurden die Berichtsunternehmen unter Beibehaltung ihrer Hochrechnungsfaktoren den Größenklassen entsprechend ihrer tatsächlichen Beschäftigtenzahl zum Erhebungszeitpunkt neu zugeordnet. Dabei wurden auch die Meldungen von Unternehmen mit weniger als zehn Arbeitnehmern, die trotz fehlender Berichtspflicht ausgefüllte Erhebungsbogen eingereicht hatten, in die Aufbereitung einbezogen. Antwortausfälle wurden in keinem Fall ersetzt, da Auskunftsverweigerungen u. dgl. nur in sehr geringem Maße vorkamen. Als Ergebnisse der Erhebung über die betriebliche Altersversorgung 1973 wurden die Anzahl der begünstigten Arbeitnehmer, die Höhe der Versorgungsleistungen pro Arbeitnehmer und die Gesamtaufwendungen der Unternehmen für die betriebliche Altersversorgung, jeweils aufgegliedert nach Unternehmensgrößenklassen und Arten der Altersversorgung, ausgewiesen. Die Ergebnisse wurden vom Bundesministerium für Arbeit und Sozialordnung in der Zeitschrift "Arbeits- und sozialstatistische Mitteilungen" (Jahrgang 1975 Seite 228 ff., 270 ff.) veröffentlicht.*) Die Erhebung über die betriebliche Altersversorgung wurde für das Berichtsjahr 1976 bzw. für den Erhebungsstichtag 31. Dezember 1976 nach grundsätzlich dem gleichen Erhebungsplan wie 1973 wiederholt. Der Berichtskreis der Erhebung von 1976 bestand im produzierenden Gewerbe aus neu ausgewählten Unternehmen aus dem Anschriftenmaterial der Personalkostenerhebung der Europäischen Gemeinschaften für das Jahr 1975 und in den übrigen Wirtschaftsbereichen aus denselben Unternehmen wie bei der Erhebung von 1973. Der Auswahlplan für die Neuauswahl aus der Personalkostenerhebung 1975 entsprach dem bei der Erhebung von 1973 angewendeten Auswahlplan; allerdings wurden die Unternehmen, die nach ihren Angaben zur Personalkostenerhebung keine betriebliche Altersversorgung hatten, nicht mehr aussortiert, sondern bei der Erhebung über die betriebliche Altersversorgung miterfaßt.

182 Rückgang der Landwirtschaft

Ein Ziel des Gesetzes zur Änderung des Gesetzes über die Lohnstatistik vom 4. August 1971 (Bundesgesetzblatt 1971 Teil I S. 1217)

*) vgl. Hermann Berié und Marion Wiese: Arten und Ausmaß der betrieblichen Altersversorgung. In: Arbeits- und sozialstatistische Mitteilungen Jahrgang 1975, S. 228 ff., 270 ff.

bestand darin, die jährliche Verdiensterhebung in der Landwirtschaft dem in diesem Wirtschaftsbereich eingetretenen Strukturwandel anzupassen. Die in der Verdiensterhebung zu erfassenden Arbeitergruppen wurden in der Weise geändert, daß ab Berichtsmonat September 1971 bei den weiblichen angelernten Arbeitern nicht mehr die Monatslöhner, sondern stattdessen die Stundenlöhner in die Erhebung einbezogen wurden. Die Untergrenze der zu erfassenden Betriebe wurde gleichzeitig von 20 auf 30 ha landwirtschaftlicher Nutzfläche heraufgesetzt. Die wichtigste Änderung bestand darin, daß nicht mehr wie nach dem Gesetz über die Lohnstatistik von 1956 "im Durchschnitt bis zu 10 vom Hundert", sondern"bis zu höchstens 3500"Arbeiter zu erfassen waren. Die Änderung von einem Prozentsatz auf eine absolute Zahl war notwendig, weil wegen des zu erwartenden weiteren Rückgangs der Zahl der familienfremden Arbeiter in der Landwirtschaft der Prozentsatz eine zu geringe Zahl von Erfaßten für die Stichprobe erbracht hätte. Die Berichtsbetriebe wurden für die Erhebungen ab September 1971 neu ausgewählt. Bei der Berechnung des Auswahlplans wurde von der Überlegung ausgegangen, wieviele Arbeiter zur Erzielung hinreichend genauer Ergebnisse von der Stichprobe erfaßt werden müssen. Die notwendige Anzahl der Arbeiter wurde je Arbeitergruppe, Betriebsgrößenklasse und Bundesland unter Zugrundelegung eines relativen Standardfehlers von 5 % für das ungünstigste Merkmal - d. h. das Merkmal mit der größten relativen Streuung (als ungünstigstes Merkmal in diesem Sinne erwiesen sich die gesetzlichen Abzüge) - auf Grund von Variationskoeffizienten festgelegt, die durch Auszählung der Individualangaben der Verdiensterhebung in der Landwirtschaft für die Erhebungsmonate September 1966 und 1967 berechnet wurden. Da jedoch nicht die einzelnen Arbeiter, sondern die Betriebe die Auswahleinheiten waren, mußte je Bundesland, Arbeitergruppe und Betriebsgrößenklasse ein unterschiedlicher Anteil von Betrieben ohne familienfremde Arbeitskräfte berücksichtigt werden; der hiermit verbundene Untergruppeneffekt konnte allerdings vernachlässigt werden, weil als Ergebnisse der Erhebung nur Verhältniswerte nachzuweisen waren. Aus der für die Stichprobe erforderlichen Anzahl der Arbeiter wurde die Anzahl der zu erfassenden Betriebe berechnet, wozu je Arbeitergruppe die Kenntnis über die mittlere

Anzahl der landwirtschaftlichen Betriebe, die zusammen einen Arbeiter der betreffenden Gruppe beschäftigten, benötigt wurde. Die Unterschiede im Arbeitskräftebesatz der Betriebe für die einzelnen Arbeitergruppen hätten dazu geführt, daß bei einer einheitlichen vorgegebenen Genauigkeit für alle Gruppen die je Gruppe erforderlichen Betriebszahlen sehr uneinheitlich gewesen wären. Daher wurden die Genauigkeitsanforderungen bei den einzelnen Arbeitergruppen im endgültigen Auswahlplan so weit gegeneinander abgestuft, daß sich je Arbeitergruppe innerhalb der Gruppe der Monatslöhner einerseits und innerhalb der Gruppe der Stundenlöhner andererseits etwa die gleiche notwendige Anzahl von Stichprobenbetrieben ergab, d. h. bei den Arbeitergruppen, die sonst einen zu großen Stichprobenumfang erfordert hätten, wurde eine geringere Genauigkeit der Ergebnisse in Kauf genommen. Auswahlgrundlage für die Betriebsauswahl war die für Juli 1970 durchgeführte repräsentative Erhebung über die Arbeitskräfte in landwirtschaftlichen Betrieben. Die Berichtsbetriebe der Verdiensterhebung wurden gesondert in jeder Schicht - Schichten waren die Betriebsgrößenklassen innerhalb jedes Bundeslandes - nach dem systematischen Auswahlverfahren ausgewählt. Dabei zeigte sich, daß die im Auswahlplan berechneten Stichprobenumfänge so groß waren, daß in allen Schichten für die Monatslöhner sämtliche und für die Stundenlöhner 25 % der in der Landarbeitskräfteerhebung erfaßten Betriebe mit ständigen familienfremden Arbeitskräften zur Verdiensterhebung herangezogen werden mußten. In einigen Bundesländern wurden sogar über den Auswahlplan hinaus auch für die Stundenlöhner sämtliche Betriebe der Landarbeitskräfteerhebung in die Verdiensterhebung einbezogen. Die erfaßten individuellen Verdienst- und Arbeitszeitangaben der Berichtsbetriebe wurden bei der Aufbereitung in den Statistischen Landesämtern auf 100 % der Grundgesamtheit hochgerechnet; zu diesem Zweck wurde für jeden einzelnen Berichtsbetrieb ein Hochrechnungsfaktor festgelegt, der sich als Produkt aus dem jeweiligen Auswahlabstand laut Auswahlplan der Verdiensterhebung und dem Auswahlabstand laut Auswahlplan der Landarbeitskräfteerhebung ergab. Für die Behandlung von Antwortausfällen wurde das im Jahre 1964 in der Verdiensterhebung in der Landwirtschaft eingeführte Verfahren beibehalten (vgl. Seite 136). Bei dem Berichtskreiswechsel vom September 1971 wurden in einigen Bundesländern mit Hilfe von "Umrechnungsfaktoren" die Ergebnisse des alten Berichtskreises mit denen des neuen Berichtskreises in durchlaufenden bruchfreien Zeitreihen verknüpft; dieses Verfahren wurde von der vierteljährlichen Verdiensterhebung in Industrie und Handel übernommen (vgl. Seite 93). Die Neuauswahl der Berichtsbetriebe vom September 1971 hatte nicht den gewünschten Erfolg, d. h. sie erbrachte wider Erwarten weniger erfaßte Arbeiter, als nach dem Auswahlplan notwendig gewesen wären. Daraufhin wurden bei der Erhebung für September 1972 in allen Bundesländern sowohl für die Monatslöhner als auch für die Stundenlöhner sämtliche Betriebe der Auswahlgrundlage zur Berichterstattung herangezogen; gleichzeitig wurde auf die Erfassung der meist ohne familienfremde Arbeitskräfte arbeitenden Betriebe mit weniger als 50 ha landwirtschaftlicher Nutzfläche verzichtet. In dieser Form wurde die Verdiensterhebung in der Landwirtschaft vorerst letztmalig für September 1973 durchgeführt, da ab 1974 entsprechende Erhebungen der Europäischen Gemeinschaften stattfanden.

Bereits für die Berichtsmonate April und September 1971 wurden auf Wunsch der Europäischen Gemeinschaften in einer Probeerhebung ohne Auskunftspflicht in der Bundesrepublik Deutschland rund 250 gezielt aus Auflistungen der Landarbeitskräfteerhebung vom Juli 1970 ausgewählte landwirtschaftliche Betriebe zweimal nach den Verdiensten ihrer Arbeiter befragt. Die Betriebsauswahl und die Befragung - letztere unter Einsatz von Interviewern - wurden von den Statistischen Landesämtern, die Aufbereitung der Erhebungsbogen zentral vom Statistischen Bundesamt vorgenommen. Eine umfassende Erhebung mit Auskunftspflicht der Arbeitgeber fand dann ebenfalls unter Einsatz von Interviewern erstmalig im Jahre 1974 auf Grund der vom Rat der Europäischen Gemeinschaften erlassenen "Verordnung Nr. 677 zur Durchführung einer Erhebung über die Verdienste der ständig in der Landwirtschaft beschäftigten Arbeiter" vom 21. März 1974 (Amtsblatt der Europäischen Gemeinschaften 1974 Nr. L 83 S. 4) statt. Danach waren repräsentativ ausgewählte landwirtschaftliche Betriebe mit Ausnahme solcher Betriebe, die ausschließlich oder überwiegend in der Landschaftsgärtnerei, der Jagd oder der Ausführung landwirtschaftlicher Nebentätigkeiten tätig waren, zu erfassen. Als Erhebungszeitraum sah die EG-Verordnung einen beliebigen Monat des Jahres 1974, vorzugsweise den April, vor. In der Bundesrepublik Deutschland wurde dagegen der in der nationalen Verdiensterhebung in der Landwirtschaft übliche Erhebungsmonat September auch für die EG-Erhebung beibehalten. Die Berichtsbetriebe hatten die verlangten Verdienst-, Arbeitszeit- und sonstigen Angaben für jeden zu erfassenden Arbeiter einzeln zu machen. Die EG-Kommission stellte Richtlinien für den Stichprobenplan auf und regelte die Einzelheiten der Erhebung, vor allem Form und Inhalt des Fragebogens; die Befragung und die Aufbereitung zu Ergebnissen für Mitgliedstaaten - in der Bundesrepublik Deutschland zu Bundes- und Landesergebnissen - oblag den nationalen statistischen Ämtern, in der Bundesrepublik Deutschland in Zusammenarbeit zwischen dem Statistischen Bundesamt und den Statistischen Landesämtern. Die Aufwendungen der statistischen Ämter für die Erhebung gingen nach der EG-Verordnung, die im übrigen in jedem Mitgliedstaat unmittelbar galt, "zu Lasten der im Haushaltsplan der Europäischen Gemeinschaften für diesen Zweck bereitgestellten Mittel". Die EG-Verdiensterhebung in der Landwirtschaft erfaßte Betriebe unabhängig von der Größe ihrer landwirtschaftlichen Nutzfläche mit mindestens einem ständigen vollbeschäftigten familienfremden Arbeiter. In die Erhebung einbezogen wurden darüberhinaus nur Arbeiter, die im Erhebungsmonat ihr volles Arbeitsentgelt erhielten. Im übrigen wurden männliche und weibliche Monatslöhner und Stundenlöhner erfaßt. Die einzelnen Arbeiter waren durch die Berichtsbetriebe bzw. die Interviewer vorgegebenen "Qualifikationsgruppen" - ähnlich den in der nationalen deutschen Lohnstatistik üblichen Leistungsgruppen - zuzuordnen. Das Statistische Bundesamt stellte zu diesem Zweck im Einvernehmen mit den Sozialpartnern Richtlinien über die Eingliederung der tariflichen Lohngruppen in die Qualifikationsgruppen auf. Ferner waren die Arbeiter entsprechend ihrer individuellen Tätigkeit nach Hauptproduktionsrichtungen zu untergliedern. Die zeitraumbezogenen Individualangaben waren grundsätzlich für den ganzen Monat September 1974 zu machen; wenn der Lohnabrechnungszeitraum nicht genau einen Monat, sondern vier Wochen betrug, wurden die Angaben bei der Aufbereitung in den Statistischen Landesämtern pro Betrieb auf einen Monat umgerechnet. Nach dem Plan

der EG-Kommission sollten in der Bundesrepublik Deutschland mindestens 7 000 und höchstens 10 000 Betriebe als Auswahleinheiten erfaßt werden. Auswahlgrundlage war die landwirtschaftliche Betriebszählung 1971. Der Auswahlplan sah eine zweistufige Auswahl vor, und zwar wurden in der ersten Stufe Gemeinden und in der zweiten Stufe Betriebe in diesen Gemeinden ausgewählt. Zunächst wurden die Betriebe der Auswahlgesamtheit innerhalb jeder Gemeinde nach drei Größenklassen (Schichten) entsprechend ihrer Arbeiterzahl (Betriebe mit 1 bis 2 Arbeitern, Betriebe mit 3 bis 9 Arbeitern, Betriebe mit 10 oder mehr Arbeitern) gruppiert.
Der für das Bundesgebiet insgesamt vorgesehene Stichprobenumfang wurde nach einer vorgegebenen Genauigkeitsabstufung (Exponent 0,3) unter Verwendung der in der Auswahlgrundlage ermittelten Besetzungszahlen auf die Bundesländer verteilt. Der auf die einzelnen Länder entfallende Stichprobenumfang wurde ebenfalls nach vorgegebener Genauigkeitsabstufung (Exponent 0,2) auf die drei Betriebsschichten verteilt; bei dieser Berechnung wurden Mittelwert und Varianz je Schicht mittels einer Rechteckverteilung abgeschätzt. Es ergab sich, daß die mittlere und die obere Betriebsschicht in allen Ländern total erfaßt werden mußten. Für die untere Betriebsschicht wurden für die erste Auswahlstufe (Gemeindeauswahl) je Land unterschiedliche auf Betriebe bezogene Auswahlabstände und Zufallsstartzahlen festgelegt, mit denen dann über die nach Gemeinden angeordneten Betriebe der Auswahlgesamtheit die Stichprobengemeinden im systematischen Auswahlverfahren ausgewählt wurden, indem jeweils diejenige Gemeinde in die Auswahl gelangte, deren kumulative Betriebszahl die Auswahlnummer - das ist die Zufallsstartzahl zuzüglich des Vielfachen des Auswahlabstandes - erreichte oder gerade überschritt. Die Gemeinden wurden mit ungleichen Wahrscheinlichkeiten ausgewählt, wobei die Auswahlwahrscheinlichkeit proportional zur Anzahl der Betriebe war. In der zweiten Auswahlstufe (Betriebsauswahl) wurden in den ausgewählten Gemeinden sämtliche Betriebe der unteren Betriebsschicht in die Stichprobe einbezogen. Die in der Stichprobe ermittelten Individualangaben wurden bei der Aufbereitung in den Statistischen Landesämtern auf 100 % der Grundgesamtheit hochgerechnet, wobei sich der jeweilige Hochrechnungsfaktor pro Betrieb unveränderlich aus dem Auswahlplan als Produkt aus dem Auswahlab-

stand der ersten Stufe und dem Auswahlabstand der zweiten Stufe ergab. Im Falle "unechter Antwortausfälle" - dabei handelte es sich neben den nicht mehr bestehenden Betrieben auch um Betriebe, die keine familienfremden ständigen vollbeschäftigten Arbeiter mehr hatten - wurden die betreffenden Betriebe wie üblich ersatzlos aus dem Berichtskreis gestrichen. Mit"echten Antwortausfällen" (Auskunftsverweigerung u. a.) brauchte wegen des Interviewereinsatzes in der Regel nicht gerechnet zu werden; wenn diese Fälle wider Erwarten bei mehr als 5 % der Berichtsbetriebe doch auftraten, wurde ein Ausgleich durch Dopplung der Angaben vergleichbarer Berichtsbetriebe vorgenommen. Für die Ergebniserstellung wurden die Berichtsbetriebe unter Umständen abweichend von der Auswahlgrundlage entsprechend den tatsächlichen Verhältnissen zur Erhebungszeit den Hauptproduktionsrichtungen sowie den Größenklassen nach der Arbeiterzahl und den Größenklassen nach der landwirtschaftlichen Nutzfläche neu zugeordnet. Erhebungsmerkmale waren vor allem der Barlohn, die gesetzlichen Abzüge, die Arbeitszeit und der für Naturalleistungen eventuell vom Lohn einbehaltene Betrag; ferner war anzugeben, ob der Arbeiter neben seinem Barlohn Kost oder Unterkunft erhielt. Die individuellen Verdienstangaben wurden nur zu Durchschnittsverdiensten pro Arbeiter aufbereitet; Häufigkeitsverteilungen nach Verdienstklassen wurden nicht aufgestellt. Die EG-Verordnung Nr. 677 galt nur für eine einzige Erhebung im Jahre 1974, nach der amtlichen Begründung war jedoch eine "regelmäßig durchzuführende jährliche Erhebung über die Effektivverdienste der landwirtschaftlichen Arbeitnehmer unter Berücksichtigung bestimmter individueller Merkmale wie Geschlecht, Alter und berufliche Qualifikation" vorgesehen (Bundesratsdrucksache Nr. 142/74 vom 18. Februar 1974). Daraufhin fanden auch in den folgenden Jahren jeweils für den Erhebungsmonat September unter Heranziehung desselben Berichtskreises wie 1974 derartige Erhebungen statt. Rechtsgrundlagen der Erhebungen für 1975 und 1976 waren die vom Rat der Europäischen Gemeinschaften erlassenen Verordnungen Nr. 1103 vom 28. April 1975 und Nr. 1035 vom 30. April 1976 (Amtsblatt der Europäischen Gemeinschaften 1975 Nr. L 110 S. 2 und 1976 Nr. L 118 S. 3). In diesen Verordnungen wurde die Bestimmung über die Kostenerstattung durch die Europäischen Gemeinschaften in der Weise neu gefaßt, daß die Mitgliedstaaten nunmehr "für die Durchführung der Erhebung proportional zur Zahl der befragten Betriebe einen Pauschalbetrag aus den im Haushaltsplan der Europäischen Gemeinschaften für diesen Zweck bereitgestellten Mitteln" erhielten. Die Ergebnisse der EG-Verdiensterhebungen in der Landwirtschaft für das Bundesgebiet wurden vom Statistischen Bundesamt in der Fachserie M Reihe 14 (Stuttgart-Mainz 1976 ff.) veröffentlicht.*)

183 Grenzen der Belastbarkeit

Der in den vergangenen Jahrzehnten - insbesondere seit dem Zweiten Weltkrieg - erfolgte Aufbau und Ausbau der amtlichen Lohnstatistik hat zu einem solchen Umfang der lohnstatistischen Erhebungen geführt, daß eine Weiterentwicklung in der gleichen Richtung nicht möglich bzw. nicht sinnvoll erscheint. Die Grenzen einer Weiterentwicklung zeigen sich in verschiedener Hinsicht sowohl bei den Auskunftspflichtigen und den statistischen Ämtern als auch bei den Konsumenten der lohnstatistischen Daten. Als in den sechziger Jahren zu den auf Grund des Gesetzes über die Lohnstatistik vom 18. Mai 1956 (Bundesgesetzblatt 1956 Teil I S. 429) in drei- bis fünfjährigen Abständen durchgeführten Gehalts- und Lohnstrukturerhebungen in der gewerblichen Wirtschaft entsprechende Erhebungen der Europäischen Gemeinschaften traten, war man bestrebt, beide Erhebungen jeweils organisatorisch zusammenzulegen, um die finanzielle und arbeitsmäßige Belastung bei den Berichtsbetrieben und den statistischen Ämtern so gering wie möglich zu halten. Da die Gehalts- und Lohnstrukturerhebungen der Europäischen Gemeinschaften eine sechsjährige Periodizität vorsahen, wurde durch das Gesetz zur Änderung des Gesetzes über die Lohnstatistik vom 4. August 1971 (Bundesgesetzblatt 1971 Teil I S. 1217) für die nationalen Strukturerhebungen eine Periodizität von nunmehr drei bis sechs Jahren vorgeschrieben. Auf diese Weise wurde sichergestellt, daß die nationalen und die europäischen Gehalts- und Lohnstrukturerhebungen auch weiterhin organisatorisch zusammengelegt werden können.

---

*) vgl. auch Dietrich Kunz, Ursula Schulz: Die Neugestaltung der laufenden Verdienststatistik in der Landwirtschaft. In: Wirtschaft und Statistik Jahrgang 1976, S. 543 ff.

Die finanziellen und arbeitsmäßigen Grenzen der Belastbarkeit durch lohnstatistische Erhebungen machen sich besonders in den Fällen empfindlich bemerkbar, in denen die öffentliche Hand gleichzeitig als Erhebungs- und Aufbereitungsstelle und als Berichtsstelle auftritt. Die "Ständige Konferenz der Innenminister der Länder" faßte auf ihrer Sitzung am 22. April 1971 in Bonn den Beschluß, den Bundesminister des Innern zu bitten, so bald wie möglich die rechtlichen Voraussetzungen zur Einführung einer laufenden Verdiensterhebung im öffentlichen Dienst durch entsprechende Änderung des Gesetzes über die Lohnstatistik von 1956 zu schaffen. Bis zu dieser Gesetzesänderung sollte die Erhebung als Repräsentativerhebung in Bund und Ländern auf freiwilliger Basis durchgeführt werden. Der Beschluß der Innenministerkonferenz konnte mit vertretbarem Aufwand nicht realisiert werden. Nur in Hamburg fand von 1971 bis 1974 eine vierteljährliche Verdiensterhebung im öffentlichen Dienst statt, die dann jedoch im Zuge von Sparmaßnahmen wieder eingestellt wurde.

Eine Grenze für die Weiterentwicklung der lohnstatistischen Erhebungen zeigt sich auch darin, daß die Berichtsstellen in einer zunehmenden Zahl von Fällen die verlangten Auskünfte verweigern bzw. erst nach mehrfacher Mahnung und Einleitung von Bußgeldverfahren erteilen. In dieser Hinsicht bereiten besonders die Personalkostenerhebungen der Europäischen Gemeinschaften im produzierenden Gewerbe erhebungstechnische Schwierigkeiten. In ungewöhnlich zahlreichen schriftlichen Eingaben an die Statistischen Landesämter beklagen sich die auskunftspflichtigen Unternehmen und die Unternehmensverbände, daß nach ihrer Meinung mit den umfangreichen Erhebungsbogen und schwierigen Fragen der Personalkostenerhebungen die Grenze des Zumutbaren überschritten wird.

Die maschinelle Aufbereitung hat dazu geführt, daß die Ergebnistabellen der lohnstatistischen Erhebungen ohne wesentlichen Mehraufwand durch Darstellung aller möglichen Merkmalskombinationen sehr viel zahlreicher und umfangreicher werden konnten als bei der früheren manuellen Aufbereitung. Für die Konsumenten der lohnstatistischen Daten ergeben sich damit zunehmende Schwierigkeiten bei der Verarbeitung dieser großen Datenmengen bzw. beim

Heraussuchen der für sie relevanten Daten. Als Beispiel dafür, daß auch die Aufnahmekapazität der Konsumenten der weiteren Entwicklung möglicherweise eine Grenze setzt, kann das überaus umfangreiche Ergebnismaterial der letzten Personalkostenerhebungen im produzierenden Gewerbe angesehen werden. So umfaßt zum Beispiel die vom Landesamt für Datenverarbeitung und Statistik Nordrhein-Westfalen herausgegebene Veröffentlichung der Ergebnisse der Personalkostenerhebung 1972 in drei Bänden insgesamt 1352 Seiten, davon 1289 Tabellenseiten.*)

184 <u>Methodische Fortschritte</u>

Nach dem im Jahre 1964 eingeführten Aufbereitungsverfahren wurden in der vierteljährlichen Verdiensterhebung in Industrie und Handel die von den Berichtsbetrieben gemeldeten Verdienst- und Arbeitsstundensummen pro Schicht aufaddiert und anschließend auf 100 % der Grundgesamtheit hochgerechnet, indem die Schichtsummen - gegebenenfalls noch unter Berücksichtigung eines Ergänzungsfaktors für echte Antwortausfälle - mit einem allen Betrieben der betreffenden Schicht gemeinsamen Hochrechnungsfaktor multipliziert wurden (vgl. Seite 132). Statt dieser "Hochrechnung pro Schicht" mußte für Betriebe, die aus besonderen Gründen aus ihrer ursprünglichen Schicht in eine "Sonderschicht" umgesetzt werden mußten, eine "Hochrechnung pro Betrieb" - das bedeutete Multiplikation der vom Betrieb gemeldeten Summen mit einem betriebsspezifischen Hochrechnungsfaktor und erst danach Bildung von Schichtsummen - vorgenommen werden. Die unterschiedliche Behandlung der Normalschichten und der Sonderschichten brachte für die Praxis der Aufbereitung einige Schwierigkeiten mit sich. Ab Erhebungsmonat April 1974 wurde in der vierteljährlichen Verdiensterhebung ein neues Programm für die maschinelle Aufbereitung verwendet, das die "Hochrechnung pro Betrieb" nunmehr für alle Schichten vorsah. Der seitdem pro Betrieb laut Auswahlplan festgelegte Hochrechnungsfaktor wurde durch den weiterhin pro Schicht für jeden Erhebungsmonat neu ermittelten Ergänzungsfaktor korrigiert. Die Hochrech-

---

*)vgl. Landesamt für Datenverarbeitung und Statistik Nordrhein-Westfalen: Die Personalkosten im produzierenden Gewerbe Nordrhein-Westfalens 1972. Beiträge zur Statistik des Landes Nordrhein-Westfalen Hefte 330, 331, 332. Düsseldorf 1975.

nung erfolgte dann durch Multiplikation der Summenangaben jedes einzelnen Betriebes mit dem auf diese Weise korrigierten jeweiligen Hochrechnungsfaktor. Infolge der allgemein vorgenommenen "Hochrechnung pro Betrieb" konnte ab 1974 auf die Bildung von Sonderschichten verzichtet werden. Die früher in den Sonderschichten enthaltenen Betriebe wurden denjenigen Schichten zugeordnet, denen sie auf Grund ihres Wirtschaftszweiges und ihrer Größenklasse tatsächlich angehörten. Da die Ergebnisse nur nach Wirtschaftszweigen und nicht nach Größenklassen aufzugliedern waren, brauchte die Zugehörigkeit der Betriebe zu den Schichten nur hinsichtlich des Wirtschaftszweiges bei jeder Befragung neu festgelegt zu werden, während hinsichtlich der Größenklasse die Schichtzugehörigkeit in der Auswahlgrundlage beibehalten werden konnte. Auch die früher in den Sonderschichten aufbereiteten zusammengefaßten Unternehmensmeldungen - d. h. Sammelmeldungen für mehrere in der Stichprobe erfaßte Zweigbetriebe eines Unternehmens - wurden jeweils den Schichten zugeordnet, denen der Wirtschaftszweig des Unternehmens im Erhebungsmonat und die Größenklasse des Unternehmens in der Auswahlgrundlage entsprachen. Bei der für jede Erhebungseinheit einzeln vorgenommenen Hochrechnung spielte keine Rolle, wenn durch die Neuzuordnung der Betriebe bzw. Unternehmen zu den Schichten in eine Schicht Einheiten mit verschiedenen Hochrechnungsfaktoren gelangten.

Eine Abschätzung der den repräsentativen lohnstatistischen Erhebungen anhaftenden Stichprobenfehler wurde von den statistischen Ämtern bisher nur sporadisch und meist nur auf Grund der Verhältnisse in den Auswahlgrundlagen, jedoch in der Regel nicht auf Grund der in den Erhebungen tatsächlich ermittelten Daten vorgenommen. Laufende Fehlerrechnungen auf Grund der Erhebungsdaten fanden bisher nur bei der vierteljährlichen Verdiensterhebung in Industrie und Handel und nur in Nordrhein-Westfalen statt. Hier wurden zunächst die Standardfehler der durchschnittlichen Bruttostundenverdienste der männlichen Arbeiter der Leistungsgruppe 1 in zehn ausgewählten Industriezweigen aus den Ergebnissen der vierteljährlichen Verdiensterhebung für die Berichtsmonate Januar und April 1972 berechnet*). Mit der laufenden Berechnung der Standardfehler der durchschnittlichen Bruttostundenverdienste bzw. der durchschnittlichen Bruttomonatsverdienste der männlichen und weiblichen Arbeiter bzw. Angestellten aller Leistungsgruppen in sämtlichen erfaßten Wirtschaftszweigen wurde in Nordrhein-Westfalen anläßlich der Neuauswahl der Berichtsbetriebe der vierteljährlichen Verdiensterhebung im Oktober 1972 begonnen**). In der wirtschaftssystematischen Gliederung fielen aus diesen Fehlerrechnungen zunächst nur Ergebnisse für die einzelnen Wirtschaftszweige - d. h. für die kleinsten systematischen Einheiten - , jedoch nicht für Wirtschaftsbereiche als Zusammenfassungen von jeweils mehreren Wirtschaftszweigen an. Anläßlich der Neuprogrammierung der vierteljährlichen Verdiensterhebung im Jahre 1974 wurde das nordrhein-westfälische System der Fehlerrechnung vervollständigt***). Ab Januar 1974 bezogen sich die in den laufenden Fehlerrechnungen ermittelten Standardfehler nicht nur auf die durchschnittlichen Bruttostundenverdienste und Bruttomonatsverdienste der Arbeiter bzw. Angestellten, sondern auch auf die durchschnittlichen Bruttowochenverdienste sowie bezahlten Wochenarbeitszeiten und wöchentlichen Mehrarbeitszeiten der Arbeiter. Die Standardfehler wurden seitdem nicht nur für die einzelnen Wirtschaftszweige, sondern auch für sämtliche zusammengefaßten Wirt-

---

*) vgl. Wolfgang Gerß: Stichprobentheoretische Grenzen der Aussagefähigkeit der amtlichen laufenden Verdiensterhebung, dargestellt mit Hilfe von Zahlenmaterial für das Land Nordrhein-Westfalen. In: WSI-Mitteilungen (Zeitschrift des Wirtschafts- und Sozialwissenschaftlichen Instituts des Deutschen Gewerkschaftsbundes GmbH), Jahrgang 1973 S. 35 ff.

**) vgl. W. Gerß: Einführung laufender Fehlerrechnungen in der repräsentativen Verdiensterhebung. In: Statistische Rundschau für das Land Nordrhein-Westfalen, herausgegeben vom Landesamt für Datenverarbeitung und Statistik Nordrhein-Westfalen, Jahrgang 1974 S. 109 ff.

***) vgl. W. Gerß: Laufende Fehlerrechnungen in der Verdiensterhebung - Methodische Grundlagen und Auswertungsmöglichkeiten. In: Statistische Rundschau für das Land Nordrhein-Westfalen, herausgegeben vom Landesamt für Datenverarbeitung und Statistik Nordrhein-Westfalen, Jahrgang 1975 S. 379 ff.

schaftsbereiche bis hinauf zu den Bereichen "Gesamtindustrie" bzw. "Industrie, Handel, Kredit- und Versicherungsgewerbe insgesamt" ausgewiesen. Die Ergebnisse der nordrhein-westfälischen Fehlerrechnungen wurden zusammen mit den in der vierteljährlichen Verdiensterhebung anfallenden Durchschnittsverdiensten bzw. durchschnittlichen Arbeitszeiten laufend in den vom Statistischen Landesamt bzw. Landesamt für Datenverarbeitung und Statistik Nordrhein-Westfalen herausgegebenen "Statistischen Berichten Nr. N I 1" veröffentlicht.

185 Zentralisierungstendenzen

Entsprechend dem föderativen Aufbau der Bundesrepublik Deutschland wurden die amtlichen lohnstatistischen Erhebungen seit dem Zweiten Weltkrieg grundsätzlich in Zusammenarbeit zwischen dem Statistischen Bundesamt und den Statistischen Landesämtern durchgeführt, wobei mit den eigentlichen Erhebungsarbeiten und den Aufbereitungsarbeiten bis zur Erstellung der Ergebnisse für die Bundesländer das Schwergewicht der Arbeiten bei den Statistischen Landesämtern lag, während das Statistische Bundesamt für die methodische Vorbereitung und die Zusammenfassung der Landesergebnisse zu den Ergebnissen für das Bundesgebiet zuständig war. Abweichend von dem Normalfall wurde bei Erhebungen mit einer besonders geringen Zahl von Erhebungseinheiten bereits in den fünfziger und sechziger Jahren ein Teil der Aufbereitungsarbeiten von den Statistischen Landesämtern auf das Statistische Bundesamt verlagert. Bei den für die Jahre 1959 bis 1964 durchgeführten Personalkostenerhebungen der Europäischen Gemeinschaften im produzierenden Gewerbe wurden die Ergebnistabellen mit Bundes- und Landesergebnissen zentral im Statistischen Bundesamt aufgestellt. Die umfangreicheren Personalkostenerhebungen für 1966 und 1969 wurden dagegen wie üblich dezentral in den Statistischen Landesämtern aufbereitet. Bei der Personalkostenerhebung der Europäischen Gemeinschaften im Straßenverkehrsgewerbe 1967 oblag die Unternehmensauswahl, die Befragung und die Prüfung der Erhebungsbogen den Statistischen Landesämtern, die Tabellierung der Bundesergebnisse und der Landesergebnisse für Bayern - für die anderen Bundesländer wurden keine Ergebnisse aufbereitet - dem Statistischen Bundesamt. In den siebziger Jahren traten in verstärktem Maße Bestrebungen auf, einen Teil der Aufbereitungsarbeiten statt von den Statistischen Landesämtern vom Statistischen Bundesamt durchführen zu lassen. Diese Bestrebungen wurden mit Sachzwängen der maschinellen Aufbereitung begründet - der Einsatz von Großrechenanlagen wurde auch bei mittelgroßen Erhebungen nur dann für lohnend gehalten, wenn die erhobenen Daten nur an einer Stelle verarbeitet würden - und mit der Hoffnung verbunden, daß durch die zentrale Aufbereitung zumindest die Erstellung der Bundesergebnisse beschleunigt werden könnte. Bei der Personalkostenerhebung der Europäischen Gemeinschaften im produzierenden Gewerbe 1972 sollten nach dem ursprünglichen Aufbereitungsplan die Landesergebnisse wie üblich von den Statistischen Landesämtern und das Bundesergebnis vom Statistischen Bundesamt erstellt werden. Das Statistische Bundesamt bot sich dann an, auch die Tabellierung sämtlicher Landesergebnisse zentral zu übernehmen. Dieses Angebot wurde von den Statistischen Landesämtern von Nordrhein-Westfalen, Bayern und Baden-Württemberg abgelehnt, von den übrigen Landesämtern dagegen angenommen. In gleicher Weise wurden bei der Personalkostenerhebung der Europäischen Gemeinschaften im Handel, Bank- und Versicherungsgewerbe 1974 die Landesergebnisse für Nordrhein-Westfalen, Bayern und Baden-Württemberg von den Statistischen Landesämtern, die Landesergebnisse für die übrigen Länder dagegen zentral vom Statistischen Bundesamt aufbereitet, nachdem die - manuell aufbereitete - Personalkostenerhebung 1970 noch in allen Ländern die übliche Arbeitsteilung zwischen den statistischen Ämtern aufgewiesen hatte. Bei der Erhebung über die betriebliche Altersversorgung 1973 wurden die Erhebungs- und Aufbereitungsarbeiten bis zur Prüfung der Erhebungsbogen von den Statistischen Landesämtern, die Tabellierung der Bundesergebnisse und der Landesergebnisse für Nordrhein-Westfalen, Bayern und Baden Württemberg - für die übrigen Bundesländer wurden keine gesonderten Ergebnisse erstellt - vom Statistischen Bundesamt vorgenommen. Bei der seit 1974 durchgeführten jährlichen Verdiensterhebung der Europäischen Gemeinschaften in der Landwirtschaft erfolgte die Betriebsauswahl, die Befragung, die manuelle Prüfung und die maschinelle Plausibilitätskontrolle durch die Statistischen Landesämter; das Statistische Bundesamt erhielt anschließend die erhobenen Einzeldaten auf Magnetbändern zur zentralen Tabellierung von Ergebnissen für das Bundesgebiet und die Bundesländer.

Bei einigen Erhebungen der Europäischen Gemeinschaften wurde ein Teil der Aufbereitungsarbeiten von den nationalen statistischen Ämtern auf das Statistische Amt der Europäischen Gemeinschaften verlagert. Die Gehalts- und Lohnstrukturerhebungen der Europäischen Gemeinschaften im produzierenden Gewerbe 1966 und 1972 sowie im Handel, Bank- und Versicherungsgewerbe 1974 wurden bis einschließlich zur Plausibilitätskontrolle von den nationalen statistischen Ämtern - vor allem den Statistischen Landesämtern - bearbeitet. Die Einzelauskünfte wurden dann über das Statistische Bundesamt dem Statistischen Amt der Europäischen Gemeinschaften zur Verfügung gestellt, das daraus die für die EG-Kommission bestimmten Tabellen mit Ergebnissen für die Mitgliedstaaten und Regionen - im Falle der Bundesrepublik Deutschland für das Bundesgebiet und die Bundesländer - zentral aufstellte.

2

Das System der Lohnstatistik der Bundesrepublik Deutschland und seine Vorläufer im Deutschen Reich

21 Nationale Lohnstatistik

211 Tariflohnstatistik

Bei der nationalen amtlichen Lohnstatistik - d. h. den auf Grund nationaler Rechtsvorschriften für nationale wirtschafts- und sozialpolitische Zwecke durchgeführten lohnstatistischen Untersuchungen - ist zwischen der Sammlung und statistischen Auswertung der tariflichen Lohn- und Gehaltssätze und der Erfassung der effektiven Arbeitnehmerverdienste zu unterscheiden. Die Tarifverträge wurden bereits vor dem Ersten Weltkrieg vom Kaiserlichen Statistischen Amt gesammelt und zu einer jährlichen Tarifstatistik ausgewertet, die jedoch keine Tariflohnstatistik war, sondern nur wenige lohnstatistische Ergänzungen enthielt. Die lohnstatistischen Ergänzungen erfolgten unregelmäßig und bestanden vor allem aus Häufigkeitsverteilungen der tarifgebundenen Betriebe und deren Arbeiter nach Tariflohnklassen und nach Lohnzuschlagsklassen; ferner wurden teilweise die tariflichen Untergrenzen der Entlohnung sowie vereinzelt durchschnittliche Tariflöhne ausgewiesen. Die Tarifstatistik erreichte eine erhebliche Aufwertung, als sie nach dem Ersten Weltkrieg in dem neu eingeführten amtlichen "Tarifarchiv" - der Sammlung der von den Tarifparteien den zuständigen Behörden einzureichenden Tarifvertragsabschriften - bzw. dem "Tarifregister" - dem Verzeichnis der für allgemeinverbindlich erklärten Tarifverträge - auf eine laufend vervollständigte Materialbasis zurückgreifen konnte, die nunmehr auch die Angestelltentarife umfaßte. Die Tarifstatistik wurde unter Beteiligung verschiedener Behörden mit jährlicher Periodizität bis zu ihrer Einstellung im Jahre 1933 fortgeführt. Die Einstellung erfolgte mit der Aufhebung der Tarifautonomie und der Einführung von Tarifordnungen.

Das amtliche Tarifarchiv wurde nicht nur zu der Tarifstatistik ausgewertet, sondern bildete auch die Grundlage für die vom Statistischen Reichsamt seit 1922 durchgeführte monatliche Tariflohnstatistik. Diese erste Tariflohnstatistik berücksichtigte nur die tariflichen Lohnsätze der höchsten tarifmäßigen Altersstufe der gelernten und der ungelernten Arbeiter in den Hauptsitzen der wichtigsten Gewerbegruppen. Aus den tariflichen Einzellohnsätzen wurden durchschnittliche tarifliche Stunden- und Wochenlöhne als gewogene arithmetische

Mittelwerte mit den Arbeiterzahlen als Gewichte berechnet. Im Jahre 1931 wurde die Tariflohnstatistik unter Beibehaltung ihres Hauptzweckes - der monatlichen Ermittlung durchschnittlicher Tariflohnsätze - reformiert. Wie früher wurden nur ausgewählte tarifliche Lohnsätze erfaßt, wobei jedoch die Repräsentation durch Ausweitung wesentlich verbessert wurde. Als Arbeitergruppen wurden nicht mehr nur gelernte und ungelernte Arbeiter, sondern fünf Gruppen - und zwar männliche Facharbeiter, angelernte Arbeiter und Hilfsarbeiter sowie weibliche Fach- und angelernte Arbeiter (zusammengefaßt) und Hilfsarbeiter - unterschieden. Während früher bei den ungelernten Arbeitern nur der Zeitlohn und bei den gelernten Arbeitern entweder nur der Stück- oder nur der Zeitlohn - je nach dem Überwiegen der einen oder der anderen Lohnform - erfaßt wurde, wurde nunmehr für jede Arbeitergruppe ein gewogener Durchschnittssatz aus beiden Lohnformen berechnet. In der reformierten Tariflohnstatistik wurden nur noch tarifliche Stundenlöhne ermittelt, und zwar als gewogene arithmetische Mittel der Einzellohnsätze - Stundenlohnsätze bzw. Akkordrichtsätze pro Stunde - mit vorerst konstant gehaltenen Gewichten. Als Gewichte dienten die Gesamtzahlen der in den einzelnen Gewerben bzw. Arbeitergruppen im Durchschnitt der Jahre 1928 bis 1930 tatsächlich beschäftigten - d. h. nicht arbeitslosen - Arbeiter. Das Statistische Reichsamt führte die monatliche Tariflohnstatistik nach der Reform bis gegen Ende des Zweiten Weltkrieges unverändert fort.

In Verbindung mit der Industrieberichterstattung vom April 1949 fand bei sämtlichen Industriebetrieben eine einmalige Zusatzerhebung über die Tariflöhne der Industriearbeiter statt, durch die die tariflichen Lohnsätze für die einzelnen Arbeitergruppen und Ortsklassen sowie die Anzahl der auf sie entfallenden Arbeiter erfaßt wurden. Die Ergebnisse dieser Erhebung bildeten die Grundlage für die Wiederaufnahme der Tariflohnstatistik, die daraufhin mit vierteljährlicher Periodizität - jeweils für die Monate März, Juni, September und Dezember - in der Weise durchgeführt wurde, daß die Statistischen Landesämter für ihr Gebiet in Anlehnung an das Verfahren des Statistischen Reichsamtes tarifliche Durchschnittslöhne berechneten und diese dem Statistischen Amt des Vereinigten Wirtschaftsgebietes bzw. dem Statistischen Bundesamt zur Zusammenfassung zu Gesamtdurchschnitten zur Verfügung stellten. Als Durchschnittslöhne wurden weiterhin durchschnittliche tarifliche Stundenlohnsätze als gewogene arithmetische Mittel für Arbeiter der höchsten tariflichen Altersstufe nach Industriezweigen und den fünf vom Statistischen Reichsamt eingeführten Arbeitergruppen ermittelt. Als Gewichte wurden dabei im allgemeinen die in der Erhebung vom April 1949 ermittelten Besetzungszahlen der Arbeiter unverändert weiterverwendet. Das Material für die laufende Bearbeitung der Tariflohnstatistik wurde den bei den obersten Arbeitsbehörden erneut eingerichteten amtlichen Tarifarchiven entnommen. Die Berechnung tariflicher Durchschnittslöhne wurde Ende 1951 eingestellt. Statt dessen wurden bei der Ende der fünfziger Jahre erfolgten Wiederaufnahme der Tariflohnstatistik - die seitdem vom Statistischen Bundesamt zentral durchgeführt wird - vierteljährliche Tariflohnindizes aufgestellt, und zwar zunächst für die Monate Februar, Mai, August und November und seit 1964 für die Monate Januar, April, Juli und Oktober. Als Tariflohnindizes wurden Indizes der tariflichen Stundenlöhne und Wochenlöhne der Arbeiter und Monatsgehälter der Angestellten in der gewerblichen Wirtschaft und bei Gebietskörperschaften sowie ein Index der Tariflöhne in der Landwirtschaft berechnet. Die Berechnung erfolgte nach dem Modell des Preisindex von Laspeyres unter Verwendung von Gewichten, die mehrere Jahre lang konstant gehalten wurden. In die Indexberechnung für die gewerbliche Wirtschaft und die Gebietskörperschaften gingen grundsätzlich nur Zeitlohnsätze ausgewählter Tarifverträge ein, die insgesamt etwa 75 % der Arbeiter bzw. Angestellten repräsentierten. Dabei wurden nur die Zeitlohnsätze der höchsten tarifmäßigen Altersstufe - d. h. für die Angestellten die sogenannten Endgehälter - und der höchsten tariflichen Ortsklasse verwendet. Die Gewichte ergaben sich vor allem aus den jeweils neuesten Arbeiter- bzw. Angestelltenzahlen der Gehalts- und Lohnstrukturerhebungen in der gewerblichen Wirtschaft, die mit den jahresdurchschnittlichen Tariflohn- bzw. -gehaltssätzen des Indexbasisjahres multipliziert wurden. Das Gewichtungsschema und die zeitliche Basis der Indexreihen wurden in mehrjährigen Abständen erneuert. Bei der bisher letzten Umbasierung wurde als Basis der Jahresdurchschnitt 1970 eingeführt; die Arbeitnehmerzahlen der Gewichte wurden der Gehalts- und Lohnstrukturerhebung in der gewerblichen Wirtschaft 1966 entnommen. Für die gewerbliche Wirtschaft und die Gebietskörperschaften berechnete das Statistische Bundesamt nicht nur Tarifindizes, sondern stellte auch die im jeweiligen Berichtszeitraum eingetretenen prozentualen Erhöhungen der tariflichen Stundenlöhne bzw. Monatsgehälter der Arbeiter bzw. Angestellten nach Erhöhungsklassen zusammen. Die Methodik des Index der Tariflöhne in der Landwirtschaft wich in einigen Punkten von der der anderen Tarifindizes ab. In diesen Index wurden ausgewählte Arbeiterlohngruppen aus sämtlichen landwirtschaftlichen Tarifverträgen einbezogen. Als Lohnsätze wurden Zeitlohnsätze - Stundenlöhne bzw. Monatslöhne - für Arbeiter der höchsten tarifmäßigen Altersstufe in allen Ortsklassen verwendet. Der Index der Tariflöhne in der Landwirtschaft wurde gesondert als Index der Stundenlöhne, als Index der Monatslöhne und als Gesamtlohnindex (Durchschnitt aus Stunden- und Monatslöhnen) aufgestellt. Die zeitliche Basis und das Gewichtungsschema dieser Indizes wurden jeweils gleichzeitig mit den nichtlandwirtschaftlichen Tarifindizes in mehrjährigen Abständen erneuert. In das Gewichtungsschema ging im Gegensatz zu den nichtlandwirtschaftlichen Tarifindizes nicht der durchschnittliche Tariflohn, sondern ausschließlich die Anzahl der Arbeiter nach den Ergebnissen der jeweils letzten landwirtschaftlichen Betriebszählung ein.

Unabhängig vom Statistischen Bundesamt wurde von der Deutschen Bundesbank seit 1957 ein monatlicher "Index des Tariflohn- und -gehaltsniveaus" auf Stunden- und auf Wochenverdienstbasis - später auf Stunden- und auf Monatsverdienstbasis - berechnet, der Arbeiter, Angestellte und Beamte zusammenfaßte und damit die Tariflohnentwicklung von ca. 85 % aller Arbeitnehmer repräsentierte. Dieser Index verwendete Beschäftigtenzahlen als Gewichte, die innerhalb eines Jahres konstant gehalten, jedoch von Jahr zu Jahr der Beschäftigtenentwicklung angepaßt wurden .

212 Effektivverdienststatistik

2121 Laufende Verdiensterhebungen

21211 Vierteljährliche Verdiensterhebung in Industrie und Handel

Die Effektivverdienststatistik kann in laufende Verdiensterhebungen - die in regelmäßigen meist kürzeren Abständen die Verdienstentwicklung beobachten sollen - und in Gehalts- und Lohnstrukturerhebungen - die einmalig oder in größeren bzw. unregelmäßigen Abständen die Verdienststruktur untersuchen sollen - unterteilt werden. Zu den laufenden Verdiensterhebungen gehören Erhebungen in verschiedenen Wirtschaftsbereichen mit höchstens jährlicher Periodizität. Das Statistische Reichsamt führte ab 1935 nach dem Lohnsummenverfahren vierteljährliche Verdiensterhebungen für die Industriearbeiter durch, und zwar für die Monate März, Juni, September und Dezember jedes Jahres. Zu diesen Erhebungen wurden gezielt ausgewählte Berichtsbetriebe laufend herangezogen, die grundsätzlich alle Arbeiter zu erfassen hatten, die unmittelbar oder mittelbar für den eigentlichen Produktionsprozeß tätig waren und nach einer Tarifordnung des betreffenden Gewerbes entlohnt wurden. Die Arbeiter wurden wie in der Tariflohnstatistik des Statistischen Reichsamtes nach fünf Arbeitergruppen gegliedert. Außer den Angaben für diese Arbeitergruppen wurden in den einzelnen Industriezweigen gesonderte Angaben für bestimmte typische Berufe erfragt. Jeder Berichtsbetrieb hatte für eine in dem jeweiligen Berichtsmonat fallende Lohnabrechnungsperiode pro Arbeitergruppe die Anzahl der Arbeiter und der insgesamt bezahlten Arbeitsstunden sowie die Bruttolohnsumme, die Nettolohnsumme und die Summe der Arbeitgeberbeiträge zur Sozialversicherung zu melden. Das Statistische Reichsamt berechnete daraus zunächst für jeden Betrieb pro Arbeitergruppe "Betriebsdurchschnitte" als Verhältniswerte, vor allem den durchschnittlichen Stundenverdienst und den durchschnittlichen Wochenverdienst. Aus diesen Betriebsdurchschnitten wurden durch Gewichtung mit der Anzahl der Arbeitsstunden bzw. der Anzahl der Arbeiter der einzelnen Betriebe als gewogene arithmetische Mittel die übergeordneten Durchschnittswerte für die Fabrikations- und Gewerbezweige berechnet. Neben Durchschnittsverdiensten ermittelte das Statistische Reichsamt auch

Verdienstindizes für übergeordnete Gewerbebereiche, die dadurch gekennzeichnet waren, daß die Gewichte jeweils nur für zwei unmittelbar aufeinanderfolgende Erhebungen konstant gehalten wurden, und zwar wurden die Gewichte des früheren der beiden verglichenen Erhebungsmonate für die jeweils folgende Erhebung - und nur für diese - beibehalten. Als Gewichte wurden für den Index der Stundenverdienste die Anzahl der Arbeitsstunden und für den Index der Wochenverdienste die Anzahl der Arbeiter verwendet; die Gewichtszahlen wurden dabei aus den Lohnsummenerhebungen selbst gewonnen. Die zeitliche Basis der Indexreihen bezog sich zunächst auf den Monat Dezember 1935 und später auch auf den Jahresdurchschnitt 1936. Neben diesen Indizes für übergeordnete Gewerbebereiche wurden vom Statistischen Reichsamt auch "Indizes" für einzelne Gewerbezweige ausgewiesen, bei denen es sich jedoch lediglich um einfache Meßzahlen aus den in den beiden zu vergleichenden Erhebungsmonaten festgestellten Durchschnittsverdiensten jeweils sämtlicher Betriebe des betreffenden Gewerbezweiges ohne Ausschaltung von Gewichtsveränderungen handelte. Das Statistische Reichsamt führte letztmalig für den Berichtsmonat März 1943 eine Lohnsummenerhebung für die Industriearbeiter durch.

Nach dem Zweiten Weltkrieg führten die Statistischen Landesämter der britischen und der amerikanischen Besatzungszone erstmalig für Juni 1946 wieder eine Lohnsummenerhebung der Industriearbeiter durch. Methodik, Periodizität und Berichtsmonate wurden zunächst weitgehend von den Lohnsummenerhebungen des Statistischen Reichsamtes übernommen. Die Statistischen Landesämter gingen dabei jedoch unabhängig voneinander und teilweise uneinheitlich vor. Ab 1949 übernahm das Statistische Amt des Vereinigten Wirtschaftsgebietes bzw. später das Statistische Bundesamt die Koordinierung und methodische Leitung der vierteljährlichen Lohnsummenerhebungen. Die Länder der französischen Zone wurden ab 1950 in diese Erhebungen einbezogen. Die Erhebungen fanden bis September 1951 für die Monate März, Juni, September und Dezember jedes Jahres statt. Im Dezember 1951 fiel die Erhebung mit Rücksicht auf die für November 1951 durchgeführte Gehalts- und Lohnstrukturerhebung aus. Ab Anfang 1952 wurden als Erhebungsmonate Februar, Mai, August und November verwendet. Vom Statistischen Reichsamt wurde auch das Prinzip der gezielten Auswahl von Berichtsbetrieben sowie das Summenverfahren und die Abgrenzung der fünf Arbeitergruppen übernommen. Erfaßt wurden weiterhin nur die für die betreffende Branche "produktionseigentümlichen" Arbeiter. Die von den Berichtsbetrieben gemeldeten Monatssummen wurden in den Statistischen Landesämtern für das jeweilige Landesgebiet zu durchschnittlichen Bruttostunden- und Bruttowochenverdiensten sowie zu durchschnittlich bezahlten Wochenarbeitszeiten und wöchentlichen Mehrarbeitszeiten pro Arbeiter nach Arbeitergruppen und Industriezweigen aufbereitet. Bei den Durchschnittswerten für die einzelnen Industriezweige handelte es sich um Verhältniswerte aus den erhobenen Summen. Aus diesen Verhältniswerten wurden gewogene arithmetische Mittel für übergeordnete Wirtschaftsgruppen bzw. die Gesamtheit der erfaßten Gewerbe berechnet, wobei als "Wägungszahlen" die Beschäftigtenzahlen der von den Arbeitsämtern durchgeführten Arbeitseinsatzstatistik bzw. ab 1949 einheitlich die Gesamtarbeiterzahlen der Industrieberichterstattung dienten. Aus den für jedes Land festgestellten Durchschnittswerten wurden vom Statistischen Amt des Vereinigten Wirtschaftsgebietes bzw. dem Statistischen Bundesamt bei den Bruttostundenverdiensten durch Wägung mit der in den Lohnerhebungen ermittelten Anzahl der Arbeitsstunden und bei den Bruttowochenverdiensten durch Wägung mit den aus der Industrieberichterstattung gewonnenen Gesamtarbeiterzahlen gewogene arithmetische Mittel für das Vereinigte Wirtschaftsgebiet bzw. das Bundesgebiet berechnet. Neben Durchschnittsverdiensten wurden für das Vereinigte Wirtschaftsgebiet bzw. Bundesgebiet auch Verdienstindizes ermittelt. Aus den Lohnsummenerhebungen des Statistischen Reichsamtes für das Jahr 1938 lagen Angaben über die durchschnittlichen Bruttostunden- und -wochenverdienste für die damaligen "Treuhänderbezirke" vor. Die Durchschnittsverdienste dieses Basisjahres für das Vereinigte Wirtschaftsgebiet bzw. Bundesgebiet wurden als gewogene arithmetische Mittel aus den Durchschnittsverdiensten der den Ländern der Westzonen möglichst entsprechenden Treuhänderbezirke errechnet, wobei als Gewichte die Arbeiterzahlen einer "Arbeitsbucherhebung" vom 25. Juni 1938 sowie früherer Individuallohnerhebungen des Statistischen Reichsamtes verwendet wurden. Auf der Basis 1938 wurden für die Nachkriegszeit Indizes der Bruttostunden- und -wochenverdienste berechnet, wobei variable Gewichte aus dem jeweiligen neuesten Berichtsmonat der Indexberechnung zugrundegelegt wurden. Die Lohnsummenerhebungen der Nachkriegszeit waren unter anderem auch dadurch gekennzeichnet, daß die Auswahl der Berichtsbetriebe von den Statistischen Landesämtern teilweise uneinheitlich mit willkürlichen Auswahlsatzdifferenzierungen und laufenden Änderungen des Berichtskreises durch Heranziehung von Ersatzbetrieben für ausgefallene Betriebe vorgenommen wurde. Für den Berichtsmonat September 1949 fand die Lohnsummenerhebung der Industriearbeiter in erweitertem Umfang mit zusätzlichen Erhebungsmerkmalen statt. Neben den vierteljährlich erfragten Merkmalen wurden der Nettoverdienst, die Zuschläge für Über-, Sonntags- und Feiertagsarbeit, die gesetzlichen Abzüge und die tarifliche Altersstufe erfaßt; außerdem hatten die Betriebe anzugeben, wieviele Arbeiter jeweils bestimmten vorgegebenen Monatsverdienstklassen angehörten. Als Ergänzung zur vierteljährlichen Industriearbeiterlohnstatistik wurde ferner für den Berichtsmonat Mai 1949 eine einmalige Erhebung über die Effektivverdienste der Angestellten in Industrie, Handel, Bank- und Versicherungsgewerbe durchgeführt, wobei in ausgewählten Betrieben nach dem Summenverfahren jeweils sämtliche erwachsenen Angestellten mit einem Bruttogehalt bis zu 600 DM monatlich erfaßt wurden. Die summarischen Angaben bezogen sich auf Altersklassen sowie auf "Leistungsgruppen", d. h. Angestelltengruppen, zu denen die Angestellten nach ihrer Qualifikation entsprechend ihrer Berufsausbildung und ihren Tätigkeitsmerkmalen von den Betrieben selbst zusammenzufassen waren. Erhebungsmerkmale waren vor allem der Bruttoverdienst (aufgegliedert nach Grundgehalt und verschiedenen Zulagen bzw. Zuschlägen), die gesetzlichen Abzüge und der Nettoverdienst sowie die betriebsüblichen Jahreszuwendungen.

Ab Anfang 1957 wurden die vierteljährlichen Lohnsummenerhebungen reformiert. Die nunmehr als "vierteljährliche Verdiensterhebung in Industrie und Handel" bezeichneten Erhebungen fanden für Arbeiter in den Wirtschaftsbereichen verarbeitende Industrie, Bergbau, Bauhauptgewerbe und Energiewirtschaft und Wasserversorgung sowie für Angestellte darüber hinaus in den Wirtschaftsbereichen Handel, Kreditwirtschaft und Versicherungsgewerbe statt. Neben dem Summenverfahren wurden auch das Verfahren der Berechnung von Verhältniswerten - vor allem durchschnittlichen Bruttostunden- und -wochenverdiensten je Arbeiter und durchschnittlichen Bruttomonatsverdiensten je Angestellten - und vorerst auch die Erhebungsmonate - Februar, Mai, August und November - beibehalten. Der Kreis der Berichtsbetriebe wurde neu ausgewählt, wobei vom Statistischen Bundesamt Richtlinien zur einheitlichen Handhabung der Auswahl in allen Bundesländern aufgestellt wurden. In jedem Wirtschaftszweig und in jeder vorgegebenen Beschäftigtengrößenklasse wurden so viele Betriebe als Berichtsbetriebe gezielt ausgewählt, daß etwa 25 % - in einigen Wirtschaftszweigen etwa 10 % - der Arbeitnehmer der Grundgesamtheit erfaßt wurden. Innerhalb dieser Richtlinien blieb die Bestimmung der einzelnen Berichtsbetriebe den Statistischen Landesämtern überlassen. In den Wirtschaftszweigen mit etwa 10 %iger Erfassung wurden die erfaßten Summenangaben bei der Aufbereitung in den Statistischen Landesämtern auf die allgemeine Erfassungsquote von 25 % hochgerechnet. Wegen der einheitlichen bzw. rechnerisch vereinheitlichten Erfassungsquote der Arbeitnehmer konnte bei der Verhältniswertberechnung sowohl für die einzelnen Wirtschaftszweige als auch für übergeordnete Wirtschaftsbereiche auf eine besondere Gewichtung bzw. Hochrechnung der Summenangaben auf 100 % der Arbeitnehmer der Grundgesamtheit verzichtet werden. Der 1957 festgelegte Kreis der Berichtsbetriebe blieb grundsätzlich so lange unverändert erhalten, bis auf Grund neuerer Auswahlgrundlagen eine generelle Neuauswahl vorgenommen wurde; dies geschah erst wieder im Jahre 1964. Die Berichtsbetriebe hatten die erfragten Summenangaben wie früher für bestimmte Arbeitnehmergruppen zu melden, wobei nunmehr auch die für die jeweiligen Betriebe nicht produktionseigentümlichen Arbeitskräfte einzubeziehen waren. Die Arbeitnehmergruppen wurden neu als "Leistungsgruppen" gebildet, und zwar wurden drei Leistungsgruppen der Arbeiter und fünf Leistungsgruppen der Angestellten - die oberste Leistungsgruppe der Angestellten blieb allerdings aus der vierteljährlichen Verdiensterhebung ausgeschlossen - unterschieden. Die Berichtsbetriebe hatten ihre Arbeitnehmer selbst den Leistungsgruppen zuzuordnen; hierzu wurden ihnen neben detaillierten Beschreibungen der Tätigkeitsmerkmale auch Richtlinien über die Zuordnung der tariflichen Lohn- und Gehaltsgruppen zu den statistischen Leistungsgruppen zur Verfügung gestellt. Die Indizes der Effektivverdienste wurden im Zuge der Reform von 1957 auf eine neue methodische Grundlage gestellt und nunmehr nach dem Modell des Preisindex von Laspeyres unter Verwendung von Gewichten berechnet, die mehrere Jahre lang konstant gehalten wurden. Das Statistische

Bundesamt ermittelte danach vierteljährliche Indizes der durchschnittlichen Bruttostundenverdienste der Industriearbeiter, Bruttowochenverdienste der Industriearbeiter und Bruttomonatsverdienste der Angestellten in Industrie und Handel. Die in jedem Bundesland, jedem Wirtschaftszweig und jeder Arbeiter- bzw. Angestelltengruppe - differenziert nach Geschlecht und Leistungsgruppe - konstant gehaltenen Gewichte wurden durch Multiplikation von Arbeitnehmerzahlen - die vor allem der jeweils letzten Gehalts- und Lohnstrukturerhebung in der gewerblichen Wirtschaft entnommen wurden - mit den in der Verdiensterhebung ermittelten jahresdurchschnittlichen Bruttoverdiensten des jeweiligen Basisjahres gebildet. Das Gewichtungsschema und die zeitliche Basis der Indexreihen wurden in mehrjährigen Abständen aktualisiert; die bisher letzte Neuberechnung erbrachte Indizes auf der Basis des Jahresdurchschnitts 1970 und beruhte auf Gewichten, die sich als Produkte der Arbeitnehmerzahlen der Gehalts- und Lohnstrukturerhebung in der gewerblichen Wirtschaft 1966 und der Jahresdurchschnittsverdienste der Verdiensterhebung für 1970 ergaben.

Ab Anfang 1964 wurde die vierteljährliche Verdiensterhebung in Industrie und Handel abermals reformiert. Die Berichtsmonate wurden auf Januar, April, Juli und Oktober verlegt. Der Kreis der Berichtsbetriebe wurde nach einem detaillierten Stichprobenplan nunmehr als Zufallsstichprobe neu ausgewählt. Die Betriebe der Grundgesamtheit wurden vor der Auswahl nach Bundesländern, Wirtschaftszweigen und Beschäftigtengrößenklassen geschichtet und innerhalb dieser Schichten in bestimmter Reihenfolge angeordnet. Die Auswahl erfolgte dann gesondert in jeder Schicht nach dem systematischen Auswahlverfahren, wobei in den einzelnen Schichten ggf. unterschiedliche Auswahlsätze bestimmt wurden, um eine "optimale" Aufteilung des Gesamtstichprobenumfangs auf die Schichten zu erhalten. Bei der praktischen Stichprobenziehung wurde das systematische Auswahlverfahren durch "Rotation" in der Weise modifiziert, daß dann nicht immer der bei der Anwendung des vorgesehenen Auswahlabstandes zu erfassende Betrieb ausgewählt wurde, wenn dieser Betrieb bereits zum alten Berichtskreis gehört hatte. In diesen Fällen wurde statt des zunächst bestimmten der nächstfolgende bisher nicht erfaßte Betrieb ausgewählt, falls ein solcher in der betreffenden Schicht innerhalb des Auswahlabstandes vorhanden war. Das Summenverfahren, die Bildung von Arbeitnehmergruppen bzw. Leistungsgruppen und das Verfahren der Verhältniswertberechnung wurden beibehalten. Die von den Stichprobenbetrieben gemeldeten Summen wurden bei der Aufbereitung in den Statistischen Landesämtern in jeder Schicht addiert und auf 100 % der Grundgesamtheit hochgerechnet, wobei die Hochrechnung nicht mehr nach der Anzahl der erfaßten Beschäftigten, sondern nach der Anzahl der erfaßten Betriebe vorgenommen wurde. Da innerhalb einer Schicht alle Betriebe denselben gleichbleibenden Hochrechnungsfaktor hatten, konnte die Hochrechnung "pro Schicht" vorgenommen werden; lediglich für Betriebe, die aus besonderen Gründen ihre Schicht gewechselt hatten, mußte in einer für jeden in Frage kommenden Wirtschaftszweig eingerichteten "Sonderschicht" eine Hochrechnung "pro Betrieb" erfolgen. Die im Zeitablauf konstant gehaltenen Hochrechnungsfaktoren mußten im Falle von "echten Antwortausfällen" durch variable Ergänzungsfaktoren entsprechend vergrößert werden. Bei "unechten Antwortausfällen" wurden die betreffenden Betriebe dagegen ersatzlos aus dem Berichtskreis gestrichen. Nach grundsätzlich dem gleichen Verfahren wie 1964 wurde für die vierteljährliche Verdiensterhebung Ende 1972 abermals ein neuer Kreis von Berichtsbetrieben ausgewählt. Der Auswahlplan sah dabei eine verstärkte Differenzierung der durchschnittlichen Auswahlsätze in den Bundesländern vor. Der Stichprobenumfang wurde nunmehr innerhalb der Wirtschaftszweige auf die Beschäftigtengrößenklassen (Schichten) "optimal", der Gesamtstichprobenumfang auf die Wirtschaftszweige dagegen nach einer vorgegebenen Genauigkeitsabstufung aufgeteilt. Eine weitere methodische Änderung ergab sich für die vierteljährliche Verdiensterhebung ab 1974. Die Aufbereitung wurde nunmehr so organisiert, daß die früher nur in den Sonderschichten angewendete Hochrechnung "pro Betrieb" in allen Schichten vorgenommen wurde. Daher konnte ab 1974 auf die Bildung von Sonderschichten verzichtet werden. Die früher in den Sonderschichten enthaltenen Betriebe wurden denjenigen Schichten zugeordnet, denen sie auf Grund ihres Wirtschaftszweiges und ihrer Größenklasse tatsächlich angehörten. Die Hochrechnungsfaktoren der einzelnen Betriebe konnten somit auch innerhalb einer Schicht voneinander abweichen.

21212 Bruttojahresverdiensterhebung in Industrie und Handel

Die Berichtsbetriebe der vierteljährlichen Verdiensterhebung in Industrie und Handel wurden ab Berichtsjahr 1971 jährlich in zusätzlichen Summenerhebungen nach den Bruttojahresverdiensten ihrer während des ganzen Berichtsjahres dem Betrieb angehörenden Arbeiter und Angestellten befragt. Die erfaßten Jahresverdienste waren Gesamtverdienste und umfaßten neben den laufend gezahlten Verdienstbestandteilen auch sämtliche einmaligen oder unregelmäßigen Zahlungen. Die Bruttojahresverdiensterhebungen verwendeten nicht nur denselben Berichtskreis wie die vierteljährlichen Verdiensterhebungen, sondern schlossen sich auch in dem Aufbereitungsverfahren eng an die vierteljährlichen Erhebungen an; insbesondere wurden die Verfahren der Hochrechnung und der Behandlung von Antwortausfällen übernommen. Entsprechend dem Berichtskreiswechsel der vierteljährlichen Erhebung von 1972 wurde auch in der Jahreserhebung ab Berichtsjahr 1972 ein neuer Kreis von Berichtsbetrieben erfaßt. Die erfaßten Bruttojahresverdienstsummen wurden bei der Aufbereitung in den statistischen Ämtern nach der Hochrechnung und Ergänzung von echten Antwortausfällen für die einzelnen Wirtschaftszweige und Bundesländer zu Verhältniswerten (durchschnittlichen Bruttojahresverdiensten je Arbeiter bzw. je Angestellten) verrechnet.

21213 Verdiensterhebung im Handwerk

Im Jahre 1957 wurde eine seitdem als Summenerhebung - mit ergänzenden Individualangaben für Arbeiter in Betrieben mit weniger als zehn Beschäftigten - durchgeführte laufende Verdiensterhebung mit halbjährlicher Periodizität eingeführt, die Arbeiter, Angestellte und Lehrlinge bzw. Anlernlinge in repräsentativ ausgewählten Betrieben bestimmter Zweige des produzierenden Handwerks erfaßte. Berichtsmonate waren der Mai und der November jedes Jahres. Als Berichtsbetriebe wurden in jeder Schicht (Beschäftigtengrößenklassen innerhalb der zu erfassenden Handwerkszweige gesondert in jedem Bundesland) der Grundgesamtheit so viele Betriebe ausgewählt, daß die Erfassung von 10 % der Arbeitnehmer der Grundgesamtheit pro Schicht auf Dauer gesichert war. Die Auswahl der Berichtsbetriebe erfolgte grundsätzlich zufällig nach dem systematischen Auswahlverfahren, in der obersten Betriebsgrößenklasse dagegen gezielt. Der ausgewählte Berichtskreis blieb bis zur generellen Neuauswahl auf Grund einer neueren Auswahlgrundlage - die Neuauswahl erfolgte im Jahre 1966 - grundsätzlich unverändert. Als Ergebnisse der Verdiensterhebung im

Handwerk wurden vor allem durchschnittliche Bruttostunden- und Bruttowochenverdienste der nach drei Arbeitergruppen (Vollgesellen, Junggesellen, übrige Arbeiter) gegliederten Arbeiter sowie Bruttoverdienstsummen - d. h. keine Durchschnittsverdienste - der Angestellten, Lehrlinge und Anlernlinge ausgewiesen; ferner wurde angegeben, wieviele Arbeiter von ihren Arbeitgebern volle Kost bzw. Unterkunft erhielten. Den Berichtsbetrieben wurden für die von ihnen selbst vorzunehmende Zuordnung der Arbeiter nach Arbeitergruppen vom Statistischen Bundesamt aufgestellte Richtlinien über die Eingliederung der handwerklichen Tarifgruppen in die statistischen Arbeitergruppen zur Verfügung gestellt.

Ab 1966 wurde ein neuer Berichtskreis zur Verdiensterhebung im Handwerk herangezogen. Hierzu wurde die Grundgesamtheit wie bei der Auswahl von 1957 geschichtet. Für die Berechnung des neuen Auswahlplans wurde eine Genauigkeitsabstufung zwischen den Handwerkszweigen vorgegeben; eine derartige Abstufung zwischen den Bundesländern unterblieb, da jedes Land von vorn herein die maximale Anzahl von Berichtsbetrieben festgelegt hatte, zu deren Erfassung es bereit war.

Die auf diese Weise für die einzelnen Handwerkszweige jedes Landes sich ergebenden Stichprobenumfänge wurden jeweils "optimal" mit entsprechend unterschiedlichen Auswahlsätzen auf die Schichten verteilt. Die Bestimmung der Berichtsbetriebe erfolgte nach dem systematischen Auswahlverfahren, wobei wie bei der vierteljährlichen Verdiensterhebung in Industrie und Handel zur Entlastung der bisherigen Berichtsbetriebe eine "Rotation" vorgenommen wurde. Die von den Stichprobenbetrieben gemeldeten Summenangaben wurden bei der Aufbereitung schichtweise addiert und anschließend pro Schicht auf 100 % der Grundgesamtheit hochgerechnet. Während bei "unechten Antwortausfällen" die betreffenden Betriebe ersatzlos im Berichtskreis gestrichen wurden, wurden bei "echten Antwortausfällen" die fehlenden Angaben mit Hilfe eines "Ergänzungsfaktors" pro Schicht hinzugeschätzt.

21214 Verdiensterhebung in der Landwirtschaft

Im Jahre 1957 wurden laufende Individuallohnerhebungen bei repräsentativ ausgewählten Betrieben in der Landwirtschaft eingeführt. Die Auswahl war so zu bemessen, daß im Durchschnitt bis zu 10 % der Arbeiter der Grundgesamtheit erfaßt wurden. In die Erhebungen wurden nur die im Stundenlohn oder im Monatslohn stehenden landwirtschaftlichen Arbeiter einbezogen. Die Erhebungen fanden bis Ende 1958 mit halbjährlicher Periodizität - Erhebungsmonate waren März und September - und danach jährlich einmal für September statt. In den ausgewählten Betrieben, die entsprechend ihrer landwirtschaftlichen Nutzfläche nach Größenklassen gegliedert waren - dabei kamen nur Betriebe ab 20 ha für die Erhebung in Frage -, wurden grundsätzlich sämtliche Arbeiter der höchsten tarifmäßigen Altersstufe einzeln erfaßt. Bei der Aufbereitung in den Statistischen Landesämtern wurden die Arbeiter entsprechend den Berufsbezeichnungen und tariflichen Lohngruppen zu Qualifikationsgruppen zusammengefaßt. Die Verdiensterhebung in der Landwirtschaft erfaßte ausschließlich die Barverdienste. Die Aufbereitung führte nur zu Durchschnittsverdiensten als Verhältniswerte. Häufigkeitsverteilungen nach Verdienstklassen wurden trotz des Individualverfahrens nicht gebildet. Neben durchschnittlichen Bruttostunden- und Bruttomonatsverdiensten wurden ab 1965 auch durchschnittliche gesetzliche Abzüge ausgewiesen. Bei der Auswahl der Berichtsbetriebe wurde angestrebt, in den einzelnen Bundesländern so viele Betriebe zu erfassen, daß jedes Land proportional zu der Anzahl seiner landwirtschaftlichen Arbeitskräfte im Bundesergebnis vertreten war. Anzahl und Quoten der auszuwählenden Betriebe wurden für die einzelnen Bundesländer und Betriebsgrößenklassen unterschiedlich festgelegt. Die Bestimmung der Berichtsbetriebe erfolgte zufällig nach dem systematischen Auswahlverfahren. Als sich nach der ersten Erhebung zeigte, daß die gewünschte Anzahl der erfaßten Arbeiter nicht erreicht wurde, wurde für die folgenden Erhebungen die Zufallsstichprobe durch gezielt ausgewählte Berichtsbetriebe ergänzt.

Ab 1964 wurde für die Verdiensterhebung in der Landwirtschaft ein neuer Berichtskreis herangezogen. Die Auswahl erfolgte nunmehr ausschließlich nach dem systematischen Auswahlverfahren, und zwar wiederum als geschichtete Stichprobe mit unterschiedlichen Auswahlsätzen pro Schicht (Größenklasse nach der landwirtschaftlichen Nutzfläche). Zur Entlastung der bisherigen Berichtsbetriebe wurde bei der Neuauswahl eine "Rotation" vorgenommen. Die erfaßten individuellen Verdienstangaben der Berichtsbetriebe wurden bei der Aufbereitung in den Statistischen Landesämtern innerhalb jeder Schicht addiert und anschließend pro Schicht auf den einheitlichen Satz von 10 % der Grundgesamtheit hochgerechnet bzw. reduziert. Bei "unechten" Antwortausfällen wurden die betreffenden Betriebe ersatzlos aus dem Berichtskreis gestrichen; bei "echten" Antwortausfällen wurden dagegen die fehlenden Angaben pro Schicht mit Hilfe eines "Ergänzungsfaktors" hinzugeschätzt. Ab 1964 wurde die Zuordnung der Arbeiter zu Qualifikationsgruppen nicht mehr von den Statistischen Landesämtern, sondern von den Betrieben selbst vorgenommen.

Die Verdiensterhebung in der Landwirtschaft mußte ab 1971 dem in diesem Wirtschaftsbereich eingetretenen Strukturwandel angepaßt werden. Die Untergrenze der zu erfassenden Betriebe wurde auf 30 ha landwirtschaftlicher Nutzfläche heraufgesetzt. Die Anzahl der maximal zu erfassenden Arbeiter wurde nicht mehr durch einen Prozentsatz (10 % der Arbeiter der Grundgesamtheit), sondern durch eine absolute Zahl (3 500 Arbeiter) festgelegt. Die Berichtsbetriebe wurden neu ausgewählt. Bei der Berechnung des Auswahlplans wurde von der Überlegung ausgegangen, wieviele Arbeiter zur Erzielung hinreichend genauer Ergebnisse von der Stichprobe erfaßt werden müssen. Die notwendige Anzahl der Arbeiter wurde je Arbeitergruppe, Betriebsgrößenklasse und Bundesland festgelegt. Aus der für die Stichprobe erforderlichen Anzahl der Arbeiter wurde die Anzahl der zu erfassenden Betriebe berechnet. Dabei wurden die Genauigkeitsanforderungen bei den einzelnen Arbeitergruppen so weit gegeneinander abgestuft, daß sich je Arbeitergruppe innerhalb der Gruppe der Monatslöhner einerseits und innerhalb der Gruppe der Stundenlöhner andererseits etwa die gleiche notwendige Anzahl von Stichprobenbetrieben ergab. Die Berichtsbetriebe wurden gesondert in jeder Schicht nach dem systematischen Auswahlverfahren ausgewählt. Die erfaßten individuellen Verdienstangaben der Berichtsbetriebe wurden bei der Aufbereitung in den Statistischen Landesämtern auf 100 % der Grundgesamtheit hochgerechnet, indem für jeden einzelnen Betrieb ein Hochrechnungsfaktor festgelegt wurde. Die Neuauswahl der Berichtsbetriebe von 1971 hatte nicht den gewünschten Erfolg, d. h. sie erbrachte wider Erwarten weniger erfaßte Arbeiter, als nach dem Auswahlplan notwendig gewesen wären. Daraufhin wurde bei der Erhebung für 1972 bei gleichzeitiger Erhöhung der Anzahl der Berichtsbetriebe in den oberen Größenklassen auf die Erfassung der Betriebe mit weniger als 50 ha landwirtschaftlicher Nutzfläche verzichtet. In dieser Form wurde die Verdiensterhebung in der Landwirtschaft vorerst letztmalig für September 1973 durchgeführt.

21215 Bergarbeiterlohnstatistik

Die preußischen Oberbergämter führten ab 1872 durch Befragung der Bergwerksbesitzer zunächst uneinheitlich Erhebungen über die tatsächlichen Löhne der Bergarbeiter durch. Im Jahre 1887 erließ der zuständige preußische Minister Richtlinien an die Oberbergämter, nach denen die weiteren lohnstatistischen Erhebungen nach einheitlichen Methoden und regelmäßig mit vierteljährlicher Periodizität stattzufinden hatten. Die bergbehördliche Lohnstatistik erfaßte sämtliche entsprechend der Art ihrer Tätigkeit nach Gruppen gegliederten Arbeiter. Es handelte sich um Lohnsummenerhebungen, aus deren Befragungsergebnissen als Verhältniswerte Durchschnittslöhne pro Arbeiter bzw. pro Schicht ermittelt wurden. Dabei wurde die jeweilige Lohnsumme zunächst auf die durchschnittliche Anzahl der Arbeiter bezogen, die berechnet wurde, indem das arithmetische Mittel zwischen den Arbeiterbeständen am Anfang und am Ende jedes Monats und aus diesen Monatsmitteln das Mittel für Vierteljahre und für Jahre gebildet wurde. Ab 1913 wurde die Lohnsumme auf die Anzahl der"Vollarbeiter"bezogen, die sich als Quotient aus der Anzahl der überhaupt verfahrenen Arbeitstage und der Anzahl der Arbeitstage des Erhebungszeitraums ergab. Ab 1921 wurde die Anzahl der Vollarbeiter als Quotient aus der Gesamtzahl der verfahrenen Arbeitsschichten abzüglich der Schichten für Überarbeit und der Anzahl der Arbeitstage des Erhebungszeitraums berechnet. Daneben wurde ab 1921 auch die Anzahl der "angelegten Arbeiter" - d. h. der Quotient aus der Gesamtzahl der verfahrenen Arbeitsschichten abzüglich der Schichten für Überarbeit zuzüglich der entgangenen Schichten und der Anzahl der Arbeitstage des Erhebungszeitraums - als Bezugsgröße verwendet.
Ab 1933 wurden nur noch die angelegten Arbeiter berechnet und auf den Begriff des Vollarbeiters verzichtet. Die laufenden lohnstatistischen Erhebungen der Bergbehörden waren zunächst auf Preußen beschränkt, fanden später als Teil der "Reichsmontanstatistik" im ganzen Reichsgebiet statt und wurden nach dem Zweiten

Weltkrieg als "Schichten- und Lohnstatistik" im Bundesgebiet weitergeführt. Die bergbehördliche Lohnstatistik erstreckte sich immer auf den gesamten Bergbau und erfaßte als Totalerhebung sämtliche Betriebe. Daneben führte das Statistische Reichsamt unabhängig von den Bergbehörden auf Grund von Nachweisungen der Zechenverbände eine besondere monatliche Statistik über die Effektivverdienste der Arbeiter im Stein- und Braunkohlenbergbau durch, die im Summenverfahren durchschnittliche Barverdienste pro Schicht und pro Monat je angelegten Arbeiter nach Arbeitergruppen lieferte. Nach dem Zweiten Weltkrieg wurde auch die allgemeine Bergarbeiterlohnstatistik der Oberbergämter von der vierteljährlichen auf monatliche Periodizität umgestellt. In der britischen Zone wurde der Kohlenbergbau monatlich statt von den Bergbehörden nunmehr von der neugeschaffenen Institution "Deutsche Kohlenbergbauleitung" erfaßt, wobei neben durchschnittlichen Bruttobarverdiensten auch durchschnittliche Gesamteinkommen (einschl. Naturalleistungen) ermittelt wurden. Nach Auflösung der Deutschen Kohlenbergbauleitung wurde im Jahre 1954 die "Statistik der Kohlenwirtschaft e. V." gegründet, der die Durchführung der Bergarbeiterlohnstatistik in fast dem gesamten Kohlenbergbau übertragen wurde. Kleinere Teile des Kohlenbergbaus wurden wie der gesamte Nichtkohlenbergbau weiterhin von den Oberbergämtern direkt zur Bergarbeiterlohnstatistik herangezogen. Auch für den Nichtkohlenbergbau wurden durchschnittliche Bruttobarverdienste und Gesamteinkommen ermittelt. Ab 1957 wurde in den amtlichen Veröffentlichungen zur Bergarbeiterlohnstatistik die Anzahl der durchschnittlich angelegten Arbeiter genauer definiert als Quotient aus der Gesamtzahl der im Erhebungszeitraum verfahrenen Arbeitsschichten - vermindert um die Zahl der Schichten für Über-, Sonn- und Feiertagsarbeit sowie der an Ruhetagen verfahrenen Schichten und vermehrt um die Zahl der wahrgenommenen Freizeitschichten, der Ruhetagsschichten mit und ohne Lohnausgleich, der Ausbildungsschichten und der entgangenen Schichten - und der Anzahl der Arbeitstage dieses Zeitraums. Da ab 1960 für den Steinkohlenbergbau aufgrund tariflicher Vereinbarungen die Ruhetage entfielen, wurden im Interesse der Vergleichbarkeit auch für den übrigen Bergbau die Arbeitstage ohne Ruhetage ermittelt. Infolgedessen galt als Anzahl der durchschnittlich angelegten Arbeiter ab 1960 der Quotient aus der Gesamtzahl der im Erhebungszeitraum verfahrenen

Arbeitsschichten - vermindert um die Zahl der Schichten für Mehr-, Sonn- und Feiertagsarbeit und vermehrt um die Zahl der Ausbildungsschichten und der entgangenen Schichten - und der Anzahl der effektiven Arbeitstage (ohne Ruhetage) dieses Zeitraums. Bei grundsätzlicher Aufrechterhaltung der Totalerhebung wurden ab 1966 in die Schichten- und Lohnstatistik des Steinkohlenbergbaus Betriebe mit einer verwertbaren Tagesförderung von weniger als 100 Tonnen und einer Belegschaft von weniger als 100 Personen - d. h. Kleinzechen und Stollenbetriebe - nicht mehr einbezogen. Als Ergebnisse der Bergarbeiterlohnstatistik werden nach dem gegenwärtigen Stand in der Form von Durchschnittsbeträgen je angelegten Arbeiter und je verfahrene bzw. vergütete Schicht Angaben über den "Leistungslohn" - definiert als bares Bruttoarbeitsentgelt für tatsächlich verfahrene Schichten unter Ausschluß von Mehrarbeitszuschlägen, Sozialzuschlägen und sonstigen "wirtschaftlichen Beihilfen", worunter Naturalleistungen wie z. B. Kohlendeputate zu verstehen sind - und das "errechnete Gesamteinkommen" - Summe aus Leistungslohn, Mehrarbeitszuschlägen, Sozialzuschlägen, Urlaubs- und Feiertagsbezahlung sowie Wert der sonstigen wirtschaftlichen Beihilfen - unter Ausgliederung des Betrages für Bergmannsprämien, vermögenswirksame Leistungen und Einmalzahlungen (Weihnachtsgeld, Gratifikationen, zusätzliches Urlaubsgeld, Leistungsbonus) ausgewiesen.

2122 Gehalts- und Lohnstrukturerhebungen

21221 Gehalts- und Lohnstrukturerhebung in der gewerblichen Wirtschaft

Die jeweils für verschiedene Wirtschaftsbereiche durchgeführten Gehalts- und Lohnstrukturerhebungen haben gemeinsam, daß die Verdienst- und sonstigen Angaben im Individualverfahren - d. h. gesondert für die einzelnen Arbeitnehmer - erhoben werden. Die erste umfassende Gehalts- und Lohnstrukturerhebung fand für den Berichtsmonat Februar 1920 statt. Zu dieser Erhebung wurden gezielt ausgewählte Betriebe aller nichtlandwirtschaftlichen Gewerbegruppen mit Ausnahme des Bergbaus herangezogen. Innerhalb der ausgewählten Betriebe wurden sämtliche Arbeiter und Angestellten erfaßt; Erhebungsmerkmale waren dabei neben dem Verdienst die wesentlichen verdienstbestimmenden persönlichen Merkmale. In die Aufbereitung der Arbeiter wurden dagegen nur bestimmte typische Berufsarten einbezogen, für die dann durchschnittliche Stunden- und Monatsverdienste berechnet wurden. Die Befragung der Berichtsbetriebe wurde von den Statistischen Landesämtern durchgeführt, die nach einheitlichen Richtlinien des Statistischen Reichsamtes zunächst für jeden einzelnen Betrieb Durchschnittsverdienste der Arbeiter berechneten. Diese "Betriebsdurchschnitte" wurden vom Statistischen Reichsamt unter Berücksichtigung der Arbeiterzahl pro Betrieb zu gewogenen "Ortsdurchschnitten" für jede Gemeinde zusammengezogen. Im Gegensatz zur Lohnstatistik der Arbeiter wurde die Gehaltsstatistik der Angestellten nicht zu Durchschnittsverdiensten für bestimmte Berufsarten, sondern zu einer Gehaltsklassenstatistik - d. h. zu Häufigkeitsverteilungen nach Gehaltsklassen - für die entsprechend den Tätigkeitsmerkmalen nach vier Gruppen gegliederten versicherungspflichtigen Angestellten verarbeitet.

Im September 1927 führte das Statistische Reichsamt ohne Beteiligung der Statistischen Landesämter eine Individualerhebung über die Effektivverdienste der Arbeiter in der Textilindustrie durch. Dabei wurden in gezielt ausgewählten Betrieben jeweils sämtliche Arbeiter erfaßt, die zu bestimmten Arbeitergruppen gehörten. Erhebungsmerkmale waren neben dem Verdienst und den verdienstbestimmenden Merkmalen unter anderem auch der Tariflohnsatz, die gesetzlichen Abzüge und der Arbeitgeberbeitrag zur Sozialversicherung. Als Ergebnisse wurden vor allem Häufigkeitsverteilungen der Arbeiter nach Verdienstklassen und gewogene Durchschnittsverdienste ausgewiesen. Die Individuallohnerhebung in der Textilindustrie wurde mit geringfügigen Abwandlungen im September 1930 und im September 1933 wiederholt. Ähnliche Individuallohnerhebungen über die Verdienststruktur der Arbeiter fanden in ebenfalls dreijährigen Abständen in verschiedenen Erhebungszeiträumen der Jahre 1928 bis 1934 nacheinander für die wichtigsten anderen Industriezweige statt. Eine erneute Individualerhebung der Angestelltenverdienste wurde vom Statistischen Reichsamt nur noch für den Monat Februar 1934 durchgeführt, und zwar beschränkt auf die Angestellten des Bankgewerbes. Dabei wurden "fast alle wichtigeren" Betriebe des Bankgewerbes und in diesen Betrieben sämtliche versicherungspflichtigen kaufmännischen Angestellten erfaßt. Weitere Gehalts- und Lohnstrukturerhebungen im Individualverfahren wurden vom Statistischen Reichsamt für Teile der gewerblichen Wirtschaft noch im März 1936 und im Juni 1938 veranstaltet. Die Erhebung vom März 1936 beschränkte sich auf das Bäckerhandwerk des Wirtschaftsgebiets Niedersachsen; erfaßt wurden in ausgewählten Betrieben jeweils sämtliche Arbeiter und Lehrlinge. Die Erhebung vom Juni 1938 bezog sich auf die metallverarbeitende Industrie des Reichsgebietes und erfaßte ebenfalls in ausgewählten Betrieben grundsätzlich sämtliche Arbeiter. Im Gegensatz zu den anderen Individualerhebungen wurden für die Erhebung von 1938 keine Häufigkeitsverteilungen, sondern nur Durchschnittswerte als Ergebnisse ausgewiesen.

Nach dem Zweiten Weltkrieg fand erstmalig für den Berichtsmonat November 1951 eine Gehalts- und Lohnstrukturerhebung in der gewerblichen Wirtschaft statt, die nunmehr entsprechend dem in der Bundesstatistik üblichen Verfahren in Zusammenarbeit zwischen dem Statistischen Bundesamt und den Statistischen Landesämtern durchgeführt wurde. Die Erhebung erfaßte gleichmäßig in allen Bundesländern sowie in allen Wirtschaftszweigen des Erhebungsbereichs sämtliche Betriebe ab zehn Beschäftigten und von den Betrieben mit weniger als zehn Beschäftigten nach dem systematischen Auswahlverfahren jeden siebten Betrieb. Die erfaßten Betriebe mit weniger als zehn Beschäftigten hatten individuelle Angaben für alle Arbeiter und Angestellten zu machen, die Betriebe ab zehn Beschäftigten nur für die Arbeiter und Angestellten, deren Familiennamen mit bestimmten für alle Betriebe gleichen Buchstaben begannen. Als Maßstab für die Qualifikation der Arbeitnehmer wurde ein Leistungsgruppenschema aufgestellt. Die Leistungsgruppen wurden nach der Berufsausbildung und Berufserfahrung sowie nach den tatsächlichen Tätigkeitsmerkmalen gebildet. Bei den Arbeitern wurden drei Leistungsgruppen, bei den Angestellten fünf Leistungsgruppen unterschieden. Die Zuordnung der einzelnen Arbeiter und Angestellten zu den Leistungsgruppen wurde nicht den Betrieben überlassen, sondern nach einheitlichen Gesichtspunkten - in erster Linie auf Grund von eigens für diesen Zweck ausgearbeiteten Richtlinien über die Eingliederung der tariflichen Lohn- und Gehaltsgruppen in die statistischen Leistungsgruppen - in den Statistischen Landesämtern vorgenommen. Erhebungsmerkmale waren vor allem der Bruttoverdienst im Erhebungsmonat nach Lohnform mit gesonderter Angabe der Mehrarbeits- bzw. Sonn- oder Feiertagsbezahlung, die gesetzlichen Abzüge, der Arbeitgeberbeitrag zur Sozialversicherung, die Jahressonderzuwendung für das Jahr 1951 sowie verdienstbestimmende persönliche Merkmale. Als Ergebnisse wurden in erster Linie durchschnittliche Stunden-, Wochen- und Monatsverdienste sowie Häufigkeitsverteilungen nach Verdienstklassen ausgewiesen.

Im Jahre 1957 fand abermals eine Gehalts- und Lohnstrukturerhebung in der gewerblichen Wirtschaft statt, wobei für Oktober 1957 in ausgewählten Betrieben (örtliche Einheiten) vor allem die Verdienste ausgewählter Arbeiter und Angestellter im Individualverfahren sowie für das Jahr 1957 in ausgewählten Unternehmen (rechtliche Einheiten) die sozialen Nebenleistungen für sämtliche Arbeitnehmer im Summenverfahren erfaßt wurden. Im eigentlichen Gehalts- und Lohnstrukturteil der Erhebung wurden in der ersten Stufe des Auswahlverfahrens aus der nach Beschäftigtengrößenklassen geschichteten Grundgesamtheit die Berichtsbetriebe nach dem systematischen Auswahlverfahren ausgewählt, indem von Größenklasse zu Größenklasse unterschiedliche, dagegen in allen Bundesländern und allen Wirtschaftszweigen einheitliche Auswahlsätze angewandt wurden. In der zweiten Stufe des Auswahlverfahrens wurden die von den Berichtsbetrieben zu erfassenden Arbeitnehmer nach bestimmten Anfangsbuchstaben der Familiennamen ausgewählt, die hier ebenfalls lediglich zu von Größenklasse zu Größenklasse unterschiedlichen Auswahlsätzen führten. Die in Frage kommenden Anfangsbuchstaben der Familiennamen wurden nicht für alle Betriebe gleich festgelegt; vielmehr wurde das Verfahren der alternierenden Buchstabenauswahl mit rotierenden Alphabetabschnitten angewendet. Für eventuelle "echte Antwortausfälle" wurden von vornherein zufällig ausgewählte Reservebetriebe miterfaßt und bei Bedarf in die Aufbereitung einbezogen. Der Gehalts- und Lohnstrukturteil der Erhebung erfaßte grundsätzlich monatliche Verdienstangaben; die von den Betrieben gemeldeten Angaben, die sich nicht genau auf den Erhebungsmonat bezogen, wurden bei der Aufbereitung in den Statistischen Landesämtern betriebsweise auf einen Zeitraum von der Länge des Oktober 1957 umgerechnet. Die monatlichen Verdienstangaben für die Arbeiter wurden bei der Aufbereitung unter anderem je Wirtschaftszweig mit Hilfe eines "Reduktionsfaktors" zu durchschnittlichen Wochenangaben verrechnet. Zu den Erhebungsmerkmalen des Gehalts- und Lohnstrukturteils gehörte unter anderem auch der Tariflohn bzw. das Tarifgehalt. Im Erhebungsteil "soziale Nebenleistungen" der Erhebung von 1957 wurden in den Wirtschaftsbereichen Industrie, Baugewerbe und Handel sämtliche Unternehmen mit mindestens 20 Arbeitnehmern erfaßt, von denen mindestens ein Zweigbetrieb zum Gehalts- und Lohnstrukturteil ausgewählt worden war. Bei der Aufbereitung wurden die von den Unternehmen mit 20 bis 99 Arbeitnehmern gemeldeten Summenangaben pauschal mit dem Hochrechnungsfaktor 2 hochgerechnet; bei den Unternehmen mit 100 oder mehr Arbeitnehmern wurde dagegen auf eine Hochrechnung verzichtet. Die Berichtsunternehmen lieferten für sämtliche bei ihnen beschäftigten Arbeiter und Angestellten vor allem summarische Angaben über die Personalkosten und Personalnebenkosten in sehr detaillierter Gliederung nach Aufwandsarten.

Während auf eine Wiederholung des Erhebungsteiles "soziale Nebenleistungen" verzichtet wurde, fand für den Berichtsmonat Oktober 1962 abermals eine repräsentative Gehalts- und Lohnstrukturerhebung in der gewerblichen Wirtschaft im Individualverfahren statt. Im Gegensatz zu der Erhebung von 1957 waren die Auswahlsätze bei der Erhebung von 1962 nicht in allen Bundesländern einheitlich, wobei allerdings die länderweise Differenzierung nicht nach statistisch-methodischen Gesichtspunkten, sondern nach Kostengesichtspunkten von den Statistischen Landesämtern selbst vorgenommen wurde. Im Gegensatz zu der Erhebung von 1957 wurden ferner bei der Erhebung von 1962 neben Ergebnissen nach Wirtschaftszweigen auch Ergebnisse nach Beschäftigtengrößenklassen ermittelt; daher mußten nunmehr bei der Aufbereitung die Betriebe eventuell abweichend von der Auswahlgrundlage nach Wirtschaftszweigen und Größenklassen entsprechend den tatsächlichen Verhältnissen im Erhebungsmonat neu zugeordnet werden. In der Erhebung von 1962 wurden als zusätzliche Merkmale die Lohnabrechnungsform der Arbeiter (Stundenlohn, fester Wochenlohn oder fester Monatslohn) und summarisch die betriebliche Arbeitszeiteinteilung (Fünf- oder Sechstagewoche) erfaßt.

Die nächste Gehalts- und Lohnstrukturerhebung in der gewerblichen Wirtschaft wurde für Oktober 1966 durchgeführt, dabei waren für Arbeiter und Angestellte individuelle Verdienstangaben außer für den Erhebungsmonat auch für das Jahr 1966 zu machen. Nach dem für diese Erhebung aufgestellten Stichprobenplan wurden die Betriebe der Auswahlgesamtheit erst nach Wirtschaftszweigen und dann nach Beschäftigtengrößenklassen (Schichten) sortiert und innerhalb der Schichten in bestimmter Reihenfolge angeordnet. Die Auswahl der Berichtsbetriebe erfolgte nach dem systematischen Auswahlverfahren gesondert in jeder Schicht. Die Auswahlsätze für die Betriebsauswahl waren in allen Bundesländern gleich, dagegen von Größenklasse zu Größenklasse und unter Berücksichtigung einer vorgegebenen Genauigkeitsabstufung auch von Wirtschaftszweig zu Wirtschaftszweig unterschiedlich. Der Gesamtauswahlsatz für die in die Stichprobe aufzunehmenden Arbeitnehmer - d. h. das Produkt aus dem Auswahlsatz der ersten Stufe (Betriebsauswahl) und dem Auswahlsatz der zweiten Stufe (Arbeitnehmerauswahl) - sollte in allen Größenklassen im Durchschnitt aller Wirtschaftszweige gleich sein. Daraus folgte, daß in den nach unterschiedlichen Auswahlsätzen ausgewählten Betrieben auch unterschiedliche Auswahlsätze für die

Auswahl der Arbeitnehmer in Ansatz zu bringen waren. Die Bestimmung der von den Berichtsbetrieben in die Stichprobe aufzunehmenden Arbeitnehmer erfolgte nach dem Verfahren der alternierenden Buchstabenauswahl. Bei der Aufbereitung in den Statistischen Landesämtern wurden im Falle "echter Antwortausfälle" die fehlenden Angaben durch Dopplung der Angaben eines Berichtsbetriebes aus derselben Schicht geschätzt; im Falle "unechter Antwortausfälle" wurden die betreffenden Betriebe ersatzlos aus dem Berichtskreis gestrichen. Wegen der von Wirtschaftszweig zu Wirtschaftszweig unterschiedlichen Auswahlsätze mußte eine Hochrechnung der Stichprobenergebnisse auf 100 % der Grundgesamtheit vorgenommen werden, wobei die individuellen Verdienstangaben jedes einzelnen erfaßten Arbeitnehmers mit einem Hochrechnungsfaktor multipliziert wurden. In der Erhebung von 1966 wurde als zusätzliches Merkmal der Gesamtbruttojahresverdienst unter Ausgliederung der Weihnachtsgratifikation erfaßt.

In weitgehender methodischer Übereinstimmung mit der Erhebung von 1966 wurde für Oktober 1972 abermals eine Gehalts- und Lohnstrukturerhebung in der gewerblichen Wirtschaft durchgeführt. Die Auswahlsätze für die Betriebsauswahl wurden nunmehr von Größenklasse zu Größenklasse,von Wirtschaftszweig zu Wirtschaftszweig und von Bundesland zu Bundesland nach vorgegebener Genauigkeitsabstufung unterschiedlich festgelegt. Die Auswahlsätze für die Arbeitnehmerauswahl waren nach Betriebsgrößenklassen unterschiedlich, dagegen innerhalb jeder Größenklasse grundsätzlich für alle Wirtschaftszweige und alle Bundesländer gleich. In der Erhebung von 1972 wurde neben den Angaben für den Erhebungsmonat auch der Gesamtbruttojahresverdienst für 1972 unter Ausgliederung sämtlicher einmaligen bzw. unregelmäßigen Zahlungen erfaßt.

21222 Gehalts- und Lohnstrukturerhebung in der Landwirtschaft

Das Statistische Reichsamt führte für das Kalenderjahr 1937 bzw. das Wirtschaftsjahr 1936/37 erstmalig eine Strukturerhebung im Individualverfahren über die Effektivverdienste der Arbeiter in der Landwirtschaft durch. Es handelte sich um eine Repräsentativerhebung, zu der Berichtsbetriebe gezielt ausgewählt wurden. Erhebungsmerkmale waren vor allem der Jahresbarverdienst, die Naturalleistungen nach Arten und Mengen, die gesetzlichen Abzüge sowie verdienstbestimmende persönliche Merkmale. Die Bewertung der Naturalleistungen erfolgte bei der Aufbereitung im Statistischen Reichsamt vor allem mit Hilfe von Daten der amtlichen Preisstatistik. Die für die einzelnen Arbeiter erfaßten Verdienstangaben wurden zu Durchschnittsverdiensten aufbereitet; die Verdienststreuung wurde lediglich in der Form einer Auszählung der Fälle über- bzw. unterdurchschnittlicher Lohnzahlung nachgewiesen.

Für das Berichtsjahr 1950 fand in Zusammenarbeit zwischen dem Statistischen Amt des Vereinigten Wirtschaftsgebietes bzw. dem Statistischen Bundesamt und den Statistischen Landesämtern eine Lohnstrukturerhebung in der Landwirtschaft statt, bei der mit Hilfe von Interviewern repräsentativ ausgewählte Betriebe und in diesen Betrieben jeweils alle ständig beschäftigten familienfremden Arbeiter einzeln erfaßt wurden. Während des Erhebungszeitraums wurden sechs Teilerhebungen für jeweils zwei Monate durchgeführt, in denen Angaben für jeden Arbeiter und jeden einzelnen Monat zu machen waren. Die Auswahl der Berichtsbetriebe aus den Landkreisen erfolgte, indem zunächst in jedem Landkreis eine größere Anzahl von geeigneten Betrieben gezielt und dann daraus eine kleinere Anzahl von Betrieben als Berichtsbetriebe zufällig ausgewählt wurde. In jedem Stadtkreis bzw. jeder kreisfreien Stadt wurden die Berichtsbetriebe direkt gezielt ausgewählt. Bei der Auswahl war zu beachten, daß sich die Berichtsbetriebe nach vorgegebenen Anteilen auf Betriebsgrößenklassen nach der landwirtschaftlichen Nutzfläche verteilten. Erhebungsmerkmale waren vor allem der Bruttoverdienst, die gesetzlichen Abzüge, Arten und Mengen der empfangenen Naturalleistungen - die Bewertung wurde ähnlich wie bei der Erhebung von 1937 erst nachträglich von den Statistischen Landesämtern vorgenommen - und verdienstbestimmende persönliche Merkmale. Die individuellen Verdienstangaben wurden lediglich zu Durchschnittsverdiensten pro Stunde und pro Jahr aufbereitet.

Die nächste Individualerhebung in der Landwirtschaft wurde als repräsentative Gehalts- und Lohnstrukturerhebung für das Berichtsjahr vom 1. Februar 1953 bis zum 31. Januar 1954 veranstaltet. Zu dieser Erhebung wurden landwirtschaftliche Betriebe in einem zweistufigen Auswahlverfahren zufällig ausgewählt, wobei sowohl in der ersten als auch in der zweiten Stufe unterschiedliche Auswahlsätze in den nach der landwirtschaftlichen Nutzfläche gebildeten Betriebsgrößenklassen angewendet wurden. In der ersten Auswahlstufe wurden je Bundesland aus den in eindimensionale Ordnung gebrachten kreisangehörigen Gemeinden nach dem systematischen Auswahlverfahren bestimmte Gemeinden ausgewählt. In der zweiten Auswahlstufe wurden dann innerhalb der einzelnen ausgewählten Gemeinden ebenfalls nach dem systematischen Auswahlverfahren die Berichtsbetriebe ausgewählt. Wenn in einer ausgewählten Gemeinde keine Betriebe der jeweils gewünschten Größenklasse vorhanden waren, wurde entweder eine benachbarte Gemeinde erfaßt oder eine Ersatzgemeinde zufällig ausgewählt. Die kreisfreien Städte bzw. Stadtkreise wurden sämtlich in die Erhebung einbezogen; auch hier wurden die Berichtsbetriebe nach dem systematischen Auswahlverfahren gesondert in jeder Größenklasse bestimmt. Die Berichtsbetriebe hatten Angaben für grundsätzlich jeden der bei ihnen beschäftigten Arbeiter und Angestellten zu melden. Dabei hatten die größeren Berichtsbetriebe die erfragten Angaben für jeden Monat des ganzen Erhebungsjahres zu machen. Die kleineren Berichtsbetriebe hatten nur für die Monate Februar, Mai, September und November des Erhebungsjahres Meldungen abzugeben. Bei besonders ausgeprägter Berichtsunwilligkeit der Berichtsbetriebe wurden teilweise nachträglich Ersatzbetriebe erfaßt, indem von den Statistischen Landesämtern zunächst solche Gemeinden gezielt ausgewählt wurden, in denen im allgemeinen gut berichtet worden war; diese Gemeinden hatten dann selbst eine vorgegebene Anzahl von Ersatzbetrieben zu benennen. Auch im Falle von "unechten Anwortausfällen" wurden größenmäßig vergleichbare Ersatzbetriebe ausgewählt. Wenn die von den Betrieben gemeldeten Individualangaben sich nicht genau auf einen Monat bezogen, wurden sie bei der Aufbereitung in Monatswerte umgerechnet. Wenn für einen Arbeitnehmer in einem Erhebungsmonat zum Beispiel wegen Krankheit nur ein verringerter Verdienst angegeben war, wurde eine Hochschätzung auf den vollen erreichbaren Monatsverdienst vorgenommen. Analog wurden aus den Verdienstangaben der nur in vier Monaten erfaßten Arbeitnehmer die gesamten Jahresverdienste geschätzt. Wenn die Angaben für einen Arbeitnehmer in einem einzelnen Erhebungsmonat ganz fehlten, wurden sie auf Grund der entsprechenden Daten aus den benachbarten Erhebungsmonaten geschätzt. Wegen der unterschiedlichen Auswahlsätze in den Betriebsgrößenklassen war ferner eine Hochrechnung der Stichprobendaten auf 100 % der Grundgesamtheit erforderlich. In der Erhebung von 1953/54 wurde als zusätzliches Merkmal der Arbeitgeberbeitrag zur Sozialversicherung erfaßt. Als Ergebnisse wurden in erster Linie durchschnittliche Stunden-, Monats- und Jahresverdienste und Häufigkeitsverteilungen nach Verdienstklassen ausgewiesen.

Für das Berichtsjahr vom 1. Februar 1962 bis zum 31. Januar 1963 wurde abermals eine Gehalts- und Lohnstrukturerhebung in der Landwirtschaft durchgeführt, die in ausgewählten Betrieben grundsätzlich sämtliche familienfremden landwirtschaftlichen Arbeitskräfte erfaßte. Die einzelnen Arbeiter wurden bei der Aufbereitung in den Statistischen Landesämtern nach ihrer Qualifikation und ihren Tätigkeitsmerkmalen zu Arbeitergruppen zusammengefaßt. Von den Angestellten wurden nur männliche Inspektoren und Verwalter in die Erhebung einbezogen. Die Berichtsbetriebe hatten in vier Teilerhebungen zu je drei Monaten für jeden Monat des Berichtsjahres individuelle Angaben zu liefern, und zwar über die im Stundenlohn stehenden Arbeiter für alle zwölf Monate, über die im Monatslohn stehenden Arbeiter sowie die Angestellten dagegen nur für einen Monat (September 1962). Die Berichtsbetriebe waren aus den nach Größenklassen entsprechend der landwirtschaftlichen Nutzfläche geschichteten Betrieben der Auswahlgesamtheit mit nach Größenklassen unterschiedlichen Auswahlsätzen auszuwählen; daher mußte bei der Ermittlung von Durchschnittsergebnissen für die Gesamtheit der Betriebe eine Hochrechnung der erfaßten Angaben auf 100 % der Grundgesamtheit vorgenommen werden. Für die Realisierung des Auswahlplans standen den Statistischen Landesämtern mehrere alternative Auswahlverfahren zur Verfügung. In Nordrhein-Westfalen wurden zunächst gesondert in jeder Größenklasse die Betriebe der Grundgesamtheit regional nach Gemeinden sortiert, wobei die Reihenfolge der Gemeinden einer Anordnung in Serpentinenlinie entsprechend ihrer geographischen Lage entsprach. Aus der auf diese Weise geordneten Grundgesamtheit wurden dann nach dem systematischen Auswahlverfahren unter Beachtung der nach Betriebsgrößenklassen unterschiedlichen Auswahlabstände bestimmte Betriebe ausgewählt. Als Berichtsbetriebe wurden schließlich außer den systematisch ausgewählten Betrieben entsprechend den unterschiedlichen Auswahlsätzen jeweils einige in der Anordnung der Grundgesamtheit unmittelbar darauffolgende Betriebe bestimmt. In die Stichprobe gelangten demnach nicht isoliert ausgewählte Betriebe, sondern ganze Klumpen regional benachbarter Betriebe. In der Erhebung von 1962/63 wurde als zusätzliches Merkmal für den Berichtsmonat Oktober 1962 für die einzelnen im Stundenlohn stehenden Arbeiter die zu zahlende Miete für eventuell bereitgestellte Werkswohnungen erfaßt; aus diesen Angaben wurde bei der Aufbereitung durch Vergleich mit dem geschätzten tatsächlichen Mietwert der Wohnung der jeweilige "Mietvorteil" berechnet.

21223 Lohnstrukturerhebung in der Forstwirtschaft

Im Rahmen der Individualerhebungen des Statistischen Reichsamtes fand für das Forstwirtschaftsjahr vom 1. Oktober 1939 bis zum 30. September 1940 erstmalig eine Strukturerhebung über die Effektivverdienste der Arbeiter in der Forstwirtschaft statt. Zu der Erhebung wurde eine gezielte repräsentative Auswahl von Betrieben der staatlichen, kommunalen und privaten Forstwirtschaft herangezogen. In den ausgewählten Betrieben wurden sämtliche männlichen und weiblichen Waldarbeiter der höchsten tariflichen Altersstufe einzeln erfaßt. Erhebungsmerkmale waren vor allem der Bruttobarverdienst sowie Arten und Mengen der Naturalleistungen, deren Bewertung dann bei der Aufbereitung im Statistischen Reichsamt in erster Linie mit Hilfe von Daten der amtlichen Preisstatistik erfolgte. Die individuellen Verdienstangaben wurden ausschließlich zu durchschnittlichen Bruttostundenverdiensten aufbereitet.

Die erste Lohnstrukturerhebung in der Forstwirtschaft nach dem Zweiten Weltkrieg wurde in Zusammenarbeit zwischen dem Statistischen Amt des Vereinigten Wirtschaftsgebietes bzw. dem Statistischen Bundesamt und den Statistischen Landesämtern für das Berichtsjahr vom 1. Oktober 1949 bis zum 30. September 1950 durchgeführt. Dabei wurden mit Hilfe von Interviewern repräsentativ ausgewählte staatliche, kommunale, körperschaftliche und private Forstbetriebe und in diesen Betrieben jeweils alle Arbeiter einzeln erfaßt. Während des Erhebungszeitraums fanden zwei Teilerhebungen für jeweils drei Monate und eine Teilerhebung für sechs Monate statt, in denen Angaben für jeden Arbeiter und jeden einzelnen Monat zu machen waren. Die Berichtsbetriebe wurden gezielt ausgewählt, wobei als allgemeine Richtlinie galt, daß die erfaßten Arbeiter zu vorgegebenen Anteilen auf die o. a. Besitzarten entfallen sollten; außerdem war bei privaten Betrieben eine Größenklassengliederung nach der Forstfläche mit höheren Auswahlsätzen für die Kleinbetriebe zu berücksichtigen. Erhebungsmerkmale waren vor allem der Bruttobarverdienst, die gesetzlichen Abzüge, Arten und Mengen der empfangenen Naturalleistungen - die Bewertung erfolgte nachträglich in den Statistischen Landesämtern - und verdienstbestimmende persönliche Merkmale. Die als Ergebnisse ausgewiesenen durchschnittlichen Stunden- und Jahresverdienste wurden berechnet, nachdem die Angaben über die in der Erhebung erfaßten Arbeiter auf 100 % aller Forstarbeiter hochgerechnet worden waren. Die dazu notwendigen Totalzahlen der Forstarbeiter wurden Unterlagen der forstwirtschaftlichen Verwaltungsbehörden entnommen.

Für das Berichtsjahr vom 1. Oktober 1952 bis zum 30. September 1953 wurde abermals eine Lohnstrukturerhebung in der Forstwirtschaft als repräsentative Individualerhebung veranstaltet. Diese Erhebung erfaßte sämtliche staatlichen und kommunalen Forstbetriebe eines bestimmten Größenbereichs und in diesen Betrieben sämtliche Haumeister sowie diejenigen sonstigen männlichen und weiblichen Waldarbeiter, deren Familiennamen mit bestimmten für alle Betriebe gleichen Buchstaben begannen. Das Erhebungsjahr wurde in vier Berichtsquartale aufgeteilt, wobei jedoch Angaben pro Arbeiter für jeden einzelnen Monat zu machen waren. In der Erhebung von 1952/53 wurden als zusätzliche Merkmale die Urlaubsvergütung, der Lohnfortzahlungsbetrag bei Krankheit und der Arbeitgeberbeitrag zur Sozialversicherung erfaßt. Aus den individuellen Verdienstangaben wurden durchschnittliche Stunden- und Jahresverdienste sowie Häufigkeitsverteilungen nach Verdienstklassen berechnet. Die Lohnsummen der total erfaßten Haumeister wurden dabei durch Multiplikation mit einem "Reduktionsfaktor" auf das Niveau der Lohnsummen der repräsentativ erfaßten Arbeiter umgerechnet.

In weitgehender methodischer Übereinstimmung mit der Erhebung von 1952/53 wurde für das Berichtsjahr vom 1. Oktober 1961 bis zum 30. September 1962 wiederum eine Lohnstrukturerhebung in der Forstwirtschaft durchgeführt. Der Auswahlplan entsprach dem der Erhebung von 1952/53, allerdings beschränkte sich die Erhebung von 1961/62 neben den Haumeistern auf die ständig beschäftigten männlichen Waldarbeiter der höchsten tarifmäßigen Altersstufe. Ferner ergab sich dadurch eine Vereinfachung, daß das Erhebungsjahr nicht mehr in Berichtsquartale aufgeteilt wurde; die Betriebe wurden vielmehr nur zu einer einmaligen Berichterstattung für das gesamte Forstwirtschaftsjahr herangezogen. Die Naturalleistungen wurden erstmalig nicht mehr erfaßt.

21224 Gehalts- und Lohnstrukturerhebung im Erwerbsgartenbau

Im Erwerbsgartenbau wurde bisher erst einmal eine Gehalts- und Lohnstrukturerhebung durchgeführt, und zwar für den Berichtsmonat Mai 1962. Zu dieser Repräsentativerhebung wurden nach dem systematischen Auswahlverfahren einheitlich in allen Bundesländern 50 % der Erwerbsgartenbaubetriebe mit familienfremden Arbeitskräften unabhängig von der Betriebsgröße als Berichtsbetriebe ausgewählt. Die Berichtsbetriebe hatten Individualangaben für grundsätzlich sämtliche Arbeiter und Angestellten zu melden. Erhebungsmerkmale waren vor allem der Bruttobarverdienst, die Naturalleistungen nach Arten und Mengen, die gesetzlichen Abzüge und verdienstbestimmende persönliche Merkmale. Die Naturalleistungen wurden bei der Aufbereitung in den Statistischen Landesämtern mit Hilfe der für Zwecke der Sozialversicherung festgelegten Sätze bzw. mit Hilfe von Daten der amtlichen Preisstatistik bewertet. Die individuellen Verdienstangaben wurden zu durchschnittlichen Stunden- und Monatsverdiensten und Häufigkeitsverteilungen nach Verdienstklassen aufbereitet.

21225 Gehalts- und Lohnstrukturerhebung im öffentlichen Dienst

Für den Berichtsmonat September 1950 fand erstmalig eine Individualerhebung über die Effektivverdienste im öffentlichen Dienst in den Ländern des Vereinigten Wirtschaftsgebietes mit Ausnahme von Bayern statt. Die Erhebung erstreckte sich auf sämtliche Gebietskörperschaften, Eigenbetriebe und Eigengesellschaften von Gebietskörperschaften sowie die der Aufsicht einer Gebietskörperschaft unterstehenden Körperschaften, Anstalten und Stiftungen des öffentlichen Rechts und die Verwaltungen der Grund- und Sondervermögen der öffentlichen Hand; ausgenommen waren lediglich die Gemeinden mit weniger als 1 000 Einwohnern. Bei diesen Dienststellen wurden einheitlich diejenigen aktiven Bediensteten (Beamte, Angestellte, Arbeiter, Personen in Ausbildung) und Versorgungsempfänger erfaßt, deren Familiennamen mit vorgegebenen für alle Dienststellen gleichen Buchstaben begannen. Erhebungsmerkmale waren vor allem der Brutto- und Nettoverdienst, Angaben über die Eingruppierung bzw. Qualifikation und weitere in den Strukturerhebungen übliche persönliche Merkmale. Die individuellen Verdienstangaben wurden zu durchschnittlichen Monatsverdiensten bzw. bei den Arbeitern auch zu durchschnittlichen Wochen- und Stundenverdiensten aufbereitet. Das Statistische Bundesamt schrieb die in der Erhebung ermittelten Durchschnittsverdienste nachträglich fort, indem es darauf eine spätere Erhöhung der Grundvergütungen pauschal aufschlug.

Eine weitere Individualerhebung über die Effektivverdienste im öffentlichen Dienst wurde im gesamten Bundesgebiet für den Berichtsmonat September 1968 durchgeführt. In die Erhebung wurden sämtliche Dienststellen und nichtrechtsfähigen Wirtschaftsunternehmen der Gebietskörperschaften einschl. Bundesbahn und Bundespost, die Sozialversicherungsträger sowie die jeweils zugehörigen Sondervermögen einbezogen; ausgenommen waren außer den Gemeinden mit weniger als 1 000 Einwohnern in Nordrhein-Westfalen auch die amtsangehörigen Gemeinden mit weniger als 10 000 Einwohnern. In diesen Berichtsstellen wurden jeweils ausgewählte Beamte, Richter, DO-Angestellte der Sozialversicherungsträger, Angestellte und

Arbeiter erfaßt; Versorgungsempfänger und Personen in Ausbildung blieben ausgeschlossen. Für die Auswahl der Bediensteten wurde eine Schichtung zunächst nach Beschäftigungsbereichen (Behörden und Einrichtungen, Wirtschaftsunternehmen, Sozialversicherungsträger) und dann nach Dienstherren (Bund, Länder, Gemeinden und Gemeindeverbände) vorgenommen. Die Auswahlsätze für die Bedienstetenauswahl wurden für alle Berichtsstellen innerhalb einer Schicht einheitlich, von Schicht zu Schicht jedoch grundsätzlich unterschiedlich nach einer vorgegebenen Genauigkeitsabstufung festgelegt. Die Berichtsstellen wählten dann selbst die von ihnen zu erfassenden Bediensteten in einigen Fällen nach dem systematischen Auswahlverfahren, in der Regel jedoch nach bestimmten - innerhalb einer Schicht für alle Berichtsstellen gleichen - Anfangsbuchstaben der Familiennamen aus. Die von den Berichtsstellen gemeldeten individuellen Verdienstangaben wurden bei der Aufbereitung auf 100 % der Grundgesamtheit hochgerechnet. Wenn die Angaben für die Arbeiter sich nicht genau auf den Erhebungsmonat bezogen, wurden sie bei der Aufbereitung in Monatsangaben umgerechnet. Die Monatsangaben für die Arbeiter wurden ferner zur Berechnung von Wochenergebnissen auf durchschnittliche Wochenangaben reduziert. Sämtliche Bediensteten wurden nach ihren Besoldungs- bzw. Vergütungs- oder Lohngruppen von den statistischen Ämtern den in der amtlichen Effektivverdienststatistik üblichen Leistungsgruppen zugeordnet. Erhebungsmerkmale waren vor allem der nach seinen Bestandteilen aufgegliederte Bruttoverdienst, die gesetzlichen Abzüge und verdienstbestimmende persönliche Merkmale. Als Ergebnisse wurden vor allem durchschnittliche Stunden-, Wochen- und Monatsverdienste sowie Häufigkeitsverteilungen nach Verdienstklassen ausgewiesen.

213 Lohnstatistische Sonderuntersuchungen

2131 Erhebung über die Vermögensbildung der Arbeitnehmer

Zur nationalen Lohnstatistik gehören neben der Tariflohnstatistik und der Effektivverdienststatistik gelegentliche Erhebungen über Spezialfragen im Rahmen der statistischen Untersuchung der Arbeitnehmereinkommen. Um Daten zur Erfolgskontrolle des Ersten Vermögensbildungsgesetzes vom 12. Juli 1961 (Bundesgesetzblatt 1961 Teil I S. 909) zu erhalten, wurde für das Berichtsjahr 1963 bei repräsentativ ausgewählten Unternehmen eine Erhebung über die Vermögensbildung der Arbeitnehmer durchgeführt. Die Auswahlsätze waren nach Beschäftigtengrößenklassen und Wirtschaftsbereichen differenziert. Die Berichtsunternehmen wurden aus der zunächst nach Beschäftigtengrößenklassen und dann nach Wirtschaftszweigen geschichteten Grundgesamtheit pro Schicht nach dem systematischen Auswahlverfahren ausgewählt. Bei der Aufbereitung wurden die Berichtsunternehmen den Größenklassen und Wirtschaftszweigen entsprechend den tatsächlichen Verhältnissen im Erhebungsjahr neu zugeordnet. Die Angaben der Berichtsunternehmen wurden gesondert für jedes einzelne Unternehmen auf 100 % der Grundgesamtheit hochgerechnet. Als Ergebnisse der Erhebung wurden vor allem Angaben über die Anzahl der vermögenswirksame Leistungen anbietenden Unternehmen, die Anzahl der begünstigten Arbeitnehmer und die Durchschnittsbeträge der vermögenswirksamen Leistungen pro Arbeiter und pro Angestellten ausgewiesen.

2132 Erhebung über die betriebliche Altersversorgung

Für das Berichtsjahr 1973 bzw. zum Erhebungsstichtag 31. Dezember 1973 wurde bei ausgewählten Unternehmen der gewerblichen Wirtschaft mit Ausnahme des Baugewerbes eine Erhebung über Arten und Umfang der betrieblichen Altersversorgung durchgeführt. Die Berichtsunternehmen hatten summarische Angaben für grundsätzlich alle Arbeiter und Angestellten unter gesonderter Erfassung der leitenden Angestellten zu machen. Der Erhebungsbogen enthielt teilweise ungewöhnliche Fragen. So sollten die Unternehmen durch eine Modellrechnung die für ihre Arbeitnehmer theoretisch erreichbare Altersversorgung ermitteln; ferner sollten sie ihre Arbeitnehmer selbst schwerpunktmäßig den einzelnen Typen der Altersversorgung zuordnen. Vor der Auswahl wurden die Unternehmen der Grundgesamtheit unter Verzicht auf eine Schichtung nach Bundesländern erst nach Wirtschaftszweigen und dann nach Beschäftigtengrößenklassen (Schichten) sortiert. Die Aufteilung des im voraus festgesetzten Gesamtstichprobenumfangs auf die Schichten erfolgte "optimal" mit prinzipiell unterschiedlichen Auswahlsätzen in den einzelnen Schichten. Die Berichtsunternehmen wurden nach dem systematischen Auswahlverfahren gesondert in jeder Schicht bestimmt, und zwar im allgemeinen wie üblich aus dem Material einer Totalerhebung (Arbeitsstättenzählung 1970), für das produzierende Gewerbe dagegen aus einer Repräsentativerhebung (Personalkostenerhebung der Europäischen Gemeinschaften für das Jahr 1972). Im produzierenden Gewerbe wurden von den in der ersten Phase - d. h. zur Stichprobe für die Personalkostenerhebung - ausgewählten Unternehmen zunächst diejenigen aussortiert, die nach ihren Angaben zur Personalkostenerhebung keine betriebliche Altersversorgung hatten. Auf die verbleibenden Unternehmen wurde dann in der zweiten Auswahlphase der Auswahlplan der Erhebung über die betriebliche Altersversorgung angewendet. Bei der Aufbereitung wurden für die im Anschluß an die erste Phase aussortierten Unternehmen die benötigten Daten nach den aus der Personalkostenerhebung bereits vorliegenden Angaben übernommen und mit den neu ermittelten Daten der bei der Erhebung über die betriebliche Altersversorgung erfaßten Unternehmen in den Ergebnissen zusammengefaßt. Sämtliche Stichprobenergebnisse wurden pro Unternehmen auf 100 % der Grundgesamtheit hochgerechnet. Bei der Aufbereitung wurden die Berichtsunternehmen den Größenklassen entsprechend ihrer tatsächlichen Beschäftigtenzahl zum Erhebungszeitpunkt neu zugeordnet. Von einer Ersetzung "echter Antwortausfälle" - die nur in sehr geringem Maße vorkamen - wurde abgesehen. Als Ergebnisse der Erhebung wurden die Anzahl der begünstigten Arbeitnehmer, die Höhe der Versorgungsleistungen pro Arbeitnehmer und die Gesamtaufwendungen der Unternehmen für die betriebliche Altersversorgung, jeweils aufgegliedert nach Unternehmensgrößenklassen und Arten der Altersversorgung - nicht nach Wirtschaftszweigen -, ausgewiesen. Die Erhebung über die betriebliche Altersversorgung wurde für das Berichtsjahr 1976 bzw. zum Erhebungsstichtag 31. Dezember 1976 nach grundsätzlich dem gleichen Erhebungsplan wie 1973 wiederholt, wobei die Berichtsunternehmen des produzierenden Gewerbes aus dem Anschriftenmaterial der Personalkostenerhebung der Europäischen Gemeinschaften für 1975 neu ausgewählt, die übrigen Berichtsunternehmen dagegen aus der Stichprobe der Erhebung von 1973 übernommen wurden.

22 Inter- und supranationale Lohnstatistik der Europäischen Gemeinschaften

221 Laufende Verdiensterhebungen

2211 Harmonisierte Verdiensterhebung in Industrie und Handel

Die in der Bundesrepublik Deutschland amtlicherseits durchgeführte inter- und supranationale Lohnstatistik beruht ausschließlich auf Rechtsvorschriften der Europäischen Gemeinschaften oder Vereinbarungen ihrer Mitgliedstaaten und ist in erster Linie für Zwecke der gemeinsamen europäischen Wirtschafts- und Sozialpolitik bestimmt. Dabei ist zwischen der laufenden Beobachtung der Entwicklung der Effektivverdienste, der einmaligen oder in mehrjährigen Abständen wiederholten Untersuchung der effektiven Lohn- und Gehaltsstruktur und der Erfassung der gesamten Personalkosten zu unterscheiden. Zuständig für die Bearbeitung dieser Erhebungen ist das Statistische Amt der Europäischen Gemeinschaften, in der Regel in Zusammenarbeit mit den nationalen statistischen Ämtern, d. h. in der Bundesrepublik Deutschland mit dem Statistischen Bundesamt und den Statistischen Landesämtern. Mit der Zusammenstellung vergleichbarer laufender Daten über die Effektivverdienste im gesamten Gebiet der Europäischen Gemeinschaften wurde im Jahre 1964 begonnen. Zunächst wurden die durchschnittlichen Bruttostundenverdienste der"manuell beschäftigten" Arbeiter im produzierenden Gewerbe einschl. Bergbau und Baugewerbe für die Berichtsmonate April und Oktober jedes Jahres ausgewiesen. Für die Beschaffung der Ausgangsdaten dieser international harmonisierten Verdienststatistik wurden keine eigenen Erhebungen durchgeführt; vielmehr wurden die in den Mitgliedsländern bestehenden nationalen laufenden Verdiensterhebungen den Wünschen der Europäischen Gemeinschaften so weit angepaßt, daß die Ergebnisse neben nationalen Zwecken gleichzeitig den Zwecken der EG-Kommission dienen konnten. Als Datenquelle der harmonisierten Verdienststatistik wurde in der Bundesrepublik Deutschland die vierteljährliche Verdiensterhebung in Industrie und Handel verwendet. Die harmonisierte Verdienststatistik wurde ab Oktober 1972 auf die durchschnittlichen Bruttomonatsverdienste der Angestellten in Industrie, Handel, Kreditwirtschaft und Versicherungsgewerbe ausgedehnt.

2212 Erhebung über die Arbeiterverdienste in der Landwirtschaft

Im Jahre 1974 fand erstmalig eine eigenständige EG-Erhebung über die Verdienste der ständig in der Landwirtschaft beschäftigten Arbeiter statt, in der repräsentativ ausgewählte landwirtschaftliche Betriebe unabhängig von der Größe ihrer landwirtschaftlichen Nutzfläche mit Hilfe von Interviewern erfaßt wurden. Erhebungszeitraum war in der Bundesrepublik Deutschland der Monat September. Die Berichtsbetriebe hatten Individualangaben für grundsätzlich jeden ihrer Arbeiter zu liefern. Die einzelnen Arbeiter waren durch die Berichtsbetriebe bzw. die Interviewer nach ihren Tätigkeitsmerkmalen bzw. ihren tariflichen Lohngruppen vorgegebenen Qualifikationsgruppen sowie den Hauptproduktionsrichtungen zuzuordnen. Die zeitraumbezogenen Individualangaben waren grundsätzlich für den ganzen Monat September 1974 zu machen; bei einem abweichenden Lohnabrechnungszeitraum wurde bei der Aufbereitung eine Umrechnung in Monatswerte vorgenommen. Der Auswahlplan sah eine zweistufige Auswahl vor, und zwar wurden in der ersten Stufe Gemeinden und in der zweiten Stufe Betriebe in diesen Gemeinden ausgewählt. Zunächst wurden die Betriebe der Auswahlgesamtheit innerhalb jeder Gemeinde nach Größenklassen (Schichten) entsprechend ihrer Arbeiterzahl gruppiert. Der für das Bundesgebiet im voraus festgesetzte Gesamtstichprobenumfang wurde nach einer vorgegebenen Genauigkeitsabstufung auf die Bundesländer, der auf die einzelnen Länder entfallende Stichprobenumfang ebenfalls nach vorgegebener Genauigkeitsabstufung auf die Betriebsschichten verteilt. Soweit die Betriebsschichten nicht total erfaßt wurden, wurden für die erste Auswahlstufe schichtweise je Land unterschiedliche auf Betriebe bezogene Auswahlabstände und Zufallsstartzahlen festgelegt, mit denen dann über die nach Gemeinden angeordneten Betriebe der Auswahlgesamtheit die Stichprobengemeinden im systematischen Auswahlverfahren ausgewählt wurden, indem jeweils diejenige Gemeinde in die Auswahl gelangte, deren kumulative Betriebszahl die Auswahlnummer - das ist die Zufallsstartzahl zuzüglich des Vielfachen des Auswahlabstandes - erreichte oder gerade überschritt. In der zweiten Auswahlstufe wurden in den ausgewählten Gemeinden sämtliche Betriebe in die Stichprobe einbezogen. Die in der Stichprobe ermittelten Individualangaben wurden pro Betrieb bei der Aufbereitung auf 100 % der Grundgesamtheit hochgerechnet. Bei "unechten Antwortausfällen" wurden die betreffenden Betriebe ersatzlos aus dem Berichtskreis gestrichen; wenn trotz des Interviewereinsatzes in einer größeren Zahl von Fällen"echte Antwortausfälle" auftraten, wurden diese durch Dopplung der Angaben vergleichbarer Berichtsbetriebe ersetzt. Für die Ergebniserstellung wurden die Berichtsbetriebe entsprechend den tatsächlichen Verhältnissen zur Erhebungszeit den Hauptproduktionsrichtungen sowie den Größenklassen - sowohl nach der Arbeiterzahl als auch nach der landwirtschaftlichen Nutzfläche - neu zugeordnet. Erhebungsmerkmale waren vor allem der Barlohn, die gesetzlichen Abzüge und der für Naturalleistungen eventuell vom Lohn einbehaltene Betrag; ferner war anzugeben, ob der Arbeiter neben seinem Barlohn Kost oder Unterkunft erhielt. Die individuellen Verdienstangaben wurden nicht zu Häufigkeitsverteilungen, sondern nur zu Durchschnittsverdiensten pro Arbeiter aufbereitet. Die EG-Verdiensterhebung in der Landwirtschaft wurde auch in den folgenden Jahren - in der Bundesrepublik Deutschland jeweils für den Erhebungsmonat September - unter Heranziehung desselben Berichtskreises wie 1974 durchgeführt.

222 Gehalts- und Lohnstrukturerhebungen

2221 Gehalts- und Lohnstrukturerhebung im produzierenden Gewerbe

Als erste Lohnstrukturerhebung der Europäischen Gemeinschaften wurde für Oktober 1966 eine Individualerhebung in Industrie und produzierendem Handwerk durchgeführt. Die Erhebung fand gleichzeitig mit der nationalen Gehalts- und Lohnstrukturerhebung in der gewerblichen Wirtschaft 1966 statt und wurde so organisiert, daß durch Erfassung der gleichen Erhebungseinheiten und unter Verwendung der gleichen Erhebungsformulare mit einer einzigen Befragung sowohl die Informationsbedürfnisse der Bundesrepublik Deutschland als auch die der Europäischen Gemeinschaften befriedigt werden konnten. Für die EG-Erhebung waren in ausgewählten Betrieben jeweils nur ausgewählte Arbeiter zu erfassen. Die von der EG-Kommission für den Stichprobenplan festgelegte Rahmenregelung war so flexibel, daß sie ohne besondere Schwierigkeiten mit dem Stichprobenplan der nationalen Erhebung in Einklang gebracht werden konnte. Nach den EG-Richtlinien waren im Durchschnitt aller Wirtschaftszweige kleine Betriebe repräsentativ mit jeweils sämtlichen Arbeitern, mittlere Betriebe repräsentativ mit jeweils einem Teil der Arbeiter und große Betriebe total mit jeweils einem Teil der Arbeiter zu erfassen.

Der Gesamtstichprobenumfang war auf die Wirtschaftszweige "optimal" - d. h. bei der Betriebsauswahl mit prinzipiell unterschiedlichen Auswahlsätzen pro Wirtschaftszweig - aufzuteilen. Die EG-Richtlinien legten ferner für jeden Mitgliedstaat und jeden Wirtschaftszweig die mindestens zu erfassende Gesamtarbeiterzahl fest. Die in die Stichprobe einzubeziehenden Arbeiter waren nach einem nicht näher vorgeschriebenen Verfahren der Zufallsauswahl zu bestimmen; die in der Bundesrepublik Deutschland übliche Auswahl nach den Anfangsbuchstaben der Familiennamen wurde auch in den Niederlanden und Belgien angewendet, während in Frankreich die Arbeiter nach den Geburtsmonaten und in Italien mit Hilfe von Zufallszahlentafeln ausgewählt wurden.

In weitgehender methodischer Übereinstimmung mit der Erhebung von 1966 wurde für Oktober 1972 abermals eine repräsentative Individualerhebung im gesamten produzierenden Gewerbe durchgeführt, und zwar nunmehr als Gehalts- und Lohnstrukturerhebung unter Einbeziehung von Arbeitern, Angestellten, Meistern und Führungskräften. Die Erhebung fand als supranationale Erhebung der Europäischen Gemeinschaften entsprechend dem 1966 praktizierten Verfahren gleichzeitig und als organisatorische Einheit mit der nationalen Gehalts- und Lohnstrukturerhebung in der gewerblichen Wirtschaft 1972 statt. Zu erfassen waren wiederum in ausgewählten Betrieben jeweils ausgewählte Arbeitnehmer. Als Erhebungszeitraum galt für die Arbeiter der Oktober 1972 und für die übrigen Arbeitnehmer hinsichtlich der Monatsangaben - vor allem Monatsverdienste - der Oktober 1972 und hinsichtlich der Jahresangaben - gesamte Bruttojahresverdienste mit gesonderter Angabe der einmaligen bzw. unregelmäßigen Zahlungen - das Jahr 1972.

2222 Gehalts- und Lohnstrukturerhebung im Handel, Bank- und Versicherungsgewerbe

Im Jahre 1974 fand für den Wirtschaftsbereich Handel, Bank- und Versicherungsgewerbe eine Gehalts- und Lohnstrukturerhebung der Europäischen Gemeinschaften statt, die erstmalig organisatorisch nicht mit einer gleichartigen nationalen Erhebung verbunden wurde. Danach waren in ausgewählten Unternehmen die Verdienste von jeweils ausgewählten Arbeitern und Angestellten individuell zu erfassen. Sämtliche Arbeitnehmer wurden bei der Aufbereitung einheitlich nach "Qualifikationsgruppen" aufgegliedert, die aus den in der amtlichen deutschen Lohnstatistik üblichen Leistungsgruppen der Arbeiter bzw. der Angestellten gebildet werden konnten. Erhebungszeiträume waren für die Monatsverdienste der Oktober 1974 und für die Jahresangaben - Bruttojahresverdienste mit gesondertem Nachweis der einmaligen oder unregelmäßigen Zahlungen - das Jahr 1974. Die Unternehmen der Auswahlgesamtheit wurden vor der Auswahl innerhalb jedes Bundeslandes erst nach Wirtschaftszweigen und dann nach Beschäftigtengrößenklassen (Schichten) sortiert. Der für das Bundesgebiet von vorn herein festgesetzte Gesamtstichprobenumfang wurde zunächst auf die Bundesländer verteilt, indem die Auswahlsätze pro Land prinzipiell unterschiedlich nach vorgegebener Genauigkeitsabstufung bestimmt wurden. Der sich damit ergebende Gesamtstichprobenumfang pro Land wurde anschließend ebenfalls nach einer vorgegebenen Genauigkeitsabstufung und entsprechend differenzierten Auswahlsätzen auf die Wirtschaftszweige und Größenklassen verteilt. Die Bestimmung der Stichprobenunternehmen erfolgte schichtweise nach dem systematischen Auswahlverfahren (erste Auswahlstufe). Die Stichprobendaten wurden bei der Aufbereitung auf 100 % der Grundgesamtheit hochgerechnet. Für die Ergebniserstellung wurden die erfaßten Unternehmen mit ihren Arbeitnehmern nach den tatsächlichen Verhältnissen im Berichtszeitraum den Wirtschaftszweigen, Größenklassen sowie den Bundesländern neu zugeordnet. Bei "echten Antwortausfällen" wurde eine Dopplung der Angaben vergleichbarer Berichtsunternehmen vorgenommen, bei "unechten Antwortausfällen" wurden die betroffenen Unternehmen ersatzlos aus dem Berichtskreis gestrichen. In der zweiten Auswahlstufe hatten die Berichtsunternehmen nach dem Verfahren der alternierenden Buchstabenauswahl bestimmte Arbeitnehmer auszuwählen. Zur Ermittlung der Auswahlsätze für die Arbeitnehmerauswahl wurde die von vorn herein festgesetzte Gesamtzahl der in der Bundesrepublik Deutschland zu erfassenden Arbeitnehmer nach vorgegebenen Genauigkeitsabstufungen zuerst auf die Bundesländer und dann auf die einzelnen Unternehmensschichten je Land verteilt, wobei zusätzlich zu beachten war, daß in jedem Wirtschaftszweig eine vorgegebene Mindestzahl von Arbeitnehmern erfaßt werden sollte. Die Gesamtauswahlsätze - deren Kehrwerte als Hochrechnungsfaktoren verwendet wurden - ergaben sich schließlich als Produkte aus den Auswahlsätzen der ersten Stufe (Unternehmensauswahl) und der zweiten Stufe (Arbeitnehmerauswahl). Hinsichtlich der Erhebungsmerkmale und der Einzelheiten der Aufbereitung hielt sich die Gehalts- und Lohnstrukturerhebung 1974 im Rahmen der früheren Strukturerhebungen im produzierenden Gewerbe.

223 Personalkostenerhebungen

2231 Personalkostenerhebung im produzierenden Gewerbe

Die Personalkostenerhebungen der Europäischen Gemeinschaften erfassen über die den einzelnen Arbeitnehmern direkt zuzurechnenden Bruttoverdienste hinaus sämtliche einzelnen, mehreren oder allen Arbeitnehmern direkt oder indirekt zugute kommenden Aufwendungen. Als Vorläufer derartiger Erhebungen im produzierenden Gewerbe fand für das Berichtsjahr 1955 in neun europäischen Staaten - darunter die Bundesrepublik Deutschland - eine Erhebung der Internationalen Arbeitsorganisation über die Aufwendungen der Unternehmen für ihre Arbeitnehmer statt. Die praktische Durchführung der Erhebung oblag in der Bundesrepublik Deutschland ausschließlich dem Statistischen Bundesamt. Die Erhebung erstreckte sich auf freiwillig berichtende Unternehmen in nur wenigen Industriezweigen. Als Ergebnisse fielen Angaben über sämtliche nach Aufwandsarten gegliederten Personalkosten und Personalnebenkosten an.

Seit dem Berichtsjahr 1959 führte das Statistische Amt der Europäischen Gemeinschaften in Zusammenarbeit mit den nationalen statistischen Ämtern - in der Bundesrepublik Deutschland dem Statistischen Bundesamt und den Statistischen Landesämtern - zunächst jährliche und später in dreijährigen Abständen wiederholte Personalkostenerhebungen im produzierenden Gewerbe mit Auskunftspflicht der Arbeitgeber durch. Die für die Berichtsjahre 1959 bis 1964 durchgeführten jährlichen Erhebungen erstreckten sich jeweils auf ausgewählte Industriezweige, und zwar wurden die für das Jahr

1959 erfaßten Zweige im Jahre 1962, die für das Jahr 1960 erfaßten Zweige im Jahre 1963 und die für das Jahr 1961 erfaßten Zweige im Jahre 1964 abermals in die Erhebung einbezogen. Es handelte sich bei diesen Erhebungen innerhalb der erfaßten Industriezweige um partielle Totalerhebungen; zu der Erhebung von 1959 wurden grundsätzlich alle Betriebe (örtliche Einheiten) mit mindestens 50 Arbeitnehmern, zu den folgenden Erhebungen in der Bundesrepublik Deutschland alle Unternehmen (rechtliche Einheiten) mit mindestens 50 Arbeitnehmern herangezogen. Ausnahmsweise wurde bei den Erhebungen von 1961 und 1964 in zwei Industriezweigen von den Unternehmen eines bestimmten Größenbereichs nur jedes zweite erfaßt und bei der Aufbereitung eine entsprechende Hochrechnung vorgenommen. Für das Berichtsjahr 1966 fand erstmalig eine repräsentative Personalkostenerhebung in sämtlichen Zweigen des produzierenden Gewerbes mit Ausnahme der Energiewirtschaft und Wasserversorgung bei ausgewählten Unternehmen - deren Angaben bei der Aufbereitung zu Totalwerten hochgerechnet wurden - mit mindestens 50 Arbeitnehmern statt. Die darauffolgende Personalkostenerhebung für das Jahr 1969 erstreckte sich auf das gesamte produzierende Gewerbe einschl. der Energiewirtschaft und Wasserversorgung und erfaßte repräsentativ ausgewählte Unternehmen mit mindestens 50 Arbeitnehmern, die grundsätzlich für jeden ihrer Betriebe unabhängig von deren Größe und Produktionsrichtung einen besonderen Erhebungsbogen auszufüllen hatten. Aufbereitungseinheiten waren sowohl der Betrieb (für Zwecke der Europäischen Gemeinschaften) als auch das Unternehmen (für deutsche Zwecke). Mit gleicher Methodik wie 1969 wurde die Personalkostenerhebung für das Jahr 1972 wiederholt, jedoch nunmehr unter Einbeziehung von Unternehmen mit mindestens zehn Arbeitnehmern. Eine abermalige Wiederholung fand im gleichen Umfang wie 1972 für das Berichtsjahr 1975 statt. Für die zukünftigen Erhebungen ist weiterhin eine dreijährige Periodizität vorgesehen.

Bei den als Repräsentativerhebungen durchgeführten Personalkostenerhebungen der Europäischen Gemeinschaften wurden die Berichtsunternehmen als geschichtete Stichproben mit prinzipiell unterschiedlichen Auswahlabständen pro Schicht nach dem systematischen Auswahlverfahren ausgewählt. Die Schichten wurden innerhalb jedes Wirtschaftszweiges als Unternehmensgrößenklassen nach der Beschäftigtenzahl oder der Arbeitnehmerzahl gebildet. Eine Schichtung der Auswahlgesamtheiten nach Bundesländern wurde nicht vorgenommen. Die Auswahlsätze wurden schichtweise nach einer vorgegebenen Genauigkeitsabstufung festgelegt. Bei der Aufbereitung wurden die

Unternehmen bzw. Betriebe - unabhängig von ihrer Schichtzugehörigkeit in der Auswahlgesamtheit - der Größenklasse und dem Wirtschaftszweig neu zugeordnet, denen sie nach ihrer Arbeitnehmerzahl und nach ihrer wirtschaftlichen Tätigkeit im Erhebungsjahr tatsächlich angehörten. Bei "unechten Antwortausfällen" wurden die betreffenden Unternehmen als Berichtsunternehmen ersatzlos gestrichen, bei "echten Antwortausfällen" wurden die ausgefallenen Angaben bei der Aufbereitung durch Dopplung der Angaben eines vergleichbaren Berichtsunternehmens ergänzt. Die in den Stichproben erfaßten Angaben wurden bei der Aufbereitung auf 100 % der Grundgesamtheit hochgerechnet, wobei für jedes Berichtsunternehmen ein eigener Hochrechnungsfaktor festgelegt wurde. Als Ergebnisse der Personalkostenerhebungen wurden in erster Linie hochgerechnete Summenangaben - zur Ergänzung auch Durchschnittsangaben pro Arbeiter und pro Angestellten - über sämtliche nach Aufwandsarten tiefgegliederten Personalkosten und Personalnebenkosten einschl. der Naturalleistungen ausgewiesen. Bei den späteren Erhebungen wurden auch Fallauszählungen vorgenommen, die Aufschluß darüber gaben, wie viele Unternehmen jeweils Personalkosten bestimmter Aufwandsarten hatten und welche Beträge diese Unternehmen dafür aufwendeten. Im Rahmen der Fallauszählungen fielen unter anderem detaillierte Angaben über die Vermögensbildung der Arbeitnehmer an.

2232 Personalkostenerhebung der Montanunion in den EGKS-Industrien

Die Europäische Gemeinschaft für Kohle und Stahl (Montanunion) führte seit dem Berichtsjahr 1953 in Zusammenarbeit mit den zuständigen nationalen Unternehmensverbänden ohne Einschaltung der nationalen statistischen Ämter bei sämtlichen Betrieben der EGKS-Industrien (Steinkohlenbergbau, Eisenerzbergbau, Eisen- und Stahlindustrie) jährliche Erhebungen über die Aufwendungen für die Arbeiter durch. Diese Erhebungen finden nach wie vor als jährliche Totalerhebungen des Statistischen Amtes der Europäischen Gemeinschaften statt, das in der Bundesrepublik Deutschland unmittelbar mit der Statistik der Kohlenwirtschaft e. V., dem Betriebswirtschaftlichen Institut der Eisenhüttenindustrie bzw. der Wirtschaftsvereinigung Eisen- und Stahlindustrie und dem Unternehmensverband Eisenerzbergbau zusammenarbeitet.

2233 Personalkostenerhebung im Handel, Bank- und Versicherungsgewerbe

Für das Berichtsjahr 1970 veranstaltete das Statistische Amt der Europäischen Gemeinschaften in Zusammenarbeit mit den nationalen statistischen Ämtern erstmalig eine Personalkostenerhebung bei Unternehmen des Einzelhandels sowie des Bank- und des Versicherungsgewerbes. Im Einzelhandel, im Versicherungsgewerbe und bei genossenschaftlichen Kreditinstituten waren Unternehmen mit mindestens 20 Arbeitnehmern, im übrigen Bankgewerbe sämtliche Unternehmen zu erfassen. Bei den kleineren Einzelhandelsunternehmen wurde die Erhebung grundsätzlich als Repräsentativerhebung mit einem einheitlichen Auswahlsatz von 50 %, bei den größeren Einzelhandelsunternehmen sowie in den anderen Wirtschaftsbereichen als (ggf. partielle) Totalerhebung durchgeführt. Die Angaben der repräsentativ erfaßten Unternehmen wurden auf 100 % der Grundgesamtheit hochgerechnet. Die Einzelheiten der Aufbereitung - wie Bestimmung der Hochrechnungsfaktoren, Zuordnung zu Größenklassen und Wirtschaftszweigen, Behandlung von Antwortausfällen u. dgl. - sowie die Erhebungsmerkmale und Form der Ergebnisse entsprachen dem Verfahren, das auch bei den EG-Personalkostenerhebungen im produzierenden Gewerbe angewandt wurde.

Eine weitere Personalkostenerhebung fand für das Berichtsjahr 1974 im Groß- und Einzelhandel sowie im Bank- und im Versicherungsgewerbe statt, und zwar nunmehr allgemein im Stichprobenverfahren bei Unternehmen mit mindestens zehn Arbeitnehmern. Die Auswahl der Berichtsunternehmen wurde im Auswahlplan und bei der praktischen Ziehung der Stichprobe mit der ersten Auswahlstufe (Unternehmensauswahl) der Gehalts- und Lohnstrukturerhebung der Europäischen Gemeinschaften im Handel, Bank- und Versicherungsgewerbe 1974 gekoppelt. Auswahlgrundlage, Schichtung, Auswahlsätze und praktiziertes Auswahlverfahren für die Unternehmensauswahl waren bei der Personalkostenerhebung und der Gehalts- und Lohnstrukturerhebung identisch. Durch die Festlegung jeweils unterschiedlicher Zufallsstartzahlen in den nicht total erfaßten Schichten wurden jedoch bei den beiden Erhebungen so weit wie möglich verschiedene Unternehmen in die Stichprobe einbezogen. Die Hochrechnung, die Zuordnung der Berichtsunternehmen zu Wirtschaftszweigen, Größenklassen und

Bundesländern und die Behandlung von Antwortausfällen erfolgten bei der Personalkostenerhebung ebenfalls wie bei der Gehalts- und Lohnstrukturerhebung; allerdings wurden bei der Personalkostenerhebung im Gegensatz zur Gehalts- und Lohnstrukturerhebung wegen des einstufigen Auswahlverfahrens die Auswahlabstände der Unternehmensauswahl als Hochrechnungsfaktoren verwendet. Die Erhebungsmerkmale einschl. der Form der Ergebnisse entsprachen bei der Personalkostenerhebung im Handel, Bank- und Versicherungsgewerbe 1974 denen der Personalkostenerhebungen im produzierenden Gewerbe. Derartige Erhebungen im Handel, Bank- und Versicherungsgewerbe finden nach den Plänen der Kommission der Europäischen Gemeinschaften weiterhin in dreijährigen Abständen statt.

2234 Personalkostenerhebung im Straßenverkehrsgewerbe

Auf Veranlassung der Europäischen Gemeinschaften wurde für das Berichtsjahr 1967 eine repräsentative Personalkostenerhebung im Straßenverkehrsgewerbe durchgeführt, zu der in der Bundesrepublik Deutschland Unternehmen mit mindestens fünf Arbeitnehmern herangezogen wurden. Hinsichtlich der Erhebungs- und Aufbereitungsorganisation, den Erhebungsmerkmalen und der Form der Ergebnisse entsprach diese Erhebung weitgehend den Personalkostenerhebungen im produzierenden Gewerbe. Die Berichtsunternehmen wurden als geschichtete Stichprobe nach dem systematischen Auswahlverfahren ausgewählt. Die Schichten waren definiert als Beschäftigtengrößenklassen innerhalb der einzelnen Verkehrszweige; eine Schichtung nach Bundesländern wurde nicht vorgenommen. Die Auswahlsätze wurden für die einzelnen Schichten nach stichprobentheoretischen Erfordernissen prinzipiell unterschiedlich festgelegt. Die Stichprobendaten wurden bei der Aufbereitung pro Schicht auf 100 % der Grundgesamtheit hochgerechnet . Die Berichtsunternehmen wurden für die Ergebniserstellung den Verkehrszweigen und Größenklassen nach den tatsächlichen Verhältnissen im Erhebungszeitraum neu zugeordnet. Die Behandlung von Antwortausfällen erfolgte wie bei den Personalkostenerhebungen in den anderen Wirtschaftsbereichen.

3

Die historische Entwicklung und der gegenwärtige Stand der methodischen Grundlagen der deutschen Lohnstatistik

31 Die Rechtsgrundlagen

311 Art der Rechtsvorschrift

Die der amtlichen Lohnstatistik zugrundeliegenden Rechts- und Verwaltungsvorschriften enthalten vor allem Regelungen über die Berichtsstellen bzw. die auskunftspflichtigen Personen, den Umfang der Auskunftspflicht, die Folgen einer Verletzung der Auskunftspflicht, die Amtsverschwiegenheit bzw. die Geheimhaltungspflicht der Auskunftsberechtigten und die Verteilung der bei den Erhebungsbehörden anfallenden Kosten. Als Rechtsgrundlagen der deutschen Lohnstatistik kommen Gesetze, Rechtsverordnungen und Regierungserlasse in Frage. Als älteste gesetzliche Grundlage für lohnstatistische Erhebungen ist das Allgemeine Berggesetz vom 24. Juni 1865 (Gesetzsammlung für die Königlichen Preußischen Staaten 1865 Seite 705) anzusehen. Durch § 79 dieses Gesetzes wurden die Bergwerksbesitzer generell verpflichtet, in den dafür festgesetzten Zeiträumen und Formen der Bergbehörde die vom zuständigen Minister vorgeschriebenen statistischen Nachrichten einzureichen. Das Allgemeine Berggesetz bildet bis in die Gegenwart die Grundlage der laufenden Bergarbeiterlohnstatistik. Eine gesetzliche Regelung der gesamten Lohnstatistik erfolgte erstmalig durch das Gesetz betreffend Lohnstatistik vom 27. Juli 1922 (Reichsgesetzblatt 1922 Teil I Seite 656), das bis zum Jahre 1949 in kraft war. Nachdem mit dem Gesetz über die Errichtung eines Statistischen Amtes des Vereinigten Wirtschaftsgebietes vom 21. Januar 1948 (Gesetzblatt der Verwaltung des Vereinigten Wirtschaftsgebietes 1948 Seite 19) der allgemeine Rahmen für die amtliche Statistik nach dem Zweiten Weltkrieg gesetzt worden war, wurde die Lohnstatistik durch das Gesetz über Lohnstatistik vom 22. August 1949 (Gesetzblatt der Verwaltung des Vereinigten Wirtschaftsgebietes 1949 Seite 265) neu geregelt. Diese Rechtsvorschriften des Vereinigten Wirtschaftsgebietes wurden hinsichtlich des allgemeinen Rahmens durch das Gesetz über die Statistik für Bundeszwecke (Stat Ges) vom 3. September 1953 (Bundesgesetzblatt 1953 Teil I Seite 1314) - das unter anderem den Grundsatz der Gesetzmäßigkeit der amtlichen Statistik festlegte, nach dem statistische Erhebungen in der Regel durch Gesetze und in bestimmten Ausnahmefällen durch Rechtsverordnungen vorgeschrieben werden mußten - und hinsichtlich der Lohnstatistik durch das Gesetz über die Lohnstatistik vom 18. Mai 1956 (Bundesgesetzblatt 1956 Teil I Seite 429) abgelöst. Das Gesetz über die Lohnstatistik von 1956 stellt bis in die Gegenwart das "Grundgesetz" der amtlichen deutschen Effektivverdienststatistik dar; da es jedoch den öffentlichen Dienst ausschloß, mußte für die Gehalts- und Lohnstrukturerhebung im öffentlichen Dienst 1968 mit dem Gesetz über eine Statistik des Personals, der Dienstbezüge, Vergütungen und Löhne im öffentlichen Dienst vom 15. Mai 1968 (Bundesgesetzblatt 1968 Teil I Seite 385) eine eigene Rechtsgrundlage geschaffen werden. Das lohnstatistische Gesetz von 1956 wurde durch das Gesetz zur Änderung des Gesetzes über die Lohnstatistik vom 4. August 1971 (Bundesgesetzblatt 1971 Teil I Seite 1217) neueren Erfordernissen angepaßt, indem vor allem laufende Bruttojahresverdiensterhebungen in Industrie und Handel eingeführt sowie eine Reform der jährlichen Verdiensterhebung in der Landwirtschaft vorgenommen wurden. Für die Tariflohnstatistik wurde das Tarifvertragsgesetz (TVG) vom 9. April 1949 (Gesetzblatt der Verwaltung des Vereinigten Wirtschaftsgebietes 1949 Seite 55) - Neufassung vom 25. August 1969 (Bundesgesetzblatt 1969 Teil I Seite 1323) - von besonderer Bedeutung. Das Tarifvertragsgesetz stellt zwar nicht unmittelbar die Rechtsgrundlage der Tariflohnstatistik dar, ermöglicht jedoch durch die zentrale Sammlung der Tarifverträge erst deren umfassende lohnstatistische Auswertung.

Bereits bei der ersten umfassenden amtlichen Lohnerhebung - der Individualerhebung vom Februar 1920 - erwies es sich als notwendig, der Erhebungsarbeit der statistischen Ämter eine besondere Rechtsvorschrift mit Verbindlichkeit über den Kreis der beteiligten Behörden hinaus zugrundezulegen. Zu diesem Zweck wurde die Verordnung zur Sicherung der Durchführung der Lohnstatistik für den Monat Februar 1920 vom 9. März 1920 (Reichsgesetzblatt 1920 Seite 309) erlassen. Die eine lohnstatistische Auswertung ermöglichende amtliche Sammlung von Tarifverträgen im "Tarifarchiv" wurde erstmalig durch eine Nachtragsverordnung vom 31. Mai 1920 (Reichsgesetzblatt 1920 Seite 1128) zu der im Jahre 1918 erlassenen Tarifvertragsverordnung - die dann im Jahre 1928 neugefaßt wurde - begründet. Später wurden Rechtsverordnungen der Reichs- bzw. der Bundesregierung als Grundlagen der Lohnstatistik nur noch in Verbindung mit bereits bestehenden Gesetzen erlassen. Zu dem Gesetz betreffend Lohnstatistik vom 27. Juli 1922 ergingen Ausführungsverordnungen vom 14. Juli 1927 (Reichsgesetzblatt 1927 Teil I Seite 185) und vom 8. August 1938 (Reichsgesetzblatt 1938 Teil I Seite 1013). Nach dem Zweiten Weltkrieg wurde die Gültigkeit der auf dem Gebiete der Statistik in kraft getretenen Gesetze des Vereinigten Wirtschaftsgebietes durch die "Erstreckungsverordnung" vom 31. März 1950 (Bundesgesetzblatt 1950 Seite 81) auf die französische Besatzungszone ausgedehnt. Besondere für die Lohnstatistik relevante Rechtsverordnungen wurden am 7. Juni 1949 (Gesetzblatt der Verwaltung des Vereinigten Wirtschaftsgebietes 1949 Seite 89) in Verbindung mit dem Tarifvertragsgesetz vom 9. April 1949 und am 22. Dezember 1951 (Bundesanzeiger 1951 Nr. 249) in Verbindung mit dem Gesetz über Lohnstatistik vom 22. August 1949 erlassen. Von der Möglichkeit, statistische Erhebungen durch Rechtsverordnungen in Verbindung mit dem Gesetz über die Statistik für Bundeszwecke vom 3. September 1953 vorzuschreiben, wurde auf dem Gebiet der Lohnstatistik bisher zweimal Gebrauch gemacht, und zwar mit einer Verordnung vom 22. April 1964 (Bundesanzeiger 1964 Nr. 80) bei der Erhebung über die Vermögensbildung der Arbeitnehmer für das Jahr 1963 und mit einer Verordnung vom 11. März 1974 (Bundesgesetzblatt 1974 Teil I Seite 681) bei der Erhebung über die betriebliche Altersversorgung für das Jahr 1973. Das Gesetz über die Lohnstatistik vom 18. Mai 1956 ermächtigte die Bundesregierung, durch Rechtsverordnungen nähere Einzelheiten über die in mehrjährigen Abständen durchzuführenden Gehalts- und Lohnstrukturerhebungen zu bestimmen; derartige Verordnungen wurden bisher am 7. Februar 1957 (Bundesanzeiger 1957 Nr. 30), am 8. August 1961 (Bundesanzeiger 1961 Nr. 153), am 20. Mai 1966 (Bundesanzeiger 1966 Nr. 98) und am 24. April 1972 (Bundesgesetzblatt 1972 Teil I Seite 729) erlassen. Mit der Gründung der Europäischen Wirtschaftsgemeinschaft traten als neue Art von Rechtsvorschriften supranationale Verordnungen des Rates der Europäischen Wirtschaftsgemeinschaft - bzw. später des Rates der Europäischen Gemeinschaften - auf, die auf den Vertrag zur Gründung der Europäischen Wirtschaftsgemeinschaft vom 27. Juli 1957 (Bundesgesetzblatt 1957 Teil II Seite 753) gestützt waren und unmittelbar in jedem Mitgliedstaat galten. Solche EG-Verordnungen wurden im Bereich der Lohnstatistik seit 1960 in größerer Zahl erlassen ; sie bildeten die Rechtsgrundlagen der auf Veranlassung der Europäischen Gemeinschaften durchgeführten Personalkostenerhebungen und Gehalts- und Lohnstrukturerhebungen sowie der jährlichen EG-Erhebungen über die Arbeiterverdienste in der Landwirtschaft.

Regierungserlasse sind als selbständige Vorschriften nur gegenüber Behörden bzw. Behördenangehörigen wirksam, kommen daher als Rechtsgrundlagen der Lohnstatistik - vor allem soweit private Personen bzw. Institutionen zu Auskünften herangezogen werden - nur ergänzend in Zusammenhang mit Gesetzen oder Verordnungen in Frage. Mit derartigen ergänzenden Erlassen - auch bezeichnet als "Bestimmungen" oder "Anordnungen" - wurden bereits die allgemeinen statistischen bzw. statistisch relevanten Vorschriften des Allgemeinen Berggesetzes vom 24. Juni 1865, der Tarifvertragsverordnung in der Fassung von 1928 und der lohnstatistischen Verordnungen vom 14. Juli 1927 und vom 8. August 1938 konkretisiert. Bei der Lohn- und Gehaltserhebung vom Februar 1920 wurde zunächst versucht, die Erhebung lediglich auf Grund eines an die Landesregierungen gerichteten gemeinsamen Erlasses des Reichswirtschaftsministers und des Reichsarbeitsministers vom 30. Januar 1920 durchzuführen; im Verlauf der weiteren Arbeiten erwies sich jedoch die rechtliche Absicherung durch die erwähnte Verordnung vom 9. März 1920 als notwendig. In der ersten Zeit nach dem Zweiten Weltkrieg fanden die vierteljährlichen Lohnsummenerhebungen der Industriearbeiter auf Grund eines Erlasses des Alliierten Kontrollrates vom 27. April 1946 statt. Die späteren für die Lohnstatistik relevanten Regierungserlasse ergänzten jeweils ein Gesetz des Vereinigten Wirtschaftsgebietes bzw. ein Bundesgesetz oder eine

Rechtsverordnung der Bundesregierung. Von besonderer Bedeutung wurde die Gemeinsame Anordnung der Verwaltungen des Vereinigten Wirtschaftsgebietes zur Durchführung von Statistiken vom 1. Juni 1949 (Öffentlicher Anzeiger für das Vereinigte Wirtschaftsgebiet 1949 Nr. 50), die sich auf das Gesetz über die Errichtung eines Statistischen Amtes des Vereinigten Wirtschaftsgebietes vom 21. Januar 1948 bezog und bis zum Inkrafttreten des Lohnstatistischen Gesetzes vom 18. Mai 1956 die Grundlage der vierteljährlichen Lohnsummenerhebungen bildete. Als Ergänzung zu dem Gesetz vom 21. Januar 1948 ergingen ferner "Anordnungen" des Direktors der Verwaltung für Arbeit des Vereinigten Wirtschaftsgebietes zur Durchführung der Erhebung über die Tariflöhne der Industriearbeiter vom April 1949 und der Angestelltenverdiensterhebung vom Mai 1949. In Verbindung mit dem Gesetz über Lohnstatistik vom 22. August 1949 ordnete der Direktor der Verwaltung für Arbeit des Vereinigten Wirtschaftsgebietes durch einen Erlaß bzw. durch "Bestimmungen" die vierteljährliche Fortschreibung der Tariflohnstatistik sowie die Durchführung der Lohnstrukturerhebungen in der Landwirtschaft und der Forstwirtschaft von 1949/50 an. Auf Grund der Verordnung zur Durchführung einer Statistik der Gehalts- und Lohnverhältnisse vom 22. Dezember 1951 erließ der Bundesminister für Arbeit mehrmals "Bestimmungen" zur Regelung von Einzelheiten der Gehalts- und Lohnstrukturerhebung in der gewerblichen Wirtschaft 1951, der Lohnstrukturerhebung in der Forstwirtschaft 1952/53 und der Gehalts- und Lohnstrukturerhebung in der Landwirtschaft 1953/54. Seit dem Inkrafttreten des Gesetzes über die Statistik für Bundeszwecke vom 3. September 1953 kommen Regierungserlasse als ergänzende Rechtsgrundlagen für die amtliche Statistik nicht mehr in Frage.

312 Auskunftspflichtige Personen

In der amtlichen Lohnstatistik werden als auskunftspflichtige Personen in der Regel die Arbeitgeber - das heißt die Inhaber bzw. Leiter der Betriebe bzw. Unternehmen - herangezogen. Nach den neueren lohnstatistischen Rechtsvorschriften - vor allem dem Gesetz über die Lohnstatistik vom 18. Mai 1956 sowie den

Verordnungen des Rates der Europäischen Gemeinschaften - sind ausschließlich die Arbeitgeber auskunftspflichtig. Analog werden bei den Gehalts- und Lohnstrukturerhebungen im öffentlichen Dienst und bei den Lohnstrukturerhebungen in der Forstwirtschaft die Auskünfte von den Leitern der Beschäftigungsstellen bzw. der Lohn- und Gehaltsabrechnungsstellen eingeholt. Für die Sammlung der Tarifverträge im amtlichen Tarifarchiv - das die Grundlage der Tariflohnstatistik bildet - gehen die benötigten Auskünfte in Form von Tarifvertragsabschriften abgesehen von den Firmentarifverträgen statt von den einzelnen Arbeitgebern von den Arbeitgeberverbänden bzw. den Gewerkschaften als Tarifvertragsparteien ein. Verbände als Berichtsstellen traten darüberhinaus im Rahmen der amtlichen Lohnstatistik nur bei der monatlichen Statistik des Statistischen Reichsamtes über die Arbeiterverdienste im Kohlenbergbau auf, zu der die Zechenverbände - allerdings ohne Auskunftspflicht - Nachweisungen lieferten. Die direkte Befragung der Arbeitnehmer nach ihren Verdiensten hat in der amtlichen deutschen Lohnstatistik - im Gegensatz zu den nichtamtlichen lohnstatistischen Erhebungen der Gewerkschaften, die sich unmittelbar an ihre Mitglieder wandten - abgesehen von früheren sporadischen Versuchen keine Bedeutung erlangt; soweit dieses Verfahren angewandt wurde, bestand für die befragten Arbeitnehmer keine gesetzliche Auskunftspflicht. Bei den von 1892 bis 1902 durchgeführten Erhebungen der Kommission für Arbeiterstatistik wurden die Fragebogen je zur Hälfte von Arbeitgebern und von Arbeitnehmern ausgefüllt. Auch bei der im Auftrage der Kommission für Arbeiterstatistik im Jahre 1898 durchgeführten Erhebung über gewerbliche Kinderarbeit wurden die Schulkinder als "Arbeitnehmer" direkt nach der Höhe ihrer Löhne befragt. Die direkte Befragung von Einkommensempfängern wurde später nur noch bei der vom Statistischen Landesamt Schleswig-Holstein veranstalteten Erhebung über die Einkommensschichtung im Jahre 1949 angewendet. Soweit die lohnstatistischen Rechtsgrundlagen neben der Auskunftspflicht auch die Pflicht zur unterschriftlichen Bestätigung der erteilten Auskünfte festlegten, wurden die Arbeitnehmer bzw. ihre Vertreter häufiger zur Mitwirkung herangezogen. Bei der Lohn- und Gehaltserhebung vom Februar 1920 waren die von den Arbeitgebern ausgefüllten

Fragebogen im Falle der Individualzählblätter von den einzelnen Arbeitnehmern und im Falle der Betriebsbogen von den Obmännern der Arbeiter-bzw. Angestelltenvertretungen mitzuzeichnen. Analog hatten bei den auf Grund der lohnstatistischen Verordnung vom 14. Juli 1927 durchgeführten Erhebungen neben den Betriebsleitern auch die einzelnen Arbeitnehmer bzw. die Betriebsräte Unterschriften zu leisten. Die Verordnung vom 8. August 1938 erwähnte dagegen nur noch die Auskunfts- und Unterzeichnungspflicht der Unternehmer. Nach dem Zweiten Weltkrieg wurde durch das Gesetz über Lohnstatistik vom 22. August 1949 neben der Unterzeichnungspflicht der befragten Arbeitgeber wiederum die Unterschrift des Betriebsrates vorgeschrieben. Unterschriften der einzelnen Arbeitnehmer unter Individualzählblätter bzw. besondere "Belege über geleistete Bar- und Naturallöhne" wurden darüberhinaus bei den Strukturerhebungen in der Landwirtschaft von 1950 und 1953/54 sowie in der Forstwirtschaft von 1949/50 eingeholt. Die späteren lohnstatistischen Erhebungen sahen nur noch die Unterschriften der auskunftspflichtigen Arbeitgeber vor.

Neben den an der Lohnzahlung direkt beteiligten Arbeitgebern und Arbeitnehmern wurden in der amtlichen Lohnstatistik ausnahmsweise auch die Leiter bestimmter Behörden als Auskunftspersonen herangezogen. Bei den von 1874 bis 1922 durchgeführten Erhebungen über die vereinbarten Monatsheuern von Seeleuten gaben die Seemannsämter die statistischen Meldungen ab. Seit 1892 wurden für Zwecke der Sozialversicherung auf Grund von Schätzungen der Gemeindebehörden laufend die "ortsüblichen Tagelöhne" - später bezeichnet als "Ortslöhne" - ermittelt.

313 Umfang der Auskunftspflicht

Die Auskunftspflicht wurde durch das Gesetz über die Statistik für Bundeszwecke vom 3. September 1953 für die nationale amtliche Statistik allgemein in der Weise definiert, daß die Befragten die verlangten Antworten wahrheitsgemäß, vollständig, fristgemäß und grundsätzlich unentgeltlich zu geben sowie die Richtigkeit der Angaben durch Unterschrift zu bestätigen haben.

Durch das Gesetz zur Durchführung der Verordnung Nr. 70/66/EWG (Agrarstrukturerhebungsgesetz) vom 23. Dezember 1966 (Bundesgesetzblatt 1966 Teil I Seite 682) wurden die Bestimmungen des Gesetzes über die Statistik für Bundeszwecke über die Auskunftspflicht ausdrücklich auf supranationale statistische Erhebungen der Europäischen Gemeinschaften ausgedehnt. Die Auskunftspflicht umfaßt in erster Linie die Pflicht zur Ausfüllung und Unterzeichnung sowie zur portofreien Rücksendung der Erhebungsbogen an die auskunftsberechtigten statistischen Ämter; bei einigen lohnstatistischen Erhebungen - den Lohnstrukturerhebungen in der Landwirtschaft und der Forstwirtschaft von 1949/50 sowie den jährlichen Erhebungen der Europäischen Gemeinschaften über die Arbeiterverdienste in der Landwirtschaft - trat an die Stelle der Ausfüllung und Rücksendung die Auskunftserteilung an Interviewer. Die Auskunftspflicht umfaßt ferner in einigen Fällen die Pflicht zur Zusammenfassung buchhalterischer Einzelpositionen - Bildung von Lohnsummen und Arbeitsstundensummen für Arbeitnehmergruppen bei den im Lohnsummenverfahren durchgeführten Verdiensterhebungen, Ermittlung von Jahresverdienstsummen bei der Bruttojahresverdiensterhebung in Industrie und Handel und den Gehalts- und Lohnstrukturerhebungen in der gewerblichen Wirtschaft - und die Pflicht zur Zuordnung der einzelnen Arbeitnehmer zu Leistungsgruppen bzw. Qualifikations- oder Arbeitergruppen bei den laufenden Verdiensterhebungen in Industrie und Handel, im Handwerk und in der Landwirtschaft. Soweit bei den repräsentativen Gehalts- und Lohnstrukturerhebungen in einer zweiten Auswahlstufe bestimmte Arbeitnehmer auszuwählen waren, gehörte zur Auskunftspflicht auch die Vornahme dieser Arbeitnehmerauswahl in der Regel nach den Anfangsbuchstaben der Familiennamen bzw. in einzelnen Fällen nach dem systematischen Auswahlverfahren. Bei den Personalkostenerhebungen der Europäischen Gemeinschaften gingen die verlangten Angaben zum Teil über die aus der Buchhaltung unmittelbar zu entnehmenden Daten bzw. die aus Buchhaltungspositionen zu errechnenden Daten hinaus; in diesen Fällen wurde von den Berichtsunternehmen verlangt, selbst Schätzungen vorzunehmen. Durch eine besonders umfassende Auskunftspflicht waren auch die Erhebungen über die betriebliche Altersversorgung von 1973 und 1976 gekennzeichnet; hier sollten die Berichtsunternehmen durch eine Modellrechnung die für ihre Arbeitnehmer theoretisch erreichbare Altersversorgung ermitteln sowie ihre Arbeitnehmer selbst schwerpunktmäßig den einzelnen Typen der Altersversorgung zuordnen. Bei früheren lohnstatistischen Erhebungen umfaßte die Auskunftspflicht ferner die Vorlage der Buchhaltungsunterlagen zur Nachprüfung der gelieferten Angaben durch die auskunftsberechtigten statistischen Ämter; derartige Bestimmungen enthielten die lohnstatistischen Verordnungen vom 14. Juli 1927 und vom 8. August 1938 sowie das Gesetz über Lohnstatistik vom 22. August 1949. Da die neueren Rechtsgrundlagen der Lohnstatistik solche Nachprüfungen nicht mehr ausdrücklich vorsehen, ist den statistischen Ämtern die Einsichtnahme in die Geschäftsbücher der Auskunftspflichtigen nicht mehr möglich.

Während in der Effektivverdienststatistik die Auskunftspflicht generell durch die Ausfüllung von besonderen statistischen Erhebungsformularen erfüllt wird, beruht die Tariflohnstatistik auf der Auswertung von Abdrucken bzw. Abschriften der vollständigen Tarifvertragstexte, die von den Tarifvertragsparteien an die für die Führung des amtlichen Tarifarchivs zuständigen Behörden eingesandt werden.

314 Verletzung der Auskunftspflicht

Um die Erfüllung der statistischen Auskunftspflicht zu sichern, sehen die Rechtsgrundlagen der Lohnstatistik für den Fall einer Verletzung der Auskunftspflicht Sanktionen vor. Das Allgemeine Berggesetz vom 24. Juni 1865 enthielt für den Fall einer Übertretung der im § 79 festgelegten Vorschrift ursprünglich keine Strafbestimmung, die jedoch durch eine spätere Änderung eingefügt wurde. In der bis in die Gegenwart gültigen Fassung dieses Gesetzes wird eine Übertretung des § 79 grundsätzlich mit Geldstrafe bis 10 000 DM bestraft. Die die Rechtsgrundlage der Lohn- und Gehaltserhebung vom Februar 1920 bildende Verordnung vom 9. März 1920 sah bei Auskunftsverweigerung oder wissentlich falscher Auskunft eine Geldstrafe bis 20 000 Mark vor. Nach dem

Gesetz betreffend Lohnstatistik vom 27. Juli 1922 war bei Zuwiderhandlung gegen auf Grund dieses Gesetzes erlassene Bestimmungen auf Anordnung der Reichsregierung eine Geldstrafe bis 100 000 Mark möglich. Nach den lohnstatistischen Verordnungen vom 14. Juli 1927 und vom 8. August 1938-hier nur auf ausdrücklichen Antrag des Präsidenten des Statistischen Reichsamtes - konnte bei einer Verletzung der Auskunftspflicht ebenfalls eine Geldstrafe verhängt werden. Das Gesetz über Lohnstatistik vom 22. August 1949 sah bei einer Verletzung der Auskunftspflicht auf Antrag des Leiters eines auskunftsberechtigten statistischen Amtes eine Geldstrafe bis 1000 DM vor. Nach den bis in die Gegenwart gültigen Bestimmungen des Gesetzes über die Statistik für Bundeszwecke vom 3. September 1953 stellt die Verletzung der statistischen Auskunftspflicht eine Ordnungswidrigkeit dar, die mit einer Geldbuße bis zu 10 000 DM geahndet werden kann. Diese Vorschrift gilt nicht nur für die gesamte nationale amtliche Statistik, sondern auf Grund des Agrarstrukturerhebungsgesetzes vom 23. Dezember 1966 auch für die supranationalen statistischen Erhebungen der Europäischen Gemeinschaften.

Die Einreichung von Tarifvertragsabschriften durch die Tarifvertragsparteien sollte auf Grund der das amtliche Tarifarchiv begründenden Verordnung vom 31. Mai 1920 durch die Androhung einer Ordnungsstrafe bis 300 RM sichergestellt werden. Analog konnte auf Grund der in Verbindung mit dem Tarifvertragsgesetz vom 9. April 1949 erlassenen Durchführungsverordnung vom 7. Juni 1949 im Falle einer Verletzung der Auskunftspflicht eine Ordnungsstrafe bis 300 DM durch den Direktor der Verwaltung für Arbeit des Vereinigten Wirtschaftsgebietes oder die oberste Arbeitsbehörde des betroffenen Landes festgesetzt werden. Die bis in die Gegenwart gültige Neufassung des Tarifvertragsgesetzes vom 25. August 1969 sah stattdessen eine der Höhe nach nicht ausdrücklich begrenzte Geldbuße wegen Ordnungswidrigkeit vor, die von den für die Ahndung von Ordnungswidrigkeiten zuständigen Verwaltungsbehörden festzusetzen war.

315 Geheimhaltungspflicht

Die Angehörigen der auskunftsberechtigten statistischen Ämter haben über die allgemeine Amtsverschwiegenheit - die von den Beamtengesetzen des Bundes bzw. des Reiches und der Länder vorgeschrieben und in die für die nichtbeamteten Mitarbeiter des öffentlichen Dienstes gültigen Tarifverträge aufgenommen wurde - hinaus besondere statistische Geheimhaltungsbestimmungen zu beachten. Die statistische Geheimhaltungspflicht beinhaltet das grundsätzliche Verbot der Weitergabe statistischer Einzelangaben - d. h. Angaben einzelner Auskunftspflichtiger - durch die auskunftsberechtigten Ämter sowohl an Privatpersonen als auch an andere Behörden einschließlich der vorgesetzten Ministerien. Im Rahmen der Lohnstatistik enthielt erstmalig die Verordnung vom 14. Juli 1927 die Bestimmung, daß Einzelangaben vom Statistischen Reichsamt geheimzuhalten waren; eine Verletzung der Geheimhaltungspflicht wurde mit einer Geldstrafe bedroht. Die lohnstatistische Verordnung vom 8. August 1938 schrieb in gleicher Weise die Geheimhaltung von Einzelangaben vor. Das Gesetz über Lohnstatistik vom 22. August 1949 übernahm die Geheimhaltungspflicht und bestimmte, daß die erfragten Daten nur zu statistischen Zwecken verwendet werden durften. Nach dem Gesetz über die Statistik für Bundeszwecke vom 3. September 1953 sind in der gesamten amtlichen Statistik Einzelangaben über persönliche oder sachliche Verhältnisse, die für eine Bundesstatistik gemacht werden, vom Statistischen Bundesamt bzw. den Statistischen Landesämtern geheimzuhalten, soweit die Weitergabe nicht in der die betreffende statistische Erhebung anordnenden Rechtsvorschrift ausdrücklich zugelassen und in den Erhebungsvordrucken bekanntgegeben worden ist. Im Falle einer Verletzung der Geheimhaltungspflicht sieht das Gesetz von 1953 auf Antrag des Verletzten eine Freiheitsstrafe oder eine Geldstrafe oder beide Strafen vor; diese Strafbestimmung wurde in geringfügig geänderter Form in § 203 Absatz 2 des Strafgesetzbuches (STGB) in der Neufassung vom 2. Januar 1975 (Bundesgesetzblatt 1975 Teil I Seite 1) übernommen. Auf Grund des Agrarstrukturerhebungsgesetzes vom 23. Dezember 1966 gelten die nationalen statistischen Geheimhaltungsbestimmungen auch für die supranationalen statistischen Erhebungen der Europäischen Gemeinschaften. Darüberhinaus erwähnen auch die den europäischen lohnstatistischen Erhebungen zugrundeliegenden Rechtsverordnungen des Rates der Europäischen Gemeinschaften die Pflicht zur Geheimhaltung von Einzelauskünften.

316 Kostenregelung

Die Verteilung der bei den Erhebungsbehörden anfallenden Kosten wurde für die Lohnstatistik ausdrücklich erstmalig durch das Gesetz betreffend Lohnstatistik vom 27. Juli 1922 geregelt, und zwar in der Weise, daß die Kosten, die den Ländern durch die auf Grund dieses Gesetzes angeordneten Erhebungen erwuchsen, vom Reich zu tragen waren. Nach dem Zweiten Weltkrieg wurde eine Neuregelung der Kostenverteilung erforderlich. Nach Artikel 83 des Grundgesetzes für die Bundesrepublik Deutschland vom 23. Mai 1949 (Bundesgesetzblatt 1949 Seite 1) führen die Länder die Bundesgesetze grundsätzlich als eigene Angelegenheit und damit in eigener Finanzverantwortung aus. Dementsprechend schrieb das Gesetz über die Statistik für Bundeszwecke vom 3. September 1953 in seiner ursprünglichen Fassung allgemein vor (§ 8): "Die Kosten der Bundesstatistiken tragen der Bund und die Länder nach den bei ihnen entstehenden Arbeiten, soweit nicht durch Gesetz oder Rechtsverordnung etwas anderes bestimmt wird." Im Jahre 1955 wurde der § 8 auf folgende Weise neu gefaßt: "Die Kosten der Bundesstatistiken werden, soweit sie bei den Bundesbehörden entstehen, vom Bund, im übrigen von den Ländern getragen." Kostenerstattungen von einer Gebietskörperschaft an eine andere kommen demnach für die nationale Lohnstatistik nicht mehr in Frage. Dagegen ist bei der supranationalen Lohnstatistik der Europäischen Gemeinschaften grundsätzlich eine Kostenübernahme durch die Gemeinschaften vorgesehen. Die in den Jahren 1960 bis 1974 erlassenen lohnstatistischen Verordnungen des Rates der Europäischen Gemeinschaften bestimmten, daß die Erhebungskosten "zu Lasten der in den Haushaltsplänen der Europäischen Gemeinschaften für diesen Zweck bereitgestellten Mittel" gingen. Da die in den Haushaltsplänen bereitgestellten Mittel jedoch im allgemeinen zur Kostendeckung nicht ausreichten,waren nicht unerhebliche Zuschüsse aus den Haushalten der Mitgliedstaaten erforderlich. Die vom Rat der Europäischen Gemeinschaften erlassene Verordnung Nr. 328 über die Durchführung einer Arbeitskostenerhebung in der Industrie vom 10. Februar 1975 (Amtsblatt der Europäischen Gemeinschaften 1975 Nr. L 37 Seite 1) enthielt erstmalig die folgende klarere Kostenregelung: "Die Mitgliedstaaten erhalten für die Durchführung der Erhebung einen der Zahl der befragten Betriebe oder Unternehmen entsprechenden Pauschalbetrag. Dieser Betrag geht zu Lasten der im Haushaltsplan der Europäischen Gemeinschaften für diesen Zweck bereitgestellten Mittel." In dieser Weise wird seitdem in allen lohnstatistischen Verordnungen der Europäischen Gemeinschaften die Kostenverteilung zwischen den beteiligten Behörden geregelt.

32 Die organisatorischen Grundlagen

321 Erhebungsbehörden

Die amtliche Lohnstatistik wurde wie die gesamte amtliche Statistik im Deutschen Reich und in der Bundesrepublik Deutschland in der Regel als "ausgelöste Statistik" betrieben, das heißt die Erhebungen wurden von organisatorisch verselbständigten, aus der sonstigen Verwaltung herausgelösten Spezialbehörden durchgeführt. Die zentrale Erhebungsbehörde war ab 1872 das Kaiserliche Statistische Amt - dessen im Jahre 1902 eingerichtete für Lohnstatistik zuständige Abteilung für Arbeiterstatistik ein gewisses Eigenleben führte -, ab 1919 das Statistische Reichsamt, ab 1948 das Statistische Amt des Vereinigten Wirtschaftsgebietes und ab 1950 das Statistische Bundesamt. Unter der Koordination des Statistischen Reichsamtes traten in der Lohnstatistik erstmalig bei der Lohn- und Gehaltserhebung vom Februar 1920 die Statistischen Landesämter als dezentrale Erhebungsbehörden auf. Die späteren lohnstatistischen Erhebungen bis 1945 wurden dagegen von der Vorbereitung über die Befragung der Berichtsstellen bis zur Zusammenstellung der Ergebnisse vom Statistischen Reichsamt allein durchgeführt. In den Jahren 1946 bis 1948 fanden die lohnstatistischen

Erhebungen - es handelte sich ausschließlich um die laufenden Lohnsummenerhebungen der Industriearbeiter - in der alleinigen Zuständigkeit der Statistischen Landesämter statt, deren Arbeiten in der britischen Zone von dem Statistischen Amt für die britische Besatzungszone koordiniert wurden. Eigene Erhebungen eines Statistischen Landesamtes fanden im Rahmen der Lohnstatistik auch noch im Jahre 1949 statt, als das Statistische Landesamt Schleswig-Holstein selbständig eine Repräsentativerhebung über die Einkommensschichtung sowie in Zusammenarbeit mit der Handwerkskammer eine Zeitlang eine laufende Lohnstatistik im Handwerk veranstaltete. Im übrigen galt hinsichtlich der Arbeitsteilung zwischen den statistischen Ämtern in der amtlichen Lohnstatistik ab 1949 die seitdem allgemein übliche Regelung, daß die Statistischen Landesämter die Arbeiten von der Auswahl und der Befragung der Berichtsstellen bis zur Erstellung der Landesergebnisse ausführten und das Statistische Amt des Vereinigten Wirtschaftsgebietes bzw. das Statistische Bundesamt für die methodische Vorbereitung einschließlich der Ausarbeitung von Erhebungs- und Aufbereitungsrichtlinien und die Zusammenfassung der Ländergebnisse zum Gesamtergebnis zuständig war. In einigen Fällen wirkten unterhalb der Ebene der Statistischen Landesämter unter deren Anleitung noch weitere Behörden als Erhebungsbehörden mit. So wurden z. B. in Nordrhein-Westfalen die vierteljährlichen Lohnsummenerhebungen der Industriearbeiter von 1946 bis 1954 vom Statistischen Landesamt in enger Zusammenarbeit mit den Arbeitsämtern durchgeführt, denen unter anderem die Auswahl und Befragung der Berichtsbetriebe oblag. Bei den Lohnstrukturerhebungen in der Forstwirtschaft von 1952/53 und 1961/62 wurden die Erhebungsbogen den Berichtsstellen von den Statistischen Landesämtern über die Forstdezernate der Regierungspräsidenten bzw. die entsprechenden vorgesetzten Behörden übersandt und gelangten auf dem gleichen Wege zur Aufbereitung in die Statistischen Landesämter zurück. Bei der Gehalts- und Lohnstrukturerhebung in der Landwirtschaft von 1953/54 erfolgten der Versand und der Rücklauf der Erhebungsbogen zwischen den Statistischen Landesämtern und den Berichtsbetrieben jeweils über die Gemeindeverwaltungen. Die in den Gehalts- und Lohnstrukturerhebungen im öffentlichen Dienst erfaßten Berichtsstellen erhielten die Erhebungsbogen von den Statistischen Landesämtern auf dem Dienstweg über die vorgesetzten Behörden.

Von der seit 1949 üblichen Arbeitsteilung zwischen den statistischen Ämtern wurde in einigen Fällen in der Weise abgewichen, daß das Statistische Bundesamt auch die Befragung der Berichtsstellen ganz oder teilweise übernahm. Vollständig zentral wurden die Erhebung der Internationalen Arbeitsorganisation über die Aufwendungen der Unternehmen für ihre Arbeitnehmer im Jahre 1955 sowie zwei Probeerhebungen als Vorerhebungen zu Personalkostenerhebungen der Europäischen Gemeinschaften - und zwar eine Probeerhebung für 1962 über die Personalkosten im Straßenverkehrsgewerbe und eine Probeerhebung für 1966 über die Personalkosten im Einzelhandel, Bank- und Versicherungsgewerbe - durchgeführt. Bei den übrigen in der amtlichen Lohnstatistik bisher durchgeführten Probeerhebungen - eine Probeerhebung für 1961 über die Vermögensbildung der Arbeitnehmer sowie je eine Probeerhebung für April und September 1971 als Vorerhebungen zu den Erhebungen der Europäischen Gemeinschaften über die Arbeiterverdienste in der Landwirtschaft - erfolgte dagegen die Befragung der Berichtsstellen entsprechend der üblichen Arbeitsteilung durch die Statistischen Landesämter. Teilweise zentralisiert wurden die Gehalts- und Lohnstrukturerhebungen im öffentlichen Dienst durchgeführt, bei denen das Statistische Bundesamt direkt die zum Bund gehörenden Dienststellen und die Statistischen Landesämter die Dienststellen im Bereich der Länder und Gemeinden erfaßten. Um eine zentral bearbeitete Statistik handelt es sich schließlich auch bei der seit 1958 in neuer Form durchgeführten amtlichen Tariflohnstatistik. Hier berechnet das Statistische Bundesamt auf Grund des Datenmaterials des amtlichen Tarifarchivs ohne Beteiligung der Statistischen Landesämter - allerdings wird daneben in einigen Bundesländern wie z. B. Bayern vom Statistischen Landesamt selbständig eine laufende landeseigene Tariflohnstatistik nach dem Verfahren des Statistischen Bundesamtes durchgeführt - verschiedene vierteljährliche Indices der Tariflöhne und -gehälter.

Unabhängig vom Statistischen Bundesamt wertet die Deutsche Bundesbank seit 1957 das amtliche Tarifarchiv ebenfalls zentral zu einem monatlichen Index des Tariflohn- und -gehaltsniveaus aus. Über die hier erörterte Zentralisierung der eigentlichen Erhebungsarbeiten - d.h. der Befragung der Berichtsstellen in der Effektivverdienststatistik sowie der Datenübernahme aus dem Tarifarchiv in der Tariflohnstatistik - hinaus wurde bei einigen lohnstatistischen Erhebungen abweichend von der seit 1949 üblichen Arbeitsteilung auch ein Teil der Aufbereitungsarbeiten von den Statistischen Landesämtern auf das Statistische Bundesamt verlagert (vgl. Seite 180).

In der inter- und supranationalen Lohnstatistik traten neben die nationalen Erhebungsbehörden weitere Institutionen. Die für das Jahr 1955 veranstaltete Erhebung über die Aufwendungen der Unternehmen für ihre Arbeitnehmer wurde vom Statistischen Bundesamt auf Grund eines vom Internationalen Arbeitsamt aufgestellten Erhebungsplans durchgeführt. Die supranationalen Erhebungen der Europäischen Gemeinschaften - Personalkostenerhebungen im produzierenden Gewerbe, im Handel, Bank- und Versicherungsgewerbe und im Straßenverkehrsgewerbe, Gehalts- und Lohnstrukturerhebungen im produzierenden Gewerbe und im Handel, Bank-, und Versicherungsgewerbe sowie laufende Erhebungen über die Arbeiterverdienste in der Landwirtschaft - wurden vom Statistischen Amt der Europäischen Gemeinschaften koordiniert. Das Statistische Amt der Europäischen Gemeinschaften arbeitete dabei grundsätzlich mit den nationalen statistischen Ämtern - in der Bundesrepublik Deutschland dem Statistischen Bundesamt und den Statistischen Landesämtern - in der für den jeweiligen Mitgliedstaat üblichen Weise zusammen; d. h. den Statistischen Landesämtern oblag unter anderem die Befragung der Berichtsstellen nach allgemeinen Anweisungen des Statistischen Bundesamtes. Lediglich bei der Erfassung der zum Zuständigkeitsbereich der Europäischen Gemeinschaft für Kohle und Stahl gehörenden Berichtsstellen im Rahmen der Personalkostenerhebungen im produzierenden Gewerbe - im Falle des Steinkohlenbergbaus und des Eisenerzbergbaus immer, im Falle der Eisen- und Stahlindustrie teilweise - arbeitete das Statistische Amt der Europäischen Gemeinschaften unter Umgehung der nationalen statistischen Ämter mit den zuständigen nationalen Unternehmensverbänden zusammen, die die Befragung ihrer Mitgliedsunternehmen übernahmen und die ausgefüllten Erhebungsbogen direkt dem Statistischen Amt der Europäischen Gemeinschaften zusandten. In gleicher Weise wurden die jährlichen Personalkostenerhebungen der Europäischen Gemeinschaft für Kohle und Stahl in den EGKS-Industrien in direkter Zusammenarbeit zwischen der Hohen Behörde der Montanunion bzw. später dem Statistischen Amt der Europäischen Gemeinschaften und den nationalen Unternehmensverbänden durchgeführt.

Von dem Prinzip der "ausgelösten Statistik" gab es in der amtlichen Lohnstatistik nur wenige Ausnahmen. Im Jahre 1876 wurden Erhebungen über die Frauen- und Kinderarbeit in den Fabriken und über die Verhältnisse der Lehrlinge, Gesellen und Fabrikarbeiter abgeschlossen, deren Bearbeitung nicht im Kaiserlichen Statistischen Amt, sondern im Reichskanzleramt - das in dieser Angelegenheit mit den Landesregierungen zusammenarbeitete - erfolgte, weil derartige Daten in der damaligen Zeit als politisch besonders brisant empfunden wurden. In den Jahren 1892 bis 1902 veranstaltete die von der Reichsregierung eingesetzte "Kommission für Arbeiterstatistik" mehrere statistische Erhebungen, die sich in erster Linie auf die Arbeitszeit in verschiedenen Gewerbezweigen bezogen und teilweise auch lohnstatistische Daten erbrachten; lediglich die technische Abwicklung dieser Erhebungen wurde dem Kaiserlichen Statistischen Amt übertragen. Die Kommission für Arbeiterstatistik führte ferner im Jahre 1898 eine Erhebung über die gewerbliche Kinderarbeit außerhalb der Fabriken in Zusammenarbeit mit den einzelnen Staatsregierungen durch, bei der unter anderem einige lohnstatistische Daten anfielen; auch die Ergebnisse dieser Erhebung wurden im Kaiserlichen Statistischen Amt zusammengestellt. Im Jahre 1940 führte die "Deutsche Arbeitsfront" in Zusammenarbeit mit dem Reichsarbeitsministerium und den Abeitsämtern ohne Beteiligung des Statistischen Reichsamtes eine lohnstatistische Erhebung durch.

Die laufende Bergarbeiterlohnstatistik wird bis in die Gegenwart von den Oberbergämtern unter Aufsicht der für den Bergbau zuständigen Ministerien der Länder unabhängig von den statistischen Ämtern bearbeitet. Für die Festsetzung der "ortsüblichen Tagelöhne" bzw. später der "Ortslöhne" sowie der durchschnittlichen Jahresarbeitsverdienste landwirtschaftlicher Arbeitnehmer für Zwecke der Sozialversicherung waren stets die Oberversicherungämter ebenfalls ohne Beteiligung der statistischen Ämter zuständig. Auch die Sammlung der Tarifverträge in den amtlichen Tarifarchiven, die bis in die Gegenwart die Vorstufe der tariflohnstatistischen Auswertungen bildet, gehörte grundsätzlich nicht zum Aufgabenbereich der statistischen Ämter, sondern oblag den Dienststellen der Arbeitsverwaltung. Das zentrale amtliche Tarifarchiv wurde erstmalig im Jahre 1920 beim Reichsamt für Arbeitsvermittlung eingerichtet, das nicht nur die Tarifvertragstexte sammelte, sondern auch auf besonderen statistischen Erhebungsbogen ergänzende Angaben von den Zentralverbänden der Arbeitnehmer einholte . Das Reichsamt für Arbeitsvermittlung wurde unter Beibehaltung seiner Zuständigkeit für das Tarifarchiv im Jahre 1922 in Reichsarbeitsverwaltung und im Jahre 1927 in Reichsanstalt für Arbeitsvermittlung und Arbeitslosenversicherung umbenannt. Im Jahre 1928 wurde die Führung des Tarifarchivs dem Statistischen Reichsamt übertragen, dem die Tarifvertragsparteien nunmehr die Vertragstexte direkt einzureichen hatten. Nach dem Zweiten Weltkrieg wurden die Tarifverträge nicht nur im zentralen Tarifarchiv, sondern auch in neu eingerichteten amtlichen Tarifarchiven der Länder, auf deren Gebiet sich der jeweilige Tarifvertrag erstreckte, gesammelt. Die Tarifarchive werden seit 1949 beim Direktor der Verwaltung für Arbeit des Vereinigten Wirtschaftsgebietes bzw. dem Bundesminister für Arbeit und Sozialordnung sowie bei den obersten Arbeitsbehörden der Länder geführt.

322 Berichtsstellen

Berichtsstellen der amtlichen Statistik sind diejenigen Institutionen, deren Leiter als auskunftpflichtige Personen (vgl. Seite 233) von den Erhebungsbehörden zur Berichterstattung aufgefordert werden. Als Berichtsstellen der amtlichen Lohnstatistik kommen im allgemeinen nur Betriebe als örtliche Einheiten in Frage. Zu den Gehalts- und Lohnstrukturerhebungen im öffentlichen Dienst wurden analog die Dienststellen bzw. Verwaltungsstellen der Behörden und öffentlichen Einrichtungen sowie gegebenenfalls die öffentlichen Betriebe, zu den Lohnstrukturerhebungen in der Forstwirtschaft die Forstämter bzw. Forstbetriebe herangezogen. Unternehmen als rechtliche Einheiten wurden in der nationalen Lohnstatistik bisher nur in wenigen Fällen als Berichtsstellen verwendet, und zwar bei der Erhebung über die sozialen Nebenleistungen in Verbindung mit der Gehalts- und Lohnstrukturerhebung für 1957, der Erhebung über die Vermögensbildung der Arbeitnehmer für 1963 und den Erhebungen über die betriebliche Altersversorgung für 1973 und 1976. In der inter- und supranationalen Lohnstatistik kommen dagegen Unternehmen als Berichtsstellen häufiger vor. Bei der Erhebung der Internationalen Arbeitsorganisation für das Jahr 1955 wurden Unternehmen nach ihren Aufwendungen für ihre Arbeitnehmer befragt. Bei den Personalkostenerhebungen der Europäischen Gemeinschaften im produzierenden Gewerbe wurden ab Berichtsjahr 1960 in der Bundesrepublik Deutschland Unternehmen-in den anderen EG-Ländern dagegen Betriebe - als Berichtsstellen erfaßt. Auch bei den Personalkostenerhebungen der Europäischen Gemeinschaften im Straßenverkehrsgewerbe 1967 sowie im Handel, Bank- und Versicherungsgewerbe 1970 und 1974 wurden die Auskünfte zumindest in der Bundesrepublik Deutschland von den Unternehmen eingeholt. Unternehmen wurden ferner bei der Gehalts- und Lohnstrukturerhebung der Europäischen Gemeinschaften im Handel, Bank- und Versicherungsgewerbe 1974 als Berichtsstellen verwendet. Dagegen wurden bei den jährlichen Personalkostenerhebungen der Europäischen Gemeinschaft für Kohle und Stahl in den EGKS-Industrien immer Betriebe befragt. Bei den Gehalts- und

Lohnstrukturerhebungen der Europäischen Gemeinschaften im produzierenden Gewerbe waren wie bei den nationalen deutschen Gehalts- und Lohnstrukturerhebungen ebenfalls Betriebe die Berichtsstellen. Die Personalkostenerhebung der Europäischen Gemeinschaften im produzierenden Gewerbe für das Jahr 1959 erfaßte auch in der Bundesrepublik Deutschland grundsätzlich Betriebe, in Ausnahmefällen auf besonderen Antrag auch Unternehmen.

323 Erhebungsformulare

Die von den Berichtsstellen der amtlichen Lohnstatistik auszufüllenden Erhebungsformulare unterschieden sich zunächst danach, ob es sich um eine im Summenverfahren oder im Individualverfahren durchgeführte Erhebung handelte. Bei den Summenerhebungen waren pro Berichtsstelle die Angaben für den ganzen Betrieb oder das ganze Unternehmen bzw. für die Gesamtheit der zu erfassenden Arbeitnehmer in einen einzigen Fragebogen einzutragen. Derartige Summenfragebogen bestanden in der Regel aus einem einzigen Blatt (vierteljährliche Verdiensterhebung in Industrie und Handel, Bruttojahresverdiensterhebung in Industrie und Handel, Verdiensterhebung im Handwerk) oder aus zwei Blättern (Personalkostenerhebung der Europäischen Gemeinschaften im Straßenverkehrsgewerbe und im Handel, Bank- und Versicherungsgewerbe, Erhebung über die Vermögensbildung der Arbeitnehmer, Erhebung über die betriebliche Altersversorgung); besonders umfangreiche Summenfragebogen aus mehreren Blättern wurden lediglich bei den Personalkostenerhebungen der Europäischen Gemeinschaften im produzierenden Gewerbe verwendet. Bei der Verdiensterhebung im Handwerk hatten die Betriebe mit weniger als zehn Beschäftigten neben dem Summenfragebogen eine "Hilfsliste" mit ergänzenden Individualangaben für die einzelnen Arbeitnehmer auszufüllen; in die Aufbereitung in den Statistischen Landesämtern ging jedoch nur der Summenfragebogen ein, während die Hilfsliste ausschließlich der manuellen Vorkontrolle diente. Bei den Personalkostenerhebungen der Europäischen Gemeinschaften im produzierenden Gewerbe ab Berichtsjahr 1969 brauchten nur die Einbetriebsunternehmen lediglich einen einzigen Unternehmensfragebogen auszufüllen; die Mehrbetriebsunternehmen hatten dagegen summarische Meldungen in einem besonderen Fragebogen für jeden ihrer Zweigbetriebe abzugeben.

Auch bei den Individualerhebungen wurden summarische Fragebogen für diejenigen Angaben verwendet, die die ganze Berichtsstelle bzw. die Gesamtheit der Arbeitnehmer der Berichtsstelle betrafen. Daneben traten jedoch entsprechend der besonderen Aufgabenstellung der Individuallohnerhebungen meist verhältnismäßig umfangreiche bzw. zahlreiche Erhebungsformulare, in die die erfragten Individualangaben für jeden einzelnen zu erfassenden Arbeitnehmer einzutragen waren. Die summarischen Fragebogen der Individualerhebungen wurden meist ausdrücklich nach der Art der jeweiligen Berichtsstelle bezeichnet, d. h. als "Betriebsbogen" (Gehalts- und Lohnstrukturerhebungen in der gewerblichen Wirtschaft, in der Landwirtschaft und im Erwerbsgartenbau) oder als "Unternehmensbogen" (Gehalts- und Lohnstrukturerhebung der Europäischen Gemeinschaften im Handel, Bank- und Versicherungsgewerbe). Bei den Gehalts- und Lohnstrukturerhebungen im öffentlichen Dienst wurde für die summarischen Fragebogen die allgemeine Bezeichnung "Berichtsstellenbogen" vorgezogen, weil die Bezeichnung "Dienststellenbogen" möglicherweise Anlaß zu Mißverständnissen gegeben hätte. Bei der Individuallohnerhebung vom Februar 1920 hatte jeder Berichtsbetrieb zwei Betriebsbogen auszufüllen, und zwar einen Arbeitersammelfragebogen und einen Angestelltensammelfragebogen. Die Erhebungsformulare für die Individualangaben traten entweder in der Form der Erhebungslisten - in die die Angaben für jeden zu erfassenden Arbeitnehmer in jeweils einer Zeile einzutragen waren - oder in der Form der Individualzählblätter - bei denen für jeden Arbeitnehmer ein besonderes Blatt auszufüllen war - auf. Erhebungslisten wurden bei den vom Statistischen Reichsamt von 1927 bis 1934 veranstalteten Individuallohnerhebungen in verschiedenen Industriezweigen,der Individuallohnerhebung in der metallverarbeitenden Industrie 1938, den nach dem Zweiten Weltkrieg durchgeführten Gehalts- und Lohnstrukturerhebungen in der gewerblichen Wirtschaft, der Lohnstrukturerhebung in der Forstwirtschaft 1961/62, der Gehalts- und Lohnstrukturerhebung der Europäischen Gemeinschaften im Handel, Bank- und Versicherungsgewerbe 1974 (die Erhebungsformulare der Gehalts- und Lohnstrukturerhebungen der Europäischen Gemeinschaften im produzierenden Gewerbe 1966 und 1972 waren identisch mit den Formularen der gleichzeitigen nationalen Strukturerhebungen in der gewerblichen Wirtschaft) und bei den jährlichen - nationalen bzw. ab 1974 europäischen - Verdiensterhebungen in der Landwirtschaft verwendet. Individualzählblätter wurden bei der Lohn- und Gehaltserhebung vom Februar 1920, der Individualerhebung im Bankgewerbe 1934, der Lohnstrukturerhebung in der Landwirtschaft 1937, den Lohnstrukturerhebungen in der Forstwirtschaft 1949/50 und 1952/53, den Gehalts- und Lohnstrukturerhebungen in der Landwirtschaft 1953/54 und 1962/63 sowie im Erwerbsgartenbau 1962 und bei den Gehalts- und Lohnstrukturerhebungen im öffentlichen Dienst 1950 und 1968 verwendet. Bei der Lohnstrukturerhebung in der Landwirtschaft 1950 wurden die Individualangaben länderweise unterschiedlich entweder auf Erhebungslisten oder auf Individualzählblättern erfaßt. Neben den von den Berichtsstellen auszufüllenden Fragebogen gehörten bei den Summenerhebungen und den Individualerhebungen ergänzende "Erläuterungen" bzw. "Definitionen" oder "Richtlinien" zu den Erhebungsformularen.

Die Arbeit der Erhebungsbehörden und der Berichtsstellen könnte wesentlich erleichtert werden, wenn die erfragten Daten statt auf Erhebungsformularen auf maschinell zu verarbeitenden Datenträgern übermittelt würden. Derartige Versuche haben jedoch für die amtliche Lohnstatistik bisher kaum Bedeutung erlangt. Bei der Individuallohnerhebung in der metallverarbeitenden Industrie 1938 reichten die Berichtsbetriebe dem Statistischen Reichsamt teilweise Originallochkarten oder Lochkartendoppel ein, teilweise wurden auch in der Buchhaltung anfallende Lohnlisten im Statistischen Reichsamt direkt abgelocht. Bei der Gehalts- und Lohnstrukturerhebung im öffentlichen Dienst 1968 wurden in Nordrhein-Westfalen die Landesbeamten und Richter statt auf Individualzählblättern durch Auswertung der im Statistischen Landesamt Nordrhein-Westfalen - das im Auftrage des

Landesamtes für Besoldung und Versorgung Nordrhein-Westfalen für die maschinelle Berechnung der Bezüge zuständig war - auf Datenträgern vorliegenden Besoldungsunterlagen erfaßt. Von einigen kommunalen Berichtsstellen wurden dem Statistischen Landesamt Nordrhein-Westfalen zur Strukturerhebung 1968 statt der Individualzählblätter Individuallochkarten eingereicht.

324 Art der Datenübermittlung

Die Erhebungsformulare der amtlichen Lohnstatistik werden den Berichtsstellen grundsätzlich postalisch übersandt und gelangen nach Ausfüllung auf dem gleichen Wege wieder an die Erhebungsbehörden zurück. Nur in wenigen Fällen wurde vom Postversand zugunsten des Einsatzes von Interviewern abgesehen.
Im amtlichen bzw. halbamtlichen Bereich fand die erste lohnstatistische Erhebung im Interviewerverfahren im Jahre 1887 statt, als die Berufsgenossenschaft der Buchdrucker eine Erhebung bei ihren Mitgliedsunternehmen durchführte; die Interviewer wurden dabei für ihre Aufgabe von den unteren Verwaltungsbehörden vereidigt. Bei der Erhebung der Kommission für Arbeiterstatistik über gewerbliche Kinderarbeit außerhalb der Fabriken im Jahre 1898 wurden im allgemeinen Volksschullehrer als Interviewer eingesetzt. Bei der Lohnstrukturerhebung in der Landwirtschaft 1937 übernahmen die "Kreisgefolgschaftswarte" der "Kreisbauernschaften" unter anderem die Verteilung der Erhebungsbogen an die Betriebsleiter und deren Anleitung bei der Ausfüllung der Fragebogen sowie die erste Prüfung und Berichtigung der Angaben. Nach dem Zweiten Weltkrieg beschränkte sich der Einsatz von Interviewern in der amtlichen Lohnstatistik auf einige Erhebungen im Bereich der Land- und Forstwirtschaft. Die Lohnstrukturerhebung in der Landwirtschaft 1950 wurde mit Hilfe von Interviewern - vorzugsweise Mitarbeitern der Landwirtschaftskammern und der Landwirtschaftsschulen - durchgeführt. Bei der Lohnstrukturerhebung in der Forstwirtschaft 1949/50 wurden die Interviewer vor allem von den forstwirtschaftlichen Verwaltungsbehörden gestellt. Die späteren Struturerhebungen in der Land- und Forstwirtschaft fanden ohne Interviewer mit Hilfe des üblichen Postversands

statt. Bei der laufenden Verdiensterhebung in der Landwirtschaft wurden für die erste Befragung im März 1957 insbesondere zur Erledigung von Rückfragen bei den Berichtsbetrieben teilweise Interviewereingesetzt, die von den Landwirtschaftsschulen und Wirtschaftsberatungsstellen der Landwirtschaftskammern gestellt wurden; die folgenden Erhebungen wurden nur noch postalisch durchgeführt. Die jährlichen Erhebungen der Europäischen Gemeinschaften über die Arbeiterverdienste in der Landwirtschaft fanden bisher in fast allen Bundesländern im Interviewerverfahren statt. Als Interviewer wurden dabei in den einzelnen Bundesländern unterschiedliche Personenkreise eingesetzt, in Nordrhein-Westfalen z. B. neben Angehörigen des Landesamtes für Datenverarbeitung und Statistik Nordrhein-Westfalen vor allem Personen, die sich bereits als Interviewer bei den Erhebungen des Mikrozensus qualifiziert hatten. Abweichend von dem allgemeinen Verfahren wurden die EG-Verdiensterhebungen in der Landwirtschaft in Baden-Württemberg ab 1974 und in Nordrhein-Westfalen ab 1976 postalisch durchgeführt.

325 Sonderbehandlung des Bergbaus

Bei der Erfassung des Bergbaus wies die Organisation der lohnstatistischen Erhebungen immer einige Besonderheiten auf. Zunächst verfügt der Bergbau in der Bergarbeiterlohnstatistik über eigene laufende Effektivverdiensterhebungen, die im Gegensatz zu den Erhebungen in den anderen Wirtschaftsbereichen nicht von den statistischen Ämtern, sondern von den zuständigen Fachbehörden - den Oberbergämtern - bearbeitet werden. Auch in der Effektivverdienststatistik der statistischen Ämter wird der Bergbau seit jeher in besonderer Weise behandelt. Die Lohn- und Gehaltserhebung vom Februar 1920 und die späteren vom Statistischen Reichsamt durchgeführten Individuallohnerhebungen und Lohnsummenerhebungen der Industriearbeiter schlossen den Bergbau aus. Die lohnstatistische Rechtsverordnung vom 14. Juli 1927 (Reichsgesetzblatt 1927 Teil I Seite 185) bestimmte ausdrücklich, daß für neue lohnstatistische Erhebungen im Bergbau die Zustimmung des Reichsrats erforderlich war, während die Erhebungen in den anderen Wirtschaftsbereichen durch den Reichswirtschaftsminister lediglich im Benehmen mit dem Reichsarbeitsminister im Erlaßwege angeordnet werden konnten. Um die lohnstatistische Lücke im Bereich des Bergbaus so weit wie möglich zu schließen und den Bergbau in die laufenden Indexberechnungen der Effektivverdienste einzubeziehen, führte das Statistische Reichsamt auf Grund von freiwilligen Nachweisungen der Zechenverbände eine monatliche Statistik über die Effektivverdienste der Arbeiter im Stein- und Braunkohlenbergbau durch. Auch nach dem Zweiten Weltkrieg blieb der Bergbau zunächst aus der allgemeinen Lohnstatistik der statistischen Ämter ausgeschlossen. Die bergbehördliche Lohnstatistik wurde nach 1945 von den Oberbergämtern der Westzonen bzw. des Bundesgebietes weitergeführt; dabei wurde jedoch in der britischen Zone der Kohlenbergbau statt von den Bergbehörden von der neugeschaffenen Institution "Deutsche Kohlenbergbauleitung" erfaßt. Durch Verhandlungen zwischen den statistischen Ämtern und den Oberbergämtern bzw. der Deutschen Kohlenbergbauleitung konnten die Lohnerhebungen im Kohlenbergbau und die vierteljährlichen Lohnsummenerhebungen der Industriearbeiter methodisch einander schrittweise angenähert werden. In der amerikanischen Zone erhielten die Statistischen Landesämter bereits ab 1947 Kopien der Meldungen der Kohlenbergwerke zur Bergarbeiterlohnstatistik, um sie für Zwecke der vierteljährlichen Lohnsummenerhebungen selbst aufzubereiten. In der britischen Zone übernahm die Deutsche Kohlenbergbauleitung ab 1949 die Aufbereitung zu Landesergebnissen, die dann den Statistischen Landesämtern und dem Statistischen Amt des Vereinigten Wirtschaftsgebietes bzw. dem Statistischen Bundesamt zum Einbau in die Ergebnisse der Industriearbeiterlohnstatistik zur Verfügung gestellt wurden. Nach Auflösung der Deutschen Kohlenbergbauleitung wurde im Jahre 1954 die "Statistik der Kohlenwirtschaft e.V." als ein in Bonn eingetragener Verein mit Geschäftsstellen in Essen (für den Steinkohlenbergbau) und Köln (für den Braunkohlenbergbau) gegründet. Der Statistik der Kohlenwirtschaft e.V. wurde die Aufgabe übertragen, die Bergarbeiterlohnstatistik in fast dem gesamten Kohlenbergbau durchzuführen und weiterhin fertig aufbereitete Landesergebnisse den statistischen Ämtern zum Einbau in die vierteljährlichen Lohnsummenerhebungen zu liefern. Erst ab Anfang 1956 gelang es, den gesamten Bergbau voll vergleichbar in die allgemeinen Lohnsummenerhebungen einzubeziehen. Während der Kohlenbergbau nunmehr die allgemein angewandte lohnstatistische Methode übernahm, wurde der Nichtkohlenbergbau in der laufenden Industriearbeiterlohnstatistik neu erfaßt. Die volle Vergleichbarkeit bezog sich allerdings nur auf die Ergebnisse der Erhebungen; in der Erhebungs- und Aufbereitungsorganisation bestanden dagegen auch nach 1956 erhebliche Abweichungen von dem normalen Verfahren. Die Grundlage für die Datenerfassung in den Bergbaubetrieben bildete nach wie vor grundsätzlich die Bergarbeiterlohnstatistik. Im Kohlenbergbau bereitete die Statistik der Kohlenwirtschaft e.V. weiterhin die Einzelmeldungen zur Bergarbeiterlohnstatistik für Zwecke der vierteljährlichen Lohnsummenerhebung zu Durchschnittsergebnissen für die in Frage kommenden Bundesländer auf. Die Statistischen Landesämter erhielten statt der Einzelmeldungen der Betriebe des Kohlenbergbaus lediglich ihr aggregiertes Landesergebnis. Die ab 1957 vorgenommene Erfassung und Aufbereitung der Verdienstangaben für die Angestellten des Kohlenbergbaus erfolgte in gleicher Weise wie bei den Arbeitern. Im Nichtkohlenbergbau lieferten die zuständigen Oberbergämter den Statistischen Landesämtern für die Arbeiter in gleicher Weise aggregierte Verdienst- und Arbeitszeitangaben als Landesdurchschnitte wie im Kohlenbergbau. Für die Erfassung der Angestellten des Nichtkohlenbergbaus in der vierteljährlichen Summenerhebung verteilten die Oberbergämter dagegen die ihnen von den Statistischen Landesämtern gesammelt zur Verfügung gestellten Erhebungsbogen zur Ausfüllung an die einzelnen Bergbaubetriebe und sandten die ausgefüllten Erhebungsbogen gesammelt wieder an die Statistischen Landesämter zur Aufbereitung zurück. Bei den Gehalts- und Lohnstrukturerhebungen in der gewerblichen Wirtschaft wurde ebenfalls die Statistik der Kohlenwirtschaft e.V. eingeschaltet, die die Erhebungsbogen an die Betriebe des Kohlenbergbaus verteilte, nach der Ausfüllung wieder einsammelte und nach Überprüfung zur Aufbereitung an die Statistischen Landesämter zurücksandte. Der Nichtkohlenbergbau wurde dagegen in den Gehalts-

und Lohnstrukturerhebungen nicht über die Oberbergämter, sondern wie die anderen Wirtschaftsberiche unmittelbar von den Statistischen Landesämtern erfaßt.

Die Vorteile der Einschaltung der Statistik der Kohlenwirtschaft e.V. und der Oberbergämter bei der Durchführung der allgemeinen amtlichen Lohnstatistik bestehen zunächst darin, daß der gesamte Bergbau in den laufenden Verdiensterhebungen und der Kohlenbergbau in den Strukturerhebungen total erfaßt werden können, während in den übrigen Wirtschaftsbereichen eine Beschränkung auf eine repräsentative Auswahl von Berichtsstellen erforderlich ist. Für die statistischen Ämter ist diese Zusammenarbeit außerdem verlockend, weil sie ihnen eine nicht unerhebliche Arbeitsersparnis bringt, die besonders zu Buche schlägt, wenn die genannten Stellen die Aufbereitung zu fertigen Landesergebnissen übernehmen. Ferner können die fachlich ausschließlich auf den Bergbau ausgerichteten Erhebungsstellen bergbauspezifische Besonderheiten in der Entlohnung möglicherweise besser beurteilen als die allgemein statistisch tätigen Ämter. Dem steht die Gefahr gegenüber, daß trotz aller Integrationsbemühungen die lohnstatistischen Ergebnisse für den Bergbau mit denjenigen für die anderen Wirtschaftsbereiche eventuell doch nicht voll vergleichbar sind, weil vielleicht interne Aufbereitungsrichtlinien in den Erhebungsstellen des Bergbaus einerseits und in den statistischen Ämtern andererseits voneinander abweichen bzw. unterschiedlich aufgefaßt werden, ohne daß derartige Abweichungen den statistischen Ämtern immer bekannt werden. In den Fällen, in denen von den Erhebungsstellen des Bergbaus nur die aggregierten Landesergebnisse den statistischen Ämtern übermittelt werden, haben diese keine Möglichkeit,die Meldungen der einzelnen Berichtsstellen einer Vollzähligkeits- bzw. Vollständigkeits- oder Plausibilitätskontrolle zu unterziehen. Darüberhinaus können rechtliche Bedenken dagegen erhoben werden, daß die Statistik der Kohlenwirtschaft e.V. als private Institution mit der Durchführung amtlicher statistischer Erhebungen hoheitliche Funktionen ausübt. Obwohl die Arbeitgeber des Kohlenbergbaus nach dem Gesetz über die Lohnstatistik vom 18. Mai 1956 (Bundesgesetzblatt 1956

Teil I Seite 429) in gleicher Weise wie die Arbeitgeber der anderen Wirtschaftsbereiche auskunftspflichtig und somit in gleicher Weise den Bestimmungen des Gesetzes über die Statistik für Bundeszwecke vom 3. September 1953 (Bundesgesetzblatt 1953 Teil I Seite 1314) über die Auskunftspflicht unterworfen sind, könnte im Falle einer Verletzung der Auskunftspflicht zur vierteljährlichen Verdiensterhebung kein Bußgeldverfahren durchgeführt werden, weil die Statistik der Kohlenwirtschaft e.V. als private Institution dazu nicht befugt wäre und die statistischen Ämter - die nur die aggregierten Landesergebnisse erhalten - gar nicht erfahren, ob alle Arbeitgeber ihrer Auskunftspflicht ordnungsgemäß nachgekommen sind.

33 Die Repräsentation

331 Auswahl von Erhebungsgegenständen

Ein zentrales Problem der amtlichen Lohnstatistik bilden die mit der Repräsentation zusammenhängenden Fragen, die in erster Linie die Stichprobenziehung, daneben aber auch die Auswahl von Erhebungsgegenständen über die Stichprobeneinheiten hinaus betreffen. Derartige repräsentativ ausgewählte Erhebungsgegenstände kommen vor allem in der Tariflohnstatistik vor, bei der man stets bestrebt war, das überaus vielfältige Erscheinungsbild der Tarifverträge dadurch überschaubar zu machen, daß man sich auf bestimmte Gegenstände beschränkte, die dann stellvertretend die gesamte Breite der tarifvertraglichen Wirklichkeit widerspiegeln sollten. Die im Jahre 1922 eingeführte Tariflohnstatistik des Statistischen Reichamtes erfaßte nur die Tariflohnsätze der höchsten tarifmäßigen Altersstufe in den Hauptsitzen der wichtigsten Gewerbegruppen. Ab 1931 wurden die Tariflohnsätze - ebenfalls nur der höchsten tariflichen Altersstufe - für ausgewählte Gewerbegruppen, Berufsarten und Tarifgebiete bzw. Orte oder Ortsklassen sowie ausgewählte tarifliche Lohnzuschläge einbezogen. Der gegen Ende der fünfziger Jahre aufgenommenen Berechnung von Indices der Tariflöhne und -gehälter in der gewerblichen Wirtschaft und bei Gebietskörperschaften lagen ausgewählte Tarifverträge zugrunde, deren Auswahl nach der Anzahl der betroffenen Arbeitnehmer vorgenommen wurde; und zwar wurden in jedem einzelnen Wirtschaftszweig die Tarifverträge mit der größten Arbeiter- bzw. Angestelltenzahl ausgewählt, solange bis 75 % der in dem betreffenden Wirtschaftszweig beschäftigten Arbeiter bzw. Angestellten durch die Verträge repräsentiert waren. Außerdem beschränkten sich diese Tarifindices auf bestimmte Lohn- bzw. Gehaltsgruppen - seit der Umbasierung auf das Jahr 1970 werden dagegen in den ausgewählten Tarifverträgen sämtliche Lohn- und Gehaltsgruppen einbezogen - sowie auf die höchste tarifmäßige Altersstufe bzw. die tariflichen Endgehälter und auf die höchste tarifliche Ortsklasse. Der Index der Tariflöhne in der Landwirtschaft umfaßte im Gegensatz zu den anderen Tarifindices die Lohnsätze sämtlicher Tarifverträge für alle Ortsklassen, beschränkte sich jedoch auf ausgewählte Lohngruppen sowie ebenfalls auf die höchste tarifmäßige Altersstufe.

In der Effektivverdienststatistik wurden in einigen Fällen bestimmte Berufe oder Wirtschaftszweige ausgewählt, die eine größere Gruppe bzw. die Gesamtheit der Berufe oder Wirtschaftszweige repräsentieren sollten. Bei der Lohn- und Gehaltserhebung vom Februar 1920 wurden in die Aufbereitung der Arbeiterverdienste nur typische Berufsarten einbezogen; die von 1927 bis 1934 durchgeführten Individuallohnerhebungen erfaßten jeweils nur ausgewählte Arbeitergruppen. Die vierteljährlichen Lohnsummenerhebungen des Statistischen Reichsamtes erbrachten unter anderem gesonderte Ergebnisse für bestimmte typische Berufe. Nach dem Zweiten Weltkrieg wurden ausgewählte Wirtschaftszweige zur Repräsentation größerer Wirtschaftsbereiche bei der halbjährlichen Verdiensterhebung im Handwerk, der Erhebung der Internationalen Arbeitsorganisation über die Personalaufwendungen von 1955 und den Personalkostenerhebungen der Europäischen Gemeinschaften im produzierenden Gewerbe für die Jahre 1959 bis 1964 erfaßt.

Bei einigen lohnstatistischen Erhebungen, die die Verdienstentwicklung während eines ganzen Jahres aufzeigen sollten, wurden statt dieses Jahres zur Arbeitserleichterung nur bestimmte über das Jahr verteilte kürzere Erhebungszeiträume verwendet. Im Jahre 1891 veranstaltete die "Badische Fabrikinspektion" im Raum Mannheim eine lohnstatistische Erhebung, bei der die Verdienste in einer Reihe genau bezeichneter Wochen, die so weit wie möglich die im Laufe des Jahres vorkommenden Unterschiede in der Lohnhöhe ausgleichen sollten, ermittelt wurden. Die vierteljährlichen Lohnsummenerhebungen wurden für vier ausgewählte Erhebungsmonate jedes Jahres durchgeführt, und zwar von 1935 bis 1951 für März, Juni, September und Dezember, von 1952 bis 1963 für Februar, Mai, August und November und ab 1964 für Januar, April, Juli und Oktober. Die Erhebungsmonate der vierteljährlichen Lohnsummenerhebungen waren seit 1949 gleichzeitig die Berichtsmonate der vierteljährlichen Tariflohnstatistik. Für die halbjährliche Verdiensterhebung im Handwerk wurden bisher immer die Erhebungsmonate Mai und November ausgewählt. Bei der Gehalts- und Lohnstrukturerhebung in der Landwirtschaft 1953/54 wurde für die kleineren Berichtsbetriebe die Verdienstentwicklung während des Erhebungsjahres durch die Verdienstmeldungen der Monate Februar, Mai, September und November repräsentiert.

332 Stichprobenziehung

3321 Auswahlgrundlagen

Die amtlichen lohnstatistischen Erhebungen wurden nur in wenigen Fällen als Totalerhebungen durchgeführt. Reine Totalerhebungen waren immer die Bergarbeiterlohnstatistik und die Personalkostenerhebungen der Europäischen Gemeinschaft für Kohle und Stahl. Die Personalkostenerhebungen der Europäischen Gemeinschaften im produzierenden Gewerbe von 1959 bis 1964 erfaßten in den in die jeweilige Erhebung einbezogenen Wirtschaftszweigen grundsätzlich als partielle Totalerhebungen von einer bestimmten Arbeitnehmerzahl an sämtliche Betriebe bzw. Unternehmen. Auch die Personalkostenerhebung der Europäischen Gemeinschaften im Einzelhandel, Bank- und Versicherungsgewerbe für 1970 fand zum größten Teil als partielle Totalerhebung statt. Abgesehen von diesen Ausnahmefällen beschränkten sich die lohnstatistischen Erhebungen auf die Erfassung repräsentativ ausgewählter Berichtsstellen bzw. Erhebungseinheiten. Die mit der Stichprobenziehung zusammenhängenden Fragen sind damit für die Lohnstatistik von besonderer Bedeutung.

Die erste Voraussetzung für die Durchführung von Repräsentativerhebungen ist die Beschaffung geeigneter Auswahlgrundlagen, aus denen die Stichprobeneinheiten ausgewählt werden können. Als Auswahlgrundlagen der Lohnstatistik dienten gewöhnlich die Anschriftenlisten früherer nichtlohnstatistischer Totalerhebungen. So wurde für die lohnstatistischen Erhebungen in den verschiedenen Wirtschaftsbereichen die jeweils letzte Arbeitsstättenzählung, Handwerkszählung, Handels- und Gaststättenzählung, landwirtschaftliche Betriebszählung, Gartenbauerhebung, Totalerhebung zur Industrie- und zur Bauberichterstattung, Unternehmenserhebung in der Industrie und im Bauhauptgewerbe sowie der Zensus im produzierenden Gewerbe und der Verkehrszensus als Auswahlgrundlage verwendet. Wenn ausnahmsweise keine geeigneten Anschriftenlisten aus amtlichen Totalerhebungen vorlagen, wurden stattdessen auch private bzw. verbandseigene Anschriftenverzeichnisse ausgewertet. In wenigen Fällen wurden die Berichtsstellen lohnstatistischer Erhebungen aus Auswahlgrundlagen ausgewählt, die als Ergebnisse von Repräsentativerhebungen bereits selbst Stichproben darstellten. Die Berichtsbetriebe der laufenden Verdiensterhebung in der Landwirtschaft wurden bei der erstmaligen Stichprobenziehung im Jahre 1957 aus den Betriebsauflistungen der repräsentativen Landarbeitskräfteerhebung von 1956 und bei der Neuauswahl im Jahre 1971 aus den Auflistungen der repräsentativen Landarbeitskräfteerhebung von 1970 ausgewählt. Auswahlgrundlagen der Erhebungen über die betriebliche Altersversorgung für 1973 und 1976 waren im Bereich des produzierenden Gewerbes die repräsentativen Personalkostenerhebungen der Europäischen Gemeinschaften von 1972 und 1975.

3322 Auswahl- und Erhebungseinheiten

Vor der Stichprobenziehung ist zu klären, welche Art von Einheiten als Stichprobeneinheiten ausgewählt werden sollen (Auswahleinheiten) und auf welche Art von Einheiten sich die zu erfragenden Angaben beziehen sollen (Erhebungseinheiten). In der Regel sind die Auswahleinheiten mit den Erhebungseinheiten identisch. Ausnahmsweise kann sich jedoch eine Auswahleinheit aus mehreren Erhebungseinheiten zusammensetzen; es kommt auch vor, daß zunächst Einheiten ausgewählt werden, die dann selbst überhaupt keine Erhebungseinheiten sind. Als Auswahl- und gleichzeitig Erhebungseinheiten kommen in der amtlichen Lohnstatistik vor allem Betriebe als örtliche Einheiten - bei den Gehalts- und Lohnstrukturerhebungen im öffentlichen Dienst stattdessen Dienst- bzw. Verwaltungsstellen -, Unternehmen als rechtliche Einheiten sowie Arbeitnehmer vor.

Die einzelnen Arbeitnehmer kommen lediglich für die im Individualverfahren durchgeführten Erhebungen als Auswahl- und Erhebungseinheiten in Frage, und zwar werden sie hier nicht direkt, sondern in der zweiten Stufe eines zweistufigen Auswahlverfahrens ausgewählt. Die direkte einstufige Auswahl von Personen wurde in der amtlichen Lohnstatistik bisher nur bei der Erhebung des Statistischen Landesamtes Schleswig- Holstein über die Einkommensschichtung von 1949 angewendet. Die Möglichkeit, daß eine Auswahleinheit in mehrere Erhebungseinheiten zerfiel, war in der amtlichen Lohnstatistik in verschiedener Form gegeben. So waren teilweise bei den vierteljährlichen Lohnsummenerhebungen und bei den Gehalts- und Lohnstrukturerhebungen in der gewerblichen Wirtschaft unter bestimmten Voraussetzungen gesonderte Meldungen für fachliche Betriebsteile als Erhebungseinheiten abzugeben, obwohl nur ganze Betriebe Auswahleinheiten waren. Bei den Personalkostenerhebungen der Europäischen Gemeinschaften im produzierenden Gewerbe waren seit dem Berichtsjahr 1969 Auswahleinheiten die Unternehmen, Erhebungseinheiten dagegen die zu diesen Unternehmen gehörenden Betriebe. Bei den im Lohnsummenverfahren durchgeführten laufenden Verdiensterhebungen wurden Betriebe als Auswahleinheiten verwendet; Erhebungseinheiten waren neben den Betrieben selbst auch bestimmte aus den Arbeitnehmern dieser Betriebe zu bildende Arbeitnehmergruppen, für die summarische Verdienstangaben zu liefern waren. In wenigen Fällen wurden in der amtlichen Lohnstatistik bei Anwendung des zweistufigen Auswahlverfahrens in der ersten Stufe Einheiten ausgewählt, die bei der Befragung nicht als Erhebungseinheiten verwendet wurden. Bei den repräsentativen Erhebungen der Kommission für Arbeiterstatistik von 1892 bis 1902 wurden in der Regel in der ersten Stufe Orte bzw. Stadtbezirke ausgewählt, in denen dann Betriebe und deren Arbeitnehmer als Erhebungseinheiten erfaßt wurden. In ähnlicher Weise - allerdings nach anderen Auswahlkriterien - wurden bei der Gehalts- und Lohnstrukturerhebung in der Landwirtschaft 1953/54 und bei den jährlichen Erhebungen der Europäischen Gemeinschaften über die Arbeiterverdienste in der Landwirtschaft in der ersten Stufe Gemeinden ausgewählt; Erhebungseinheiten waren dagegen ausschließlich die in der zweiten Stufe ausgewählten Betriebe und deren Arbeitnehmer.

3323 Auswahlverfahren

Die in der amtlichen Lohnstatistik angewendeten Auswahlverfahren hatten stets den Zweck, aus den Einheiten der Auswahlgrundlagen jeweils eine Teilmenge herauszugreifen, die die Grundgesamtheit im Hinblick auf das Erhebungsziel hinreichend genau repräsentierte. Derartige repräsentative Teilmengen wurden in der Lohnstatistik des Deutschen Reichs grundsätzlich im Wege der gezielten Auswahl bestimmt. Ausnahmsweise - so bei einigen Erhebungen der Kommission für Arbeiterstatistik in den Jahren 1892 bis 1902 - begnügte man sich auch mit der Erfassung weniger typischer Einzelfälle. Bei der gezielten Auswahl eines repräsentativen Berichtskreises arbeiteten die Statistischen Ämter vielfach mit anderen sachverständigen Institutionen zusammen. Solche Institutionen waren Reichsarbeitsgemeinschaften der Arbeitgeber und Arbeitnehmer (Lohn- und Gehaltserhebung vom Februar 1920), Arbeitgeber- und Arbeitnehmerverbände (Individuallohnerhebungen von 1927 bis 1934), Organisationen der gewerblichen Wirtschaft und Fachämter der Deutschen Arbeitsfront (Lohnsummenerhebungen ab 1935) und die Kreisgefolgschaftswarte der Kreisbauernschaften (Lohnstrukturerhebung in der Landwirtschaft 1937). Soweit nach dem Zweiten Weltkrieg noch das Verfahren der gezielten Auswahl angewendet wurde, wurden als sachverständige Institutionen die Arbeitsämter (vierteljährliche Lohnsummenerhebungen vor 1957, z. B. in Nordrhein-Westfalen bis 1954), die Arbeitsverwaltungen im Einvernehmen mit den Industrie- und Handelskammern, den Fachverbänden und entsprechenden Organisationen (Angestelltenverdiensterhebung vom Mai 1949) sowie eigens für diesen Zweck gebildete "Landesausschüsse" mit Vertretern der Landwirtschaftsministerien, der Landwirtschaftskammern und der landwirtschaftlichen Arbeitnehmer- und Arbeitgeberverbände (Lohnstrukturerhebung in der Landwirtschaft 1950) bzw. der Landwirtschaftskammern, der Forstdezernate der Regierungspräsidenten, der Forstämter und der forstwirtschaftlichen Gewerkschaften und Arbeitgeberverbände (Lohnstrukturerhebung in der Forstwirtschaft 1949/50) herangezogen. Die Möglichkeit, statt der gezielten Auswahl ein Verfahren der Zufallsauswahl anzuwenden, wurde zwar bereits vom Statistischen Reichsamt gesehen, jedoch insbesondere für die Lohnsummenerhebungen als ungeeignet abgelehnt: "Die Anwendung der Stichprobenmethode" - d. h. der zufälligen Auswahl - "in der Lohnstatistik dürfte nach dem gegenwärtigen Stand von Theorie und Praxis günstigstenfalls auf Einzellohnerhebungen beschränkt sein. Da die Lohnsummenerhebungen von vornherein nur Durchschnittswerte für die erfaßten Betriebe ermitteln, und die Streuung der Einzelwerte um die Mittelwerte nicht bekannt ist und auch dem Charakter der Methode nach nicht bekannt werden kann, fehlen bei dieser Erhebungsmethode die wesentlichsten Voraussetzungen für die Anwendung der Stichprobenmethode. Das Statistische Reichsamt hat aus diesen und anderen Gründen von vornherein bei seiner Lohnstatistik seit jeher die Methode der 'bewußten' Auswahl angewendet."*) Hier wurden also fälschlicherweise nicht die Merkmale der Betriebe, sondern die Merkmale der einzelnen Arbeiter als "Einzelwerte" der Lohnsummenerhebungen angesehen. Ein Element des Zufalls war im Rahmen der Lohnstatistik des Deutschen Reichs lediglich bei einigen Erhebungen der Kommission für Arbeiterstatistik (1892 bis 1902) in den Auswahlverfahren enthalten, als die Fragebogen abwechselnd in der alphabetischen Reihenfolge der gezielt ausgewählten Firmen an deren Arbeitgeber oder Arbeitnehmer verteilt wurden.

Nach dem Zweiten Weltkrieg wurde in zunehmendem Maße auf Verfahren der Zufallsauswahl übergegangen; allerdings wurde in einer Reihe von Fällen auch noch die gezielte Auswahl angewendet. Die Berichtsstellen der Angestelltenverdiensterhebung vom Mai 1949 und der Lohnstrukturerhebung in der Forstwirtschaft 1949/50 wurden ausschließlich gezielt ausgewählt. Dasselbe galt für die Auswahl der Berichtsbetriebe der vierteljährlichen Verdiensterhebung von 1946 bis 1963, die vor 1957

*) Friedrich Behrens: Neue Wege der Lohnstatistik. In: Allgemeines Statistisches Archiv, 31. Band, Jahrgang 1942/43, Jena 1943, Seite 120.

in den Ländern ohne einheitlichen Plan mit willkürlichen Auswahlsatzdifferenzierungen und teilweise laufenden Änderungen des Berichtskreises, ab 1957 dagegen nach einem Rahmenplan des Statistischen Bundesamtes als geschichtete Auswahl unter Konstanthaltung des Berichtskreises bis zur nächsten generellen Neuauswahl mit gleichmäßiger Erfassung von so vielen Betrieben in jeder Schicht, daß etwa 25 % - in einigen Wirtschaftsbereichen etwa 10 % - der Arbeitnehmer der Grundgesamtheit einbezogen wurden, vorgenommen wurde. Die Berichtsbetriebe der Lohnstrukturerhebung in der Landwirtschaft 1950 wurden in den kreisfreien Städten ausschließlich gezielt, in den Landkreisen als Zufallsstichprobe aus einer größeren Teilmenge gezielt ausgewählter Betriebe bestimmt. Die von 1957 bis 1965 erfaßten Berichtsbetriebe der Verdiensterhebung im Handwerk wurden in der obersten Betriebsgrößenklasse gezielt, dagegen in den übrigen Größenklassen zufällig ausgewählt. Bei der Verdiensterhebung in der Landwirtschaft wurden die für den von 1957 bis 1963 erfaßten Berichtskreis grundsätzlich zufällig ausgewählten Betriebe durch zusätzlich gezielt ausgewählte Betriebe ergänzt. Bei der Gehalts- und Lohnstrukturerhebung im öffentlichen Dienst 1968 wurden als Berichtsstellen der Deutschen Bundesbahn einige Bundesbahndirektionen gezielt ausgewählt. Im übrigen erfolgte nach dem Zweiten Weltkrieg die Stichprobenziehung für die lohnstatistischen Erhebungen nur noch im Wege der Zufallsauswahl. Eine Modifikation der reinen Zufallsauswahl wurde als Auswahlverfahren erstmalig bei der Erhebung über die Einkommensschichtung in Schleswig-Holstein im Jahre 1949 angewendet, bei der alle an einem 11. November geborenen Erwerbspersonen in die Stichprobe einbezogen wurden. Bei den späteren Erhebungen wurde die Zufallsauswahl hinsichtlich der Betriebs- bzw. Unternehmensauswahl stets durch das "systematische Auswahlverfahren" mit Zufallsstartzahlen und festen Auswahlabständen simuliert. Für die Arbeitnehmerauswahl in den Gehalts- und Lohnstrukturerhebungen wurde den Berichtsstellen ebenfalls gelegentlich das systematische Auswahlverfahren angeboten; von dieser Möglichkeit wurde jedoch von den Berichtsstellen kaum Gebrauch gemacht. Das normale Verfahren der zufälligen Arbeitnehmerauswahl war die Auswahl nach den Anfangsbuchstaben der Familiennamen, die auf der Überlegung beruht, daß nach Beobachtungen über die Häufigkeit der Namensanfänge eine bestimmte Buchstabengruppe mit bestimmter Wahrscheinlichkeit einem Auswahlsatz entspricht, der innerhalb eines bestimmten Vertrauensbereichs um den laut Auswahlplan angestrebten Auswahlsatz liegt. Die Problematik der Buchstabenauswahl besteht darin, daß die Berichtsstellen zum Zwecke der "Arbeitsersparnis" vielfach nicht alle Personen mit den vorgegebenen Anfangsbuchstaben melden; diese Untererfassung, die von den Statistischen Ämtern nicht überprüft werden kann, führte dazu, daß die angestrebten Auswahlsätze für die Arbeitnehmerauswahl bei den Gehalts- und Lohnstrukturerhebungen meist unterschritten wurden. Die Buchstabenauswahl kommt als "konstante Buchstabenauswahl" und als "alternierende Buchstabenauswahl" vor. Bei der konstanten Buchstabenauswahl werden jeder Berichtsstelle die gleichen Buchstaben für die Arbeitnehmerauswahl zugewiesen (Gehalts- und Lohnstrukturerhebungen in der gewerblichen Wirtschaft 1951 und im öffentlichen Dienst 1950 und 1968, Lohnstrukturerhebungen in der Forstwirtschaft 1952/53 und 1961/62). Bei der alternierenden Buchstabenauswahl wird jedem Berichtsbetrieb in regelmäßigem Turnus eine von mehreren über das ganze Alphabet rotierenden Buchstabengruppen zugeteilt, die im voraus entsprechend den angestrebten Auswahlsätzen festgelegt wurden (übrige Gehalts- und Lohnstrukturerhebungen seit 1957). Sowohl die konstante als auch die alternierende Buchstabenauswahl kann im Falle von geschichteten Stichproben in der Weise differenziert werden, daß von Schicht zu Schicht unterschiedliche - innerhalb der Schicht konstante oder alternierende - Buchstabengruppen vorgegeben werden, die verschiedenen Auswahlsätzen für die Arbeitnehmerauswahl entsprechen (Gehalts- und Lohnstrukturerhebungen im öffentlichen Dienst 1968 und in der gewerblichen Wirtschaft seit 1957).

Die Auswahleinheiten der lohnstatistischen Erhebungen wurden bei den Summenerhebungen in einem einstufigen, bei den Individualerhebungen dagegen in einem zweistufigen oder dreistufigen Auswahlverfahren bestimmt, wobei in der dritten Stufe stets eine Totalerfassung erfolgte, während in der ersten und der zweiten Stufe in unterschiedlicher Weise Totalerhebungen oder Teilerhebungen vorgenommen wurden. Das zweistufige Auswahlverfahren kam zunächst in der Form vor, daß in ausgewählten Betrieben jeweils sämtliche Arbeiter bzw. Arbeitnehmer einzeln zu erfassen waren (Individualerhebungen des Statistischen Reichsamtes, Lohnstrukturerhebungen in der Landwirtschaft 1950 und in der Forstwirtschaft 1949/50, laufende nationale Verdiensterhebungen in der Landwirtschaft, Gehalts- und Lohnstrukturerhebungen in der Landwirtschaft 1962/63 und im Erwerbsgartenbau 1962). In einigen Fällen erfolgte die zweistufige Auswahl, indem in sämtlichen Berichtsstellen jeweils ausgewählte Arbeitnehmer erfaßt wurden (Gehalts- und Lohnstrukturerhebungen im öffentlichen Dienst 1950 und 1968, Lohnstrukturerhebungen in der Forstwirtschaft 1952/53 und 1961/62). Vielfach wurden in ausgewählten Betrieben bzw. Unternehmen (erste Stufe) jeweils ausgewählte Arbeitnehmer (zweite Stufe) in die Erhebungen einbezogen (nationale Gehalts- und Lohnstrukturerhebungen in der gewerblichen Wirtschaft, Gehalts- und Lohnstrukturerhebungen der Europäischen Gemeinschaften). In drei Stufen wurden die Auswahleinheiten erstmalig bei einigen Erhebungen der Kommission für Arbeiterstatistik (1892 bis 1902) bestimmt; hier wurden innerhalb von ausgewählten Orten bzw. Stadtbezirken in jeweils sämtlichen in Frage kommenden Betrieben alle Arbeitnehmer einzeln erfaßt. Bei der Gehalts- und Lohnstrukturerhebung in der Landwirtschaft 1953/54 wurden in ausgewählten Gemeinden (erste Stufe) ausgewählte Betriebe (zweite Stufe) nach Individualangaben für grundsätzlich sämtliche bei ihnen beschäftigten Arbeitnehmer (dritte Stufe) befragt. Bei den Erhebungen der Europäischen Gemeinschaften über die Arbeiterverdienste in der Landwirtschaft wurden in ausgewählten Gemeinden sämtliche Betriebe und in diesen Betrieben sämtliche Arbeiter einzeln einbezogen; die Gemeinden wurden dabei mit ungleichen Wahrscheinlichkeiten proportional zur Anzahl ihrer Betriebe ausgewählt.

Nachdem bereits das Statistische Reichsamt bei der Lohnstrukturerhebung in der Forstwirtschaft 1939/40 erstmalig eine

Schichtung der Auswahlgesamtheit vorgenommen und unterschiedliche Auswahlsätze in den einzelnen Schichten angewendet hatte, wurde nach dem Zweiten Weltkrieg das Verfahren der geschichteten Auswahl die Regel; nur ausnahmsweise wurde noch auf eine Schichtung verzichtet (Gehalts- und Lohnstrukturerhebung im Erwerbsgartenbau 1962, repräsentativer Teil der Personalkostenerhebung der Europäischen Gemeinschaften im Einzelhandel, Bank- und Versicherungsgewerbe 1970). Als allgemeine Schichtungsmerkmale kamen in der amtlichen Lohnstatistik die Merkmale Bundesland, Wirtschaftszweig und Betriebs- bzw. Unternehmensgrößenklasse - gemessen an der Beschäftigten- bzw. Arbeitnehmerzahl oder an der landwirtschaftlichen Nutzfläche bzw. Forstfläche - vor. Bei den Lohnstrukturerhebungen in der Forstwirtschaft wurde auch nach der Besitzart (staatliche, kommunale oder private Forstbetriebe), bei den Gehalts- und Lohnstrukturerhebungen im öffentlichen Dienst nach Beschäftigungsbereichen (Behörden und Einrichtungen, Wirtschaftsunternehmen, Sozialversicherungsträger) und nach Dienstherren (Bund, die einzelnen Länder, die Gesamtheit der Gemeinden und Gemeindeverbände jedes Landes) geschichtet. Die vierteljährliche Verdiensterhebung in Industrie und Handel sollte ab 1964 in ihren Ergebnissen nach Wirtschaftszweigen tiefer gegliedert sein als die Auswahlgrundlagen zum Zeitpunkt der Erstellung des Auswahlplans; daher wurden bei der Neuauswahl von 1964 innerhalb der Schichten teilweise noch Untergruppen gebildet, die dann durch das systematische Auswahlverfahren jeweils proportional zu ihrem Umfang erfaßt wurden. Bei den geschichteten Stichprobenerhebungen wurden die Einheiten der Auswahlgesamtheiten in jeder Schicht gewöhnlich noch in bestimmter Weise angeordnet, und zwar entweder regional (z. B. Neuauswahl der vierteljährlichen Verdiensterhebung von 1972) oder nach der Beschäftigtenzahl (z. B. Neuauswahl der vierteljährlichen Verdiensterhebung von 1964) oder auch erst regional und dann nach der Beschäftigtenzahl (z. B. Gehalts- und Lohnstrukturerhebung in der gewerblichen Wirtschaft 1966). Nach der Schichtung und Anordnung der Einheiten der Auswahlgesamtheiten waren die Stichprobeneinheiten gesondert in jeder Schicht unter Anwendung bestimmter Auswahlsätze zu bestimmen. Dabei wurde das

Modell der proportional geschichteten Auswahl mit gleichen Auswahlsätzen in allen Schichten nur bei der im Jahre 1957 vorgenommenen Betriebsauswahl der Verdiensterhebung in Industrie und Handel und der Verdiensterhebung im Handwerk und nur in der Weise angewendet, daß so viele Betriebe auszuwählen waren, daß in jeder Schicht ein grundsätzlich etwa gleich hoher Prozentsatz der Arbeitnehmer der Grundgesamtheit erfaßt wurde. Das übliche Verfahren bestand dagegen darin, die innerhalb der Schichten stets gleichbleibenden Auswahlsätze von Schicht zu Schicht zu variieren. Die Variation der Auswahlsätze erfolgte ausnahmsweise ohne stichprobentheoretische Erwägungen nach Kostengesichtspunkten (Gehalts- und Lohnstrukturerhebung in der gewerblichen Wirtschaft 1962) oder nach Gesichtspunkten der Praktibilität (z. B. Erhebung über die Vermögensbildung der Arbeitnehmer 1963), in der Regel jedoch nach dem Modell der optimal geschichteten Auswahl oder nach einer vorgegebenen Genauigkeitsabstufung. Ein prinzipiell optimale Aufteilung des Gesamtstichprobenumfangs auf die Schichten im Sinne des Satzes von Tschuprow und Neyman wurde z. B. bei der Neuauswahl der Verdiensterhebung in Industrie und Handel von 1964 und bei der Stichprobenziehung für die Erhebungen über die betriebliche Altersversorgung von 1973 und 1976 vorgenommen. Nach einer Genauigkeitsabstufung wurden die Gesamtstichprobenumfänge z. B. bei den Personalkostenerhebungen der Europäischen Gemeinschaften im produzierenden Gewerbe ab 1966 und im Handel, Bank- und Versicherungsgewerbe 1974, bei den Gehalts- und Lohnstrukturerhebungen in der gewerblichen Wirtschaft 1966 und 1972, im öffentlichen Dienst 1968 und im Handel, Bank- und Versicherungsgewerbe 1974 und bei den Stichprobenziehungen für die nationale und die europäische laufende Verdiensterhebung in der Landwirtschaft von 1971 bzw. 1974 auf die Schichten aufgeteilt. Teilweise wurde auch die optimale Aufteilung mit der Aufteilung nach einer Genauigkeitsabstufung kombiniert. Bei der Neuauswahl der Verdiensterhebung im Handwerk von 1966 wurde zwischen den Handwerkszweigen eine Genauigkeitsabstufung, bei der Aufteilung der Stichprobenumfänge je Handwerkszweig auf die Schichten dagegen eine optimale Aufteilung vorgesehen. Analog wurde bei der Neuauswahl der

Verdiensterhebung in Industrie und Handel von 1972 der Gesamtstichprobenumfang auf die Schichtgruppen - d. h. die Wirtschaftszweige - nach einer Genauigkeitsabstufung, der Stichprobenumfang je Schichtgruppe auf die Schichten optimal aufgeteilt.

Soweit als Auswahlgrundlagen für die lohnstatistischen Repräsentativerhebungen Auflistungen verwendet wurden, die selbst aus Repräsentativerhebungen stammten, ergab sich insgesamt ein zweiphasiges Auswahlverfahren. Bei der Zusammenstellung des ersten Berichtskreises der Verdiensterhebung in der Landwirtschaft im Jahre 1957 wurden aus den Betrieben der repräsentativen Landarbeitskräfteerhebung 1956 (erste Phase) die Berichtsbetriebe der Verdiensterhebung als Unterstichprobe ausgewählt (zweite Phase). Bei der Neuauswahl der Verdiensterhebung in der Landwirtschaft von 1971 bestand die Stichprobe der ersten Phase aus den Betrieben der repräsentativen Landarbeitskräfteerhebung 1970 und die Stichprobe der zweiten Phase aus den daraus ausgewählten Berichtsbetrieben der Verdiensterhebung. Die Stichprobenunternehmen der Erhebungen über die betriebliche Altersversorgung von 1973 und 1976 wurden im Bereich des produzierenden Gewerbes in einer zweiten Phase aus den Berichtskreisen der repräsentativen Personalkostenerhebungen der Europäischen Gemeinschaften von 1972 bzw. 1975 ausgewählt; in den übrigen Wirtschaftsbereichen, für die die totale Arbeitsstättenzählung 1970 Auswahlgrundlage war, wurde dagegen die übliche einphasige Auswahl vorgenommen. Ein zweiphasiges Auswahlverfahren war ursprünglich auch bei der Erhebung über die Vermögensbildung der Arbeitnehmer von 1963 geplant. Danach sollten in der ersten Phase ausgewählte Unternehmen mit einer Postkarte befragt werden, ob das Vermögensbildungsgesetz überhaupt angewendet würde; auf Grund des Ergebnisses dieser Vorbefragung sollten dann in der zweiten Phase nach differenzierteren Auswahlsätzen die mit Fragebogen zu erfassenden Berichtsunternehmen ausgewählt werden. Dieses zweiphasige Auswahlverfahren wurde von den meisten Statistischen Landesämtern wegen der zusätzlichen Kosten des Versands der Postkarten abgelehnt; praktiziert wurde stattdessen die übliche einphasige Auswahl.

Das Verfahren der einstufigen Klumpenauswahl fand in der amtlichen Lohnstatistik bisher erst einmal Anwendung, und zwar bei der Gehalts- und Lohnstrukturerhebung in der Landwirtschaft 1962/63. Für diese Erhebung standen den Statistischen Landesämtern verschiedene vom Statistischen Bundesamt aufgestellte Auswahlpläne zur Verfügung. Nach dem in Nordrhein-Westfalen angewendeten Auswahlplan wurden zunächst die Betriebe der Auswahlgesamtheit regional nach Gemeinden sortiert, wobei die Gemeinden einer geographischen Anordnung in Serpentinenlinie folgten. Als Berichtsbetriebe wurden dann nach dem systematischen Auswahlverfahren ausgewählte Betriebe sowie jeweils eine nach Schichten unterschiedlich starke Gruppe von in der Anordnung der Auswahlgesamtheit unmittelbar darauffolgenden Betrieben ausgewählt. In die Stichprobe gelangten auf diese Weise ganze Klumpen regional benachbarter Betriebe.

3324 Hochrechnung

Eine Hochrechnung der Stichprobenangaben auf 100 % der Grundgesamtheit ist in jedem Fall erforderlich, wenn - wie z. B. bei den Personalkostenerhebungen - aus den für die Berichtsstellen ermittelten Summenangaben auf die entsprechenden Summen für die Grundgesamtheit geschlossen werden soll. Wenn dagegen nur Durchschnittsangaben bzw. Verhältniswerte zu ermitteln sind, kann grundsätzlich auf eine Hochrechnung verzichtet werden, es sei denn, daß eine geschichtete Auswahl mit unterschiedlichen Auswahlsätzen in den Schichten vorgenommen wurde; in diesem Fall muß zur Berechnung von alle Schichten umfassenden Gesamtergebnissen eine Umrechnung auf einen einheitlichen Auswahlsatz oder eine Hochrechnung auf 100 % der Grundgesamtheit erfolgen. Von der Umrechnung - Hochrechnung oder Reduktion - auf einen unter 100 % liegenden einheitlichen Auswahlsatz wurde in der amtlichen Lohnstatistik nur ausnahmsweise Gebrauch gemacht. Bei den Lohnstrukturerhebungen in der Forstwirtschaft 1952/53 und 1961/62 wurden die Angaben der total erfaßten Haumeister auf das Niveau der zu einem Viertel erfaßten übrigen Arbeiter reduziert. Soweit in der Verdiensterhebung in Industrie und Handel vor 1964 in einigen Wirtschaftsbereichen die Erfassung von 10 % der Arbeitnehmer der Grundgesamtheit angestrebt wurde, wurde eine Hochrechnung auf den allgemeinen Satz von 25 % vorgenommen; bei einer beabsichtigten - z. B. im total erfaßten Bergbau - oder unbeabsichtigten Überschreitung dieses allgemeinen Satzes erfolgte eine entsprechende Reduktion. Bei der Verdiensterhebung in der Landwirtschaft wurden vor 1971 die mit von Schicht zu Schicht prinzipiell unterschiedlichen Auswahlsätzen erfaßten Stichprobendaten auf den einheitlichen Satz von 10 % der Grundgesamtheit hochgerechnet bzw. reduziert. Abgesehen von diesen Ausnahmefällen war das für die Lohnstatistik normale Hochrechnungsverfahren die Hochrechnung auf 100 % der Grundgesamtheit. Als Hochrechnungsfaktoren wurden dabei gewöhnlich die Kehrwerte der im Auswahlplan festgelegten Auswahlsätze unverändert übernommen. Gelegentlich wurden die Hochrechnungsfaktoren auch nach vollzogener Auswahl auf Grund der tatsächlichen Verhältnisse zur Zeit der Stichprobenziehung - d. h. unter Umständen abweichend von dem früher aufgestellten Auswahlplan - korrigiert; dies geschah bei den Stichprobenziehungen der Verdiensterhebung in Industrie und Handel von 1964 und 1972 und der Verdiensterhebung im Handwerk von 1966. Da diese Hochrechnungsfaktoren aus dem Auswahlplan abgeleitet wurden, bezogen sie sich stets auf die Auswahleinheiten; das bedeutete z. B. für die Verdiensterhebung in Industrie und Handel ab 1964, daß die Hochrechnung nicht mehr wie früher nach der Anzahl der erfaßten Arbeitnehmer, sondern nunmehr nach der Anzahl der erfaßten Auswahleinheiten - d. h. Betriebe - vorgenommen wurde. Bei der Hochrechnung wurden im allgemeinen jeweils die für die kleinsten vorkommenden Auswahleinheiten - Betriebe, Unternehmen, Arbeitnehmer - in der Stichprobe ermittelten Verdienst- bzw. Kostenangaben einzeln mit dem Hochrechnungsfaktor der Auswahleinheit multipliziert. So wurden z. B. die Stichprobenangaben der Personalkostenerhebungen der Europäischen Gemeinschaften gesondert für jedes einzelne Unternehmen hochgerechnet. Bei den Gehalts- und Lohnstrukturerhebungen wurden diese Angaben gesondert für jeden einzelnen erfaßten Arbeitnehmer hochgerechnet. Bei der Verdiensterhebung in Industrie und

Handel wurde eine derartige Hochrechnung je Auswahleinheit - in diesem Falle je Betrieb - erst ab 1974 generell angewendet. Vor 1974 wurden die von den Berichtsbetrieben der vierteljährlichen Verdiensterhebung gemeldeten summarischen Verdienstangaben innerhalb jeder Schicht aufaddiert und erst anschließend mit dem für alle Betriebe der betreffenden Schicht gleichen Hochrechnungsfaktor multipliziert. Diese Hochrechnung "je Schicht" mußte auf die sogenannten "Normalschichten" beschränkt bleiben; wenn ein Berichtsbetrieb nach der Stichprobenziehung z. B. seinen Wirtschaftszweig änderte, mußte er aus seiner ursprünglichen Normalschicht herausgenommen und mit seinem unveränderten Hochrechnungsfaktor der für seinen neuen Wirtschaftszweig zu bildenden "Sonderschicht" zugeordnet werden, in der dann wegen möglicherweise unterschiedlicher Hochrechnungsfaktoren der ihr angehörenden Betriebe eine Hochrechnung "je Betrieb" erforderlich war. Bei der seit 1974 in der vierteljährlichen Verdiensterhebung allgemein vorgesehenen Hochrechnung "je Betrieb" konnte auf die in der Praxis der Aufbereitung komplizierte Unterscheidung zwischen Normalschichten und Sonderschichten verzichtet werden.

Die Hochrechnungsfaktoren konnten nur dann aus dem Auswahlplan als Kehrwerte der Auswahlsätze direkt abgelesen werden, wenn eine einstufige und einphasige Auswahl vorlag. Bei einer mehrstufigen oder mehrphasigen Auswahl ergaben sich die Gesamtauswahlsätze und damit die Kehrwerte der Hochrechnungsfaktoren als Produkte aus den Auswahlsätzen der einzelnen Stufen bzw. Phasen. Bei den Gehalts- und Lohnstrukturerhebungen in der gewerblichen Wirtschaft 1966 und 1972 - die früheren Strukturerhebungen in der gewerblichen Wirtschaft konnten wegen gleicher Gesamtauswahlsätze in allen Schichten auf ein Hochrechnung verzichten - und im Handel, Bank- und Versicherungsgewerbe 1974 wurden die Hochrechnungsfaktoren als Produkte aus den reziproken Auswahlsätzen für die Betriebs- bzw. Unternehmensauswahl (erste Stufe) und den reziproken Auswahlsätzen für die Arbeitnehmerauswahl (zweite Stufe) errechnet. Analog wurden die Hochrechnungsfaktoren bei der Erhebung der Europäischen Gemeinschaften über die Arbeiterverdienste in der Landwirtschaft als Produkte aus den reziproken Auswahlsätzen für die Gemeindeauswahl (erste Stufe) und für die Betriebsauswahl (zweite Stufe) ermittelt. Die Hochrechnungsfaktoren der nationalen Verdiensterhebung in der Landwirtschaft, die ab 1971 abweichend von dem früheren Verfahren zu einer Hochrechnung auf 100 % der Grundgesamtheit führten, ergaben sich seit dieser Zeit durch Multiplikation der reziproken Auswahlsätze der ersten Auswahlphase (Stichprobe der repräsentativen Landarbeitskräfteerhebung 1970) und der zweiten Phase (Berichtskreis der Verdiensterhebung). Entsprechend wurden zur Bestimmung der Hochrechnungsfaktoren für den zweiphasigen Teil der Erhebungen über die betriebliche Altersversorgung 1973 und 1976 die Kehrwerte der Auswahlsätze der ersten Phase (Stichproben der Personalkostenerhebungen der Europäischen Gemeinschaften im produzierenden Gewerbe 1972 bzw. 1975) und der zweiten Phase (Berichtsunternehmen der Erhebungen über die betriebliche Altersversorgung) miteinander multipliziert.

Ausnahmsweise wurden die Hochrechnungsfaktoren der amtlichen Lohnstatistik nicht einfach als - eventuell nachträglich korrigierte - Funktionen der Auswahlsätze aus den Auswahlplänen abgeleitet, sondern auf Grund weiterer Informationen oder Annahmen festgesetzt. Bei der Lohnstrukturerhebung in der Forstwirtschaft 1949/50 wurden die Verdienstangaben über die in der Erhebung erfaßten Arbeiter auf 100 % aller Forstarbeiter hochgerechnet; die dazu notwendigen Totalzahlen der Forstarbeiter wurden den Akten der zentralen forstwirtschaftlichen Verwaltungsbehörden der Länder entnommen. Bei der Erhebung über die sozialen Nebenleistungen im Rahmen der Gehalts- und Lohnstrukturerhebung in der gewerblichen Wirtschaft 1957 wurde angenommen, daß von den kleinen Unternehmen - mit weniger als 100 Arbeitnehmern - die Hälfte und von den größeren Unternehmen alle erfaßt worden wären; daher wurden die Angaben der kleinen Unternehmen allgemein mit dem Hochrechnungsfaktor 2 hochgerechnet.

3325 Behandlung von Antwortausfällen

Wenn von einzelnen Berichtsstellen keine Auskünfte eingehen, ist zwischen unechten und echten Antwortausfällen zu unterscheiden. Unechte Antwortausfälle liegen vor, wenn eine Berichtsstelle zwar in der Auswahlgrundlage enthalten war, zum Zeitpunkt der Befragung jedoch nicht mehr bestand oder nicht mehr zu den erfaßten Wirtschaftsbereichen gehörte. Um echte Antwortausfälle handelt es sich, wenn bestehende und zum Erhebungsbereich gehörende Berichtsstellen die Antwort verweigern oder so spät bzw. so schlecht erteilen, daß sie nicht mehr verwertet werden kann. Da bei unechten Antwortausfällen die Berichtsstellen nicht zur Grundgesamtheit gehören und nur irrtümlich zur Berichterstattung aufgefordert wurden, ist es folgerichtig, daß derartige Berichtsstellen in der amtlichen Lohnstatistik in der Regel ersatzlos aus dem Berichtskreis gestrichen wurden; bei einigen lohnstatistischen Erhebungen wurde allerdings ein Ersatz vorgenommen. Bei der Gehalts- und Lohnstrukturerhebung in der Landwirtschaft 1953/54 wurden im Falle unechter oder echter Antwortausfälle nachträglich gezielt ausgewählte Ersatzbetriebe herangezogen. Bei der Verdiensterhebung im Handwerk von 1957 bis 1965 und bei der Gehalts- und Lohnstrukturerhebung in der Landwirtschaft 1962/63 wurden von vorn herein nach dem gleichen Verfahren wie die übrigen Berichtsbetriebe Reservebetriebe ausgewählt, laufend miterfaßt und bei Bedarf - d. h. im Falle unechter oder echter Antwortausfälle - in die Aufbereitung einbezogen. In der Verdiensterhebung in Industrie und Handel sollten vor 1964 nach den Richtlinien des Statistischen Bundesamtes unechte Antwortausfälle laufend durch neu ausgewählte vergleichbare Betriebe ersetzt werden; im Statistischen Landesamt Nordrhein-Westfalen wurde allerdings in diesen Fällen wegen methodischer Bedenken gegen die Heranziehung von Ersatzbetrieben eine ersatzlose Streichung vorgenommen.

Im Gegensatz zu den unechten Antwortausfällen gehören die "echt" ausfallenden Berichtsstellen zur Grundgesamtheit und wurden daher in der amtlichen Lohnstatistik fast immer ersetzt.

Das erwähnte Verfahren der Heranziehung von Ersatz- bzw. Reservebetrieben fand dabei außer bei den genannten Erhebungen auch in den Gehalts- und Lohnstrukturerhebungen in der gewerblichen Wirtschaft 1957 und 1962 und in der Verdiensterhebung in Industrie und Handel vor 1964 Anwendung, in denen jeweils von vorn herein Reservebetriebe ausgewählt, miterfaßt und bei Bedarf - d. h. im Falle echter Antwortausfälle - in die Aufbereitung einbezogen wurden. Bei den meisten lohnstatistischen Erhebungen wurden die echten Antwortausfälle dagegen durch Dopplung der aus der Befragung bereits vorliegenden Angaben vergleichbarer Berichtsstellen ersetzt. Diese Dopplung wurde z. B. bei den Personalkostenerhebungen der Europäischen Gemeinschaften, den Gehalts- und Lohnstrukturerhebungen in der gewerblichen Wirtschaft 1966 und 1972 und im Handel, Bank- und Versicherungsgewerbe 1974 sowie bei der Erhebung der Europäischen Gemeinschaften über die Arbeiterverdienste in der Landwirtschaft - hier wurden echte Antwortausfälle allerdings nur dann ersetzt, wenn sie besonders zahlreich auftraten - angewendet. Bei den laufenden Verdiensterhebungen in Industrie und Handel und in der Landwirtschaft ab 1964 sowie im Handwerk ab 1966 wurden echte Antwortausfälle durch einen pro Schicht ermittelten besonderen "Ergänzungsfaktor" ausgeglichen. Die Ergänzungsfaktoren bewirkten eine Vergrößerung der Hochrechnungsfaktoren und ergaben sich jeweils als Quotient aus der Anzahl der für den Erhebungsmonat berichtspflichtigen Betriebe und der Anzahl der tatsächlich antwortenden (einschließlich der ruhenden) Berichtsbetriebe. Bei der Erhebung über die betriebliche Altersversorgung 1973 wurden die echten wie die unechten Antwortausfälle in keinem Fall ersetzt, da sie nur in sehr geringem Maße vorkamen.

3326 Rotation

Bei den laufenden Verdiensterhebungen waren die statistischen Ämter stets bemüht, im Falle eines Berichtskreiswechsels die bisherigen Berichtsbetriebe so weit wie möglich von der Berichterstattung zu entbinden und durch neue Berichtsbetriebe zu ersetzen. Dies geschah, indem bei der Ziehung der neuen

Stichprobe das übliche systematische Auswahlverfahren in der Weise modifiziert wurde, daß dann nicht immer der bei der Anwendung des vorgegebenen Auswahlabstands zu erfassende Betrieb ausgewählt wurde, wenn dieser Betrieb bereits zum alten Berichtskreis gehört hatte. In diesen Fällen wurde statt des zunächst bestimmten der nächstfolgende bisher nicht erfaßte Betrieb ausgewählt, falls ein solcher in der betreffenden Schicht innerhalb des Auswahlabstandes vorhanden war. Eine derartige "Rotation", die nur in nicht total erfaßten Schichten möglich ist, wurde bei den Stichprobenziehungen der Verdiensterhebung in Industrie und Handel von 1964 und 1972, der Verdiensterhebung in der Landwirtschaft von 1964 und der Verdiensterhebung im Handwerk von 1966 vorgenommen. Bei der Stichprobenziehung der Verdiensterhebung in der Landwirtschaft von 1964 wurden über die normale Rotation hinaus so weit wie möglich auch diejenigen Betriebe ausgelassen, die zur Gehalts- und Lohnstrukturerhebung in der Landwirtschaft 1962/63 herangezogen worden waren. Eine ähnliche atypische Rotation kam bereits bei der ersten Auswahl der Berichtsbetriebe zur Verdiensterhebung in der Landwirtschaft im Jahre 1957 vor, als diejenigen Betriebe nicht ausgewählt wurden, die als Unterstichprobe innerhalb der repräsentativen Landarbeitskräfteerhebung 1956 zu einer monatlichen Berichterstattung verpflichtet waren. Bei der Erstauswahl der Berichtsbetriebe der Verdiensterhebung im Handwerk von 1957 wurden in Nordrhein-Westfalen solche zunächst ausgewählten Betriebe von der Berichterstattung freigestellt, die freiwillig an der nichtamtlichen Handwerksberichterstattung der Handwerkskammern teilnahmen.

34 Die Durchführung der Erhebung

341 Erhebungsverfahren

3411 Individualverfahren

Vor der Befragung der Berichtsstellen als der statistischen Erhebungsphase im engeren Sinne sind das Erhebungsverfahren und das Erhebungsprogramm - d. h. die Erhebungsmerkmale - festzulegen. Als Erhebungsverfahren kommen für die Lohnstatistik das Individualverfahren und das Summenverfahren in Frage. Bei dem Individualverfahren werden für jeden zur Erhebungsmasse gehörenden Arbeitnehmer die Erhebungsmerkmale individuell erfaßt. Dadurch sind sehr genaue und detaillierte Einblicke in das zu einer bestimmten Erhebungszeit bestehende Verdienstgefüge möglich. Insbesondere können Häufigkeitsverteilungen der Arbeitnehmer nach Verdienstklassen aufgestellt und die Verdienststreuung nicht nur von Berichtsstelle zu Berichtsstelle, sondern auch innerhalb jeder Berichtsstelle von Arbeitnehmer zu Arbeitnehmer gemessen werden. Die Nachteile des Individualverfahrens bestehen darin, daß es sowohl für die Berichtsstellen als auch für die Erhebungsbehörden sehr arbeits- und zeitaufwendig ist und daher erst längere Zeit nach dem Berichtszeitraum Ergebnisse liefern kann. Das Individualverfahren ist somit das angemessene Verfahren für die umfassende einmalige oder in größeren Zeitabständen wiederholte Untersuchung der Verdienststruktur.

Im Individualverfahren wurden in der frühesten Zeit der Lohnstatistik des Deutschen Reichs vor allem die Statistik der Monatsheuern von Seeleuten von 1874 bis 1922, einige Erhebungen der Kommission für Arbeiterstatistik von 1892 bis 1902 und die Erhebungen über die Löhne städtischer Arbeiter von 1902 und 1907 durchgeführt. Später folgten die Lohn- und Gehaltserhebung vom Februar 1920 sowie die Individual- bzw. Strukturerhebungen über Arbeitsverdienste in wechselnden Wirtschaftsbereichen von 1927 bis 1940. Nach dem Zweiten Weltkrieg fanden die in verschiedenen Wirtschaftsbereichen einschließlich des öffentlichen Dienstes durchgeführten Gehalts- und Lohnstrukturerhebungen im Individualverfahren statt. Von den laufenden lohnstatistischen Erhebungen wurden nur noch die nationale und die europäische Verdiensterhebung in der Landwirtschaft als Individualerhebungen durchgeführt.

3412 Summenverfahren

Die Lohnstatistik hat neben der einmaligen oder gelegentlichen Untersuchung der Verdienststruktur auch die Aufgabe, die Verdienstentwicklung laufend zu beobachten. Zu diesem Zweck kommt das langwierige Individualverfahren nicht in Frage; vielmehr muß ein Erhebungsverfahren angewendet werden, das laufend kurzfristig nach der Erhebungszeit Ergebnisse liefert, die zugunsten der Aktualität weniger genau bzw. detailliert sein können. Das angemessene Verfahren für die Beobachtung der Verdienstentwicklung ist das Summenverfahren. Beim Summenverfahren wird nicht der Verdienst für jeden einzelnen Arbeitnehmer, sondern nur die Verdienstsumme für eine ganze hinsichtlich der Tätigkeitsmerkmale und der Verdienste so weit wie möglich homogene Arbeitnehmergruppe jeweils einer Berichtsstelle erfragt. Auf diese Weise können mit relativ geringem Kosten- und Zeitaufwand statistische Angaben für einen großen Kreis von Berichtsstellen bzw. eine große Zahl von Arbeitnehmern laufend erfaßt und zu aktuellen Ergebnissen verarbeitet werden. Der Nachteil des Summenverfahrens besteht darin, daß die Verdienststreuung nur von Berichtsstelle zu Berichtsstelle und von Arbeitnehmergruppe zu Arbeitnehmergruppe, dagegen nicht innerhalb der Arbeitnehmergruppen jeweils einer Berichtsstelle von Arbeitnehmer zu Arbeitnehmer gemessen werden kann. Die Aufstellung von Häufigkeitsverteilungen der Arbeitnehmer nach Verdienstklassen ist also beim Summenverfahren nicht möglich.

In der Frühzeit der amtlichen Lohnstatistik wurde das Summenverfahren vor allem bei den vom Kaiserlichen Statistischen Amt veranstalteten Erhebungen über die Lohnverhältnisse der Jahre 1914 bis 1919 sowie bis in die Gegenwart in der Bergarbeiterlohnstatistik angewendet. Ein besonders bedeutendes Anwendungsgebiet fand das Verfahren in der vierteljährlichen Industriearbeiterlohnstatistik ab 1935. Nach dem Zweiten Weltkrieg nahm der Anteil der Summenerhebungen an den lohnstatistischen Erhebungen weiter zu. Summenerhebungen waren die erweiterte Industriearbeiterlohnerhebung vom September 1949, die Angestelltenverdiensterhebung vom Mai 1949 und später die laufenden Verdiensterhebungen in Industrie und Handel und im Handwerk, letztere mit ergänzenden Individualangaben. Als Summenerhebungen wurden auch die Personalkostenerhebungen der Montanunion ab 1953, der Internationalen Arbeitsorganisation von 1955 und der Europäischen Wirtschaftsgemeinschaft ab 1959 sowie die nationale Erhebung über soziale Nebenleistungen von 1957 durchgeführt. Im Summenverfahren fanden schließlich die Erhebung über die Vermögensbildung der Arbeitnehmer von 1963 und die Erhebungen über die betriebliche Altersversorgung von 1973 und 1976 statt.

342 Erhebungsprogramm

3421 Individuell erfaßte Merkmale

Bei den individuell erfaßten Erhebungsmerkmalen der Lohnstatistik werden die Merkmalsausprägungen für jeden einzelnen Arbeitnehmer festgestellt; diese Merkmale bilden damit das Erhebungsprogramm der Individualerhebungen. Das zentrale individuelle Merkmal war für die Lohnstatistik stets der persönliche Verdienst des Arbeitnehmers als Brutto- oder Nettoverdienst, der oft nach seinen Bestandteilen aufgegliedert wurde. Ferner wurden häufig die gesetzlichen Abzüge, der Arbeitgeberbeitrag zur Sozialversicherung und die tarifliche Lohn- oder Gehaltsgruppe - bei Beamten die gesetzliche Besoldungsgruppe - sowie gelegentlich auch der tarifliche Lohn- oder Gehaltssatz individuell erfaßt. Die dem Arbeitnehmer gewährten Naturalleistungen wurden nach Arten und Mengen und in wenigen Fällen auch nach Werten erfragt; in der Regel wurde die Bewertung jedoch nachträglich in den Statistischen Ämtern vorgenommen. Bei den Gehalts- und Lohnstrukturerhebungen wurde für die einzelnen Arbeitnehmer eine Reihe von Merkmalen ermittelt, von denen die Verdiensthöhe abhängt; als solche Merkmale kamen vor allem die Lohnform, das Geschlecht, der Familienstand, die Kinderzahl, das Lebensalter, der Beruf bzw. die ausgeübte Tätigkeit, die Qualifikation bzw. die erreichte Ausbildung, das Dienstalter bzw. die Anzahl der Berufsjahre und die Dauer der Betriebs- oder Unternehmenszugehörigkeit vor. Weitere Erhebungsmerkmale der Individualerhebungen waren die persönliche Arbeitszeit, die Anzahl der Urlaubstage, die Lohnabrechnungsform (Stundenlohn, fester Wochenlohn, Monatslohn) und der Beschäftigungsmodus (Voll- oder Teilzeitbeschäftigung).

3422 <u>Summarisch erfaßte Merkmale</u>

Die summarisch erfaßten Erhebungsmerkmale werden jeweils nur für die ganze Berichtsstelle bzw. eine ganze Arbeitnehmergruppe der Berichtsstelle ermittelt; sie sind in den Summenerhebungen die einzigen möglichen Merkmale, kommen darüberhinaus jedoch auch bei den Individualerhebungen vor, wenn statt des einzelnen Arbeitnehmers die Berichtsstelle gekennzeichnet werden soll oder wenn dieselbe Merkmalsausprägung - z. B. ein einheitlicher Tarifvertrag - für alle Arbeitnehmer der Berichtsstelle gilt. Merkmale zur Kennzeichnung der Berichtsstelle sind vor allem der Wirtschaftszweig, die Größe der Berichtsstelle - gemessen an der Anzahl der Arbeitnehmer bzw. der Beschäftigten oder gegebenenfalls an der landwirtschaftlichen Nutzfläche bzw. der Forstfläche -, der Standort, das Tarifgebiet und die tarifliche Ortsklasse, die betriebsübliche Arbeitszeit und die betriebliche Arbeitszeiteinteilung (Fünf- oder Sechstagewoche). Die für die Lohnstatistik bedeutendsten summarisch erfaßten Merkmale sind die Bruttolohn- bzw. -gehaltssumme und die Arbeitsstundensumme; daneben wurden ausnahmsweise - vor allem in der vierteljährlichen Lohnsummenerhebung des Statistischen Reichsamtes - auch die Nettolohnsumme und die Summe der Arbeitgeberbeiträge zur Sozialversicherung erfaßt. Besonders umfangreich waren die Erhebungsprogramme der Angestelltenverdiensterhebung vom Mai 1949 und der erweiterten Industriearbeiterlohnerhebung vom September 1949; hier wurden verschiedene Bestandteile des Bruttoverdienstes - z. B. die

Bezahlung für Über-, Sonn- und Feiertagsarbeit - und die gesetzlichen Abzüge summarisch erfaßt. Auch die Bergarbeiterlohnstatistik gliederte die Bruttolohnsumme nach verschiedenen Verdienstbestandteilen auf und ermittelte darüberhinaus die Wertsumme der Naturalleistungen (Kohlendeputate). Weitere summarisch erfaßte Merkmale der amtlichen Lohnstatistik waren die Personalkosten gegliedert nach Aufwandsarten einschließlich des Aufwands für Naturalleistungen, der Summe der vermögenswirksamen Leistungen und der Aufwendungen für die Altersversorgung der Arbeitnehmer (Personalkostenerhebungen der Europäischen Gemeinschaften, Erhebung über die Vermögensbildung der Arbeitnehmer, Erhebungen über die betriebliche Altersversorgung). Bei den Erhebungen über die betriebliche Altersversorgung hatten die Berichtsunternehmen nicht nur die tatsächlichen Aufwendungen, sondern auch die theoretisch von den Arbeitnehmern erreichbare Altersversorgung summarisch anzugeben.

35 Die Aufbereitung

351 Manuelles und maschinelles Verfahren

Die statistische Aufbereitung ist die Umwandlung der von den Berichtsstellen erfragten Einzelangaben in Informationen über Gesamtheiten; sie umfaßt in den Erhebungsbehörden die Arbeitsgänge von der Prüfung und eventuellen Korrektur der Einzelangaben bis zur Fertigstellung der statistischen Ergebnisse in Form von Kollektivmaßzahlen. Bei der in der amtlichen Statistik meist großen Zahl von Erhebungseinheiten war man seit langem bestrebt, die Aufbereitung mit Hilfe der maschinellen Datenverarbeitung vorzunehmen. Die lohnstatistischen Erhebungen wurden bereits im Statistischen Reichsamt teilweise mit Lochkartenmaschinen aufbereitet. Dieses Verfahren wurde nach dem Zweiten Weltkrieg im Statistischen Bundesamt und in den Statistischen Landesämtern allmählich ausgebaut. Bis gegen Ende der fünfziger Jahre gingen alle Statistischen Landesämter bei den meisten lohnstatistischen Erhebungen von der manuellen Aufbereitung auf die Aufbereitung mit Lochkartenmaschinen über. Die Lochkartenmaschinen wurden dabei in erster Linie für die

Erstellung der statistischen Ergebnisse eingesetzt, während die Plausibilitätskontrollen vorwiegend noch manuell durchgeführt wurden. Anfang der sechziger Jahre wurde das konventionelle Lochkartenverfahren in allen statistischen Ämtern durch die elektronische Datenverarbeitung ersetzt. Nunmehr konnten neben der Ergebnisberechnung und Tabellierung auch die Plausibilitätskontrollen weitgehend maschinell erfolgen. Diese vollmaschinelle Aufbereitung wurde für die gesamte amtliche Lohnstatistik die Regel. Nur einige Erhebungen mit besonders geringer Erhebungsmasse wurden weiterhin manuell bzw. mit Hilfe von Buchungsautomaten aufbereitet. Als gegen Ende der sechziger Jahre in den statistischen Ämtern leistungsfähigere EDV-Anlagen installiert wurden, konnten neben den Tabellenprogrammen vor allem die maschinellen Plausibilitätskontrollen der lohnstatistischen Erhebungen erheblich erweitert und verfeinert werden.

352 Plausibilitätskontrolle

Die von den Berichtsstellen gemeldeten lohnstatistischen Einzelangaben wurden in den Erhebungsbehörden vor der statistischen Verarbeitung stets einer eingehenden Prüfung auf wahrscheinliche Richtigkeit unterzogen. Die Prüfung erfolgte durch Vergleich der gemeldeten Einzelangaben mit gesetzlichen Bestimmungen oder tarifvertraglichen Regelungen oder mit - vor allem aus früheren Erhebungen - bereits vorliegenden Erfahrungswerten. In der Regel wurden für die Plausibilitätskontrollen Grenzwerte festgesetzt, die entweder gar nicht über - bzw. unterschritten werden durften oder die wahrscheinlich richtigen von den wahrscheinlich falschen Angaben abgrenzten; im ersten Fall bedeutete die Verletzung der Grenzwerte einen "Mußfehler", im zweiten Fall einen "Kannfehler". Ausnahmsweise ergaben sich bei lohnstatistischen Erhebungen zusätzliche Prüfmöglichkeiten. Da die Bruttojahresverdiensterhebung und die vierteljährliche Verdiensterhebung in Industrie und Handel denselben Kreis von Berichtsbetrieben erfaßten, konnten pro Betrieb die Einzelmeldungen der Jahreserhebung mit den bereits vorliegenden Einzelmeldungen der vierteljährlichen Erhebung für Zwecke der Plausibilitätskontrolle zusammengeführt werden. Bei den Erhebungen über die betriebliche Altersversorgung wurden von den Berichtsunternehmen des produzierenden Gewerbes unter anderem Angaben erfragt, die von denselben Unternehmen in ähnlicher Form bereits zu der jeweils letzten Personalkostenerhebung der Europäischen Gemeinschaften gemacht worden waren; obwohl sich die Angaben zu den beiden Erhebungen auf verschiedene Berichtsjahre bezogen, ergaben sich durch den Vergleich für jedes einzelne Unternehmen gute Prüfmöglichkeiten. Wenn bei einer lohnstatistischen Erhebung für die Plausibilitätskontrolle weder Erfahrungswerte aus früheren Erhebungen noch sonstige vorgegebene Vergleichswerte vorhanden waren, mußten die erforderlichen Grenzwerte aus den Daten der Erhebung selbst abgeleitet werden. Bei der Personalkostenerhebung der Europäischen Gemeinschaften im Straßenverkehrsgewerbe 1967 wurden aus den Angaben der Berichtsunternehmen über den Personalaufwand pro Arbeitnehmer Prüfgrößen berechnet, mit denen die unplausiblen Angaben ausgesondert werden konnten (vgl. Seite 156).

353 Umrechnung des Erhebungszeitraums

Bei den laufenden Verdiensterhebungen und den Gehalts- und Lohnstrukturerhebungen hatten die Berichtsstellen grundsätzlich Angaben für jeweils einen ganzen Erhebungsmonat zu liefern. Im Falle einer abweichenden Lohnabrechnungsperiode bestanden die Erhebungsbehörden jedoch nicht auf Angaben für genau einen Monat, sondern begnügten sich mit einer für die Berichtsstelle leichter aufzustellenden Meldung für einen kürzeren oder längeren Lohnabrechnungszeitraum, der sich so weit wie möglich mit dem eigentlichen Erhebungsmonat deckte. Bei der Aufbereitung in den statistischen Ämtern wurden dann die Angaben für die abweichende Lohnabrechnungsperiode auf einen Zeitraum von der Länge des Erhebungsmonats umgerechnet. Diese Umrechnung in Monatsangaben wurde bereits bei den vierteljährlichen Lohnsummenerhebungen des Statistischen Reichsamtes angewendet und kam nach dem Zweiten Weltkrieg vor allem bei den Gehalts- und Lohnstrukturerhebungen in der gewerblichen Wirtschaft und in der Landwirtschaft sowie bei der laufenden nationalen und europäischen Verdiensterhebung in der Landwirtschaft vor. Soweit für die Arbeiter durchschnittliche Wochenverdienste zu ermitteln waren, mußten die gemeldeten bzw. bei der Aufbereitung errechneten Monatsangaben von den Statistischen Ämtern in Wochenangaben umgewandelt werden. Die Umwandlung der Monatsangaben in Angaben für eine Durchschnittswoche wurde bei den Gehalts- und Lohnstrukturerhebungen in der gewerblichen Wirtschaft und im öffentlichen Dienst mit Hilfe eines "Reduktionsfaktors" vorgenommen. Bei der vierteljährlichen Industriearbeiterlohnstatistik nach dem Zweiten Weltkrieg bzw. später der Verdiensterhebung in Industrie und Handel wurden die Wochenangaben mit Hilfe eines "Umrechnungsfaktors" direkt aus den von den Berichtsbetrieben für den von dem Erhebungsmonat eventuell abweichenden Lohnabrechnungszeitraum gemeldeten Angaben abgeleitet; von der vorherigen Umrechnung in Monatsangaben wurde bei der vierteljährlichen Verdiensterhebung im Gegensatz zu den Gehalts- und Lohnstrukturerhebungen abgesehen.

354 Vervollständigung durch Schätzwerte

Wenn die Berichtsstellen zu einer lohnstatistischen Erhebung unplausible Angaben oder bei bestimmten Positionen des Fragebogens gar keine Angaben lieferten, wurde von den Erhebungsbehörden in der Regel zunächst versucht, diese Fälle durch Rückfragen bei den Berichtsstellen zu klären. Da jedoch die unplausiblen bzw. fehlenden Angaben teilweise - vor allem bei den lohnstatistischen Erhebungen im Bereich der Landwirtschaft - sehr häufig vorkamen und Rückfragen in diesen Fällen zu arbeitsaufwendig gewesen wären bzw. kaum Aussicht auf Erfolg geboten hätten, verzichteten die statistischen Ämter oft auf Rückfragen und korrigierten oder vervollständigten selber die Erhebungsbogen durch plausible Schätzwerte. Die Vervollständigung durch Schätzwerte kam z. B. bei der Gehalts- und Lohnstrukturerhebung in der Landwirtschaft 1953/54 in sehr vielfältiger Form vor. Bei dieser Erhebung hatten die größeren Berichtsbetriebe für jeden Monat und die kleineren Berichtsbetriebe für vier ausgewählte Monate des Erhebungsjahres unter anderem Verdienstangaben für die einzelnen Arbeitnehmer zu melden. Wenn diese Angaben für einen Arbeitnehmer in einem Berichtsmonat fehlten, wurden sie durch Einsetzen der entsprechenden Daten aus dem benachbarten Berichtsmonat oder gegebenenfalls durch Interpolation zwischen den Daten aus den beiden benachbarten Monaten geschätzt. Wenn für einen Arbeitnehmer infolge Krankheit oder Einstellung bzw. Entlassung während des Erhebungsmonats ein verringerter Verdienst gemeldet worden war, wurde eine als "Hochrechnung" bezeichnete Umrechnung auf den vollen erreichbaren Monatsverdienst vorgenommen. Im Falle der kleineren Berichtsbetriebe wurde aus den Verdienstangaben für die vier Berichtsmonate eine ebenfalls als "Hochrechnung" bezeichnete Schätzung der Jahresverdienste abgeleitet. Eine andere Art der Vervollständigung oder Korrektur durch Schätzwerte fand z. B. bei der Personalkostenerhebung der Europäischen Gemeinschaften im Straßenverkehrsgewerbe 1967 Anwendung. Hier wurden unplausible oder fehlende Angaben, die nicht durch Rückfragen geklärt werden konnten, durch Einsetzen des gewogenen arithmetischen Mittels der entsprechenden Angaben aller anderen Berichtsunternehmen derselben Schicht geschätzt, wobei als Gewichte die Arbeitnehmerzahlen der einzelnen Unternehmen dienten. Bei den erhebungstechnisch besonders schwierigen Personalkostenerhebungen der Europäischen Gemeinschaften wurden auch teilweise bereits die Berichtsunternehmen zur Abgabe von Schätzungen aufgefordert, wenn ihre Buchhaltungsunterlagen zur Erfassung der statistischen Daten nicht ausreichten. So waren z. B. bei der Aufgliederung der Personalkosten nach bestimmten Aufwandsarten, der Aufteilung einzelner Aufwandsarten auf Arbeiter und Angestellte und der detaillierten Erfassung der Arbeitsstunden von den Berichtsunternehmen gegebenenfalls Schätzwerte einzusetzen.

355 <u>Bewertung der Naturalleistungen</u>

Neben den Barverdiensten wurden in der amtlichen Lohnstatistik teilweise auch die den Arbeitnehmern von ihren Arbeitgebern gewährten Naturalleistungen erfaßt. Die Bewertung dieser Naturalleistungen wurde nur in wenigen Fällen von den Berichtsstellen selbst vorgenommen; dies Verfahren fand vor allem bei sämtlichen in der Bergarbeiterlohnstatistik (Kohlendeputate) und in den Personalkostenerhebungen erfaßten Naturalleistungen Anwendung. Bei der Gehalts- und Lohnstrukturerhebung in der Landwirtschaft 1962/63 sowie bei der laufenden nationalen und europäischen Verdiensterhebung in der Landwirtschaft wurden die gegen Entgelt gewährten Naturalleistungen von den Berichtsbetrieben nach diesen Entgelten bewertet. Ausnahmsweise wurde auf eine Bewertung der Naturalleistungen durch die Berichtsstellen oder die Erhebungsbehörden ganz verzichtet. Bei der Verdiensterhebung im Handwerk wurde hinsichtlich der Naturalleistungen nur die Anzahl der Arbeiter, die von ihren Arbeitgebern Kost und Unterkunft erhielten, erfaßt. Die Berichtsbetriebe der Erhebung der Europäischen Gemeinschaften über die Arbeiterverdienste in der Landwirtschaft hatten nur die Tatsache anzugeben, ob die einzelnen Arbeiter Kost oder Unterkunft erhielten; diese Information fiel durch eine entspechende Abgrenzung der Arbeitergruppen indirekt auch bei der nationalen Verdiensterhebung in der Landwirtschaft an. In der Regel erfolgte die Einbeziehung der Naturalleistungen in die lohnstatistischen Erhebungen jedoch in der Weise, daß die Naturalleistungen nach Arten und Mengen von den Berichtsstellen zu melden waren und bei der anschließenden Aufbereitung in den statistischen Ämtern bewertet wurden. Bei dieser Bewertung wurden verschiedene Verfahren angewendet. Das Statistische Reichsamt verwendete zu diesem Zweck bei den Lohnstrukturerhebungen in der Landwirtschaft 1937 und in der Forstwirtschaft 1939/40 vor allem Daten der amtlichen Preisstatistik - im allgemeinen Verbraucherpreise, zum Teil auch Erzeuger- und Großhandelspreise -, teilweise landwirtschaftliche Erfahrungssätze - z. B. für die Überlassung von Land u. ä. - und für die Bewertung von Kost und Unterkunft Grundsätze der Finanzämter für die steuerliche Bewertung oder Richtsätze der Heeresverwaltung für die Versorgung von Soldaten. Bei den Strukturerhebungen in der Landwirtschaft 1950 und 1953/54 sowie in der Forstwirtschaft 1949/50 und 1952/53 wurden für die Bewertung ebenfalls vor allem Daten der amtlichen Preisstatistik - nunmehr in der Regel Erzeugerpreise, teilweise Großhandelspreise und nur in besonderen Fällen Verbraucherpreise - verwendet, die beim Einsatz von Interviewern zum Teil durch deren Angaben über ortsübliche Ladenpreise ergänzt wurden. Im Rahmen der laufenden Verdiensterhebung in der Landwirtschaft wurden in den Jahren 1957 bis 1959 neben den durch die Erhebung anfallenden Barverdiensten auch Gesamtverdienste ermittelt, indem Kost und Unterkunft mit den Sätzen der Länderfinanzminister für die Berechnung von Lohnsteuern und Sozialversicherungsbeiträgen bewertet und die Werte der sonstigen Naturalleistungen aus dem mit der zwischenzeitlichen Preisentwicklung fortgeschriebenen Ergebnissen der Gehalts- und Lohnstrukturerhebung in der Landwirtschaft 1953/54 übernommen wurden. Bei der Gehalts- und Lohnstrukturerhebung in der Landwirtschaft 1962/63 wurden die unentgeltlich gewährten Naturalleistungen ebenfalls nach den Sätzen bewertet, die von den zuständigen Länderministerien für Zwecke der Sozialversicherung festgelegt worden waren. Das gleiche Verfahren wurde bei der Gehalts- und Lohnstrukturerhebung im Erwerbsgartenbau 1962 angewendet, wobei jedoch für einige Naturalleistungen, für die keine derartigen Sätze festgelegt worden waren, ersatzweise Verbraucherpreise der amtlichen Preisstatistik herangezogen wurden.

356 Form der Ergebnisse

3561 Summen

Die Ergebnisse der lohnstatistischen Erhebungen fallen je nach der Art der Erhebung in verschiedener Form an. Zunächst ist es möglich, aus den Angaben der einzelnen Berichtsstellen Summen für ganze Wirtschaftszweige oder für den gesamten Erhebungsbereich zu bilden. Solche Summen stellen für die im Summenverfahren durchgeführten Verdiensterhebungen im allgemeinen nur ein Zwischenergebnis dar, das dann weiter zu Verhältniswerten verrechnet wird; die Bruttoverdienstsummen wurden lediglich bei der Verdiensterhebung im Handwerk stets auch als Endergebnis ausgewiesen, und zwar für die Angestellten, Lehrlinge und Anlernlinge. Bei den lohnstatistischen Erhebungen, deren Ziel in der Erfassung der Aufwendungen der Arbeitgeber für ihre Arbeitnehmer in erster Linie von der Kostenseite her besteht, bilden die Summen die Hauptergebnisse; die daneben anfallenden Verhälniswerte - Personalaufwand pro Arbeitnehmer- sind hier nur als ergänzende Informationen zu betrachten. Zu diesen Erhebungen gehören die Personalkostenerhebungen der Montanunion und der Europäischen Wirtschaftsgemeinschaft, die Erhebung der Internationalen Arbeitsorganisation über die Aufwendungen der Unternehmen für ihre Arbeitnehmer von 1955 und die Erhebung über soziale Nebenleistungen im Rahmen der Gehalts- und Lohnstrukturerhebung in der gewerblichen Wirtschaft 1957. Bei den Erhebungen über die betriebliche Altersversorgung von 1973 und 1976 wurden die Summen der Aufwendungen der Unternehmen für die betriebliche Altersversorgung als Ergebnisse gleichrangig neben Verhältniswerten - Versorgungsleistungen pro Arbeitnehmer - ausgewiesen. Soweit Summen als Endergebnisse von Repräsentativerhebungen ermittelt wurden, mußten sie stets auf 100 % der Grundgesamtheit hochgerechnet werden.

3562 Durchschnitte (Mittelwerte)

Die Ergebnisse der im Individualverfahren durchgeführten lohnstatistischen Erhebungen werden - abgesehen von der Aufstellung von Häufigkeitsverteilungen nach Verdienstklassen - grundsätzlich in der Form sogenannter Durchschnittsverdienste ausgewiesen, worunter arithmetische Mittelwerte der individuellen Arbeitnehmerverdienste zu verstehen sind. Die Individualerhebungen des Statistischen Reichsamtes führten zu arithmetischen Mitteln der Verdienste der einzelnen Arbeiter bzw. Angestellten; soweit Verdienstbeträge mehrfach auftraten, wurden gewogene Mittelwerte mit Gewichten nach der Häufigkeit des Auftretens - d. h. nach der Anzahl der Arbeitnehmer, die in der jeweiligen Erhebung zu diesen Verdienstbeträgen gemeldet worden waren - berechnet. Bei den Gehalts- und Lohnstrukturerhebungen nach dem Zweiten Weltkrieg wurden ebenfalls die Individualangaben zu arithmetischen Mittelwerten verrechnet. Die Gewichtung wurde dabei gewöhnlich in Verbindung mit der Hochrechnung der Stichprobendaten dadurch vorgenommen, daß von Schicht zu Schicht unterschiedliche Hochrechnungsfaktoren verwendet wurden. Die Hochrechnungsfaktoren und damit die Gewichte für die Mittelwertberechnung ergaben sich in der Regel aus den im Auswahlplan aufgeführten Arbeitnehmerzahlen in Stichprobe und Grundgesamtheit der jeweiligen Erhebung selbst; eine Ausnahme bildete die Lohnstrukturerhebung in der Forstwirtschaft 1949/50, bei der die Totalzahlen der Forstarbeiter statt aus dem Auswahlplan der Erhebung aus Unterlagen der zentralen forstwirtschaftlichen Verwaltungsbehörden der Länder entnommen wurden.

Arithmetische Mittelwerte als Form lohnstatistischer Ergebnisse kamen ferner in der früheren Tariflohnstatistik bei der Berechnung tariflicher Durchschnittslöhne vor. Die Tariflohnstatistik wies ab 1922 mit den Arbeiterzahlen gewogene arithmetische Mittel der einzelnen Tariflohnsätze aus. Bei der Reform der Tariflohnstatistik von 1931 wurden die Gewichte für die Mittelwertberechnung genauer als teilweise geschätzte Gesamtzahlen der in den einzelnen Gewerben bzw. Arbeitergruppen im Durchschnitt der Jahre 1928 bis 1930 tatsächlich beschäftigten - d. h. nicht arbeitslosen - Arbeiter festgelegt; diese Gewichte wurden in den folgenden Jahren konstant gehalten. Auch nach dem Zweiten Weltkrieg wurden in der Tariflohnstatistik von 1949 bis 1951 gewogene arithmetische Mittel der einzelnen Tariflohnsätze berechnet, wobei die - ebenfalls konstant gehaltenen - Gewichte nunmehr Arbeiterzahlen aus der tariflohnstatistischen Sondererhebung zur Industrieberichterstattung vom April 1949 waren.

3563 Verhältniswerte

Bei den im Summenverfahren durchgeführten Verdiensterhebungen liefern die Berichtsstellen verschiedene Summenangaben, aus denen bei der Aufbereitung in den Erhebungsbehörden als statistische Endergebnisse Verhältniswerte berechnet werden. Diese Verhältniswerte werden im Sprachgebrauch der amtlichen Lohnstatistik wie die arithmetischen Mittelwerte der Individualerhebungen und der früheren Tariflohnstatistik als Durchschnittsverdienste bzw. Durchschnittslöhne bezeichnet. Verhältniswerte kommen in der Lohnstatistik in verschiedener Form vor. Die laufenden Verdiensterhebungen in Industrie und Handel und im Handwerk weisen für die Arbeiter durchschnittliche Stundenverdienste (Monatslohnsumme dividiert durch monatliche Arbeitsstundensumme), durchschnittliche Wochenverdienste (Wochenlohnsumme dividiert durch Anzahl der Arbeiter) und durchschnittliche Wochenarbeitszeiten (wöchentliche Arbeitsstundensumme dividiert durch Anzahl der Arbeiter) aus. Weitere Verhältniswerte sind der durchschnittliche Monatsverdienst für die Angestellten als Quotient aus der Monatsgehaltssumme und der Anzahl der Angestellten (vierteljährliche Verdiensterhebung in Industrie und Handel) sowie der durchschnittliche Jahresverdienst für die Arbeiter und Angestellten als Quotient aus der Jahreslohn- bzw. -gehaltssumme und der Anzahl der Arbeiter bzw. Angestellten (Bruttojahresverdiensterhebung in Industrie und Handel). Die Bergarbeiterlohnstatistik liefert nach dem gegenwärtigen Stand als Ergebnisse die Verhältniswerte Monatslohnsumme dividiert durch Anzahl der durchschnittlich angelegten Arbeiter und Monatslohnsumme dividiert durch monatliche Anzahl der verfahrenen bzw. vergüteten Schichten. In der Form der Verhältniswerte fielen teilweise auch die Ergebnisse der im Summenverfahren durchgeführten Erhebung über die Vermögensbildung der Arbeitnehmer von 1963 an, und zwar jeweils als Quotient aus der Summe der vermögenswirksamen Leistungen und der Anzahl der Arbeitnehmer. Die nationale und die europäische laufende Verdiensterhebung in der Landwirtschaft wurden zwar immer als Individualerhebungen durchgeführt, jedoch über die nachträgliche Bildung von Summen in gleicher Weise wie die laufenden Summenerhebungen nur zu den in den Verdiensterhebungen allgemein üblichen Verhältniswerten aufbereitet.

Die Methode, nach der die als Ergebnisse der laufenden Verdiensterhebungen ausgewiesenen Verhältniswerte ermittelt wurden, wurde mehrfach geändert. Das Statistische Reichsamt berechnete bei der Aufbereitung der vierteljährlichen Industriearbeiterlohnstatistik zunächst Verhältniswerte für jeden einzelnen Betrieb. Aus diesen Verhältniswerten wurden dann gewogene arithmetische Mittel für die Wirtschaftszweige gebildet, wobei als Gewichte für die durchschnittlichen Stundenverdienste die Anzahl der Arbeitsstunden und für die durchschnittlichen Wochenverdienste die Anzahl der Arbeiter der einzelnen Betriebe verwendet wurden.

Bei der Wiederaufnahme der vierteljährlichen Lohnsummenerhebung nach dem Zweiten Weltkrieg wurde die Aufbereitung in der Weise geändert, daß Verhältniswerte nicht mehr für die einzelnen Betriebe, sondern nur noch für jeweils den ganzen Industriezweig eines Landes gebildet wurden. Daraus wurden anschließend gewogene arithmetische Mittel für die übergeordneten Wirtschaftsbereiche berechnet; als Gewichte dienten statt der Arbeiterzahlen der Berichtsbetriebe der Lohnerhebung nunmehr von 1946 bis 1948 in der britischen Zone die Beschäftigtenzahlen der Arbeitseinsatzstatistik der Arbeitsämter und ab 1949 in allen Ländern die Gesamtarbeiterzahlen der Industrieberichterstattung. Aus den pro Land ermittelten Durchschnittsverdiensten wurden gewogene arithmetische Mittel für das Vereinigte Wirtschaftsgebiet bzw. das Bundesgebiet berechnet; Gewichte waren dabei für die durchschnittlichen Stundenverdienste die Anzahl der Arbeitsstunden aus der Lohnerhebung und für die durchschnittlichen Wochenverdienste die Gesamtarbeiterzahlen aus der Industrieberichterstattung in den einzelnen Ländern. Ab 1957 wurden bei den laufenden Verdiensterhebungen in Industrie und Handel und im Handwerk Verhältniswerte nicht mehr nur für die einzelnen Wirtschaftszweige, sondern in gleicher Weise auch für die übergeordneten Wirtschaftsbereiche gebildet. Wegen der einheitlichen bzw. rechnerisch vereinheitlichten Erfassungsquote der Arbeitnehmer in den einzelnen Schichten war dabei eine besondere Gewichtung nicht mehr erforderlich. Auch nach der abermaligen Reform der Verdiensterhebung in Industrie und Handel von 1964 - in der Verdiensterhebung im Handwerk entsprechend ab 1966 - wurden auf jeder Aggregationsstufe als Endergebnisse ausschließlich Verhältniswerte gebildet, jedoch nunmehr als Quotienten aus jeweils hochgerechneten Summen, wobei durch die Verwendung unterschiedlicher Hochrechnungsfaktoren in den einzelnen Schichten die wegen der unterschiedlichen Erfassungsquoten jetzt notwendige Gewichtung erzielt wurde.

36 Die Weiterverarbeitung der Ergebnisse

361 Jahresdurchschnitte

Die aus der Aufbereitung der lohnstatistischen Erhebungen anfallenden Ergebnisse wurden von den statistischen Ämtern teilweise zu bestimmten Maßzahlen weiterverarbeitet sowie mit ergänzenden Informationen zur Beurteilung der Aussagefähigkeit der Daten versehen. Die für jeweils vier Erhebungsmonate eines Jahres ermittelten Ergebnisse der vierteljährlichen Verdiensterhebung in Industrie und Handel sollten in erster Linie die kurzfristige Entwicklung der Effektivverdienste aufzeigen. Um diese Erhebung daneben für die Darstellung der längerfristigen Verdienstentwicklung nutzbar zu machen, wurden aus den Ergebnissen für die vier Erhebungsmonate jedes Jahres stets auch Jahresdurchschnitte berechnet. Diese Jahresdurchschnitte ergaben sich als gewogene arithmetische Mittel aus den durchschnittlichen Verdiensten bzw. Arbeitszeiten der einzelnen Erhebungsmonate. Vor 1964 konnte das Verfahren der Berechnung von Jahresdurchschnitten verhältnismäßig einfach gehalten werden, da die Erhebungsmonate - Februar, Mai, August, November - symmetrisch zur Jahresmitte lagen. Als Gewichte konnten unter diesen Umständen einfach die auf 100 % der Grundgesamtheit hochgerechneten Arbeitnehmerzahlen der Berichtsbetriebe der Verdiensterhebung in den einzelnen Erhebungsmonaten verwendet werden. Dabei war unerheblich, ob die Monatswerte während eines Kalenderjahres wie in der Regel bei den Verdiensten einem deutlich aufwärtsgerichteten Trend folgten oder ob sie wie im allgemeinen bei den Arbeitszeiten während eines Kalenderjahres keine merkliche Trendveränderung aufwiesen. Ab 1964 mußte auf Grund der neuen - zur Jahresmitte nicht mehr symmetrisch liegenden - Erhebungsmonate der vierteljährlichen Verdiensterhebung (Januar, April, Juli, Oktober) das Verfahren der Berechnung von Jahresdurchschnitten hinsichtlich der Verdienste geändert werden. Für die Arbeitszeiten konnte wegen des Fehlens einer wesentlichen Trendveränderung innerhalb eines Jahres das frühere Verfahren der einfachen Gewichtung der vier Monatsergebnisse beibehalten werden. Für die Verdienste hätte sich dagegen mit der einfachen Gewichtung bei dem starken Aufwärtstrend aus den vorverlegten neuen Erhebungsmonaten ein geschätzter Jahresdurchschnitt ergeben, der meist deutlich unter dem wahren Jahresdurchschnitt gelegen hätte. Daher wurden ab 1964 für die Berechnung von Jahresdurchschnitten der Verdienste die Ergebnisse der einzelnen Erhebungsmonate nicht mehr nur nach den hochgerechneten Arbeitnehmerzahlen, sondern darüberhinaus nach der relativen Lage des jeweiligen Erhebungsmonats zur Jahresmitte gewichtet (vgl. Seite 145).

362 Indices

3621 Gewichtung

Zur Messung der reinen Lohnentwicklung wurden die Ergebnisse der laufenden lohnstatistischen Erhebungen teilweise zu Indices weiterverarbeitet. Die Gewichte für die Indexberechnungen wurden bei den verschiedenen Indices in unterschiedlicher Weise bestimmt. Das Statistische Reichsamt verwendete für seine Indices der effektiven Industriearbeiterverdienste - die aus den Ergebnissen der vierteljährlichen Lohnsummenerhebungen berechnet wurden - als Gewichte bei den Stundenverdiensten die Anzahl der bezahlten Arbeitsstunden und bei den Wochenverdiensten die Anzahl der Arbeiter; die Gewichte wurden dabei ausschließlich aus den Lohnsummenerhebungen selbst gewonnen. In gleicher Weise ergaben sich die Gewichte bei den ab 1949 im Rahmen der vierteljährlichen Industriearbeiterlohnstatistik vom Statistischen Amt des Vereinigten Wirtschaftsgebietes bzw, dem Statistischen Bundesamt wieder aufgenommenen Indexberechnungen.

Ende der fünfziger Jahre unterzog das Statistische Bundesamt seine Indexberechnungen einer grundlegenden Reform. Für die neuen Indices der durchschnittlichen Bruttostundenverdienste und Bruttowochenverdienste der Industriearbeiter wurden die Gewichte bestimmt, indem die Arbeiterzahlen der jeweils letzten abgeschlossenen Gehalts- und Lohnstrukturerhebung in der gewerblichen Wirtschaft mit den jahresdurchschnittlichen Bruttostunden- bzw. Bruttowochenverdiensten der vierteljährlichen Verdiensterhebung für das Wägungsjahr multipliziert wurden. Die Arbeiterzahlen der Gehalts- und Lohnstrukturerhebungen wurden dabei grundsätzlich unverändert übernommen; nur bei der Gehalts- und Lohnstrukturerhebung in der gewerblichen Wirtschaft 1951 erfolgte eine Fortschreibung der Arbeiterzahlen auf das damalige Wägungsjahr 1954 mit Hilfe anderer Statistiken, vor allem der Industrieberichterstattung und der Bauberichterstattung. Analog wurde die Gewichtung bei dem neu eingeführten Index der durchschnittlichen Bruttomonatsverdienste der Angestellten in Industrie und Handel vorgenommen. Bei den ebenfalls neu eingeführten Indices der tariflichen Stundenlöhne der Arbeiter und der tariflichen Monatsgehälter der Angestellten in der gewerblichen Wirtschaft und bei Gebietskörperschaften ergaben sich die Gewichte als Produkte aus den Arbeiter- bzw. Angestelltenzahlen der jeweils letzten abgeschlossenen Gehalts- und Lohnstrukturerhebung in der gewerblichen Wirtschaft und den jahresdurchschnittlichen Tariflohn- bzw. -gehaltssätzen des Wägungsjahres. Die Arbeiter- und Angestelltenzahlen wurden dabei im Falle der Gehalts- und Lohnstrukturerhebung 1951 wiederum vor allem mit der Industrie - und der Bauberichterstattung auf das Wägungsjahr 1954 fortgeschrieben, im Falle der Gehalts- und Lohnstrukturerhebung 1957 teilweise durch Daten des Mikrozensus und der Industrieberichterstattung ergänzt und im übrigen immer unverändert aus den Gehalts- und Lohnstrukturerhebungen übernommen. Analog wurde auch ein Index der tariflichen Wochenarbeitszeit der Arbeiter berechnet; der Index der tariflichen Wochenlöhne der Arbeiter in der gewerblichen Wirtschaft und bei Gebietskörperschaften ergab sich dann durch Multiplikation des Index der tariflichen Stundenlöhne mit dem Index der tariflichen Wochenarbeitszeit. Für den Index der Tariflöhne der Arbeiter in der Landwirtschaft wurden als Gewichte ausschließlich die Arbeiterzahlen der jeweils letzten abgeschlossen landwirtschaftlichen Betriebszählung verwendet. Diese Arbeiterzahlen wurden grundsätzlich unverändert übernommen und nur im Falle der landwirtschaftlichen Betriebszählung 1949 entsprechend dem ersten Wägungszeitraum der Indexberechnung mit Hilfe der Statistik der Arbeitsverwaltung auf den Durchschnitt der Wirtschaftsjahre

1950/51 bis 1952/53 umgerechnet.

3622 Basiszeitraum

Die Effektivverdienstindices des Statistischen Reichsamtes wurden zunächst auf der Basis Dezember 1935 und später auch auf der Basis des Jahresdurchschnitts 1936 berechnet. Bei der Wiederaufnahme dieser Indexberechnungen ab 1949 wurde als Basis zunächst der September 1938 und später der Jahresdurchschnitt 1938 verwendet. Seit der Reform der Indexberechnungen Ende der fünfziger Jahre muß infolge des neuen Berechnungsverfahrens neben der zeitlichen Basis - d.h. dem Zeitpunkt, für den die Indexreihe den Wert 100 erhält - jeweils auch die Wägungsbasis - d. h. der Zeitpunkt, für den die nunmehr mehrere Jahre lang konstant gehaltenen Gewichte ermittelt wurden - festgesetzt werden; nach den früheren Berechnungsverfahren war die Wägungsbasis dagegen durch das Verfahren selbst vorgegeben. Die neuen Effektivverdienstindices erhielten als zeitliche Basis zunächst den Jahresdurchschnitt 1950 und als Wägungsbasis den Jahresdurchschnitt 1954. Einige Jahre später wurde sowohl für die zeitliche Basis als auch für die Wägungsbasis der Jahresdurchschnitt 1958 festgelegt. Bei der nächsten Umbasierung wurde als zeitliche Basis der Jahresdurchschnitt 1962 verwendet, während der Jahresdurchschnitt 1958 als Wägungsbasis beibehalten wurde. Bei der bisher letzten Umbasierung wurde der Jahresdurchschnitt 1970 sowohl als zeitliche Basis als auch als Wägungsbasis eingeführt. Die Indices der Tariflöhne und -gehälter in der gewerblichen Wirtschaft und bei Gebietskörperschaften stimmten mit einer Ausnahme hinsichtlich der zeitlichen Basen und der Wägungsbasen mit den Effektivverdienstindices überein; nur im Falle der zeitlichen Basis von 1950 wurde statt des Jahresdurchschnitts der Monat November verwendet. Die Indices der Tariflöhne in der Landwirtschaft wurden zunächst auf der zeitlichen Basis November 1950 und auf der Wägungsbasis "Durchschnitt der Wirtschaftsjahre 1950/51 bis 1952/53" berechnet. Einige Jahre später wurde als zeitliche Basis der Jahresdurchschnitt 1958 festgelegt, während die Wägungsbasis vorerst beibehalten wurde. Bei der Umbasierung auf die zeitliche Basis

Jahresdurchschnitt 1962 wurde die Wägungsbasis Jahresdurchschnitt 1960, bei der Umbasierung auf die zeitliche Basis Jahresdurchschnitt 1970 die Wägungsbasis Jahresdurchschnitt 1971 eingeführt.

3623 Berechnungsverfahren

Das Statistische Reichsamt berechnete seine Effektivverdienstindices grundsätzlich nach dem Modell des Preisindex von Laspeyres, d. h. die Gewichte eines früheren Erhebungszeitraums wurden konstant gehalten. Die Besonderheit dieses Berechnungsverfahrens bestand darin, daß die Gewichte jeweils nur für zwei unmittelbar aufeinanderfolgende Erhebungszeiträume konstant gehalten wurden, mit anderen Worten: Die Gewichte des früheren von zwei in vierteljährlichen Abständen aufeinanderfolgenden verglichenen Erhebungsmonaten wurden für die jeweils folgende Erhebung - und nur für diese - beibehalten. Auf diese Weise wurden Indices nur für übergeordnete Gewerbebereiche - d.h. Zusammenfassungen von Gewerbezweigen - berechnet; für die einzelnen Gewerbezweige wurden dagegen statt echter Indices lediglich einfache Meßzahlen aus den Durchschnittsverdiensten der vierteljährlichen Lohnsummenerhebungen gebildet.

Bei der ab 1949 erneut aufgenommenen Berechnung von Effektivverdienstindices wurde im Gegensatz zu dem Verfahren des Statistischen Reichsamtes das Modell des Preisindex von Paasche verwendet. Danach wurden der Indexberechnung variable Gewichte aus dem jeweiligen neuesten Erhebungszeitraum zugrundegelegt. Bei der Reform der Indexberechnungen Ende der fünfziger Jahre ging das Statistische Bundesamt allgemein wieder auf das Modell des Preisindex von Laspeyres über, und zwar nunmehr in der üblichen Form, nach der die Gewichte mehrere Jahre lang konstant gehalten wurden, bis sie für ein neues Wägungsjahr neu festgelegt wurden.

Ab 1957 berechnete die Deutsche Bundesbank monatliche Indices des Tariflohn- und -gehaltsniveaus. Dabei wurden die Gewichte innerhalb eines Jahres konstant gehalten, jedoch abweichend von dem Verfahren des Statistischen Bundesamtes von Jahr zu Jahr neu festgelegt.

363 Angaben zur Genauigkeit

3631 Pauschale Vorbehalte

Die Ergebnisse der lohnstatistischen Repräsentativerhebungen wurden oft mit ergänzenden Angaben zur Genauigkeit versehen, um auf die gegenüber Totalerhebungen infolge der Stichprobenfehler eingeschränkte Aussagefähigkeit der Daten hinzuweisen. Nach der bisher üblichen Praxis der statistischen Ämter wurden in die lohnstatistischen Veröffentlichungen jedoch nicht die Ergebnisse echter Fehlerrechnungen auf Grund der Erhebungsdaten, sondern nur pauschale Vorbehalte aufgenommen. Diese Vorbehalte wurden teilweise aus im voraus aufgestellten Fehlerrechnungen auf Grund von Daten der Auswahlgrundlagen - derartige vorläufige Fehlerrechnungen wurden für die Ausarbeitung der Auswahlpläne benötigt - abgeleitet. Die pauschalen Vorbehalte erfolgten in der Form, daß je nach der Anzahl der in den Repräsentativerhebungen erfaßten Arbeitnehmer bestimmte Zahlenwerte gar nicht veröffentlicht oder zur Betonung der eingeschränkten Aussagefähigkeit in den Veröffentlichungen in Klammern gesetzt wurden. Im Rahmen der vierteljährlichen Lohnsummenerhebungen wies bereits das Statistische Reichsamt nur Durchschnittswerte nach, die sich auf mehr als 20 erfaßte Arbeiter bezogen; bei weniger erfaßten Arbeitern wurden die Zahlenangaben durch Punkte ersetzt. Nach dem Zweiten Weltkrieg wurde für die amtliche Lohnstatistik zunächst die folgende, als wiederkehrende Bemerkung in die Statistischen Jahrbücher für die Bundesrepublik Deutschland aufgenommene allgemeine Regelung getroffen: "Durchschnitte, die auf weniger als 20 erfaßten Personen beruhen, sind in Klammern gesetzt worden, da der Aussagewert dieser Angaben infolge der verhältnismäßig geringen Repräsentation von Zufälligkeiten bestimmt sein kann. Wenn durch Zusammenfassung solcher Durchschnitte zu einem Gesamtdurchschnitt die Zahl der erfaßten Personen 20 übersteigt, eine Einklammerung der Angaben also unterbleibt, so muß doch beachtet werden, daß auch dieser Gesamtdurchschnitt noch mit einem statistischen Fehler behaftet sein kann."*) Um die Mitte der sechziger Jahre wurde der allgemeine Vorbehalt für die veröffentlichten Ergebnisse der Lohnstatistik neu geregelt: "Durchschnittsangaben für mindestens 10, aber weniger als 30 erfaßte Beschäftigte sind in Klammern gesetzt, weil diese Werte auf Grund des hohen Zufallsfehlers (einfacher relativer Standardfehler über 5 %) noch unsicher sind. Durchschnittsangaben für weniger als 10 erfaßte Beschäftigte werden nicht mehr nachgewiesen" (diese Angaben wurden zunächst durch Punkte, seit 1968 durch Schrägstriche ersetzt). "Besetzungszahlen von weniger als 50 erfaßten Beschäftigten dürfen wegen ihres hohen Zufallsfehlers (einfacher relativer Standardfehler größer als 15 %) **) nicht verallgemeinert werden; sie werden aber veröffentlicht, um den Benutzern beliebige Zusammenfassungen zu aussagefähigen Ergebnissen zu ermöglichen." ***) Dabei muß nochmals betont werden, daß die Angaben über die Höhe des Stichprobenfehlers nicht durch echte Fehlerrechnungen auf Grund der Erhebungsdaten ermittelt wurden, sondern vorläufige Fehlerabschätzungen auf Grund der Verhältnisse in den Auswahlgrundlagen darstellen. Von den für die amtliche Lohnstatistik allgemein geltenden Vorbehalten wurde bei einigen lohnstatistischen Erhebungen abgewichen. Besonders einschränkend war der Vorbehalt bei der laufenden Verdiensterhebung in der Landwirtschaft ab 1971; hier wurde bei weniger als 10 erfaßten Arbeitern ein relativer Standardfehler von im allgemeinen über 10 % (keine Veröffentlichung von Durchschnittswerten), bei 10 bis 49 erfaßten Arbeitern ein relativer Standardfehler von im allgemeinen 5 bis 10 % (Durchschnittswerte in Klammern gesetzt) und bei mindestens 50 erfaßten Arbeitern noch ein relativer Standardfehler von im allgemeinen bis zu 5 % (uneingeschränkte Veröffentlichung von Durchschnittswerten) angegeben. Bei den Gehalts- und Lohnstruk-

*) Statistisches Bundesamt: Statistisches Jahrbuch für die Bundesrepublik Deutschland, z. B. Jahrgang 1954 Seite 477.
**) gemeint war vermutlich 1,5 %
***) Statistisches Bundesamt: Statistisches Jahrbuch für die Bundesrepublik Deutschland, z. B. Jahrgang 1965 Seite 503.

turerhebungen in der gewerblichen Wirtschaft 1966 und 1972 wurde bei weniger als 20 in der Stichprobe erfaßten Arbeitnehmern (relativer Standardfehler bei Durchschnittsangaben mehr als 5 %, bei Summenangaben mehr als 20 %) von einer Veröffentlichung abgesehen; bei 20 bis unter 50 erfaßten Arbeitnehmern (relativer Standardfehler bei Durchschnittsangaben zwischen 3 % und 5 %, bei Summenangaben zwischen 13 % und 20 %) wurden die Ergebnisse in Klammern gesetzt und ebenfalls erst bei mindestens 50 erfaßten Arbeitnehmern (relativer Standardfehler bei Durchschnittsangaben unter 3 %, bei Summenangaben unter 13 %) uneingeschränkt veröffentlicht. Mit einem entsprechenden Vorbehalt wurden auch die veröffentlichten Durchschnitts- und Summenangaben der Gehalts- und Lohnstrukturerhebung im öffentlichen Dienst 1968 versehen; jedoch wurden hier bei jeder Anzahl von erfaßten Arbeitnehmern etwas niedrigere relative Standardfehler angegeben.

Wenn im Rahmen von Gehalts- und Lohnstrukturerhebungen Häufigkeitsverteilungen der Arbeitnehmer nach Verdienstklassen veröffentlicht wurden, richteten sich die pauschalen Vorbehalte nicht wie bei den Durchschnitts- und Summenangaben nach der Anzahl der erfaßten Arbeitnehmer in jeweils einem einzigen Tabellenfeld, sondern nach der Anzahl der erfaßten Arbeitnehmer in der ganzen Häufigkeitsverteilung in Verbindung mit der Anzahl der Verdienstklassen. Allgemein wurde für die Gehalts- und Lohnstrukturerhebungen geregelt, daß Häufigkeitsverteilungen mit 10 bis 15 Verdienstklassen nur bei mindestens 300 in der Stichprobe erfaßten Personen und Häufigkeitsverteilungen mit 16 bis 20 Verdienstklassen nur bei mindestens 500 erfaßten Personen veröffentlicht werden sollten; Häufigkeitsverteilungen mit weniger als 10 oder mehr als 20 Verdienstklassen wurden grundsätzlich nicht vorgesehen. Diese allgemeine Regelung wurde bei der Gehalts- und Lohnstrukturerhebung im öffentlichen Dienst 1968, deren Häufigkeitsverteilungen wegen der einheitlichen gesetzlichen bzw. tariflichen Regelungen und wegen des Wegfalls übertariflicher Zahlungen oft nur sehr wenige besetzte Verdienstklassen aufwiesen, in der Weise ergänzt, daß bei 3 besetzten Verdienstklassen mindestens 90 erfaßte Personen , bei 4 Klassen

120 Personen, bei 5 Klassen 150 Personen, bei 6 Klassen 170 Personen, bei 7 Klassen 190 Personen und bei 8 Klassen 210 Personen vorhanden sein mußten. Bei den früheren Gehalts- und Lohnstrukturerhebungen waren die Vorbehalte teilweise weniger streng; so wurden z. B. die Häufigkeitsverteilungen der Gehalts- und Lohnstrukturerhebung im Erwerbsgartenbau 1962 vollständig veröffentlicht und dabei lediglich bei weniger als 30 erfaßten Personen eingeklammert.

3632 Pläne für Fehlerrechnungen

Echte Fehlerrechnungen können nicht im voraus auf Grund der Verhältnisse in den Auswahlgrundlagen, sondern nur nachträglich auf Grund der in den Repräsentativerhebungen tatsächlich ermittelten Daten durchgeführt werden. Laufende Fehlerrechnungen auf Grund der Erhebungsdaten gab es in der amtlichen deutschen Lohnstatistik mit einer Ausnahme bisher gar nicht; lediglich in Nordrhein-Westfalen wurden ab Oktober 1972 aus den Erhebungsdaten der vierteljährlichen Verdiensterhebung in Industrie und Handel neben den üblichen Verhältniswerten laufend auch die Standardfehler berechnet (vgl. Seite 178). In der Frühzeit der deutschen Lohnstatistik wurde die Notwendigkeit von Fehlerrechnungen von den Erhebungsbehörden in keiner Weise erkannt. Bei der repräsentativen Lohn- und Gehaltserhebung vom Februar 1920 führte das Statistische Reichsamt zur Rechtfertigung der Veröffentlichung von gesonderten Ergebnissen für einzelne Gemeinden aus: "Die weitgehende örtliche Unterscheidung der Ergebnisse wird durch die starken Schwankungen der Löhne von Ort zu Ort vollkommen gerechtfertigt. Eine Zusammenziehung zu Landes- oder gar Reichsdurchschnitten würde diese bedeutsamen Unterschiede vollkommen verwischen."*) Hierin drückt sich eine bemerkenswert falsche Beurteilung der Ergebnisse von Repräsentativerhebungen aus; die starke Streuung der Stichprobendaten hätte im Gegenteil zu der Entscheidung führen

*) Statistisches Reichsamt: Lohn- und Gehaltserhebung vom Februar 1920. Statistik des Deutschen Reichs Band 293, Berlin 1921, Seite 20.

müssen, ausschließlich für größere Gebietseinheiten und damit für eine größere Zahl von erfaßten Personen Durchschnittswerte zu veröffentlichen. Später wurde die Einsicht in die Existenz des Stichprobenfehlers zumindest zaghaft angedeutet. Das Statistische Reichsamt stellte im Rahmen einer Sonderauswertung der vierteljährlichen Lohnsummenerhebungen über regionale Verdienstunterschiede fest: "Doch sind Unterschiede" - gemeint sind Unterschiede zwischen den Durchschnittsverdiensten der untersuchten Gebiete - "von einzelnen Pfennigen nicht beweiskräftig,zumal schon Abweichungen im Grad der statistischen Repräsentation der einzelnen Gewerbe den Durchschnitt leicht um ein geringes beeinflussen können."*) Trotz dieser Einsicht glaubte man, durch "sorgfältige Interpretation" der Ergebnisse der lohnstatistischen Erhebungen exakte Fehlerrechnungen ersetzen zu können: "Die durch die Ergebnisse repräsentativer Erhebungen zum Ausdruck gebrachten Lohnveränderungen müssen nur mit der nötigen Sorgfalt interpretiert werden, damit nicht durch das Wesen der Methode bedingte Zufallsschwankungen der Mittelwerte von Erhebung zu Erhebung als wesentliche Veränderungen hingestellt werden. Diese Sorgfalt in der Interpretation ist für die amtliche Lohnstatistik selbstverständlich."**)

Nach dem Zweiten Weltkrieg wurden bei der Aufstellung der Auswahlpläne der lohnstatistischen Erhebungen vom Statistischen Bundesamt oft auch echte Fehlerrechnungen in Aussicht gestellt; diese Vorhaben wurden jedoch nicht realisiert. Bei der Gehalts- und Lohnstrukturerhebung in der Landwirtschaft 1953/54 sollten erstmalig in der amtlichen Lohnstatistik Streuungsberechnungen auf Grund des Erhebungsmaterials durchgeführt werden, um eine nachträgliche Kontrolle der Zuverlässigkeit der gewonnenen Ergebnisse zu ermöglichen. Solche Pläne für Fehlerrechnungen tauchten später bei der Vorbereitung von Stichprobenziehungen

---

*) Statistisches Reichsamt: Die gebietlichen Unterschiede der Arbeitsverdienste im Deutschen Reich. In: Wirtschaft und Statistik Jahrgang 1942 Seite 282 ff.

**) Friedrich Behrens: Neue Wege der Lohstatistik. In: Allgemeines Statistisches Archiv, 31. Band, Jahrgang 1942/43, Jena 1943, Seite 120.

in zunehmender Häufigkeit auf. So sollte zum Beispiel bei der Gehalts- und Lohnstrukturerhebung in der gewerblichen Wirtschaft 1962 eine Fehlerrechnung auf Grund der Erhebungsdaten in die Aufbereitung eingebaut werden. Bei der Verdiensterhebung in Industrie und Handel wurde der Übergang von der gezielten Auswahl auf die Zufallsauswahl im Jahre 1964 damit begründet, daß auf diese Weise eine Abschätzung der Zufallsfehler möglich wurde; daher wurde bei der Neuauswahl von 1964 geplant, zur laufenden Überprüfung der Genauigkeit der Ergebnisse in das Programm der maschinellen Aufbereitung eine Fehlerrechnung einzubauen. Bei den Personalkostenerhebungen der Europäischen Gemeinschaften im produzierenden Gewerbe wurde die Einführung der vollmaschinellen Aufbereitung ab Berichtsjahr 1969 unter anderem damit begründet, daß sie die Möglichkeit bot, die Berechnung des Stichprobenfehlers oder zumindest der Grunddaten für eine Fehlerabschätzung - Summen der Merkmalswerte, ihrer Quadrate und ihrer gemischten Produkte usw. - ohne großen zusätzlichen Aufwand direkt im Zuge der Aufbereitung vorzunehmen. Anläßlich der im Jahre 1972 vorgenommenen Neuauswahl für die Verdiensterhebung in Industrie und Handel trat das Statistische Bundesamt mit der folgenden - ebenfalls nicht eingehaltenen - Zusage an die Öffentlichkeit: "Eine ausführliche Fehlerrechnung, die im nächsten Jahr durchgeführt werden wird, soll über die Höhe der Stichprobenfehler in den einzelnen Wirtschaftszweigen nähere Angaben liefern. Außerdem soll dann geprüft werden, inwieweit statistisch gesicherte Vergleiche von einem Berichtszeitraum zum anderen möglich sind."*) Auch die Neuprogrammierung der Verdiensterhebung in Industrie und Handel von 1974 erfolgte unter anderem im Hinblick auf eine eventuell durchzuführende Fehlerrechnung. Die neueren lohnstatistischen Erhebungen der Europäischen Gemeinschaften gaben auf Grund der Rahmenregelungen des Statistischen Amtes der Europäischen Gemeinschaften über die Auswahlpläne zusätzlichen Anlaß, Pläne für Fehlerrechnungen zu erwägen. Bei den von den Europäischen Gemein-

*) Statistisches Bundesamt: Ergebnisse der Verdiensterhebung in Industrie und Handel nach dem neuen und alten Berichterstatterkreis. In: Wirtschaft und Statistik Jahrgang 1973 Seite 615.

schaften veranstalteten Erhebungen über die Gehalts- und Lohnstruktur im Handel, Bank- und Versicherungsgewerbe 1974 und über die Arbeiterverdienste in der Landwirtschaft ab 1974 sollten eventuell Fehlerrechnungen durchgeführt werden; diese Fehlerrechnungen sollten im Falle der jährlichen Erhebung in der Landwirtschaft ausdrücklich laufend Informationen über die Stichprobenfehler geben und Signifikanzprüfungen zu verschiedenen Ergebnisvergleichen ermöglichen. Alle diese Erwägungen bzw. Absichtserklärungen für Fehlerrechnungen haben bisher zu keinem Ergebnis geführt.

In einigen wenigen Fällen führte das Statistische Bundesamt echte Fehlerrechnungen auf Grund der Erhebungsdaten durch, deren Ergebnisse jedoch nicht zur Beurteilung der Aussagefähigkeit der meist bereits seit längerer Zeit vorliegenden Ergebnisdaten dienten und auch nicht veröffentlicht wurden, sondern lediglich eine Grundlage für die Ausarbeitung neuer Auswahlpläne bildeten. Zur Vorbereitung der Gehalts- und Lohnstrukturerhebung in der gewerblichen Wirtschaft 1962 verwendete das Statistische Bundesamt unter anderem Ergebnisse einer internen Fehlerrechnung auf Grund des Datenmaterials der Gehalts- und Lohnstrukturerhebung 1957. Auf Wunsch des Statistischen Amtes der Europäischen Gemeinschaften führte das Statistische Bundesamt vor der Neuauswahl des Berichtskreises der Verdiensterhebung in Industrie und Handel von 1964 eine einmalige Fehlerrechnung durch, die sich auf Material des Landes Niedersachsen beschränkte. Bei der Verdiensterhebung in der Landwirtschaft nahm das Statistische Bundesamt für 1966 und 1967 für alle Bundesländer Fehlerrechnungen vor, deren Ergebnisse später bei dem Berichtskreiswechsel von 1971 in den neuen Auswahlplan eingingen.

Seit einiger Zeit arbeitet das Statistische Bundesamt an der Entwicklung eines universellen Programms für maschinelle Fehlerrechnungen, das nicht nur für lohnstatistische Erhebungen, sondern für Repräsentativerhebungen aller Art anwendbar sein soll. Diese Arbeiten wurden bisher noch nicht abgeschlossen.

Zeittafel zur Entwicklung der amtlichen deutschen Lohnstatistik

Jahr	Ereignis (in Klammern Nummern der entsprechenden Abschnitte des Kapitels 1)
1849	Eingabe der Buchdrucker an die Frankfurter Nationalversammlung zur allgemeinen Feststellung der Arbeitslöhne (111)
1872	Beginn der preußischen Bergarbeiterlohnstatistik (113)
1874-1922	Statistik der Monatsheuern von Seeleuten (113, 121)
1876	Abschluß der Erhebung über die Frauen- und Kinderarbeit in den Fabriken (112)
1876	Abschluß der Erhebung über die Verhältnisse der Lehrlinge, Gesellen und Fabrikarbeiter (112)
1878	Reichsenquêten über die Tabak-, Eisen- und Textilindustrie (112)
1887	Reichsenquête über die Lohnverhältnisse der Arbeiterinnen in der Wäschefabrikation und der Konfektionsbranche (112)
1887	Vereinheitlichung der preußischen Bergarbeiterlohnstatistik (113)
1887	Erhebung der Berufsgenossenschaft der Buchdrucker (115)
1891	Untersuchung der Badischen Fabrikinspektion über die Lage der Fabrikarbeiter im Raum Mannheim (115)
1892	Erstmalige Festsetzung ortsüblicher Tagelöhne für Zwecke der Sozialversicherung (121)
1892-1902	Kommission für Arbeiterstatistik (122)

1893	Erhebung über die Arbeits- und Gehaltsverhältnisse der Kellner und Kellnerinnen (122)
1896	Abschluß der Untersuchung über die Arbeitsverhältnisse in der Kleider- und Wäschekonfektion (122)
1898	Erhebung über gewerbliche Kinderarbeit außerhalb der Fabriken (122)
1902	Erste Erhebung über die Lohnverhältnisse städtischer Arbeiter (124)
1902-1919	Abteilung für Arbeiterstatistik beim Kaiserlichen Statistischen Amt (122, 132)
1906-1933	Tarifstatistik (123, 131, 141)
1907	Ausdehnung der preußischen Bergarbeiterlohnstatistik auf das ganze Reichsgebiet (113)
1907	Zweite Erhebung über die Lohnverhältnisse städtischer Arbeiter (124)
1912	Abschluß der Erhebung über die Arbeitsverhältnisse der Angestellten der Rechtsanwälte (122)
1914-1919	Erhebungen über die Lohnverhältnisse der Arbeiter während des Krieges (125)
1920	Individuallohn- und -gehaltserhebung in der gewerblichen Wirtschaft (135)
1920	Erstmalige Einrichtung eines amtlichen Tarifarchivs (131)
1922	Erstmalige Festsetzung von Jahresarbeitsverdiensten land- und forstwirtschaftlicher Arbeiter für Zwecke der Sozialversicherung (133)
1922	Beginn der laufenden Tariflohnstatistik (133)

1922-1943	Monatsstatistik über die Arbeiterverdienste im Kohlenbergbau (136)
1927-1934	Regelmäßige Individuallohnerhebungen in verschiedenen Industriezweigen (135)
1931	Reform der Tariflohnstatistik (133)
1934	Individualerhebung der Angestelltenverdienste im Bankgewerbe (135)
1935	Beginn der vierteljährlichen Lohnsummenerhebung der Industriearbeiter (136)
1936	Individuallohnerhebung im Bäckerhandwerk des Wirtschaftsgebietes Niedersachsen (142)
1937	Lohnstrukturerhebung in der Landwirtschaft (142)
1938	Individuallohnerhebung in der metallverarbeitenden Industrie (142)
1939/40	Lohnstrukturerhebung in der Forstwirtschaft (142)
1940	Erhebung der Deutschen Arbeitsfront über die Effektiv- und die Tariflöhne (142)
1946	Wiederaufnahme der vierteljährlichen Lohnsummenerhebung der Industriearbeiter in den Ländern (143, 144)
1946	Wiederaufnahme der Monatsstatistik über die Arbeiterverdienste im Kohlenbergbau (153)
1949	Beginn der koordinierten vierteljährlichen Lohnsummenerhebung der Industriearbeiter im Vereinigten Wirtschaftsgebiet bzw. Bundesgebiet (151)
1949	Erweiterte Industriearbeiterlohnerhebung (152)
1949	Erhebung der Angestelltenverdienste in der gewerblichen Wirtschaft (152)
1949	Erhebung über die Tariflöhne der Industriearbeiter (152)

1949 Wiedererrichtung des amtlichen Tarifarchivs (152)

1949 Wiederaufnahme der laufenden Tariflohnstatistik (152)

1949 Wiederaufnahme der Bergarbeiterlohnstatistik im Vereinigten Wirtschaftsgebiet bzw. Bundesgebiet (153)

1949 Erhebung über die Einkommensschichtung in Schleswig-Holstein (151)

1949/50 Lohnstrukturerhebung in der Forstwirtschaft (152)

1950 Lohnstrukturerhebung in der Landwirtschaft (152)

1950 Gehalts- und Lohnstrukturerhebung im öffentlichen Dienst (152)

1950 Wiederaufnahme der Festsetzungen von Ortslöhnen und von Jahresarbeitsverdiensten landwirtschaftlicher Arbeitnehmer für Zwecke der Sozialversicherung (165)

1951 Gehalts- und Lohnstrukturerhebung in der gewerblichen Wirtschaft (154)

1952/53 Lohnstrukturerhebung in der Forstwirtschaft (154)

1953 Beginn der Personalkostenerhebungen der Europäischen Gemeinschaft für Kohle und Stahl (155)

1953/54 Gehalts- und Lohnstrukturerhebung in der Landwirtschaft (154)

1955 Erhebung der Internationalen Arbeitsorganisation über die Aufwendungen der Unternehmen für ihre Arbeitnehmer (155)

1956 Einbeziehung des Bergbaus in die vierteljährliche Lohnsummenerhebung der Industriearbeiter (161)

1957 Erweiterung der Lohnsummenerhebung der Industriearbeiter zur Verdiensterhebung in Industrie und Handel (162)

1957 Beginn der Verdiensterhebung im Handwerk (162)

1957-1973 Verdiensterhebung in der Landwirtschaft (162)

1957 Gehalts- und Lohnstrukturerhebung in der gewerblichen Wirtschaft (162)

1957 Erhebung über die sozialen Nebenleistungen der Unternehmen für ihre Arbeitnehmer (162)

1957 Beginn der Berechnung des Index des Tariflohn- und -gehaltsniveaus durch die Deutsche Bundesbank (164)

1958 Reform der Tariflohnstatistik (164)

1959 Beginn der Personalkostenerhebungen der Europäischen Wirtschaftsgemeinschaft im produzierenden Gewerbe (171)

1961/62 Lohnstrukturerhebung in der Forstwirtschaft (162)

1962 Gehalts- und Lohnstrukturerhebung in der gewerblichen Wirtschaft (162)

1962 Gehalts- und Lohnstrukturerhebung im Erwerbsgartenbau (162)

1962/63 Gehalts- und Lohnstrukturerhebung in der Landwirtschaft (162)

1963 Erhebung über die Vermögensbildung der Arbeitnehmer (172)

1964 Berichtskreiswechsel der Verdiensterhebung in Industrie und Handel (172)

1964 Berichtskreiswechsel der Verdiensterhebung in der Landwirtschaft (172)

1964 Beginn der harmonisierten Verdiensterhebung der Europäischen Wirtschaftsgemeinschaft für die Arbeiter im produzierenden Gewerbe (173)

1966	Berichtskreiswechsel der Verdiensterhebung im Handwerk (172)
1966	Gehalts- und Lohnstrukturerhebung in der gewerblichen Wirtschaft (174)
1967	Personalkostenerhebung der Europäischen Wirtschaftsgemeinschaft im Straßenverkehrsgewerbe (175)
1968	Gehalts- und Lohnstrukturerhebung im öffentlichen Dienst (172)
1970	Beginn der Personalkostenerhebungen der Europäischen Wirtschaftsgemeinschaft im Handel, Bank- und Versicherungsgewerbe (175)
1971	Beginn der Bruttojahresverdiensterhebung in Industrie und Handel (181)
1971	Berichtskreiswechsel der Verdiensterhebung in der Landwirtschaft (182)
1971-1974	Verdiensterhebung im öffentlichen Dienst in Hamburg (183)
1972	Berichtskreiswechsel der Verdiensterhebung in Industrie und Handel (172)
1972	Erweiterung der harmonisierten Verdiensterhebung der Europäischen Wirtschaftsgemeinschaft auf die Angestellten in der gewerblichen Wirtschaft (173)
1972	Gehalts- und Lohnstrukturerhebung in der gewerblichen Wirtschaft (174)
1972	Beginn laufender Fehlerrechnungen für die Verdiensterhebung in Industrie und Handel in Nordrhein-Westfalen (184)
1973	Erhebung über die betriebliche Altersversorgung (181)

1974 Gehalts- und Lohnstrukturerhebung der Europäischen Wirtschaftsgemeinschaft im Handel, Bank- und Versicherungsgewerbe (175)

1974 Beginn der Erhebung der Europäischen Wirtschaftsgemeinschaft über die Arbeiterverdienste in der Landwirtschaft (182)

1974 Neuprogrammierung der Verdiensterhebung in Industrie und Handel (184)

1976 Erhebung über die betriebliche Altersversorgung (181)

Verzeichnis der Datenquellen der amtlichen deutschen Lohnstatistik *)

Deutsches Reich, laufende Daten

Tariflohnstatistik	- Wirtschaft und Statistik Jahrgänge 1922-1944; Sammlung tariflicher Einzellohnsätze in Vierteljahrshefte zur Statistik des Deutschen Reichs 1942 S. I. 3 und 1943 S. I/II. 25
Tarifstatistik	- Beiträge zur Arbeiterstatistik Nr. 4 und Nr. 8 (Berlin 1906 und 1908); Reichsarbeitsblatt 1908 XII, 1909 I und II, 1918 IV, 1919 IV, 1920 I; Sonderbeilagen zum Reichsarbeitsblatt 1909 XI, 1910 VIII, 1924 Nr. 29/30; Sonderhefte zum Reichsarbeitsblatt (4., 5., 7., 10., 12., 15., 23., 26., 27., 31., 35., 40., 43., 47., 55., 57., 58. Sonderheft; Berlin 1911 bis 1933)
Lohnsummenerhebung der Industriearbeiter	- Wirtschaft und Statistik Jahrgänge 1935-1943; Sonderauswertungen über Verdienstunterschiede nach Regionen und Ortsgrößenklassen in Wirtschaft und Statistik 1942 S. 282 und 1942 S. 425
Erhebung über die Lohnverhältnisse der Arbeiter während des Ersten Weltkrieges	- Reichsarbeitsblatt 1917 S. 643, 1918 S. 297, 1919 S. 618, 1920 S. 62
Bergarbeiterlohnstatistik	- Zeitschrift für das Berg-, Hütten- und Salinenwesen im Preußischen Staate (herausgegeben vom Ministerium für Handel, Gewerbe und öffentliche Arbeiten bzw. dessen Rechtsnachfolgern) Jahrgänge 1873-

---

*) Fußnote siehe S. 320

1933; Zeitschrift für das Berg-, Hütten- und Salinenwesen in Preußen (herausgegeben vom Reichs- und Preußischen Wirtschaftsministerium) Jahrgang 1934; Zeitschrift für das Berg-, Hütten- und Salinenwesen im Deutschen Reich (herausgegeben vom Reichs- und Preußischen Wirtschaftsministerium bzw. ab 1938 vom Reichswirtschaftsministerium) Jahrgänge 1935-1939;
Reichsarbeitsblatt Jahrgänge 1903 ff.

Monatsstatistik über die Arbeiterverdienste im Kohlenbergbau	-	Wirtschaft und Statistik Jahrgänge 1922-1939
Statistik der Monatsheuern von Seeleuten	-	Monatshefte zur Statistik des Deutschen Reichs Jahrgänge 1878-1891; Vierteljahrshefte zur Statistik des Deutschen Reichs Jahrgänge 1892-1902; Statistisches Jahrbuch für das Deutsche Reich Jahrgänge 1883-1921/22
Ortsübliche Tagelöhne bzw. Ortslöhne für Zwecke der Sozialversicherung	-	Zentralblatt für das Deutsche Reich Jahrgänge 1892 ff.; Reichsministerialblatt Jahrgänge 1923 ff.; Reichsarbeitsblatt Jahrgänge 1929 ff.
Jahresarbeitsverdienste land- und forstwirtschaftlicher Arbeiter für Zwecke der Sozialversicherung	-	Zentralblatt für das Deutsche Reich 1922 Nr. 6; Reichsministerialblatt Jahrgänge 1923-1925, zuletzt 1925 Nr. 66

Deutsches Reich, einmalige Daten

Individuallohn- und -gehaltserhebung in der gewerblichen Wirtschaft 1920	-	Statistik des Deutschen Reichs Band 293 (Berlin 1921)

Individuallohnerhebungen in verschiedenen Industriezweigen 1927-1934	- Wirtschaft und Statistik Jahrgänge 1928-1935; Vierteljahrshefte zur Statistik des Deutschen Reichs Jahrgänge 1928-1935
Individuallohnerhebung in der metallverarbeitenden Industrie 1938	- Statistisches Jahrbuch für das Deutsche Reich 1939/40 S. 350
Individualerhebung der Angestelltenverdienste im Bankgewerbe 1934	- Wirtschaft und Statistik 1934 S. 460 und 1935 S. 136; Vierteljahrshefte zur Statistik des Deutschen Reichs 1935 S. I.149
Individuallohnerhebung im Bäckerhandwerk Niedersachsens 1936	- Wirtschaft und Statistik 1936 S. 792
Lohnstrukturerhebung in der Landwirtschaft 1937	- Wirtschaft und Statistik 1941 S. 403
Lohnstrukturerhebung in der Forstwirtschaft 1939/40	- Wirtschaft und Statistik 1942 S. 80
Erhebungen über die Lohnverhältnisse städtischer Arbeiter 1902 und 1907	- Beiträge zur Arbeiterstatistik Nr. 9 (Berlin 1908)
Erhebung über die Frauen- und Kinderarbeit in den Fabriken 1876	- "Ergebnisse der über die Frauen- und Kinderarbeit in den Fabriken auf Beschluß des Bundesrats ausgeführten Erhebungen, zusammengestellt im Reichskanzleramt" (Berlin 1876)
Erhebung über die Verhältnisse der Lehrlinge, Gesellen und Fabrikarbeiter 1876	- "Ergebnisse der über die Verhältnisse der Lehrlinge, Gesellen und Fabrikarbeiter auf Beschluß des Bundesrats angestellten Erhebungen, zusammengestellt im Reichskanzleramt" (Berlin 1876)
Reichsenquêten über die Tabak-, Eisen- und Textilindustrie 1878	- Drucksachen und Sitzungsprotokolle des Bundesrats 1878

Reichsenquête über die Lohnverhältnisse der Arbeiterinnen in der Wäschefabrikation und der Konfektionsbranche 1887	- Drucksachen des Reichstags Session 1887 Nr. 83
Erhebung über die Arbeits- und Gehaltsverhältnisse der Kellner und Kellnerinnen 1893	- Drucksachen der Kommission für Arbeiterstatistik, Erhebungen Nr. 6 (Berlin 1894)
Untersuchung über die Arbeitsverhältnisse in der Kleider- und Wäschekonfektion 1896	- Drucksachen der Kommission für Arbeiterstatistik, Erhebungen Nr. 10 (Berlin 1896)
Erhebung über gewerbliche Kinderarbeit außerhalb der Fabriken 1898	- Vierteljahrshefte zur Statistik des Deutschen Reichs 1900 S. III. 97
Erhebung über die Arbeitsverhältnisse der Angestellten der Rechtsanwälte 1912	- Drucksachen des Kaiserlichen Statistischen Amtes, Abteilung für Arbeiterstatistik, Erhebungen Nr. 9 (Berlin 1912)

Bundesrepublik Deutschland, nationale Lohnstatistik, laufende Daten

Tariflohnstatistik	- Statistisches Jahrbuch für die Bundesrepublik Deutschland 1952 S. 440; "Preise Löhne Wirtschaftsrechnungen" (seit 1962 Fachserie M) Reihe 11 III (Stuttgart-Mainz 1959 ff.); Sammlung tariflicher Einzellohn- und -gehaltssätze und sonstiger tariflicher Regelungen in Reihe 11 I und II; Sammlung gesetzlicher Einzelgehaltssätze der Bundesbeamten in Reihe 11 IV
Index des Tariflohn- und -gehaltsniveaus der Deutschen Bundesbank	- Monatsberichte der Deutschen Bundesbank Jahrgänge 1967 ff.
Lohnsummenerhebung der Industriearbeiter	- Statistische Berichte Arb. Nr. VI/11/1 bis VI/11/24 (Wiesbaden 1949 ff.);

	"Preise Löhne Wirtschaftsrechnungen" Reihe 10 (Stuttgart-Köln 1955 ff.)
Vierteljährliche Verdiensterhebung in Industrie und Handel	- "Preise Löhne Wirtschaftsrechnungen" (seit 1962 Fachserie M) Reihe 15 I (Arbeiterverdienste) und II (Angestelltenverdienste) (Stuttgart 1958 ff. bzw. Stuttgart-Mainz 1962 ff.)
Bruttojahresverdiensterhebung in Industrie und und Handel	- Wirtschaft und Statistik Jahrgänge 1975 ff.
Verdiensterhebung im Handwerk	- "Preise Löhne Wirtschaftsrechnungen" (seit 1962 Fachserie M) Reihe 16 (Stuttgart-Mainz 1959 ff.)
Verdiensterhebung in der Landwirtschaft	- "Preise Löhne Wirtschaftsrechnungen" (seit 1962 Fachserie M) Reihe 14 (Stuttgart-Mainz 1958 ff.)
Bergarbeiterlohnstatistik	- Statistische Mitteilungen der Bergbehörden der Bundesrepublik Deutschland, zusammengestellt als Gemeinschaftsarbeit der Bergbehörden des Bundesgebietes (Clausthal-Zellerfeld 1951 ff.); Der Bergbau in der Bundesrepublik Deutschland, Bergwirtschaft und Statistik, zusammengestellt als Gemeinschaftsarbeit der Bergbehörden des Bundesgebietes (bzw. ab Berichtsjahr 1968 "zusammengestellt von den Bergbehörden des Bundesgebietes in Zusammenarbeit mit dem Bundesministerium für Wirtschaft" bzw. ab Berichtsjahr 1973 "zusammengestellt von den Bergbehörden der Länder in Zusammenarbeit mit dem Bundesministerium für Wirtschaft") (Clausthal-Zellerfeld 1968 ff.)

Monatsstatistik über die Arbeiterverdienste im Kohlenbergbau	- "Statistische Monatszahlen", herausgegeben vom Statistischen Amt des Vereinigten Wirtschaftsgebietes (Wiesbaden 1948-1949); Wirtschaft und Statistik Jahrgänge 1949 ff.; Statistisches Jahrbuch für die Bundesrepublik Deutschland Jahrgänge 1952 ff.
Verdiensterhebung im öffentlichen Dienst in Hamburg	- Statistische Berichte Nr. NI/S und Nr. NI1, herausgegeben vom Statistischen Landesamt der Freien und Hansestadt Hamburg (Hamburg 1971-1974)
Laufende Fehlerrechnungen für die Verdiensterhebung in Industrie und Handel in Nordrhein-Westfalen	- Statistische Berichte Nr. NI1, herausgegeben vom Statistischen Landesamt bzw. Landesamt für Datenverarbeitung und Statistik Nordrhein-Westfalen (Düsseldorf 1973 ff.)
Ortslöhne sowie Jahresarbeitsverdienste landwirtschaftlicher Arbeitnehmer für Zwecke der Sozialversicherung	- Gesetz- und Verordnungsblätter und Ministerialblätter der Bundesländer sowie Amtsblätter der Regierungsbezirke Jahrgänge 1950 ff.; keine zentrale amtliche Veröffentlichung für das Bundesgebiet

Bundesrepublik Deutschland, nationale Lohnstatistik, einmalige Daten

Gehalts- und Lohnstrukturerhebung in der gewerblichen Wirtschaft 1951	- Statistik der Bundesrepublik Deutschland Bände 90 und 91 (Stuttgart-Köln 1954)
Gehalts- und Lohnstrukturerhebung in der gewerblichen Wirtschaft 1957	- Statistik der Bundesrepublik Deutschland Band 246 Hefte 1 und 2 (Stuttgart-Mainz 1960)
Gehalts- und Lohnstrukturerhebung in der gewerblichen Wirtschaft 1962	- Fachserie M Reihe 17 I Bände 1 und 2 (Stuttgart-Mainz 1966)
Gehalts- und Lohnstrukturerhebung in der gewerblichen Wirtschaft 1966	- Fachserie M Reihe 17 I Bände 1 und 2 (Stuttgart-Mainz 1970)

Gehalts- und Lohnstrukturerhebung in der gewerblichen Wirtschaft 1972	- Fachserie M Reihe 17 I Bände 1 und 2 (Stuttgart-Mainz 1976)
Erweiterte Industriearbeiterlohnerhebung 1949	- Wirtschaft und Statistik 1949/50 S. 316 und 355, 1950 S. 40 und 274[*]
Erhebung der Angestelltenverdienste in der gewerblichen Wirtschaft 1949	- Wirtschaft und Statistik 1950 S. 68 und 444[*]
Lohnstrukturerhebung in der Landwirtschaft 1950	- Statistischer Bericht Arb. Nr. VI/16/1 (Wiesbaden 1952)
Gehalts- und Lohnstrukturerhebung in der Landwirtschaft 1953/54	- Statistik der Bundesrepublik Deutschland Band 92 Heft 2 (Stuttgart 1958)
Gehalts- und Lohnstrukturerhebung in der Landwirtschaft 1962/63	- Fachserie M Reihe 17 II (Stuttgart-Mainz 1964)
Lohnstrukturerhebung in der Forstwirtschaft 1949/50	- Statistischer Bericht Arb. Nr. VI/17/1 (Wiesbaden 1952)
Lohnstrukturerhebung in der Forstwirtschaft 1952/53	- Statistik der Bundesrepublik Deutschland Band 92 Heft 1 (Stuttgart 1957)
Lohnstrukturerhebung in der Forstwirtschaft 1961/62	- Fachserie M Reihe 17 III (Stuttgart-Mainz 1963)
Gehalts- und Lohnstrukturerhebung im Erwerbsgartenbau 1962	- Fachserie M Reihe 17 IV (Stuttgart-Mainz 1963)
Gehalts- und Lohnstrukturerhebung im öffentlichen Dienst 1950	- Statistischer Bericht Arb. Nr. VI/13/1 (Wiesbaden 1953)
Gehalts- und Lohnstrukturerhebung im öffentlichen Dienst 1968	- Fachserie M Reihe 17 V (Stuttgart-Mainz 1971)

Erhebung über die sozialen Nebenleistungen der Unternehmen für ihre Arbeitnehmer 1957	- Statistik der Bundesrepublik Deutschland Band 246 Heft 3 (Stuttgart-Mainz 1961)
Erhebung über die Vermögensbildung der Arbeitnehmer 1963	- Bundesarbeitsblatt 1965 S. 186
Erhebung über d. betriebliche Altersversorgung 1973	- Arbeits- und sozialstatistische Mitteilungen (herausgegeben vom Bundesministerium für Arbeit und Sozialordnung) 1975 S. 228 und 270 (Bonn 1975)
Erhebung über die Einkommensschichtung in Schleswig-Holstein 1949	- Statistische Monatshefte Schleswig-Holstein (herausgegeben vom Statistischen Landesamt Schleswig-Holstein) 1950 S. 166 und 409 (Kiel 1950)

Bundesrepublik Deutschland, inter- und supranationale Lohnstatistik

Harmonisierte Verdiensterhebung der Europäischen Wirtschaftsgemeinschaft in Industrie und Handel	- Fachserie M Reihe 15 I (Stuttgart-Mainz 1964 ff.) und II (Stuttgart-Mainz 1973 ff.); Sozialstatistik, herausgegeben vom Statistischen Amt der Europäischen Gemeinschaften (Brüssel - Luxemburg 1965 - 1967 und 1969 ff.); Statistische Studien und Erhebungen, herausgegeben vom Statistischen Amt der Europäischen Gemeinschaften (Brüssel-Luxemburg 1968)
Erhebung der Europäischen Wirtschaftsgemeinschaft über die Arbeiterverdienste in der Landwirtschaft	- Fachserie M Reihe 14 (Stuttgart-Mainz 1976 ff.); Sozialstatistik, herausgegeben vom Statistischen Amt der Europäischen Gemeinschaften (Brüssel-Luxemburg 1975 ff.)

Lohnstrukturerhebung der Europäischen Wirtschaftsgemeinschaft im produzierenden Gewerbe 1966	- Fachserie M Reihe 17 I Band 1 (Stuttgart-Mainz 1970); Sonderreihe der Sozialstatistik, herausgegeben vom Statistischen Amt der Europäischen Gemeinschaften (mehrere Bände, Brüssel-Luxemburg ab 1969)
Gehalts- und Lohnstrukturerhebung der Europäischen Wirtschaftsgemeinschaft im Produzierenden Gewerbe 1972	- Fachserie M Reihe 17 I Bände 1 und 2 (Stuttgart-Mainz 1976); Sonderreihe der Sozialstatistik, herausgegeben vom Statistischen Amt der Europäischen Gemeinschaften (mehrere Bände, Brüssel-Luxemburg ab 1974)
Gehalts- und Lohnstrukturerhebung der Europäischen Wirtschaftsgemeinschaft im Handel, Bank- und Versicherungsgewerbe 1974	- Keine nationale Veröffentlichung; Veröffentlichung der Europäischen Wirtschaftsgemeinschaft liegt noch nicht vor
Personalkostenerhebungen der Europäischen Wirtschaftsgemeinschaft im produzierenden Gewerbe	- "Preise Löhne Wirtschaftsrechnungen" (seit 1962 Fachserie M) Reihe 15 Sonderbeiträge (Stuttgart-Mainz 1961 ff.); Sozialstatistik, herausgegeben vom Statistischen Amt der Europäischen Gemeinschaften (Brüssel-Luxemburg 1961 ff.)
Personalkostenerhebungen der Europäischen Gemeinschaft für Kohle und Stahl	- Keine nationale Veröffentlichung; Statistische Informationen, herausgegeben von der Hohen Behörde der Europäischen Gemeinschaft für Kohle und Stahl (Luxemburg 1955 ff.); Sozialstatistik, herausgegeben vom Statistischen Amt der Europäischen Gemeinschaften (Brüssel-Luxemburg 1960 ff.)
Personalkostenerhebungen der Europäischen Wirtschaftsgemeinschaft im Handel, Bank- und Versicherungsgewerbe	- Fachserie M Reihe 15 Sonderbeiträge (Stuttgart-Mainz 1973 ff.); Sozialstatistik, herausgegeben vom Statistischen Amt der Europäischen Gemeinschaften (Brüssel-Luxemburg 1972 ff.)

Personalkostenerhebung der Europäischen Wirtschaftsgemeinschaft im Straßenverkehrsgewerbe 1967	- Wirtschaft und Statistik 1969 S. 391, 431*; Sozialstatistik (herausgegeben vom Statistischen Amt der Europäischen Gemeinschaften) 1970 Nr. 1 (Brüssel-Luxemburg 1970
Erhebung der Internationalen Arbeitsorganisation über die Aufwendungen der Unternehmen für ihre Arbeitnehmer 1955	- Wirtschaft und Statistik 1958 S. 269; Studien und Berichte des Internationalen Arbeitsamtes, Neue Folge, Nr. 52 (Genf 1959)

*) Hinweis: Die Veröffentlichungen des Statistischen Bundesamtes wurden ab Anfang 1977 neu gegliedert und mit neuen Bezeichnungen versehen.

Literaturverzeichnis

Behrens, Friedrich: Die amtlichen Lohnerhebungen. Allgemeines Statistisches Archiv, 28. Band Jahrgang 1939, S. 61-71. Jena 1939.

Behrens, Friedrich: Neue Wege der Lohnstatistik. Allgemeines Statistisches Archiv, 31. Band Jahrgang 1942/43, S. 114-138. Jena 1943.

Berié, Hermann: Die Anwendung des Vermögensbildungsgesetzes. Bundesarbeitsblatt, Jahrgang 1965, S. 186. Stuttgart-Köln 1965.

Berié, Hermann und Wiese, Marion: Arten und Ausmaß der betrieblichen Altersversorgung. Arbeits- und sozialstatistische Mitteilungen, Jahrgang 1975, S. 228. Bonn 1975.

v.d.Decken, Wolf und Schulz, Hans-Joachim: Reform der laufenden Verdiensterhebung in Industrie und Handel 1964. Wirtschaft und Statistik, Jahrgang 1964, S. 712. Stuttgart-Mainz 1964.

Deneffe, Peter: Die Angestelltenverdienste im Vereinigten Wirtschaftsgebiet im Mai 1949. Wirtschaft und Statistik, Jahrgang 1950, S. 68. Stuttgart 1950.

Deneffe, Peter: Die Arbeiterverdienste im Mai 1957. Wirtschaft und Statistik, Jahrgang 1957, S. 528. Stuttgart 1957.

Deneffe, Peter und v.d.Decken, Wolf: Die methodischen Grundlagen der laufenden Verdiensterhebungen in Industrie und Handel. Wirtschaft und Statistik, Jahrgang 1957, S. 522. Stuttgart 1957.

Deneffe, Peter und Guckes, Siegfried: Die Aufwendungen der Unternehmen für die Arbeitnehmer im Jahr 1955. Wirtschaft und Statistik, Jahrgang 1958, S. 269. Stuttgart 1958.

Deneffe, Peter und Schulz, Ursula: Zur Berechnung von Indices der Tariflöhne und Tarifgehälter. Wirtschaft und Statistik, Jahrgang 1958, S. 494. Stuttgart 1958.

Feig, Johannes: Statistik des Arbeitslohns und der Lebenshaltung. In: Die Statistik in Deutschland nach ihrem heutigen Stand, Ehrengabe für Georg von Mayr, Band II, herausgegeben von F. Zahn, München-Berlin 1911, S. 789-826.

Gerß, Wolfgang: Stichprobentheoretische Grenzen der Aussagefähigkeit der amtlichen laufenden Verdiensterhebung, dargestellt mit Hilfe von Zahlenmaterial für das Land Nordrhein-Westfalen. WSI-Mitteilungen (Zeitschrift des Wirtschafts- und Sozialwissenschaftlichen Instituts des Deutschen Gewerkschaftsbundes GmbH), Jahrgang 1973, S. 35. Köln 1973.

Gerß, Wolfgang: Neuauswahl der Berichtsbetriebe zur laufenden Verdiensterhebung und ihre methodischen Konsequenzen. Statistische Rundschau für das Land Nordrhein-Westfalen, herausgegeben vom Statistischen Landesamt Nordrhein-Westfalen, Jahrgang 1973, S. 348. Düsseldorf 1973.

Gerß, Wolfgang: Einführung laufender Fehlerrechnungen in der repräsentativen Verdiensterhebung. Statistische Rundschau für das Land Nordrhein-Westfalen, herausgegeben vom Landesamt für Datenverarbeitung und Statistik Nordrhein-Westfalen, Jahrgang 1974, S. 109. Düsseldorf 1974.

Gerß, Wolfgang: Laufende Fehlerrechnungen in der Verdiensterhebung - Methodische Grundlagen und Auswertungsmöglichkeiten. Statistische Rundschau für das Land Nordrhein-Westfalen, herausgegeben vom Landesamt für Datenverarbeitung und Statistik Nordrhein-Westfalen, Jahrgang 1975, S. 379. Düsseldorf 1975.

Horstmann, Kurt und v.d.Decken, Wolf: Neuberechnung der Indices über die Verdienste und die bezahlten Wochenstunden der Industriearbeiter. Wirtschaft und Statistik, Jahrgang 1959, S. 184. Stuttgart 1959.

Kaiserliches Statistisches Amt: Erhebungen über Arbeitslöhne in Deutschland, Uebersicht über die von Behörden und Vereinen veranstalteten Aufnahmen zur Lohnstatistik. Vierteljahrshefte zur Statistik des Deutschen Reichs, Zweiter Jahrgang 1893, Drittes Heft, S. 1-6. Berlin 1893.

Kaiserliches Statistisches Amt, Abteilung für Arbeiterstatistik: Die Fortschritte der amtlichen Arbeitsstatistik in den wichtigsten Staaten, Erster Teil Vereinigte Staaten von Amerika, Großbritannien und Irland, Frankreich, Belgien, Österreich, Deutsches Reich. Beiträge zur Arbeiterstatistik Nr. 1. Berlin 1904.

Kaiserliches Statistisches Amt, Abteilung für Arbeiterstatistik: Gebiete und Methoden der amtlichen Arbeitsstatistik in den wichtigsten Industriestaaten. Beiträge zur Arbeiterstatistik Nr. 12. Berlin 1913.

Kloß, Hans-Gustav: Index der Bruttomonatsverdienste der Angestellten in Industrie und Handel auf der Basis 1958. Wirtschaft und Statistik, Jahrgang 1962, S. 84. Stuttgart-Mainz 1962.

Krause, Friedland: Die deutsche Lohnstatistik. In: Die Statistik in Deutschland nach ihrem heutigen Stand, Ehrengabe für Friedrich Zahn, Band II, herausgegeben von Friedrich Burgdörfer, Berlin 1940, S. 1168-1179.

Kunz, Dietrich und Schulz, Ursula: Die Neugestaltung der laufenden Verdienststatistik in der Landwirtschaft. Wirtschaft und Statistik, Jahrgang 1976, S. 543. Stuttgart-Mainz 1976.

Schulz, Ursula: Zur Berechnung eines Index der Tariflöhne in der Landwirtschaft. Wirtschaft und Statistik, Jahrgang 1958, S. 596. Stuttgart 1958.

Statistisches Bundesamt: Stichproben in der amtlichen Statistik. Stuttgart-Mainz 1960.

Statistisches Reichsamt: Die amtliche Lohnstatistik in Deutschland. Statistik des Deutschen Reichs Band 293. Berlin 1921.

Statistisches Reichsamt: Die Nachprüfung und Neubearbeitung der amtlichen Tariflohnstatistik. Vierteljahrshefte zur Statistik des Deutschen Reichs, 40. Jahrgang 1931, Zweites Heft, S. 94-109. Berlin 1931.

Statistisches Reichsamt: Zur Neubearbeitung der amtlichen Tariflohnstatistik. Vierteljahrshefte zur Statistik des Deutschen Reichs, 40. Jahrgang 1931, Drittes Heft, S. 116. Berlin 1931.

Wörishoffer: Die soziale Lage der Fabrikarbeiter in Mannheim und dessen nächster Umgebung. Karlsruhe 1891.

Anhang

Die Lohnstatistik des Allgemeinen Deutschen Gewerkschaftsbundes (1919 - 1933)

Die früheste Zeit der deutschen Lohnstatistik war durch einen auffallenden Gegensatz zwischen der Zurückhaltung der Behörden einerseits und der Aktivität der Gewerkschaften andererseits gekennzeichnet (vgl. Abschnitte 114 und 122). Während die amtliche Statistik sich erst allmählich der Lohnstatistik annahm, leisteten die Gewerkschaften vielfach Pionierarbeit. Die Aufnahme amtlicher lohnstatistischer Erhebungen erfolgte teilweise als Reaktion auf entsprechende vorherige Arbeiten der Gewerkschaften und mit dem ausdrücklichen Ziel, den gewerkschaftlichen Lohnerhebungen amtliche Zahlen entgegenhalten zu können. Auch als nach dem Ersten Weltkrieg die Notwendigkeit einer umfassenden amtlichen Lohnstatistik allgemein anerkannt wurde, konnte das Statistische Reichsamt in der Phase des Aufbaus seines lohnstatistischen Systems Anregungen aus bereits vorhandenen lohnstatistischen Erhebungen insbesondere des Allgemeinen Deutschen Gewerkschaftsbundes übernehmen. Es ist daher sinnvoll, im Rahmen einer Darstellung, die sich grundsätzlich auf die amtliche Lohnstatistik beschränkt, auch kurz auf die gewerkschaftliche Lohnstatistik einzugehen.

Der Allgemeine Deutsche Gewerkschaftsbund (ADGB) wurde im Jahre 1919 als Dachorganisation der "freien Gewerkschaften" der Arbeiter gegründet und umfaßte damit insbesondere nicht die Angestelltengewerkschaften, die christlichen Gewerkschaften und die Hirsch-Duncker'schen Gewerkvereine. Die Lohnstatistik des ADGB bezog sich dementsprechend auf die Löhne der in den freien Gewerkschaften organisierten Arbeiter. Ab Berichtsmonat September 1921 nahm der ADGB eine laufende Erhebung über die Entwicklung der tariflich festgesetzten Zeitlöhne männlicher und weiblicher Vollarbeiter auf. Die Erhebung wurde grundsätzlich mit vierteljährlicher Periodizität jeweils zum Stichtag Ende März, Ende Juni, Ende September und Ende Dezember weitergeführt; in den letzten Jahren des Bestehens des ADGB wurde auf eine halbjährliche Periodizität übergegangen. In den Jahren 1922 und 1923, als infolge der Inflation die Tariflöhne innerhalb eines Monats oft mehrmals geändert wurden, wurden zusätzlich zu den Vierteljahresergebnissen auch Monatsergebnisse als gewogene arithmetische Mittel der während des Erhebungsmonats gültig gewesenen Tariflohnsätze ermittelt, wobei als Gewichte die Anzahlen der Arbeitsstunden dienten, für die die verschiedenen Lohnsätze in kraft waren. Nach 1923 wurden Monatsergebnisse - nunmehr zum Stichtag Monatsende - nur noch sporadisch ausgewiesen. Zur Vervollständigung der Zeitreihen wurden nachträglich auch Tariflöhne zu den Stichtagen Jahresende 1919 und 1920 sowie tariflohnstatistische Angaben aus den Jahren 1913 und 1914 zusammengestellt. Die Tariflohnstatistik des ADGB war in der Weise organisiert, daß die Zentralvorstände der Einzelgewerkschaften - im Falle lokaler Tarifabschlüsse nach Erkundigung bei ihren örtlichen Verwaltungsstellen - dem Bundesvorstand laufend über die Höhe der tariflich festgesetzten Zeitlöhne und die Dauer der regelmäßigen wöchentlichen Arbeitszeit berichteten. Die Berichterstattung beschränkte sich auf einen grundsätzlich gleichbleibenden Kreis ausgewählter Berufe (bzw. Wirtschaftszweige) - überwiegend "Fachberufe", in einigen Wirtschaftszweigen auch gesondert gelernte und ungelernte Berufe - und ausgewählter Orte. Während die erstmalige Auswahl der Berufe den Einzelgewerkschaften überlassen wurde, wurden die in die Berichterstattung aufzunehmenden Orte vom Bundesvorstand bestimmt. Der Bundesvorstand war dabei bestrebt, alle Bezirke des Reiches und alle Ortsklassen angemessen zu berücksichtigen; um den Arbeitsaufwand in Grenzen zu halten, wurden in die Aufbereitung jedoch nur Großstädte und einige Mittelstädte - insgesamt etwa 50 Orte - einbezogen. Die Aufbereitung oblag ausschließlich dem Bundesvorstand; sie ging von den Spitzenlöhnen - das heißt den pro Ort und Beruf festgesetzten höchsten Tariflöhnen - für Vollarbeiter der höchsten tariflichen Altersstufe aus und erbrachte Angaben über durchschnittliche tarifliche Stundenlohnsätze. Bei Berufen, in denen ausschließlich Wochenlohnfestsetzungen erfolgten, wurden die tariflichen Wochenlöhne erfaßt und im Zuge der statistischen Aufbereitung nach der für den jeweiligen Beruf an dem einzelnen Ort bestehenden regelmäßigen Wochenarbeitszeit in Stundenlöhne umgerechnet. Auf die Erfassung von Akkordlöhnen wurde verzichtet. Als Ergebnisse der Tariflohnstatistik wurden neben Auflistungen einzelner Lohnsätze nach den in die Erhebung einbezogenen Berufen und Orten durchschnittliche Tariflöhne pro Ort für die Gesamtheit der Berufe und pro Beruf für die Gesamtheit der Orte sowie Gesamtdurchschnitte aus den Ortsdurchschnitten bzw. den Berufsdurchschnitten ausgewiesen. Neben Gesamtdurchschnitten - für die Gesamtheit der Orte - wurden teilweise auch Durchschnittslöhne für die verschiedenen erfaßten Ortsklassen berechnet; außerdem wurden Häufigkeitsverteilungen der Berufe nach tariflichen Stundenlohnklassen aufgestellt. Für die landwirtschaftlichen Arbeiter und die Bergarbeiter wurden Sondertabellen aufbereitet, die zusätzliche Merkmale - bei den landwirtschaftlichen Arbeitern den Bar-, Deputat- und Gesamtlohn und bei den Bergarbeitern verschiedene Qualifikationsgruppen - enthielten und sich statt auf ausgewählte Orte auf größere Tarifbezirke bezogen, aus denen dann Reichsdurchschnitte berechnet wurden. Mit Ausnahme der erwähnten Monatsdurchschnitte der Inflationszeit handelte es sich bei den in der Tariflohnstatistik des ADGB ausgewiesenen Durchschnittslöhnen stets um ungewogene arithmetische Mittel. Diese Mittelwertbildung wurde damit begründet, daß die Tariflohnstatistik des ADGB als eigentliches Ziel den Nachweis der Entwicklung - das heißt der zeitlichen Veränderung - der Tariflöhne verfolgte und die Angaben über die durchschnittliche Lohnhöhe dazu nur als Zwischenergebnis wertete. Mit der Verwendung des ungewogenen Mittels wurde erreicht, daß bei der konstanten Anzahl von Berufen und Orten jeder tarifliche Einzellohnsatz bei jeder Erhebung mit einem konstant bleibenden Gewicht in die Durchschnittsberechnung einging und somit die Veränderungen der Durchschnittslöhne wie bei einem Index als reine Lohnänderungen unter Ausschaltung von Gewichtsänderungen interpretiert werden konnten. Allerdings wurde in kauf genommen, daß diese Gewichte nicht der wirtschaftlichen Bedeutung der einzelnen Berufe und Orte entsprachen, sondern für alle Berufe bzw. Orte gleich groß waren. Im Gegensatz zur Tariflohnstatistik des ADGB ermittelte die Tariflohnstatistik des Statistischen Reichsamtes mit den Arbeiterzahlen gewogene arithmetische Mittel der tariflichen Einzellohnsätze, weil ihr primärer Zweck in der Berechnung der durchschnittlichen Höhe der Tariflohnsätze bestand (vgl. Abschnitt 133). Die Ergebnisse der Tariflohnstatistik des ADGB wurden laufend im "Korrespondenzblatt des Allgemeinen Deutschen Gewerkschaftsbundes (Anhang Statistische Beilagen)", Jahrgänge 1922 und 1923 (Berlin 1922/23), in der "Gewerkschafts-Zeitung, Organ des Allgemeinen Deutschen Gewerkschaftsbundes",

Jahrgänge 1924 bis 1933 (Berlin 1924 bis 1933), und im "Jahrbuch des Allgemeinen Deutschen Gewerkschaftsbundes", Jahrgänge 1922 bis 1931 (Berlin 1923 bis 1932), veröffentlicht. Die letzten vom ADGB vor seiner Zerschlagung durch das nationalsozialistische Regime bekanntgegebenen lohnstatistischen Angaben beziehen sich auf den Stand Ende Dezember 1932.

Neben der laufenden Tariflohnstatistik führte der Bundesvorstand des ADGB für die Berichtswoche vom 2. bis 7. November 1925 eine einmalige Effektivverdiensterhebung im Individualverfahren in 22 ausgewählten Berufsgruppen bzw. Wirtschaftszweigen und 54 ausgewählten Orten durch. Grundlage der Erhebung bildeten rund 150 000 Lohnnachweisungen (Lohntüten und Lohnzettel), die durch die gewerkschaftlichen Ortsausschüsse unter Mitwirkung der örtlichen Gewerkschaftsleitungen von den einzelnen Arbeitern der in Frage kommenden Betriebe eingesammelt und dem Bundesvorstand zur Aufbereitung zugesandt wurden. Die in den Lohnnachweisungen erfaßten Erhebungsmerkmale waren der Effektivverdienst und die effektive Arbeitszeit (einschließlich Überstunden) in der Berichtswoche, die Lohnform (Zeit- oder Akkordlohn) sowie der Beruf bzw. Wirtschaftszweig, der Arbeitsort, das Geschlecht, die Qualifikation (gelernt, angelernt oder ungelernt), das Lebensalter, der Familienstand und die Anzahl der schulpflichtigen Kinder des Arbeiters. Aus den individuellen Verdienst- und Arbeitszeitangaben wurden durchschnittliche Stundenverdienste und Wochenarbeitszeiten pro Ort für die Gesamtheit der Berufe und pro Beruf für die Gesamtheit der Orte sowie Gesamtdurchschnitte aus diesen Ortsdurchschnitten bzw. Berufsdurchschnitten berechnet. Neben den Durchschnittswerten wurden auch Häufigkeitsverteilungen der Arbeiter nach Wochenverdienstklassen ausgewiesen. Die Durchschnitte, bei denen es sich um jeweils auf einen Arbeiter entfallende Beträge handelte, wurden als gewogene arithmetische Mittel berechnet; als Gewichte dienten die Anzahlen der in der Erhebung selbst erfaßten Arbeiter. Die Ergebnisse der Erhebung wurden im "Jahrbuch des Allgemeinen Deutschen Gewerkschaftsbundes" Jahrgang 1925 (Berlin 1926, Seite 194 ff.) veröffentlicht. Mit der Individuallohnerhebung von 1925 wollte der ADGB unter anderem Anregungen zu entsprechenden amtlichen Erhebungen über die Effektivverdienste der Arbeiter geben, die dann auch vom Statistischen Reichsamt ab 1927 in wechselnden Wirtschaftsbereichen durchgeführt wurden (vgl. Abschnitt 135).

Die Lohnstatistik des Deutschen Gewerkschaftsbundes (ab 1949)

Die gewerkschaftliche Lohnstatistik wurde nach dem Zweiten Weltkrieg als zentrale Lohnstatistik des Deutschen Gewerkschaftsbundes (DGB) in veränderter Form weitergeführt. Die Bearbeitung der Statistik wurde dem neugegründeten "Wirtschaftswissenschaftlichen Institut der Gewerkschaften GmbH" (WWI) übertragen, das später in "Wirtschafts- und Sozialwissenschaftliches Institut des Deutschen Gewerkschaftsbundes GmbH" (WSI) umbenannt wurde. Die erste eigene lohnstatistische Erhebung des WWI fand für die Jahre 1949 und 1950 statt. Es handelte sich um eine einmalige repräsentative Effektivverdiensterhebung im Individualverfahren, bei der die einzelnen Einkommensempfänger selbst durch Fragebogen und parallel laufende Interviews nach ihrem Einkommen befragt wurden. Die Vorbereitung der Erhebung und die Auswertung der erhobenen Daten lag in den Händen des WWI, mit der Befragung der Auskunftspersonen wurde das EMNID-Institut in Bielefeld beauftragt. In die Erhebung wurde eine repräsentative Auswahl sämtlicher abhängigen und selbständigen Erwerbspersonen einbezogen. Als Auswahlverfahren wurde das in der Meinungsforschung übliche Verfahren der Quotenauswahl angewendet, wobei die Quoten nach den Merkmalen Bundesland, Ortsgrößenklasse, Wirtschaftszweig, soziale Stellung (selbständig bzw. abhängig als Arbeiter, Angestellter oder Beamter) und Geschlecht gebildet wurden. Von den Auskunftspersonen wurde erfragt, in welche von insgesamt 14 vorgegebenen Einkommensklassen ihr monatliches Gesamteinkommen Anfang 1949 und im Mai 1950 fiel; dazu wurden ergänzende Fragen nach der Art und der Gliederung des Einkommens gestellt. Als Einkommen galt grundsätzlich das Bruttoeinkommen, und zwar sollten ursprünglich sämtliche Einkünfte der Erwerbspersonen und der in ihrem Haushalt lebenden Angehörigen erfaßt werden. Das anfänglich gesetzte Ziel der Ermittlung des Familieneinkommens wurde jedoch bei den abhängigen Einkomensempfängern nicht erreicht, so daß schließlich in die Ergebnistabellen weitgehend Einzeleinkommen eingingen. Als Ergebnisse der Erhebung wurden in erster Linie Häufigkeitsverteilungen der erfaßten Einkommensempfänger - gegliedert nach sozialer Stellung, Geschlecht und Wirschaftszweig - nach den vorgegebenen 14 Einkommensklassen ausgewiesen; aus den Häufigkeitsverteilungen wurden darüber hinaus auch durchschnittliche Monatseinkommen pro Person als gewogene arithmetische Mittel der geschätzten mittleren Monatseinkommen der einzelnen Einkommensklassen berechnet. Die Gewichte für diese Mittelwertbildung ergaben sich nicht aus der Erhebung selbst, sondern aus der tatsächlichen Struktur der Erwerbspersonen im Bundesgebiet. Die Ergebnisse der Einkommenserhebung von 1949/50 wurden in den "Mitteilungen des Wirtschaftswissenschaftlichen Instituts der Gewerkschaften", 3. Jahrgang (1950) Nr. 10/11 Seite 1 ff. (Köln 1950), veröffentlicht.

Seit dem Berichtsjahr 1954 führt das WWI bzw. später das WSI eine laufende Statistik der Tariflöhne und -gehälter durch. Als Materialbasis dieser Statistik dient das institutseigene Tarifarchiv, das von den Gewerkschaften laufend Ausfertigungen der abgeschlossenen Tarifverträge erhält. Die tariflohn- und -gehaltsstatistischen Auswertungen werden für die einzelnen Monate und Jahre, teilweise auch für die einzelnen Vierteljahre und Halbjahre vorgenommen, und zwar werden als Ergebnisse die während des Berichtszeitraums eingetretenen prozentualen Änderungen (Erhöhungen) der tariflichen Stundenlohnsätze und Monatsgehaltssätze von Arbeitern bzw. Angestellten für die einzelnen Wirtschaftsbereiche sowie im Durchschnitt sämtlicher Wirtschaftsbereiche ausgewiesen. Die durchschnittliche prozentuale Tarifsatzänderung wird als gewogenes arithmetisches Mittel aus den prozentualen Tarifsatzänderungen der einzelnen Tarifbereiche berechnet, wobei als Gewichte die Anzahlen der jeweils begünstigten Arbeiter bzw. Angestellten dienen. Die gewerkschaftliche Tariflohnstatistik weicht damit in der Form ihrer Ergebnisse (durchschnittliche Tarifsatzänderungen) von der Tariflohnstatistik des Statistischen Bundesamtes - das Indices nach dem Modell des Preisindex von Laspeyres ermittelt - ab (vgl. Abschnitt 164). Die Ergebnisse der gewerkschaftlichen Tariflohnstatistik werden laufend in den "WWI-Mitteilungen" (Zeitschrift des Wirtschaftswissenschaftlichen Instituts der Gewerkschaften GmbH, Jahrgänge 1955 bis 1971, Köln 1955 bis 1971) bzw. in den "WSI-Mitteilungen" (Zeitschrift des Wirtschafts- und Sozialwissenschaftlichen Instituts des Deutschen Gewerkschaftsbundes GmbH, Jahrgänge 1972 ff., Köln 1972 ff.) veröffentlicht.